ORIGIN OF LIFE:
The 5th OPTION

BY BRYANT M. SHILLER, ENG.

ORIGIN OF LIFE:

The 5th OPTION

The case for "The Rational Design Hypothesis" solution to the mystery of the origin of bio-life on our planet.

The Rational Design Hypothesis invokes a systems engineering analysis of the interactive system of biological life in order to answer the questions:

What is Life?
What is it doing here?
How did it get here?

And,

What are the consequences of the answers to these questions for the future survival of humanity and the system of biological life on our planet?

BY BRYANT M. SHILLER, ENG.

Note for Librarians: a cataloguing record for this book that includes Dewey Decimal Classification and US Library of Congress numbers is available from the Library and Archives of Canada. The complete cataloguing record can be obtained from their online database at:
www.collectionscanada.ca/amicus/index-e.html
ISBN 0-9739936-0-X
Printed in Montreal, QC, Canada

Cover image coutesy of NASA and the NSSDC

Order online at:
www.The5thOPTION.com

Dedication and Acknowledgments

This book is dedicated to:

—my children, Romy, Warren, Douglas and his wife Sonya, who bring meaning into my life;

—my wife Lillian who shows me how to live and makes life beautiful;

—friends and colleagues for their encouragement during the many years it took to bring this book to fruition;

—my good friend Marty Baker.

Thank you sincerely.

Bryant
Mar 2005

Contents

Origin of Life: THE "5th" OPTION

Preface

My personal quest for answers began as a young child having developed an insatiable appetite for finding out how things worked. It actually began as a consequence of my father, Alec, enlisting me as his helper to repair some appliance or other household gadget that had ceased to function. My dad got a thrill every time he managed to diagnose a mechanical or electrical problem and effect a remedy.

Once initiated into the game of "figure out how to fix it", I developed a healthy respect for the concept that there is a rational explanation for pretty well how everything works – if you are interested and willing to dig it out. I do not think a single appliance, radio, or telephone escaped my prying curiosity and eventually I became an expert "fixer" in my own right.

As I grew up, the only area of inquiry that could not be fathomed intuitively was electrical and electromagnetic theory. A degree in electrical engineering filled in that void and provided as well the useful background education needed to understand a host of other technical and scientific disciplines. Then a short stint in design and manufacturing engineering in the communications field afforded me two advantages: First, I was exposed to the developing fields of information theory, feed-back control systems and computer technology. Second, my employer actually paid for university night courses in psychology and philosophy. Throughout this learning process, as knowledge accumulated of how the world worked and how great thinkers thought about the world and humanity's place in it, the arrival of the space age sparked additional inquiry into extraterrestrial and cosmological issues and the like. By the time I was in my mid twenties (in the mid sixties) I was convinced that there were rational explanations for pretty well every question – whether the answers were apparent or not. I had total confidence that given enough time, man's ingenuity and logic would eventually ferret out the answers to the most complex of questions. I fully expected that even the ultimate quest for the solutions to that most vexing puzzle of the Origin of Life on our planet could and would be satisfied.

In fact that was the prevailing view of many in the scientific community following that watershed year of 1953. Two monumental events occurred that signaled the "light at the end of the tunnel" attitude among biologists with respect to a solution to the mystery of the Origin of Life here on earth. The first was the discovery by James Watson and Francis Crick of the double-helix architecture of the DNA genetic information molecule that controls all of life's functions. The second was the famous Urey-Miller experiments that for the first time demonstrated that amino and nucleic acids – essential molecules for life – can be produced artificially from chemical reactions using only water and some gases considered to be present in the primordial atmosphere of the earth some 3.8 billions of years ago.

The year 1953 ushered in a new and powerful future for molecular biology and it was expected that life's remaining secrets including the question of its abiogenetic origin (spontaneous self-generation) would be settled in relatively short order. Biologists already knew that biological processes are directed by a set of genetic instructions written in the chemical medium of DNA – blueprints, if you will – and within a couple of years (1956) had discovered how to decode and, in a sense, read the genetic language in which are written the genetic instructions that express themselves as the physical proteins organisms are made of. With the relationship between genotype (information) and phenotype (its physical expression) now understood, many in the scientific community sincerely believed we were in the home stretch, as it were, in determining how the first organisms began life. And the rest of us "science groupies" were there cheering and urging them on.

Well, that was more than fifty years ago and we are still waiting for some hint of light at the end of the abiogenesis Origin of Life tunnel. It's really amazing when you come to think of it that a half century after discovering the essence of how life works, biologists have not really come any closer to determining how biological life originated on our planet. Then again, it could be that scientists are looking in the wrong places – even in the wrong directions.

I have addressed the mystery of the Origin of Life on the planet much the same way one goes about solving a literary murder mystery. The author typically describes the events leading up to the nefarious crime and provides the details of police questioning of witnesses and suspects. The reader is then called upon to put the pieces together and find the inconsistencies between the testimonies and evidence. Then the logical conclusions should impose themselves upon the reader. What I have done is amass and pore over the many aspects of biological life. From text books, encyclopedias, articles in journals and downloaded from the internet as well as discussions with scientists and other experts I have collected the evidence that in the end have imposed upon me a set of logical conclusions culminating in the solution to life's greatest mystery. I believe that my unique advantage has been that I have operated independently with neither ulterior motive nor agenda. I have not felt any of the pressures that academics traditionally come up against to produce results that may be described as career oriented. I had the luxury of having neither a timetable nor finishing date in mind when I began the exercise. I just went with the flow of ideas as they developed. In the process, the chips have fallen according to the evidence and have forced the conclusions, as controversial as they may appear, that are herein drawn. But, it was only after I realized that the validity of those conclusions could be tested – in accordance with scientific principles – that I seriously considered committing my ideas to paper. The end result comprises The 5th OPTION.

It has occurred to me that some readers might be tempted to question the legitimacy of this kind of endeavor. How can an electrical engineer attempt to seriously explore, no less suggest, a solution to what can only be described as the most compelling question any living being can pose? Traditionally, that should be the exclusive province of cutting edge structural molecular biologists working in megafunded research labs. (And before them, in a less enlightened age, it was the exclusive domain of theologians.)

Let me explain it this way:

First: We are living in what has been aptly coined the "Information Age". This implies that both the quality and quantity of accessible information in all the realms of scientific endeavor has increased exponentially in recent times. It also relates to the fantastic methods afforded the initiated to access easily and efficiently any information requested of that global data based system. Today, virtually anybody can research the published academic and scientific literature on any subject. I have taken advantage and availed myself of these extensive resources in order to study and research my subject of inquiry: the search for the Origin of Life on the planet earth.

Second: Molecular biologists interested in Origin of Life research must of necessity restrict themselves to a narrow spectrum of inquiry. They have neither the time nor the funding to do more than one thing at a time. Therefore, they are most likely to choose a narrow channel to focus their resources and energies, albeit one that is felt to offer a reasonable chance of success. As well, scientists must be pragmatic in their choice of research direction and tend to stay clear of anything that might be considered the fringe. Future funding as well as careers and reputations can be influenced by one's choice of research and practical wisdom tends to restrict scientific inquiry to more middle of the road endeavors that have practical applications. Therefore, until recently, not too many scientists were likely to devote their careers to such a non-useful inquiry such as Origin of Life. I say "until recently" in deference to the introduction for the first time of a degree course in Origin of Life studies recently introduced and funded by NASA. I, on the other hand, have had time over the last two decades in which to pursue and explore what has become a fascinating, if sometimes obsessive subject. Most importantly, throughout the process of exploration and synthesis, I have depended on no one's permission, authorization, nor forbearance on how I spent my academic time and resources in researching my subject.

Third: An engineering background affords some distinct advantages: a) provides sufficient background knowledge to address and comprehend the technical aspects of the biological sciences; b) provides sufficient background knowledge to address the other technical disciplines such as chemistry, geology, information theory, thermodynamics, quantum theory, geology etc. that have come to bear on the subject; c) permits viewing the subject from a uniquely pragmatic "top-down" engineering point of view as opposed to the laboratory "bottom-up" mentality of biochemists.

Engineers, by nature, are pragmatic problem solvers. Engineering traditionally employs the fruits of scientific research to address and solve practical problems and create the technology that ultimately serves the needs of mankind. It aims to transform the esoteric findings derived from scientific experimentation into the power plants, manufacturing and production facilities for the systems, machines, products, raw materials and chemicals that advance society's living standards – making life easier for people in the process. In the pursuit of these goals, engineers are often called upon to combine the findings of a number of diverse scientific disciplines in order to arrive at practical solutions and to achieve specific goals. This is the traditional application of engineering principles. But those same principles are eminently suitable for the study of systems already in operation. It's called "reverse engineering". The quest for the solution to the puzzle of how and/or why life came to be on the planet earth can benefit from this kind of mentality – the engineering mentality.

Scientists have been pursuing the problem of Origin of Life from the "nuts and bolts" perspective; trying to recreate a semblance of biological life from the basic elements of inanimate chemistry. This approach, if successful, would at least demonstrate that the initial organisms that began life on earth some 3.8 billion years ago might have "self generated" in some sort of analogous fashion under the then prevailing conditions – but without the help of talented molecular biologists.

Not all scientists agree that that is the way it happened. Many believe that life is just too complicated to have just appeared as a result of some lucky encounter between the right molecular mix in the chemical soup solution of the primordial sea. These scientists point to the least complex life forms that abound on our planet and conclude that even these simple unicellular structures are way too complicated to act as models that instruct how nature alone may have done it. Take e-coli, for example. This simple bacterium is probably the best-understood organism on the planet. Scientists have used e-coli as a basic tool in the study of many aspects of microbiological inquiry. Still, its ten-thousand or so genes represent a level of complexity that so overshadows anything researchers can hope to reproduce in the test-tube using inanimate chemicals. In reality, if life began as a self-generated enterprise, one should expect that the primary first organisms that displayed life functions and gave rise to all of life thereafter would have had to be simple things indeed. But, fifty plus years after that seminal year in molecular biological discovery, scientists have failed to produce molecules that mimic life. Furthermore, the natural world seems to be devoid of examples or analogs of "proto-organisms" in various intermediate stages of transformation from the chemical format into the biological.

Self-generation of life, as one scientist put it, is analogous to a 747 jet self-assembling as a result of a hurricane sweeping through a junkyard full of spare parts. It appears to be just too complicated. The problems for self-generationists are both real and numerous and we will have ample opportunity to point them out.

I am not unaware of the sheer chutzpah attached to the publication of this kind of endeavor. However, new ideas can spark new ways of examining nagging problems. This enterprise represents an in-depth due diligence exploration of the scientific case for Origin of Life by "Rational Design". If the conclusions are borne out, the consequences for the likelihood of our species surviving its technology (present and future) are grim. As such, The 5th OPTION may also represent a timely reality check from a uniquely novel perspective. If I accomplish just that limited goal, I will feel satisfied.

Bryant M. Shiller, Eng
March 2005

Introduction

*The most beautiful thing we can experience is the mysterious. It is the
source of all true art and all science. He to whom this emotion is a
stranger, who can no longer pause to wonder and stand rapt in awe, is as
good as dead: his eyes are closed.*

—Albert Einstein

The following pages reflect the author's rational due dilligence effort at uncovering the true significance of existential being through the exploration of the mysteries of the bio-life phenomenon. The fact that the living experience is a phenomenon shared by every living thing implies that the significance of that phenomenon is shared as well. To answer the questions: "What is life?", "How did it originate?", and "Why does it exist at all?"—is to shed significant light on the questions: "What am I?" and "Why do I exist?" The interesting fact that these questions can simultaneously address and embrace religious, and philosophical concepts in addition to those of rational science—without being paradoxical in the least—yields some measure of the fundamental nature of the subject matter we shall be covering. It is my sincere wish that the reader walk away at the end of this exercise with both an improved understanding of the fundamental mechanics behind the biological life phenomenon together with some genuine recognition of the present challenges that have already begun to threaten the existence of future generations of our species. For, it is only through such understanding and recognition that one can finally come to grips with and accept their true role within the grand scheme of life.

The origin of life (OoL) on the planet earth represents a very special event in its history. Before it happened, there was probably not that much to distinguish the earth from any of the other planets in the solar system. After life began, however, its history represents an astonishing takeover. Hardly a square meter of the earth's surface has escaped life's ubiquitous influence. Therefore, it is not surprising that how life came to be represents one of the great mysteries of all time. There are presently four less-than-satisfactory solutions to the OoL mystery on the table. Our 5th Option makes the case for the Rational Design solution to the origin of life mystery.

The 5th OPTION: The Rational Design Hypothesis (RDH).

PROPOSITION:

> *Biological life is a designed system whose form and function was genetically engineered in order to fulfill a specific design intent here on the planet earth. In this respect, life is a system strategically put in operation in a specific location (our planet), not unlike the way human engineers create and put into operation all kinds of complex systems when and where they are needed in order to accomplish specific goals.*

There is no reason why one could not formulate a scientific hypothesis that states that life on earth was a designed system—the product of intelligence and placed here on planet Earth, quite possibly in order to achieve some specific purpose. Such an approach could reflect the new directions of scientific inquiry into the search for extraterrestrial intelligence (SETI) and would assume that intelligence, in one form or another, exists elsewhere in our galaxy (in order to qualify as the designer of the life system). I believe such an approach could be of tremendous value, if only to fill an existent intellectual void, that would help complete the picture of all possible OoL hypotheses. The implication of a design hypothesis for the OoL on Earth is that the planet may be a splendid habitat to support biological life, but does not necessarily qualify as a likely venue for its self-origin. A Rational Design Hypothesis might consider the design intent or purpose of the system we call bio-life to be knowable. In other words, if the life system (LS) were indeed a product of rational design, then the design intent or purpose may become evident as a consequence of a thorough and successful systems engineering analysis. If we can determine what the system does, we should also be able to understand its purpose. In the process, and with some good luck, this line of inquiry could quite possibly lead us to some strong evidence in support of a design-based OoL. As it turns out, the Rational Design Hypothesis (RDH) will prove to be—not only justifiable as an approach—but as convincing an option as any of the others currently being seriously considered. But, as we shall see, there is an important difference that favors the RDH over all of the other OoL options. That difference resides within the fact that the RDH is scientifically testable. This alone truly raises it to a distinct level of scientific relevancy. No other origin-of-life option can make that claim.

There is little disagreement that once life and the planet came together, the ability of the system of life to adapt to external changes in the planetary biosphere through processes we define under the umbrella term "evolution" were essential for its success. While the meaning of success in this case may indeed be subject to interpretation, we will narrowly define it as the ability of the system of biological life to survive and thrive over the period of billions of years since its inception on the planet. From modest beginnings, life diversified into the myriad examples of life forms we are witness to today. And, the mechanisms responsible for this state of affairs is, indeed, evolution. How did life begin? When did evolution begin? Did they begin at the same time? No sooner do you ask these simple questions, than do other questions come to mind. What was the primordial earth like at the time life was introduced?

Obviously the physical conditions of the planet back then had to have been conducive to both the introduction of the phenomenon as well as its future success. Were the conditions then such that a self-replicating organism could assemble itself from the raw chemicals on the lifeless planet? If it happened here, could it happen elsewhere? Is biochemistry and biology simply a seamless and transparent extrapolation of natural chemical and physical processes? And, if that were the case, was the second law of thermodynamics (dealing with entropy) violated in the process? Has it continuously been violated ever since life began? How did life get its "jump start"? What is the ultimate significance of the existence of biological life on our planet? These are just some of the puzzling subplots that surround the mystery of the origin and continued existence of the life phenomenon.

Are we ever going to have definitive answers to these provocative questions? Before we are through with this exercise we will encounter many more. Extensive investigation and research has taught us a great deal about some of the questions we ask. Still, much more work remains to be done before we can draw any conclusions. The 5th OPTION represents a new way of addressing the age old mystery of the "Origin of Life". Before we are through, it is safe to say you will never quite think of life in the same way again.

The first step is to define precisely the framework and the parameters within which we will work. This will help us to delineate where the different OoL paradigms agree and where they diverge. Let's begin by stating outright that once life did begin and take hold—however that came about—the mechanisms of biological evolution began to operate. That is not to say that there is universal agreement on exactly what those mechanisms are, but there is in place a concensus that the system of life on our planet has the ability to evolve, or change over time. The term evolution has broadened to refer to both the results of such changes as well as whatever operative mechanisms are involved. These permitted the system of life to both thrive and diversify over a period in excess of 3.8 billion years, in response to changes in the planet's physical habitat—that which we call the biosphere. Thus, the only issue separating the different scientific theories trying to explain the existence of life on our planet has to do with the nature of the occurrence of that distinctly singular event—the OoL itself—and the circumstances leading up to it.

The Fragility of Life

Biological life is a rather delicate phenomenon. It can only exist under extremely moderate temperature conditions and only within a protective environment furnished with the necessary materials and energy sources. At the top of the list of requirements are the presence of water in liquid form and readily available carbon from which organic compounds can be formed. It should be noted that the word "organic" carries no implication of biological origin, but rather refers to molecules based on carbon (carbon monoxide and carbon dioxide being exceptions). Dissolved in water, these organics can be made to react with one another in countless ways within the protective environment of the biological cell to produce the complex biological materials essential for life. Traditionally, this description of the environment-sensitive conditions necessary for life processes to occur is meant to convey the simple fact that biological processes are fragile. And, indeed they are.

The extent of the fragility of life becomes truly compelling when we consider that even the conditions for basic chemistry to occur in the universe are comparatively fragile and considerably rare. Just finding enough molecules that could react together becomes somewhat of a challenge when you consider that the density of interstellar space approximates as little as 500,000 atoms per cubic meter (the best earth-bound vacuum chambers can only pump down to as few as ten billion atoms per cubic meter). Sure enough, some atoms stranded in space may chemically combine to form simple molecules, however, most of the dynamic activity taking place in the universe involves stellar activity. In fact, it is only within stars that the majority of chemical elements beyond hydrogen in the Periodic Table of Elements are created. So, without stars, there is no chemistry because there are no chemicals (besides hydrogen, helium and traces of lithium). And, the reactions taking place within stars are basic thermonuclear reactions involving fusion at temperatures in the millions of degrees—much too severe for the incidence of chemical reactions.

Star activity involves the creation of the materials that, given the opportunity and a relatively moderate environment, will react chemically. The fusion reactions in stars account for their abilities in transforming simpler elements (hydrogen-1) into more complex ones (helium-4) throwing off vast amounts of energy, a la $E=mc^2$ of Einstein fame. In the case of our sun, this energy is obtained at the expense of its mass, at the rate of 4.2 million tons each and every second, converting in the process, 530 million tons of hydrogen into helium. Its core temperature is close to 15,000,000 degrees K (cooling down to about 6,000 degrees K at the surface). This is hot stuff, hotter than anything chemistry can withstand. The very fact that chemistry can and does occur here in the planetary environment of our solar system is in and of itself an important indication that this is a special environment—the relatively benign world of planets (and other space junk) composed of the stuff originally manufactured in stellar ovens. So, when we talk about the fragility of life and its survival and thriving on the planet, we are referring to a different order of magnitude again as it refers to special places. We take for granted (and understandably so) that under the appropriate physical circumstances, chemistry will spontaneously and randomly occur under the natural rules that dictate the delicate bonding interactions between atoms to form compounds. Can the same be claimed for the phenomenon of biological life? Can the assumption be made that given the sufficient and necessary conditions that could support life processes, that a self-replicating entity would develop spontaneously, function, and thrive of necessity, under the influence of the same laws of nature that permit random chemistry to occur? These are the kinds of questions that require investigation when we consider the OoL.

If biological life, as we know it, can survive only under extremely limited circumstances, it is important to understand what the sufficient and necessary conditions for life are and the circumstances that gave rise to them on our planet. Absent those conditions, regardless of how life eventually originated on the planet, it simply could not continue to exist. That is to say that if it is too hot or too cold, for example, biological reactions will not take place. We shall examine the geological history of the planet and set the stage for the arrival and thriving of Life. It goes without saying then, that regardless of how you believe life originated, the initial conditions of the biosphere that would permit the biological phenomenon to survive (and submit to the processes of evolution) would have had to be identical.

Options For Consideration

There are at present only four logical possibilities that purport to account for the presence of Life on our planet. And, these four are, by and large, representative of the diverse intellectual camps studying the issue, as well as the state of the art, in the search for the Origin Of Life (OoL). They are herein presented in the chronological order in which they appeared historically.

The First Option: Biblical Creationism

As described in the Old Testament, life on earth was part of a grand Creation (which includes that of the whole universe) which came about as an act of God. Any purpose the creator may have had is essentially considered unknowable.

The Second Option: Spontaneous Abiogenesis (SAb).

This theory states that life is a product of the planet and spontaneously self-generated (within a "chemical soup") when biology (and biochemistry) evolved naturally from physical and chemical processes. Usually referred to simply as "abiogenesis" (a-bio=outside of biology; genesis=origin) the prefix "spontaneous" specifically defines the circumstances under which abiogenesis is thought to have occurred. A host of varied and conflicting scenarios have emerged over the years to account for abiogenesis—the spontaneous self-generation origin of life. On the other hand a significant number of respected scientists assert that SAb is highly improbable.

The Third Option: Panspermia (PS).

The term literally means "seeds everywhere". The theory states that either the complex chemical base that would eventually give rise to life, or ready-made spores or seeds of life, originated somewhere else in space and somehow arrived on our planet to seed the planetary environment.

The Fourth Option: Directed Panspermia (DP).

The seeds of life were self-generated elsewhere and were deliberately sent into space and somehow arrived on our planet. This offers a novel twist over Panspermia by adding the concept of intervention by some technological entity that undertook the difficult problem of transporting existing primitive life forms into outer space. These eventually landed on our planet and served as the seed stock for biological life on earth. No particular purpose is considered.

Is That All There Is?

Spontaneous Abiogenesis, Panspermia and Directed Panspermia are the products of scientific inquiry and essentially date from the twentieth century. But, the scientific community must face up to the consequences of their present approach to the mystery of OoL in as much as:

1) After decades of intensive investigation, the SAb theories have still to yield a plausible workable solution to the OoL problem. In fact, the deeper SAb scientists dig into the complexities of building an organism from the bottom up, nuts-and-bolts approach, the deeper they find themselves in difficulties that has led many (the author included) to seek alternate rational solutions.

2) Panspermia and Directed Panspermia are lesser players in the Origin of Life mystery game and relegated to the status of logical alternatives that "cannot be entirely discounted", as some scientists have put it.

3) So preoccupied is the scientific community with the SAb bottom-up approach, they have failed to properly consider all the alternatives implicit in a design hypothesis, lumping all such ideas together under the umbrella of Creationism, and therefore, deemed to be non-scientific. The closest science has come to offering any alternative to SAb are the Panspermia and Directed Panspermia initiatives which seem to resolve some difficulties posed by SAb but raise others just as serious. These logical alternatives inspired, no doubt, by the seemingly insurmountable difficulties posed by any SAb hypothesis also suggest that any and all scientific OoL options deserve examination—if only to cover all possible bases. The fact is that the obstacles that confront the interfacing of inanimate chemistry and living biology appear to many scientists to be formidable. But, aside from the above four options, they are indeed running out of possible OoL lines of inquiry. At present, the only base left open and untried is a serious look at the design option from the strictly rational point of view. That's where this exercise—The 5th Option comes into play.

Biblical Creationism—the first option—predates the scientific way of thinking by thousands of years in one form or another. One of the dilemmas that creationism faces today is the non-empirical (i.e., non-scientific) legacy of its methodology. Before the advent of the scientific method, unquestioned religious dogma dictated the answers to nearly all-important questions. The answers they provided emanated from an ancient tradition that maintained its own esoteric logic. Today, however, religious dogma has been largely superceded where the experimental methods of empirical science can be brought to bear. Each one of us is witness to the ongoing changes in our collective understanding of the universe in which our lives are played out, resulting directly from the escalating research in all of the scientific disciplines. In contrast, religious views persist in those areas that science has as yet failed to provide adequate answers for—including the mystery of the OoL on our planet. Human nature being what it is, it can be expected that until science can provide definitive answers to the OoL question, Creationism will endure as a viable option for many—one more unproven hypothesis among a host of other likewise unproven hypotheses.

Bridging The Gap:

As things stand at present, the scientific and religious approaches to the question of OoL are not really in competition because their respective investigations in search of answers involve totally different methodologies. What competition does exist between the two is continually cast in an atmosphere of suspicion as well as disbelief (literally). The result has been an interesting effect each has had on the other resulting in both adopting and maintaining myopic intellectual postures concerning key elements each holds important with respect to life and its origin. As such, science has not as yet seen fit to consider the possibility of a scientific version of the design option Creationists hold dear. The reasons for this may lie in part with the fact, as stated, that generally speaking, scientists automatically equate design with religious Creationism; design is seen to be merely an extension of religious belief, and therefore outside of the scientific domain. The fact is that while the design concept may, of necessity, include creationism, the design concept need not be confined to religious doctrine alone, but could logically be subjected to rational scientific inquiry. In a related way, religious adherents have yet to re-consider biological evolution such that it might logically be compatible with the creationist doctrine. It is our considered belief that the time has come for each side to re-evaluate its respective positions, in the light of some recent advances in a variety of scientific disciplines that bear on these issues. A 5th option, the subject of this inquiry, goes a long way towards bridging the gap that separates the two.

No serious investigation of a rational design hypothesis can be found in the scientific OoL literature. Clearly, the design option can only be taken seriously by the scientific community if every attempt is made to separate it from its traditional religious Creationist legacy, and if it is looked at from the perspective of a purely rational approach. Then again, design is not really the province of scientists, is it? If we are going to talk design, we are, in fact, entering the realm of the engineer, because, design is what engineers do! And, the approach that engineers bring to the study and synthesis of all kinds of systems is the rigorous discipline referred to as: Systems Engineering (SE). It shall prove to be the ideal investigative tool in the systematic exploration of the form and function of the system of biological life on our planet. We will use the versatility of SE to effectively gain a unique understanding of what life is, and what it is doing here on the planet earth. The results and conclusions will effectively establish the Rational Design Hypothesis (RDH) as an important missing link in the efforts—not only to clarify the nature of the OoL question—but also to resolve a number of relevant and related issues that have so far only confused the debate. Indeed, the time is ripe for a 5th option—the RDH—to take its place among the other players seeking answers to the mystery of the OoL.

1. Back to Square One

*"The effort to understand the universe is one of the very few things that
lifts human life a little above the level of farce, and gives it some of the
grace of tragedy.*

Steven Weinberg (1933–), Physicist

Before we examine in detail the various options competing to explain the OoL, it is essential to grasp a bit of the history of the environment of our host planet that proved to be ideally suited to such a phenomenon. Today, planet Earth and the Life System (LS) it supports are bound up in a symbiotic kind of relationship such that it is almost impossible to separate the two. But, while each has and continues to affect the other in substantial ways, they remain two distinct entities. Obviously it was not always that way since life was introduced to the planet hundreds of millions of years after the planet came into being.

Could life as we know it have originated and thrived on some other planet? Or is there something compelling about our planet, something special about planet Earth that made it "the" candidate—some believe the only candidate in the universe—where life exists? We shall examine both the phenomenon of bio-Life, as well as its planetary locale, in order to try and fathom the coming together of the two. To be more precise, we shall not take it as a given that Life should, of necessity, have arisen in this particular place. The fact that it does, indeed, exist here, plus the additional fact that it came into being a specific amount of time after the birth of the planet, and not simultaneously with it, is what separates the two and gives rise to the monumental question of the OoL.

The Planet Earth and Life: A Brief Chronology

The sufficient and necessary conditions for the existence and survival of any kind of primitive biological organisms within any habitat include suitable energy sources, benign temperature limits, and protection from hazardous radiation. Biological life as we know it depends on a critical list of chemical elements and compounds—including carbon, which provides its structural basis and water used as an interaction medium. In addition, hydrogen and nitrogen have significant structural roles, phosphorus is important for energy storage and transport, and sulfur is critical for the three-dimensional configuration of proteins. Interestingly, the elements that make up the earth and upon which biological life depends predate the origin of our sun and in fact are complex products produced by earlier generations of stars. Let's begin at the beginning.

A) Cosmic Time-Line:

It is thought that our universe (matter, energy, space and time) was created in a violent explosion called the Big Bang some 13.7 billion years ago. It always amazes me when scientists describe the origin of the universe with a blow-by-blow description in terms of time and size. For example, it is stated that after several trillionths of a second (10^{-12} sec), the universe was the size of a grapefruit, or so, with temperatures in excess of a trillion degrees K. In fact, scientists have established with some degree of confidence a description of the universe back to a single billionth of a second—a moment referred to as one of "infinite temperature". Such conditions permitted the existence of only the basic building blocks of matter—so-called quarks and gluons—that would eventually combine to form protons and neutrons. And, today, the size of the universe is discussed in terms of billions upon billions of galaxies containing billions upon billions of stars and stretching untold billions of light years across (all due respects to Carl Sagan). Scientists speculate that by the time things settled down (within the first few minutes following the Big Bang), more than 99% of the universe's mass condensed into nuclei of hydrogen and helium, the two lightest elements. The rest became lithium, the next element in the periodic table. Eventually, under the influence of the local forces of gravity, gaseous matter coalesced into a vast mosaic of galaxies separated by voids in between.

It is thought that our own Milky Way Galaxy came into being some one billion years after the Big Bang, probably as a consequence of the collapse of such a vast gas cloud.[1] It is a massive spiral assemblage of a hundred billion stars, more or less, including our Sun. The area around our galaxy is populated by about twenty other galaxies bound together gravitationally that comprise a small cluster, which we fondly refer to as "the local group" (Our nearest neighbor and sister galaxy, the Andromeda Galaxy, is a mere 2.2 million light years away[2]). This, in effect, describes the stellar neighborhood in which we find ourselves. But, the most interesting aspect of galaxies are the stars that comprise them. While stars begin as gaseous hydrogen clouds that coalesce under the attraction of the forces of gravity, they only become stars when they ignite into nuclear furnaces under the intense heat and pressure brought about by those very same gravitational forces, and here is where the interesting action occurs. For it is from within these nuclear furnaces that complex matter in the form of chemical elements is created. By complex matter I refer to those elements of the Periodic Table without which chemistry (and biochemistry) could not take place. At the heart of the process is the phenomenon of fusion of the nuclei of atoms whereby stellar alchemy transforms hydrogen atoms, the original basic matter from the Big Bang, into those elements higher up on the table of elements, spewing out vast amount of energy in the process. Now, most importantly from our point of view is the fact that not all stars have the same kind of beginning. Their composition varies with the materials from which they are formed.

B) A Star Is Born:

A first generation star, one that was formed from virgin hydrogen gas around the time the galaxy came into being, can only produce a limited number of elements within its nuclear furnace. This is because at some point the process itself cannot overcome the strong nuclear forces present within the nuclei of elements already formed, and therefore there is a limit to the size and distribution of elementary particles within the atomic nucleus that can be produced by fusion. The exact number of heavier elements a star can create from the hydrogen and helium fuel within its nuclear furnace depends on the size of the star and the temperatures of its interior. Novae and supernovae are classes of stars that can produce heavier elements. (Very massive stars can produce atoms as heavy as iron but not further.) Eventually, when such a star runs out of nuclear fuel one of several things can happen, depending on its size. Once its nuclear furnace begins to wind down, the balance of forces holding the star together become upset. When the force of gravity is no longer balanced by the outward radiating explosive nuclear forces the star tends to collapse in upon itself. Smaller stars end up as so-called white dwarfs and over time slowly fade from sight. Larger stars, however, may collapse so rapidly—exploding in the process. The resulting cataclysm may produce sufficient energy to transform the original products of fusion into new elements higher up on the periodic table, reaching atoms as exotic as those of uranium and gold. Such an exploding star, referred to as a supernova, literally blows out all the new matter created, as well as that stored within the body of the star during its lifetime, and it is this material that becomes the raw stuff from which a new generation of stars (and in our case, planets as well) are created. Stars and planets that form subsequent to such a supernova inherit these heavy elements as part of the interstellar cloud from which they are formed. It is thought that our sun, defined as a yellow dwarf star, is such a second generation star, and more importantly, that our solar system results from the products of the explosion of a first generation supernova star. Furthermore, the higher and heavier elements of the periodic table were created in the intense heat and pressure that characterize the death throws of such a first generation star, without which, some of the crucial chemical raw materials of biological life, as we know it, would be missing. These include carbon, nitrogen, oxygen, phosphorus and sulfur. The consequences of this fact for the existence of life on our planet are critical, as we shall see.

So, somewhere among the 100 billion stars that comprise our disk-shaped Milky Way Galaxy sits this rather obscure solar system comprising our sun—a middle aged yellow dwarf star, and its nine known major planets (plus at least sixty planetary satellites, countless asteroids and comets), one of which (the planet Earth) serves as home to us all (biological Life). The fact that the solar system forms a single component within the Milky Way Galaxy was only discovered about 70 years ago. To provide a sense of the vastness of the dimensions involved, let's play galaxy trivial pursuit for a moment: Our nearest neighbor star—Alpha Centauri, is 4.3 light years away from our sun and within a diameter of 17 light years are sixty known stars. Our Sun, a middle-aged star is located quite far from the center of the galaxy—some 25,000 light years away. The whole galaxy (stretching a diameter of 100 thousand light years) is spinning and it is estimated that one revolution of our sun in its orbit about the galaxy center takes approximately 200 million years traveling at a radial velocity of 230 k/h.[3] And, of course, where the sun goes, it takes us all along for the ride.

c) The Planet Earth—Home Sweet Home:

The Earth, with a diameter of nearly 8000 miles, is a comparatively tiny planet. It is the third planet outward from the sun, from which it is 93 million miles distant. (The sun, at the center, is the real heavyweight in the solar system, containing within itself 99.9995% of the total mass.) The early history of our planet, from its inception some 4.5 billion years ago until the time hundreds of millions of years later when life became evident on the planet, (if someone were to look) is sketchy at best.

d) Age of the Planet—A History of Time:

The age of the planet has always been attended with controversy as well as diversity. Many of the earliest civilizations treated the earth's creation as part of the question of the origin of the Universe. The Han Chinese believed the universe was destroyed and recreated every 23,639,040 years.[4] Contrast this with Anglican archbishop James Ussher's famous calculation in 1658 of the actual moment of creation (later refined by John Lightfoot) at 9 o'clock in the morning of October 26, 4004 BCE. This would make the present age of the universe just 6 thousand years old. To top it off, he even considered his date accurate to within one year. It wasn't before the mid 18th century that the formation of the Earth was separated from that of the universe. Witness the frustration of most naturalists at the time, as represented by James Hutton in his classic "Theory of the Earth" written in 1795: "We find no vestige of a beginning, no prospect of an end".

But, some ambitious researchers were at work examining stratified rock formations and 70 years later, in 1862, Lord Kelvin, using Isaac Newton's laws and Fourier's theory of heat conduction, calculated and put forth the notion that the earth had formed somewhere between 20 and 400 million years ago. Of course, coming from a physicist—his work was resented by the geologists of the day, who questioned his audacious meddling in their domain. Besides, they had grown comfortable with the idea of "unlimited time", inasmuch as few papers were being written on geochronology. It is interesting that Charles Darwin greeted Kelvin's low-end estimate as "an odious spectre" that clashed with his own minimum 40 million year time frame required just for the evolution of complex organisms. The discovery of radioactivity in 1868 and its relationship with heat introduced a new factor into the calculations of earth formation. But, it was the discovery of radioactive decay in rocks and later the discovery of isotopes and the physical laws that specify the decay of radioelements, that eventually provided scientists with a reliable geological time scale. By the time accurately calibrated dating techniques were introduced it was realized that they finally had in their hands a way to date all of geological history. How could they be sure? Well, a sample of uranium 238 isotope, no matter what its origin, will gradually change into lead. And, this transmutation will occur at a steady rate, such that half of the uranium atoms will change into lead in 4.5 billion years[5]. There is no reason to believe that the nature or the rate of this process was any different in the very remote past when the universe was young. The history of these nuclear events is written in the chemical elements out of which the Earth and the rest of the universe are made. In 1955 Clair Paterson and colleagues of the California Institute of Technology first determined the age of the solar system by dating meteorites. This determines the primal age of the earth at 4.5 billion years. A still more accurate dating technique, "single-crystal laser fusion dating" has reduced errors to less than 1%[6]. Scientists claim to have found a clear record in the rocks of Greenland of when the Earth's first crust formed: within 100 million years after the planet itself coalesced.[7] Exactly when and how the atmosphere, seas and landmasses appeared is open to conjecture but a vague picture emerges as the scientific evidence from diverse sources is collected, shuffled and evaluated. This much is known:

E) RECIPE FOR A PLANET:

The equilibrium-condensation model[8] of how the solar system formed suggests that whether the planets of our solar system are the result of condensing gas and dust or a cloud of colliding meteorites and meteoric dust[9]—gravitational forces caused the material to accrete (come together) and the material composition of the Earth and the other planets were affected by their respective distances from the sun. The same model also strongly suggests that the formation of planets is a normal by-product of the formation of stars. An intense heat, produced by gravitational energy and radioactivity of some atoms, caused the earth to become stratified. The heavier material (nickel and iron) gravitated to the center; the lighter collected nearer the surface. Contraction produced heat and melting, such that gradually, three distinct layers have emerged.: The molten mostly iron core; the relatively pliant upper mantle; the more dense lower mantle, consisting mainly of dense silicate minerals; and the crust (consisting of less dense silicate materials), the top layer of which comprises the hydrosphere (water) and lithosphere (rocks and soil of the terrestrial surface)—both of which in turn form part of the biosphere—the habitat of life on the planet.

F) LIVING CONDITIONS:

Any planet upon which life finds itself must have the necessary characteristics and conditions that could permit the biological processes of life to function. These conditions can be defined as the narrow limits within the attribute spectrum of such a planet's biosphere which must serve as habitat for living things, that are both sufficient and necessary in order to permit the complex molecular biological reactions of life. Conditions such as moderate temperature limits, availability of water in liquid form, essential chemicals, availability of sufficient sunlight, and protection from damaging energy rays arriving from space are essential considerations in the study of the survivability of biological organisms. So, it can be assumed that prior to the advent of such suitable environmental conditions on Earth, biological life—no matter how it might have gotten here—could not have survived because the minimum conditions of a biosphere habitat for life were not yet present. Then, once the planetary biosphere conditions were sufficient to support bio-life and the origin of life event could and did take place, the life system (LS) had to be able to adapt and adjust to all kinds of dynamic changes to the biosphere that would challenge continually its very existence. It is essential to understand this relationship between the LS and the planetary biosphere upon which it is dependent, in order to comprehend the perseverance—bordering on tenacity—required of the LS to respond by way of adaptation to those changes. But, most importantly, these same responses and challenges must be faced and overcome by any proto-molecules of life that had any intention of spontaneously sprouting into an emergent life form (SAb) or, for that matter, falling to earth from outer space (PS and DPS), as these respective origin of life options would suggest. The long history of bio-life on this planet, however it originated, is testament to the reality that the LS has met these survival challenges to date and that as a survival systems go, it comes well equipped to do so. No catch phrase better characterizes the system of bio-life on our planet than its "tenacity for survival". But, conditions today are not what they were some 3.8 billion years ago when life is thought to have originated. Back then; a truly astonishing event occurred on the inanimate earth, which heretofore had no history beyond the harsh primordial conditions of the inanimate planet. For, where there existed only inanimate chemistry began somehow the life processes of biochemistry and biology. Thus, before any characterization of "tenacity" could be applied to the wonder we call life, the fledgling phenomenon had to first appear on the planet (by whatever OoL option), and then had to survive the initial ordeal as well. There are effectively two separate and distinct questions that attend any consideration of the OoL:

1) How did the phenomenon of complexity we call life get here in the first place? And then, after it began,

2) How did biological life manage to overcome the thermodynamic forces that mitigate against complexity wherever and whenever it occurs in nature? While this is an interesting question in its own right, it becomes significant once we understand that life-system survival over time requires not just the maintenance of system complexity (biological processes are by nature complex) but increases in complexity as well—simply to accommodate evolutionary processes—without which adaptation to short and long-term changing planetary conditions could not occur. These are mysteries that continue to plague the imaginations of philosophers and scientists alike. Our inquiry here continues the tradition.

g) A Recipe For Life?

Now, it would have been nice if after the planet had formed (as described above), it had gone through a period of cooling and change and eventually settled down to an equilibrium steady state. Then, any life-form(s), regardless of how it might have originated could have had a relatively easy time of settling in to such an ambient state characterized by stable and unchanging conditions. If such had been the case, then the original life form(s) and its descendents might not have had to contend with the many challenges posed by changing global conditions—changes our ancestor organisms actually had to face. The fact is that however life originated on our planet, the planet at the time was going through changes that were nothing short of revolutionary. As a result, the new biological phenomenon quickly had to adapt to "life in the fast lane" just in order to survive.

Severe convection currents within the earth's mantle caused the thin crust above to move continuously and there were no stable land masses during the time leading up to the OoL on the planet. We know from radioactive dating that the Acasta gneiss group of metamorphic rocks in northern Canada (the oldest known intact piece of the earth's surface) is nearly 4 billion years old[10]. This proves that there was some continental material only a few hundred million years after the earth's formation. The primitive atmosphere of the early earth probably was produced by the outgasing from the interior, particularly by volcanic action. As a result, the primordial atmosphere was thought to have consisted of water vapor (H_2O), nitrogen gas (N_2), and carbon dioxide (CO_2) with only trace amounts of hydrogen.

(Lightweight atoms such as hydrogen would have been lost as the earth formed due to earth gravity's inability to hold them). We call such an atmosphere "reducing" because it lacked free oxygen as opposed to the oxidizing atmosphere of today. While this estimate of the composition of the primitive earth's atmosphere is subject to revision, one thing is certain: as the earth cooled a critical temperature was reached at the surface permitting the vast amounts of water vapor to condense and form the oceans. The critical aspect derives from the fact that if you don't have water in liquid form, you can't have biological life. It's as simple (or as complicated) as that. And, once you have water, you also have a whole variety of chemical reactions that can occur within the many possible substances that can dissolve to form localized aqueous solutions.

An additional critical factor concerns the planetary distance from the sun. This is one of those very special criteria for life to exist on any planet and has been given its own classification: the "ecosphere". This refers to that small range of distances from a star (in our case, the Sun) within which temperatures are suitable for bio-life to function—where water may exist in liquid form and an atmosphere may be retained without boiling off into space. What is decisive is that specific combination of distance and energy emanating from the star's surface through space that produces just the right amount of radiated energy per square meter received at the planet's surface. Not too much, nor too little—just right.

The ecosphere of the sun includes the Moon and the planets Earth and Mars. The Moon lacks an atmosphere and water (although some evidence coming from the Clementine moon probe suggests the presence of ice)[11] and is alternately scorched and frozen between temperatures that range from—190 to +117 degrees C. And, Mars fares no better having too low an atmospheric pressure (6 millibars compared to Earth's 1013.25). Beyond the ecosphere of the Sun, both Mercury and Venus are ruled out as possible abodes of bio-life (they are too hot) as are the outer planets of the solar system (they are too cold). Seen from this perspective, the planet earth appears to be a very special locale indeed.

Were We Expecting Visitors?

It is within this delicately balanced ambiance that life originated on planet Earth. And, ever since, it has not let up for a moment. Over the course of its long history, the system of biological life has managed to weather its evolutionary storms (you and I are witness to that fact) and to date has logged some 3.8 billion years of uninterrupted activity. At the present time we have identified some 400 thousand plant species and 1.2 million animal species (many more millions have yet to be identified) that make up the LS, and it is considered that 99% of all species that ever existed have become extinct.

So, we have a dual set of dynamics at work when we attempt to describe the origin and existence of life on earth. First we have a planet in the throws of dynamic planetary forces (radioactive heating, volcanic, geologic, chemical, and weather to name just a few) upon which has somehow emerged a biological system of living things that must thrive, keep pace with, and continually adapt to its ever changing environment—all from the word go. As we shall see, this is quite a feat! But, it happened and life goes on and we want to get to the root bottom of this extraordinary phenomenon.

The history of our planet is written in its rocks and reflects the history of geological change. By the same token, until recently, the history of its inhabitants could only be be found within the fossil record strewn about geologic strata. Today, molecular biologists can peruse the genetic library of living things written in the medium of DNA that reflects the comparative history of the evolution of life. Thus geology, paleontology and molecular biology go hand in hand in the modern quest to determine the history of life on our planet, including its origins. Geologic history began when the crust first formed some 4.6 billion years ago as determined by radiometric age-dating of the oldest rocks and meteorites that avail themselves to investigators. And, of course biological evolutionary history dates from the very beginning of bio-life, or does it? As we proceed, it will become apparent that the way one considers evolution and its history is directly dependent upon how one believes life originated on the planet. We will have occasion to explore these ideas in depth. But, first we will organize the history of life on our planet along the four principle geologic eras that have been defined:

Precambrian Era: began 4.6 billion years ago; includes the first 4 billion years of earth history (85% of all geologic time); comprises Upper (later), Middle, and Lower (earlier) Precambrian; Key event— OoL on the planet some 3.8 billion years ago, remained essentially unicellular for the next 2 billion years. The Cambrian, which follows, comprises the following notable eras.

Paleozoic Era: lasted from 600 to 225 million years (10% of geologic time); Key events—all complex life forms (both aquatic and land based) evolved, three of the five greatest extinctions took place, preceding the dinosaurs.

Mesozoic Era: from 225 to 65 million years ago (4% of geologic time); Key events—mass extinction precedes Jurassic and Cretaceous periods; the dinosaurs reign over the land supreme.

Cenozoic Era: embraces last 65 million years (1.5% of Geologic time. Key events—mammals replace dinosaurs as dominant life form on land following extinction caused by catastrophic collision of planet by immense extraterrestrial object. One mammal in particular develops technology that threatens the future of land based life. (Next great extinction anticipated?)

The Oldest Fossils

Paleontologists have been searching for evidence of early life since Charles Darwin unleashed his theory of evolution upon an unsuspecting public in 1859. He argued that complex organisms arose from simpler ones and indeed, in his time, the earliest life forms known were those from the Cambrian era. The fossil record at the time of Darwin indicated that a whole cacophony of complex life forms—snails, clams, worms, trilobites—seemed to appear out of nowhere in the distant past. Any attempts to find the precursors to these ancient creatures drew a blank. It was as though the Cambrian period produced an explosion of multicelled creatures out of thin air. The fossil history that preceded this phenomenon seemed to be wiped clean. All this was about to change in 1954 when Stanley Tyler, a geologist, and Elsa Barghorn wrote an inconspicuous report in the journal Science indicating they had found on the north shore of Lake Superior microscopic fossils embedded in a 2 billion year old rock formation known as the Gunflint—inconspicuous because paleontologists at the time were reluctant to accept the evidence[12]. The fact is that, until then, they were used to seeing the multicelled, hard-bodied fossils emanating from the Cambrian period and had no way of knowing that only microscopic unicellular organisms inhabited the planet exclusively during the first 2 billion years of life history. Compounding the problem was the difficulty in accepting the premise that such organisms could be preserved in rocks during billions of years. Then J. William Schopf, a student of Barghoorn, wrote his thesis on the same Gunflint material and reopened the case that until then drew little interest. Finally in 1965, the definitive description of the discovery published a decade earlier was publicized and things have not been the same since. Schopf himself has led the way in searching for formations that might harbor evidence of early microscopic life. And, that's how he wound up in Australia searching for evidence of life stretching back to the Archean Era—the oldest segment of the Precambrian (2.5 billion years back to the formation of the planet).

The oldest evidence of life on earth is in northwestern Australia at a site, strangely enough, called the North Pole. Here in a group of sedimentary rocks 3.5 billion years old (referred to as the Warrawoona group), paleontologists have discovered fossil evidence of early life: fragile strands resembling microfossils of ancient microorganisms. These were found to resemble the matted microorganism colonies produced by so-called blue-green algae of today known as stromatolites. These and other remains of microscopic algae and bacteria have been found in well-preserved sediments and their discovery within the past several decades has pushed back our estimate of when Life on earth originated from 650 million years (as far back as the macroscopic fossil record goes) to the 3.5 billion year age of the tidal mud flats of North Pole, Australia, where early microorganisms are thought to have flourished. Then, recent discoveries of more fragile microscopic filaments embedded in 3.5 billion year old uncontaminated rock pretty well nailed down the Archean origin of these fossils[13]. In fact six different species of ancient unicellular organisms have been identified. Thus, a major piece of the puzzle of the history of Life on earth has been resolved. And, more recently, discoveries in Greenland found traces of bacteria dating back 3.85 billion years.

A Brief History of Life:

William Schopf continues to be a key player in the pursuit of Life's origins as the director of the "Center for the Study of Evolution and the Origin of Life" at UCLA. He also instigated the Precambrian Paleobiology Research Group which has produced a 632 page primer entitled "Earth's Earliest Biosphere". It attempts to describe the Archean environment, from the evolution of the early atmosphere to the origin of oxygen users to the earliest fossil evidence and geochemical signs of primitive life.

In an article for Discover Magazine written by Wallace Ravven in 1990, Schopf drew some conclusions regarding the history of life on the planet based on his extensive experience searching for and discovering ancient evidence of life. With a variety of fossils compared and analyzed, a compelling portrait of the earliest history of life has emerged:

1) Given the diversity of the species extant 3.5 billion years ago, it is probable that the whole biological process of life began in the preceding 500 million years. Before that time, the planet was probably too violent a place to have been able to support life (meteorite bombardment of the planet's surface, intense volcanic activity and too high ambient temperatures).

2) Once life originated, microorganisms were the only lifeforms in the following 2 billion years, during which time the gaseous composition of the atmosphere began to change—from reducing to oxygenating. (The source of atmospheric oxygen is considered to be cyanobacteria, ancestral forms of which have been among those fossil remains that comprise the ancient microorganism fossil record. These blue-green algae make up the top portions of modern stromatolites and are oxygen producing photosynthetic organisms. They use the sun's energy to drive their own metabolism taking in carbon dioxide and liberating free oxygen in the process.)

3) As the oceans became saturated with dissolved oxygen, rusty sediments continued to form over the 2 billion year period, continuing until all the iron ions in the water were oxidized. Only then could sufficient free oxygen flood the oceans and atmosphere for other forms of life—oxygen dependent life—to evolve. Microfossils of such life-forms have been identified in a 2.1 billion year old iron formation in northern Michigan, suggesting that free oxygen was a significant component of the atmosphere between 2 to 2.5 billion years ago.[14]

The history of life on Earth is essentially the story of how life evolved from simpler to more complex organisms since its inception some 3.8 billion years or so ago. As we have seen, for the first 2 billion years of that story, only pond scum (microorganisms) was life's sole representative on the planet. But, as noted above, important things were going on. While life began in a very harsh and unfriendly environment, it began to react within and make complex and important changes to the life-dependent biosphere. Among the most important changes was the abundance of free oxygen emanating from organisms enhabiting the oceans. But, this was not good news to most of the other microscopic inhabitants of the time. Let's face it, if they and their ancestors survived—no, flourished—for two billion years or so in an oxygen free environment, the prospect of a whole different gaseous atmosphere undoubtedly represented a whole different order of challenge. Even though the increase in oxygen came slowly, this changing gaseous environment represented a monumental threat to the vast majority of lifeforms comprising the system of life that existed then on the planet. Probably the first donors of the oxygen in our atmosphere were the lifeform we refer to as Blue-Green algae.[15] Seen today as ancient precursors to higher life-forms, these smallest and simplest organisms dating back to those ancient stromatolites of more than 3 billion years ago so "polluted" the oceans and atmosphere with oxygen (poisonous to existing life) but created, as well, the protective ozone layer in the process. This fortunate happenstance would permit life to eventually inhabit dry land, free of the lethal dangers from ultraviolet radiation. In stark constrast, the 1976 Viking life detection experiments searching for evidence of present or past life on Mars found the planet surface sterilized by ultraviolet light. Instead of life, they found superoxides that would preclude the existence of a life sustaining biota on the Martian surface.[16]

Time For A Change

Thus, life has been around nearly, but not quite, as long as the planet itself, and for most of that time, our planet was populated by microorganisms. But, the changes that were in store for the descendants of those oxygen-free organisms of that formative period of life on the planet would transform the bio-life system (LS) in unimaginable ways.

For starters, oxygen is a very toxic gas and exposure would have immediately killed off any ancestral progenitors of life. The truth be known, had the system of exclusively anaerobic life that existed 2 billion years ago been subjected to a rapid increase in oxygen exposure, life might have come to an abrupt end right there and then. It is indeed fortunate for us all that inhabit and share the planet today, that the forces of evolution were able back then to keep pace with these dramatic changes and allow our common ancestors to adapt and accommodate the modifications to the new atmospheric composition. Of course we can assume that by the time the effects of atmospheric change were being felt, there were already in existence a sufficient diversity of species on the planet such that at least some could adapt. Unquestionably many could not and became extinct in that their morphologies were totally incompatible with the directions that the biospheric conditions were heading. The change to an oxygen atmosphere (whether in the oceans or the gaseous atmosphere above) forced the total redesign in how organisms utilized and managed energy (metabolism) to fuel their biological activities. Unquestionably, many organisms were not up to those novel challenges. But, we are getting ahead of ourselves. Let's backtrack a bit.

As a result of sophisticated dating techniques and the discovery and analysis of micro and macro fossils, we have a pretty good general idea of the history of early life and the fact that vital evolutionary adaptive forces were an essential component for the survival of bio-life over eons of time. But, by far the most interesting historical period from the point of view of OoL is that which preceded life on the planet—the period which gave rise to conditions and circumstances that would permit biological Life to exist, no less thrive. We understand and take for granted the phenomenon of life once it got going. But, our essential quest is: How did it get going? Star and planet formation seem to take place under quite violent conditions and we are interested in determining what the conditions were less than 1 billion years following the assemblage of the planet that could have given rise to the life phenomenon that is so ubiquitous today. That unique event occurred during the Lower Precambrian period (3.8 billion years ago, more or less).

The Biosphere

The biosphere refers to that part of the planet within which life can function;—a thin envelope variably extending from the surface, 5 to 6 miles into the atmosphere as well as the short distance into the soil, that serves as the environment where life's biological functions take place. It comprises the exposed continents, ocean basins, water and atmosphere. It is the total ecological envelope of the planet that permits life activity. It represents the total physical environment including climate as well as the raw material constituents that living things use in creating and carrying on Life activities. The myriad organisms that play out their lives within the biosphere of the planet owe their existence primarily to the sun's energy and to the interaction of this energy with the elements and compounds found there.

It is the stage upon which all the players of life act out their designated bit parts. Now, we know that living things interact with the external environment within which bio-life can thrive—taking from it solids, liquids and gases in the form of chemical compounds and returning to it other chemical compounds as well as biological material. In the process, the biosphere changes over time in response to this give and take, as well as in response to the climactic and geological changes that naturally occur on the planet, thus creating new conditions which living things must accommodate. But, at any given moment in time, the biosphere reflects the infrastructure of habitat, materials and sources of energy— the essential resources that support all of the lifeforms that make up the LS.

The biosphere of the planet is divided up into a set of terrestrial components: the largest of these are the biomes, encompassing smaller units called habitats, which form major landscapes that reflect different patterns of biological activity. Climate plays the principal role in differentiating between one biome and another. This becomes readily apparent on mountain terrain, for example, where as many as three biomes can function between the lower slopes and the summit, each supporting different kinds of life. And the transitional space where one biome ends and another begins are refered to as "ecotones" where a biosphere phenomenon known as the "edge effect" takes place. Within these special junction zones exist species of each of the overlapping communities as well as species specifically adapted for survival within the space circumscribed by the edges of individual biomes. As might be expected,

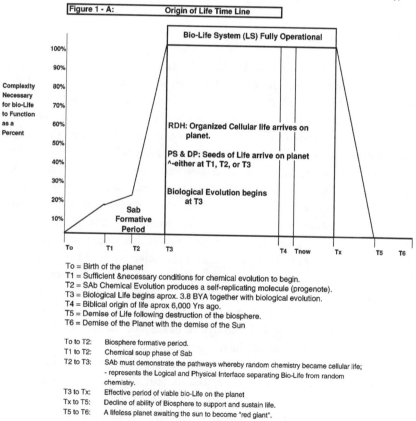

| Figure 1 - A: | Origin of Life Time Line |

To = Birth of the planet
T1 = Sufficient &necessary conditions for chemical evolution to begin.
T2 = SAb Chemical Evolution produces a self-replicating molecule (progenote).
T3 = Biological Life begins aprox. 3.8 BYA together with biological evolution.
T4 = Biblical origin of life aprox 6,000 Yrs ago.
T5 = Demise of Life following destruction of the biosphere.
T6 = Demise of the Planet with the demise of the Sun

To to T2:	Biosphere formative period.
T1 to T2:	Chemical soup phase of Sab
T2 to T3:	SAb must demonstrate the pathways whereby random chemistry became cellular life; - represents the Logical and Physical Interface separating Bio-Life from random chemistry.
T3 to Tx:	Effective period of viable bio-Life on the planet
Tx to T5:	Decline of ability of Biosphere to support and sustain life.
T5 to T6:	A lifeless planet awaiting the sun to become "red giant".

ecotones serve as cradles of biological diversity and play an important role as natural laboratories where the adaptive evolutionary experimentation of species can occur. Species venturing into these zones must deal with some novel conditions all the while remaining close enough to conditions that dominate their own environmental niche. Within these kinds of biosphere settings, all of biological life must act out its designated role. Limited in both space and time, living things function within complex relationships whose existence long preceded their own arrival on the scene of life. Not only is each participant organism a mere transient in the overall scheme of life but each ironically has also the potential to direct the whole system of life in new and important directions. The mechanisms through which this feat is accomplished is referred to as "evolution".

One thing to keep in mind as we proceed is that it is not enough to validate life as simply a product of time and chemistry because neither can account for LS complexity. Evolution, which is found nowhere else in the inanimate universe outside of the LS, is responsible for that. The point is illustrated in the graph (Fig. 1-A) which plots increasing LS complexity as a function of time, for each of the OoL options. Rest assured, complexity and how it was achieved shall figure importantly in our discussions ahead.

Evolution—More Than Just A Theory

It is the extent to which a species can modify over time its morphology, or physical makeup, in order to accommodate biosphere changes that determines long term success in the Life survival game. The mechanisms responsible for this capability are referred to under an umbrella term: "evolution". Evolution is the process by which all living things alive today have developed from the original primitive unicellular organisms that populated the planet at the beginning of life, through all of the changes that have occurred over billions of years. That evolution occurs is not subject to question, and is considered scientific fact. How it occurs is certainly open to question and subject to vigorous debate among scientists. The essential principles of "Darwinian evolution", as stated in contemporary terms, are as follows:

Start with self-replicating organisms that produce offspring incorporating random variations in their genetic information libraries. These genetic modifications can have one of three consequences:

1) They effectively damage a key genetic instruction(s) that endangers the survivability of the new offspring organism. The organism doesn't pass on the defective gene to a future generation either because it doesn't survive long enough to reproduce or because it can't reproduce;

2) The genetic modification can be neutral or benign. In other words, the random change to genetic information does not interfere with the organism's ability to reproduce and its physical expression proves to be compatible with the overall physiological makeup of the species. The mutation becomes inheritable by (and part of the gene pool of) future generations;

3) The expression of the genetic modification confers a distinct physiological advantage on its owner, permits increased survivability over time, and potentially many offspring whose descendants can benefit from it as well. Such advantages may take many forms, however it is essential they have the effect of overcoming successfully the competitive challenges for survival and reproduction of future offspring. This competition becomes keener when there is an overproduction of competitive organisms

such that some, but not all, will survive to reproduce their kind. The selection idea in "natural selection" arises from the resulting culling of the population that occurs when better "fit" individuals beat out their competition at reproducing offspring. As a result, it is their genetic information (including any which confers a competitive advantage) that gets passed on to future generations. The greater the number of such offspring, the greater the genetic influence within the gene pool of the reproducing population of survivors that have met the challenge—sometimes referred to as the "survival of the fittest". The net result produces physical changes in new generations, that result from the expression of successive changes to the genetic information of their forebears and hence, the origin of species modification and of entirely new species as well. When all is said and done, for evolution to work successfully, any physiological modifications must also accommodate any changes simultaneously occuring to a species' environmental niche conditions. Successful evolution, like the tango, thus hinges on the role of two independent participants: the changing biosphere, and the adapting lifeforms. "Adaptation" is the term that describes the phenomenon from the species point of view, as species successfully adapt over time to changing external biosphere conditions. Charles Darwin put it this way: "It is not the strongest species that survive, nor the most intelligent, but the ones most responsive to change".

Charles Darwin was not the first to propose a general theory of evolution. That distinction probably goes to a 17th century Frenchman by the name of Pierre Louis Moreau de Maupertuis, who concluded that hereditary material in the form of particles was transmitted to offspring. He even considered the role of natural selection long before it could be fully appreciated by the naturalists of his day. But, there was confusion as well. The contributions and prominent influence of a fellow countryman, Jean Baptiste Lamarck on evolutionary concepts of his day are today considered to have been on the wrong track.

"Lamarckism" is the coined phrase that defines the concept of acquired traits: that new organs arise from new needs and develop according to the extent of their use. Thus, according to this doctrine, giraffes would have developed long necks, a little at a time, because over many generations individuals stretched to reach the leaves at the top of trees. Each generation, according to Lamarckism, supposedly then passed this incremental increase in neck length to its offspring, resulting in the acquired long-neck trait. The science of genetics eventually showed that acquired traits cannot be inherited. In recent times, it is the science of molecular biology and the understanding of how genetic information is processed that has given rise to a "central dogma of molecular genetics" that stipulates the one-way direction of the flow of genetic information—from the genes to the proteins, and not the reverse. But, as we shall see, when it comes to understanding the mechanisms of evolution, even dogmas can be subject to modification—as has been demonstrated with respect to the central dogma under certain limited conditions at the molecular level.

It was Charles Darwin and fellow English naturalist Alfred R Wallace who, together in 1858, introduced the notion of "natural selection" as the main mechanism of evolution. It has been suggested that Darwin's original theory on the origin of species was an attempt to describe the system of living things according to methodological structures characteristic of "Newtonian" scientific philosophy—as laid out earlier by Charles Lyell and John Herschel[17]. The ideas put forth nearly a century and a half ago by Darwin have undergone some significant modifications and incarnations as a result of much experimentation and observation. His original ideas were essentially based on the accumulating evidence derived from fossil remains of ancient and extinct organisms together with a meticulous attention to the sometimes-subtle differences among related living species. But, even Darwinism has been subject to evolutionary changes over that period of time. Each new phase of Darwinism has been characterized by the emergence of new mathematical tools with which to build models resulting from scientific research. As well, the rediscovery of the writings of Gregor Mendel and the development of population genetics at the beginning of the twentieth century mark a major turning point in its interpretation. In 1901 Hugo de Vries proposed his mutation theory which states that variations in traits among members of a given population result from changes to the hereditary material of each organism. The original Darwinian dynamic concepts dating to the mid-nineteenth century, associated with Newtonian mechanics, had by then undergone considerable change with the introduction of the principles of statistical thermodynamics that characterized the revolution in probability theory. This second phase lasted into the 1940's and was distinguished by the application of the mathematics of probability to the statistical nature of large populations. We shall have ample opportunity to examine and explore the application and influence of statistics on species populations as it impacts on the mechanisms of evolution in general and on the concept of species adaptation to changing external biosphere conditions in particular.

The third phase of Darwinism is associated with the "molecular revolution" in biology and its aftermath. This third phase has considerably expanded the number of concepts and directions that the scientific research has taken. New schools of thought have arisen that reflect these changes. Essentially, they can be grouped into two camps: the classical Darwinians and the developmentalists.

A "Darwinian" is still defined today as an advocate of natural selection, the doctrine that the adaptiveness and diversity of organisms can be explained by differences in the reproductive success of inheritable variations. Natural selection is seen in terms of external factors such as changes in the external environment that affect survival and reproduction—leading to the actual "selection" process.

A "developmentalist", on the other hand, explains the broad range of living forms on the planet in terms of internal factors within the conditions that set up the original evolutionary processes and are built into the genetic makeup of the original organisms. Adherents point to recent indications of a more punctuated evolutionary process in which the genome itself, by means of its own internal properties, throws up highly organized alternatives for selection. In this respect you could include the discredited ideas of Lamarck within the developmental framework because they describe the essential evolution processes as feedback mechanisms, also emanating from the organism itself, although that's about as far as the comparison goes.

Modern day developmentalists, such as Stuart Kauffman are busy working on novel models based on the new dynamics of complex systems that derive from the so-called complexity revolution and the mathematics of chaos theory. This is considered to be the next phase in the quest to elucidate the mysteries that attend an understanding of the evolutionary processes of life. Contemporary developmentalists emphasize the naturally occurring self-organizing properties of biological systems, as opposed to natural selection, in explaining the adaptiveness and diversity of organisms. As yet, no new principles or rules have been detected in inanimate nature to support a theory of self organizing complexity. Still, biological systems (Life), indeed, seem to demonstrate such self-organizing properties. We shall be taking a great interest in these issues, and shall have occasion to support developmentalism from a unique vantage point as we explore the differences between life and non-life. Indeed, this will turn out to be significant within our deliberations in the pages to come.

The question can be asked as to whether, indeed, natural selection and developmentalism represent opposite sides of the evolution coin or are we only involved in an exercise in semantics? Natural selection is the mechanism of evolution that emanates from the environment and is used to describe and emphasize how the external conditions continually present the participants of life with new challenges to overcome. And, there are others, including the mechanisms of mutations that derive from both internal and external forces as well (internal DNA copying errors; damage caused by external radiation and the like). But, effectively, the question developmentalists raise is whether the long term survival of life under the tough conditions imposed by the environment could work unless there was a way for the system of life to either control or limit these kinds of external effects. Coming as they do from the outside, these effects range from slowly evolving biosphere conditions all the way to instant catastrophic change (meteor impact, for example) that, in the course of the history of life on the planet, has wrought complete destruction to large population segments as well as afforded opportunities for adaptive evolution of others. The overall system has survived them all. It is this survival capability, together with the long term ability to create new species as others become extinct, (these are separate phenomena) that emanates from life itself, that developmentalists must firmly establish in order to compete with the more traditional "natural selection" of the Darwinists. And, indeed, we believe they can. Because, the LS does, indeed, contain within itself all the necessary attributes for survival that allow it to take advantage of the very powerful mechanisms that rely on the universal rules within the laws of probability. We shall have ample opportunity to delve further into this phenomenon, for it will turn out in the end to be one of the keys to understanding the limitations of SAb on the one hand and a key argument in favor of the RDH on the other. If, indeed, developmentalism is on the right track, as we shall propose, then where does that leave Darwinism? Frankly, not much different from where it was before. There is no denying that the external biosphere acts and the participants of life react. To this degree, the direction of change in the external environmental conditions are independent of the LS. (We are ignoring the long term modifications to the planet resulting from biological processes as irrelevant to this discussion.) Survival of species depends ultimately on the survival of individual organisms that have that built-in capability. The only point we are making here is that evolution is a sum total of effects that emanates both from the external biosphere (Darwinism) as well as from within the system of life (developmentalism). Just remember, however, that in order for developmentalists to be confident that the LS does indeed control its own evolution mechanisms responsible for long term survival, it would be nice if they were able to demonstrate such built-in capabilities. From the RDH point of view, if life was, indeed, a product of deliberate design, then the description of such strategies becomes the challenge of the RDH as well. In that respect, proponents of the RDH are also developmentalists.

Before we are through, we shall enter the debate alluded to above because of its central role to the whole issue of OoL. These are the kinds of issues we intend to explore as we examine this phenomenon of biological Life on our planet pursuant to determining how it got here. But, before we do, let's examine carefully this abiogenetic "chemical soup" theory, better described as "Spontaneous Abiogenesis (SAb)", to see where its strengths lie, and, of course, to reveal any weaknesses. As we shall come to appreciate, SAb has essentially been treated by the Darwinians as their own unshakable private domain. Their unquestioned loyalty to the SAb doctrine seems to defy some of the current logic that flows from the hard evidence coming out of current research in many areas.

---

[1]Scientific American: Jan 93; p72; S van den Bergh/J Hesser (33)
[2]Galaxies: Harrison House Pub; Timothy Ferris
[3]Scientific American: Mar 81; p92; B. Bok (24B)
[4]Scientific American: Aug 89; p90; Lawrence Badash (32)
[5]Scientific American: Jan 74; p69; David N. Schramm (105)
[6]National Geographic: Mar96; p113
[7]Discover: July 92; p22; Carl Zimmer (119)
[8]Scientific American: p53; John S Lewis (69)
[9]Scientific American: p163; George W. Wetherill (104)
[10]Scientific American: Jan 93; p91; D. York (30)
[11]Discover: Jan 95; p93; (Space 1994)
[12]Discover: Oct 90; p98; (article by Wallace Ravven) (31)
[13]Sc Am: Oct 81; p 64; D. Groves et al (10A)
[14]Science: Feb 5 1993; Vol 259; p835 (Technical Comments) (113)
[15]Scientific American: May 1974, p 134; Book Review of "The Blue-Green Algae" Academic Press (66)
[16]Ames Research (Internet Download)
[17]Nature: Jan 19 95, p208 (Bk Rev:Darwin Evolving/Depew & Weber)

2. The 2nd Option—Spontaneous Abiogenesis

"Nothing is more dangerous than a dogmatic worldview—
nothing more constraining, more blinding to innovation,
more destructive of openness to novelty."
Stephen Jay Gould (1941–2002), Evolutionary Biologist

History:

Enormous successes in the understanding of how life processes function have been attained since the dawn of the age of molecular biology some five decades ago with the discovery of the shape of the DNA information molecule. But, the ability to breech the knowledge gap that separates inanimate chemistry from living biology is as illusive as ever. Some feel that part of the problem holding back answers lies in the fact that until quite recently OoL studies had not really been considered a field of study as such. Ten years ago, interest in the OoL question was concentrated within an international society of several hundred members from all walks of science worldwide—essentially hobbyists, if you will, in the subject. Funding for OoL studies was virtually non-existent and until recently, no degree was given in the field. But, all that has begun to change, with the advances being made in genetic research and the excitement generated within the prospect of unraveling the information locked up in the DNA information libraries of a variety of species. Already a number of genomes have been elucidated including the human genome decoded early in the new millennium. As these advances in genetic research continue, some origin-of-lifers believe that the keys to an understanding of the OoL mystery are to be found within the encoded basepairs that comprise an organisms genetic library. But, make no mistake about it—the only serious direction that such research has taken in the past, and will continue in the future, is in the area of abiogenesis—the spontaneous abiogenesis hypothesis of "life from chemical beginnings".

"Spontaneous abiogenesis (SAb)", better known as the "chemical soup" theory, argues that life originated within the chemical soup environment of the oceans on the planet earth when the "right" organic chemicals combined to form the first self-replicating organisms—by chance and without any kind of outside help. The earliest recorded theories promoting self-generation date back to the Greek philosophers Anaximander and Aristotle with their ideas that life arises from non-living organic matter.

During the 19th century it was thought that the forces of electricity, magnetism and radiation could produce life spontaneously from inanimate matter. It wasn't until the early twentieth century that the chemical soup theory—was proposed by biochemist A. Oparin in the 1920's and independently a little later by geneticist J. Haldane. This "Primordial Soup Theory", as it came to be called, was actually tested (in a series of experiments beginning in 1953) when Stanley L Miller, under the wing of Nobel Prize winning chemist Harold Urey, attempted to recreate what was then thought to be the reducing atmospheric conditions of the primeval earth. Within a sealed glass enclosure were combined methane, ammonia, hydrogen and water (no oxygen). The concoction was then heated and exposed to the simulated lightening of a spark discharge device. Within several days it was confirmed that several amino acids, the life essential organic compounds that link up to form proteins, had been created. The discovery created quite a stir and launched a new experimental field, *"prebiotic chemistry"*, which opened the door to much speculation among biologists as to how bio-life (biological life) might have originated from just this kind of natural chemistry. That same year James Watson and Francis Crick discovered the structure of DNA, the informational molecule in which resides the genetic instructions that direct life. To top it off, Frederick Sanger had recently determined the chemical structure of proteins. Thus was ushered in the age of molecular biology, and with it, the expectation that the very solution to the mystery of the origin of life could be just around the corner. Over the years since, numerous Miller-style experiments using different recipes of gaseous mixtures and energy sources have led to a variety of organic end products, all the while making more seductive the primordial chemical-soup theory proposed by Operin and Haldane some decades earlier. From such promising beginnings and to this day, the SAb hypothesis, an umbrella term that includes all the different abiogenetic terrestrial OoL scenarios (including primordial "chemical soup") continues to be the dominant scientific OoL paradigm.

SAb considers that life began when its constituent chemical components got together and the resulting combination acquired the ability to self-replicate, or copy itself. Then, it is thought, the forces of evolution (chemical evolution, followed by biological evolution) enabled the expansion over time from these humble chemical beginnings into the multitudes of life forms that comprise the complex system of species and organisms that make up Life on our planet today. In the laboratory, clever and sophisticated experiments are continuously being devised and set up in an attempt to influence and cajole elemental biological chemicals into the dance of life in order to try and replicate in vitro what SAb would have us believe occurred naturally within the planet's hostile environment some 3.8 billion years ago. After more than four decades of such activity, during which provocative pronouncements have proclaimed spectacular progress implying near victory, SAb supporters are not really closer to understanding how life originated on our planet than when they started. Many may consider this statement harsh in the light of some truly magnificent and successful research that has elucidated many of life's exquisite mechanisms at the minutest level. However, it seems that as biologists get closer to understanding the details, so too becomes evident how truly complicated this system of life is. It's as though every time SAb defenders come a step closer to understanding life's mysteries, they discover as well additional depths to the mystery with which they must contend.

It is our view that it is not the lack of knowledge or technical expertise in the various disciplines being applied to the task that prevents success in the SAb line of reasoning. Insurmountable obstacles attend any efforts to establish a convincing argument in favor of SAb. In short, and to put it graphically, we hope to show that there is a solid "intellectual brick wall" standing in the way of any abiogenetic SAb scenario on theoretical as well as logistical grounds. Ultimately, we believe that a totally different and alternate hypothesis—the one we shall introduce—will be able to dissolve away these same impediments: will not only be more convincing, but testable as well.

Present Status of Spontaneous Abiogenesis (SAb):

In February 3, 1994, the journal "Nature"[2] announced: "A small meeting….on the origin of life pinned down some important questions and showed how many more remained unanswered….". Under the auspices of the Ciba Foundation in London, the gathering was noteworthy, from our point of view, in that up to that point in time—little encouragement for SAb was evident. In fact, probably the only interesting news for OoL enthusiasts was the discussion on the "formation of hydrocarbons or their chemical derivatives in various kinds of molecular clouds". This news, if anything, may have offered some encouragement to those espousing Panspermia sentiments (the hypothesis that has the spores or seeds of life landing on the planet in space dust). Otherwise, the discussion turned to the efforts on delineating the actual time when the OoL did occur. It was suggested that the first self-replicating entities must have been molecules, and not organisms in the ordinary sense. Further, they must have been "autocatalytic" molecules if they were to escape the consequences of equilibrium thermodynamics (derived from the 2nd law). Also discussed was the question of why 3 billion years had elapsed before fossils of creatures with differentiated cells began appearing in the fossil record. But, from our point of view, the really telling clue to the state of the art of OoL at the time, hung on the concluding statement of the report on the meeting in the scientific journal Nature which, referring to the evolution of membrane channels following that of membranes, states: "Perhaps the next big effort, in the search for the origin of life, should be a careful reading of the journals in the hope of defining the latest dates at which such features could have arisen". I call this the "needle in the haystack" effect. First jumping from the idea that life began as self-replicating molecules then making a quantum leap, as it were, to suggesting that perhaps the secrets to OoL are to be found in biological cell membrane mechanisms. This suggests that rather than narrowing in on solutions to the secret of the OoL, researches were far from any concensus and engaged in hit-and-miss tactics. And, in the intervening years since, despite a huge influx of interest and the publication of copious scientific papers on OoL topics, nothing monumental or even memorable has transpired to effectively narrow the consensus gap. On the contrary, all of the renewed interest in research has simply spawned additional schools of thought with a predictable result: when it comes to SAb theory of OoL, agreement is in short supply.

The origin of life on the planet has a central place in the reductionists' agenda. And, scientists engaged in the SAb—OoL game, by nature are reductionists (those looking to reduce phenomena to their basic principles). They have adopted a principle of sorts by which they intend to play this game, which goes as follows:

"SAb, in order to be successful, does not have to recreate life as it exists on the earth. It would suffice to show that organisms capable of replicating themselves could plausibly have arisen from primordial inorganic matter."

In other words, they effectively want to turn the hands of the clock back to the beginning of biological time and create a chemical entity that can bridge the "chemistry-biology" gap—one that can approximate the first most primitive living thing. And, this ancient ancestor of us all, some believe, may have been a less sophisticated precursor of modern RNA (a nucleic acid—which together with DNA carries the genetic code of all living things). If they succeed, it will force us to confront another important question: Is life on earth a one-shot deal or is it simply a function of universal common forces and influences and essentially inevitable under the "right" circumstances? The answer to that question remains a mystery—and just one of many.

Let's examine some of the many schemes worked up to account for the self-generation origin of Life on our planet: Our aim here is not to get caught up in the complicated details of molecular biology but rather to provide a sense of where the scientific efforts are being waged.

RNA World:

RNA world is an umbrella term that encompasses efforts to bridge the gap that separates simple chemistry from prototypes of complex DNA based cells found in modern organisms.[3] In April 1993, scientists at the Scripps Research Institute in La Jolla California achieved a breakthrough of sorts when they produced synthetic RNA molecules that could self-replicate (make copies of themselves). As copies made more copies, it was found that this unusually talented bit of matter could "evolve", in a sense, the ability to perform new and unexpected "chemical tricks".[4] Naturally, the question for SAb enthusiasts came to mind: Is this how life got started? Perhaps, it is thought, something akin to these were the precursor molecules of modern RNA and DNA. Other scientists at MIT have designed self-assembling molecules that help to elucidate some of the essential principles of self-replication. For the past several decades, the most widely accepted recipe for the origin of life has specified DNA or RNA in lukewarm water plus other chemicals that are assumed to have been part of the primitive earth's atmosphere.[5] Indeed, it is precisely in this manner that DNA replicates in every living organism, under the surveillance of a host of enzymes—and there is the rub. Enzymes are made of proteins, which leaves us with: Where did the first proteins come from, or better yet—where did the first enzyme come from that could help the first nucleic acid (DNA or RNA) replicate? There appear to be significant logical problems that attend a DNA or RNA molecular origin of life. The cell, the basic unit of life, is comprised of proteins. These proteins derive from amino acids linked together in a polypeptide chain. Once folded, this chain becomes a protein, having both biochemical and structural properties. The instructions for the length and amino acid composition of the chain are written in the genetic language within the structure of both DNA and RNA molecules. The catch, as we have seen, is that neither DNA nor RNA can be manufactured without proteins. Question: Which came first, the DNA and RNA, or proteins? This chicken-and-egg problem was partially resolved back in 1982 when it was observed that under certain conditions RNA molecules can behave both as blueprints (RNA or DNA) and catalysts. The discovery of this highly unusual type of RNA inside a unicellular pond dweller called Tetrahymena earned its finders, Thomas Cech and Sidney Altmen of the University of Colorado at Boulder, Nobel prizes in 1989. Until then, RNA was seen simply as a carrier of genetic instructions and not a participant in the action. This particular RNA molecule is able to rearrange its internal structure by cleaving itself at specific locations and then joining certain fragments creating a new sequence and thereby altering the information it carries. Speculation then turned to the possibility that in a similar way at the beginning of life on our planet, a precursor RNA-type molecule, could have served as its own catalyst for self replication (without the help of proteins). Thus, was ushered in the SAb paradigm referred to as "RNA World". The term was coined by Walter Gilbert who described the likely steps involved:

a: The first organisms were simple self-replicating RNA molecules that came together in the chemical soup of the ocean;

b: As they evolved they learned how to synthesize proteins in order to help them replicate faster;

c: Then came lipids that could form a cell wall;

d: Finally, RNA based organisms gave rise to DNA, which served as a more efficient repository for genetic information.

The above scenario defines the grand scheme of RNA World. However, defining how each step could have derived and joining them all in a smooth transition has proven to be no small task. Many efforts are underway to both describe the intervening mechanisms and elucidate how life might have spontaneously abiogenerated from "scratch". Some noteworthy contributions to the debate follow:

ACCORDING TO MANFRED EIGEN:

a: Start with a chemical soup consisting of randomly constructed small proteins, lipids (fatty Acids), and energy rich nucleotides suitable for building nucleic acids;

b: At least one self-replicating RNA molecule forms by chance creating a so-called "quasi-species";

c: Somehow RNA molecules learn to exert control over proteins and a primitive genetic code develops;

d: A variety of actions termed "hypercycles" occur between proteins and nucleic acids;

e: Somehow, through the action of random mutations, competition arises between "compartmentalized" assortments of the same quasi-species, which compete with each other;

f: Biological evolution takes over from chemical evolution as these organisms assemble themselves into formalized cells and ultimately modern life forms evolve.

Eigen led experiments (e.g., Biebricher-Eigen-Luce experiment, 1981) have shown that RNA, with the encouragement of enzymes and other inducements introduced under laboratory conditions can adapt and evolve. Labeled "directed evolution", biologists see this as a powerful mechanism for generating new biological compounds. Others see it more as a poignant example of biological reactions requiring intelligent "direction". In the laboratory, we know it is the intelligent molecular biologists doing the directing. What we want to know is: if Life processes began on this planet all by themselves, whether an initiating "jump start" may have been required to get things going? If so, from where could it derive?

Unquestionably, it is not for a lack of imagination that supporters of RNA World find themselves bogged down in attempting to elucidate the logical steps such an OoL option might have followed. But, in fact, proponents fail to adequately address what is probably the most important step: how did RNA develop initially? What energy source could have fueled the production of the first RNA molecules? This singular challenge alone, unless met, in the end may well doom the whole notion of RNA world. Other problematic questions include, for example:

1) How did phosphorus, a relatively rare substance in nature, become a critical component of RNA? It would have had to be available in the primordial sea in sufficient quantity to actually find its way into any so-called proto-RNA molecule;

2) A key component of RNA is the sugar ribose. However, the same process that yields this sugar produces as well others that tend to prevent RNA synthesis;

3) While synthesized RNA has been shown to be able to self-replicate, it can do so only under carefully controlled laboratory conditions, i.e.: with a great deal of help. RNA turns out to be, as one scientist put it "…an inept molecule", especially when compared to proteins.

Computer Simulations:

A series of computer simulations conducted notably by U. Niessert into the behavior of quasi-species and hypercycles haven't helped raise the confidence level in such schemes. The molecular populations of simulated hypercycles are subject to error catastrophes as well as other serious calamities variously described as follows:

Population Collapse: statistical fluctuations cause the demise of one of the molecular species causing a chain reaction and the total collapse of the population. This study points up the critical importance of population size to the survival of evolving species. We shall have occasion to return to this decisive issue in the later discussions on the mechanisms of evolution.

Selfish RNA: a single RNA molecule changes to a form that replicates faster than the competition and forgets its role as a catalyst. Again, in this case as well, the problem is exacerbated by population size, but in the opposite direction

Short Circuit: occurs when a critical RNA reaction component changes its role such that it catalyzes a later reaction in the chain, thereby contracting the hypercycle into a simpler and ineffectual one.

There is a critically narrow range of population size within which the probability of all three of the above catastrophic occurrences appears sufficiently low. But alas, even then, the lifetime of such a hypercycle converges and becomes finite—hardly the divergent phenomenon required of any originating lifeform that aspires to parent us all. The net result of such studies tends to cast a large shadow upon any theory that attempts to rely upon the uncharacteristic cooperation of large populations of molecules.

Perhaps the nail-in-the-coffin argument against the very logic of RNA world was stated by Leslie Orgel of the Salk Institute who put it bluntly, referring to experiments simulating the early stages of the RNA scenario(s): "You have to get an awful lot of things right and nothing wrong". What the research into RNA world has illuminated to date is the reality that it appears to be just too complicated to be plausible. Orgel himself is inclined to believe that some less sophisticated and dissimilar molecule preceded RNA. And then, once you get away from RNA and start looking elsewhere for solutions, it's like starting from scratch. "That would be a major business," he surmised (i.e., Don't hold your breath waiting for it to happen!).

There has been some success of late in the synthesis of organic molecules that could self-replicate, but, either they do so under the most unnatural conditions, or even then, they do so too accurately to satisfy the critical conditions of evolution. In a sense, the above statement describes two of the most important barriers to any SAb solution of the OoL problem: 1] the necessity for contrived conditions; and 2] the necessity of mutability or ability to evolve. What compounds the problem further is the blatant fact that the simplest life form alive today, a bacterium, is "....so damn complicated from the point of view of the chemist that it is almost impossible to imagine how it happened". These are the thoughts of Harold P. Klein, while he was chairman of the National Academy of Sciences committee reviewing OoL research. And, in the minds of many, despite all the experiments and new knowledge, the goal seems more distant than ever before. Have we really come closer to solving the mystery of the system of self-replicating organisms on our planet since Stanley Miller's famous 1953 experiment? Let's digress for a moment and examine the concept of self-replication (one of life's most obvious traits) from the viewpoint of a mathematician.

Life and The Universal Tool Machine:

It was once considered that a self-duplicating machine was beyond comprehension.[6] The logic of that philosophical position went as follows: It's not difficult to conceive of a machine that could build some simple hand tool, but, a machine producing more complex mechanisms would in principle have to be, again, more complicated than that which it is producing i.e.: a machine reproducing itself would have to be more complicated than itself—a seemingly logical impossibility.

Then along came famed mathematician John von Neumann, who, in the 1940's, defined a "universal constructor" or self-reproducing automaton,[7]. His theoretical device resembled a universal tool machine having at its disposal a large store of parts from which it could self-assemble. Now, outfit this machine with an instructional tape encoded with the instructions for producing and assembling an identical machine. Such a tape and tool machine can then self-reproduce without any insurmountable hurdles. Undoubtedly, such a machine must exceed a minimum threshold of complexity. But, all the instructional complexities associated with the enterprise are taken over by the tape. And in principle, given a long enough tape of instructions and a long enough period of time, at the height of its complexity such a machine could conceivably carry out an arbitrary sequence of taped orders. This description has a familiar ring to it because it metaphorically describes a living organism[8]. What is the basic unit of life, the cell, if not a long tape of DNA encoded with sufficient information to inform its biological tool machine? This biological tool machine is constructed out of sequences of amino acid building blocks which when appropriately folded produce the molecular structures and catalysts of life. The replication of a cell involves nothing more than the invocation of detailed instructions on how to copy the originating structure as well as the full library of ancestral instructions themselves. The construction of the new cell utilizes surplus molecular pieces over and above that required for the normal cell operation and previously stocked within the originating cell for the anticipated purpose.

Once we accept von Neumann's logical scheme for the existence of a mechanical self replicator, the only problem we remain with is not how more complex machines (organisms) could arise from less complex ones, but rather, how could such a process begin in the first place. In other words, where would the first such von Neumann machine originate from? More to the point, in the case of biological self-replicators (organisms), we want to know where the first living self-replicating organism came from?

The following idea flourishes, according to physicist Philip Morrison's appraisal, "within a gap in the implications drawn from von Neumann's original proposition".

Crystal Genes—Life's First Organisms Were Made of Clay?

The idea is not a page taken from a biblical text nor a throwback to creationist dogma, but a rather serious attempt to depict the irregularities in crystal lattices of clay as precursors of RNA. This is the premise explored in *Genetic Takeover and The Mineral Origins of Life* by Glasgow chemist Graham Cairns-Smith. Herein he expands on ideas first put forth in 1966. His approach is two-fold: to address the logical issues at the heart of the origin of any self-replicating machine (biological organism or logical self-replicator a la von Neumann) and to set down the sufficient and necessary conditions to qualify a precursor-to-life scenario. Effectively, Cairns-Smith attempts to simplify von Neumann's criteria of flexibility and versatility, a requisite for any self replicating machine, by insisting that, in the special case of SAb, it would be sufficient to begin with some crude low-tech self-replicator. This, so long as there would be future opportunity of switching over to the von Neumann structure. Thus, no distinction need be required between the instructions for self-replication and the organism itself. The implication is that the replication mechanism could be a physical or chemical function of the atoms of the precursors to biological life themselves, and thus, a precursor candidate for life could have been inorganic and possibly mineral. It is in this spirit that Cairns-Smith introduces his novel and low-tech crystal structures as the precursors to biology. Perhaps he drew his inspiration from Irwin Schrodinger's conjecture[9] in 1945 that the gene might be a giant molecule whose structure was that of an aperiodic solid or crystal. This would explain, according to Schrodinger, why its stability or "permanence" is such that a "very considerable commotion" is required to alter its existing pattern. And, like crystals, the chromosome can reproduce itself. Cairns-Smith's scenario follows along these lines:

The first organisms contained genes, which were in all probability microcrystalline, inorganic and mineral, e.g. Clays, and not at all like DNA or RNA. They crystallized continuously from water solutions that were maintained slightly supersaturated over long periods of time.

We are all familiar with crystals of one form or another, which grow in a saturated solution and have the effect of concentrating in pure form the solute material. What makes the idea of crystal genes appealing is the nature of crystals themselves. Just about all of them have a defect structure (characteristic of the particular individual crystal) superimposed upon their crystal lattice structure, which is a universal function of the material itself. Cairns-Smith perceives, within the defects in individual crystals, an analogy to information storage. When a piece of crystal breaks off from its parent, naturally it takes with it the parent's defect structure, and when the daughter crystal grows, it will do so according to the crystal characteristics of the material from which it is formed, all the while maintaining the integrity of the defect structure particular to its parent. Of course, we are using terms such as "parent" and "daughter" as descriptive metaphors because crystals are not considered to be living entities. However, the analogy works somewhat because we are, after all, looking for the possible progenitors of living things, and SAb must assume that those were inanimate and not yet living organisms, as we understand the term. Cairnes-Smith goes on to describe broadly inheritable surface patterns as a result of the ways in which folding, twinning and surface contact typically characterize crystals. Eventually carbon atoms would have somehow "taken over" and ultimately the emerging organisms would have become independent of their silicate crystals and establish cells to contain the emergent biological machinery. At the time Cairnes-Smith put forth his ideas, most of his colleagues in the field saw his proposal as having, as he puts it: "all the qualities of a bad theory". After all these years, however, those same ideas of his keep appearing in the reviews that attempt to describe progress in the field of OoL.

The same author wrote a follow-up book in 1985 entitled: *Seven Clues To The Origin Of Life*. Within its 100 or so pages, Cairnes-Smith attempts to both delineate and overcome the many obstacles that OoL investigators have been faced with to date. In addition to providing a thorough development of his novel ideas, Cairnes-Smith serves the cause of OoL by elucidating extensively the problems and hurdles which any attempt at SAb must overcome. Appropriately and whimsically he invokes "Sherlock Holmesian" logic and metaphor in recognition of the monumental mystery of it all. Indeed, the whole community of OoL enthusiasts owes a large debt of gratitude for his clarity and business-like approach to the problems facing SAb. In particular, we, who offer alternatives to SAb, avail ourselves liberally of those very contributions, each of which represent, still today, another brick in the wall that separates the SAb of Life (the hypothesis) from the non-life that preceded it. But when all is said and done Cairnes-Smith's low-tech solution to the OoL, as imaginative as it is, suffers from some of the same congenital weaknesses of any SAb proposal—how to bridge the interface between chemicals (in this case crystalline chemicals) and basic cellular biology. The immense physical and logical interfaces that separate the animate world from its inanimate counterpart represent major obstacles preventing any facile extrapolation of the former from the latter.

Metabolism First:

Among the other contenders for SAb solutions includes an interesting scenario that sees life starting as a metabolic process driven by an energy source and taking place on the positively charged surface of mineral pyrite (so-called fool's gold), to which simple organic compounds can bond. The continuing formation of the mineral from iron and sulfur yields energy that could induce the organic compounds to react together and grow in complexity. Accordingly, the first cell might have comprised a pyrite grain enclosed within a membrane of organic compounds. Then again, how do you test such a scenario? It is interesting that these ideas were put forward by a patent attorney schooled in organic chemistry and, of course, having a passion for OoL. (Does that mean the field is open to anyone who cares to play the OoL game?)

ADDITIONAL SCENARIOS:

While surveying all the many theses put forth to account for a bottom-up SAb scenario for the OoL, I am sometimes reminded of the Academy Awards extravaganza for nominating excellence in the realm of cinema and films. The award nominations invariably turn out to be a popularity contest among the academy members. In a sense, everyone who's an OoL fan is in a position to make her or his favorite choice of nomination for "Most Imaginative OoL Scenario Likely to Succeed". In truth, there is a lot to choose from, both in substance and style. The following are added in order to fill out the roster of OoL nomination contenders:

Name: **Double-Origin Hypothesis**
Proposed by: Freeman Dyson
Description: Mathematical simplification that explores the "toy model" of cellular metabolism, interrelating three parameters required by the original living objects: a) the number of amino acid building blocks required; b) the number of distinct sorts of chemical reactions they were capable of catalyzing; c) the size of the molecular population in a chain composing such a form.
Problems: Purely mathematical model with somewhat intolerable correction requirements for a self-replicating system.[10]

Name: **Proteins First Hypothesis**
Proposed By: Sidney Fox
Description: Precursors to proteins called "proteinoids" can be prepared in the laboratory that display catalytic capabilities for a broad range of chemical reactions. When dissolved in warm water and allowed to slowly cool, large quantities of microspheres form that grow and bud off smaller spheres.
Problems: Lack hereditary mechanisms; no real capacity for life-like self-organization.[11]

Trouble in Paradise:

All the above scenarios and numerous less popular others, are grouped under the "Chemical or Primordial Soup" paradigm of SAb. They suggest that life began in the primordial sea and was fueled by the sun's energy. But, in recent years, problems and doubts have begun to plague the very foundation of these SAb ideas, in addition to the particular dilemmas faced by individual scenarios, and have given an increasing number of skeptics additional cause for encouragement and SAb supporters cause for concern:

1) *Reducing Atmosphere:* Recent laboratory experiments and computerized reconstructions of the atmosphere by James Walker of the University of Michigan and others suggest that ultraviolet radiation from the sun would have destroyed hydrogen-based molecules (methane and ammonia) in the atmosphere allowing the resultant free hydrogen to escape into space. How then could organics have formed in the absence of hydrogen? If that were the case, the major component of the then atmosphere would

have been carbon dioxide and nitrogen derived from volcanic activity. Others, such as geologist James Kasting of Pennsylvania State University,[12] raise the issue referred to as the "faint young sun" paradox. The idea is that when the earth was formed, the sun was probably 30% less luminous than at present. If the planet had then the same atmosphere composition as it does today, under those circumstances it would have been just a large iceberg. But it is known that the earth had liquid water early in its history. To account for the difference, Kasting maintains that the early atmosphere must have had a large carbon dioxide component to prevent the sun's heat energy from escaping back into space (greenhouse effect). But, high levels of CO_2 would have prevented the kind of scenario that Urey-Miller experimental results suggest.

Gustav Arrhenius, from the Scripps Institution of Oceanography and others dismiss outright the Urey-Miller experiments contending that the present earth has such a high proportion of water—a strong oxidizing agent—and that there is nothing to show that the early earth would have been water deficient. Recent calculations have shown as well that a significant amount of free oxygen could have been produced by photodissociation of water. In addition, the original idea that the early earth's atmosphere comprised methane and ammonia has not been borne out by the evidence from ancient rocks.[13] Accordingly, the atmosphere would have been more oxidized than originally thought. When zapped by lightning or other sources of energy, such an atmosphere would have yielded carbon monoxide and nitrogen oxide (the constituents of modern day smog and air pollution) rather than the organic compounds produced in the reducing atmosphere of Miller's experiments in the 1950's.[14] Geochemist Everett Shock of Washington University summed up the findings this way:

"The Miller-Urey experiment was a strong foundation because it was consistent with theories at the time. The problem is that subsequent research has swept away a lot of those ideas" (*and continues to do so*).

2) Greenhouse Effect: In addition, calculations have shown that the resultant increased carbon dioxide component would have created a greenhouse effect sufficiently extreme as to raise the temperatures at the planet surface close to the boiling point of water. As such, the atmosphere would not have been conducive to the synthesis of amino acids and other precursors of life as envisaged by the Miller.

If these findings hold, they alone might well spell the end to the chemical soup paradigm. But, even if that were the case, Stanley Miller is not going to see his pet ideas go down without a fight. In a *Scientific American* review on trends in evolution, he asserts that many OoL theories do not merit serious attention. He further complains that such work perpetuates the reputation of the OoL field as being on the fringe of science and not worthy of pursuit. As though in response, James Ferris, a chemist at Renselear Polytechnic Institute and editor of the journal *Origins of Life and Evolution of the Biosphere* counters: "We have all sorts of ingredients in the pot". "Sooner or later", he suggests, "a convincing explanation of genesis is bound to come crawling out." But typical of how things change in this business, a new discovery has appeared on the scene ever ready to offer itself up as a possible alternate explanation within the "chemical soup" paradigm.

Submarine Hydrothermal Vents:

In 1977 deep-sea hydrothermal vents were discovered off the coast of Ecuador near the Galapagos Islands teeming with life. Not just microscopic organisms, mind you, but tube worms and clams as well. Obviously the prime source of energy for these organisms cannot be sunlight. According to John B. (Jack) Corliss of NASA's Goddard Space Plight Center and a member of the team that discovered one of the first such vents, the energy and nutrients needed to sustain the life of these denizens of the deep are supplied by the sulfur compounds emanating therefrom. He argues further that these same vents could have also been the sites where life originated and, most importantly, the location deep under the ocean would have further served as refuge against all but the biggest extraterrestrial impacts, adding that such a venue would have provided: "…a nice, safe continuous process by which you can go from very simple molecules all the way to living cells and primitive bacteria". Continuous as well would have been the natural temperature gradient of the water. And wherever you find a temperature gradient you are surely to find as well chemical reactions—maybe even the one's that could possibly account for an original SAb OoL scenario.

Gunter Wachtershauser's version of an ocean-bottom OoL scenario hypothecates the transformation of basic inorganic chemicals (dissolved carbon and hydrogen rich gases) into the biological building blocks of life through the intermediary of metal sulphide minerals (such as iron pyrite) acting as catalysts. The organic chemist from the University of Regensberg thus envisions the formation of acetic acid from oxygen, hydrogen and carbon—as an important element leading to the formation of the original metabolic pathways leading to the citric acid cycle all living cells have come to depend on for their energy needs.

Further evidence in favor of a hydrothermal vent origin of life hypothesis comes from the genetic studies of single-celled microbes termed "*Archaebacteria*"—organisms considered to have undergone less evolutionary change than any other species alive. According to Carl Woese of the University of Illinois, these organisms thrive in temperatures exceeding the boiling point of water and many prefer an oxygen-free and acidic atmosphere. Some thrive in a sulfur environment; others in a high salt environment. Woese's investigation of the evolution of bacteria has revealed Archaebacteria to be a totally separate lifeform classification—as different from other bacteria as ordinary bacteria are from plants and animals.

More in support of hydrothermal vents as significant contributors to the survival of early life came from studies conducted by biologist Norman Pace, of Indiana University—but with a twist. He considers life as having originated near the earth's surface and then only later having spread to the relative security of the deep-sea vents. He conjectures that the planet's surface was probably too dangerous a place for primitive life to have survived. The deep-sea vents might have provided the ideal sanctuary for some lucky organisms, which would manage to survive to become the ancestors of all existing life. It is thought that vast communities of bacteria may continue to dwell to this day in geothermally heated cracks beneath the mid-ocean ridges. Thus, Pace's somewhat skeptical interjection does nothing to support the idea of OoL taking place at the ocean bottom. In fact, it offers the reverse by insisting that OoL was a surface phenomenon with hydrothermal vents becoming a latter-day refuge for life's early organisms.

This kind of scholarly "give and take" is characteristic of the whole field of study of OoL. It seems that for every interesting new idea, another new and critical interesting idea crops up. While this kind of intellectual activity is virtually ubiquitous throughout science, it becomes an interesting indicator of the actual progress being made within the SAb OoL option. Usually it can be said that as more researchers enter any particular field of study, in time, a general mainstream direction becomes discernible that has the effect of emphasizing a kind of general agreement on the bearing where the solutions are likely to be found. Not so—when it comes to SAb. Of coarse, there will always by intellectual mavericks within any field of study. Their efforts are essential for the progress and advancement of scientific knowledge that begins by breaking with the entrenched traditions of the past. However, as we have witnessed above, when it comes to SAb it can be claimed that there are no genuine traditions to break with. As such it becomes increasingly difficult to tell the mavericks from the mainstream. The bottom line remains that an implied consensus is sorely lacking in the SAb OoL option. There is still, indeed, plenty of room for new ideas.

Complexity and Artificial Life:

Regardless of which SAb scenario one favours, the whole proposition of SAb ultimately rests on an underlying premise: there must exist some as yet undetected principle(s) within the physical laws that control our universe—such that nature tends towards increased complexity. The idea stems from the observation in nature that organization seems to arise spontaneously from disordered conditions that are driven by no identifiable physical laws. This would theoretically account for the spontaneous self-organization process thought to be responsible for the generation of the self-replicating protomolecules that adherents of SAb consider the first necessary stages eventually leading to biological life. Despite seeming contradictions with 2nd law entropy considerations, a school of scientific thought has formed around this controversial complexity idea. I'm not just referring to a group of intellectual concepts but to the Santa Fe Institute, New Mexico—a complexity think tank where some dozen years ago some complex people began to consider new ways of addressing what they term *"complex adaptive systems"* or CAS[16]. This appears to be an umbrella term that attempts to describe the general principles, as yet undiscovered, that are thought to govern all systems of extraordinary complexity, from fields as diverse as economics, immunology, computer networks and nervous systems—to name just a few. There is a feeling among *"complexologists"* (that's really what they call themselves) that all complex systems share the same underlying principles that could constitute a kind of "enchanted criterion" that might be the basis for some *unified theory of complex systems*. Inherent in this view of reality is the concept of *"self-organized criticality"* developed by Per Bak, physicist and one of the founding members of the Santa Fe faculty. His studies of the dynamics of the sandpile in the late eighties have helped to illustrate how complexity could feasibly reside at *"the edge of chaos"*—some imagined boundary separating order from chaos. The sand pile is considered to be an elegant model of order arizing from the multiple interactions of a system's simple constituent parts and as a bonus, the paradigm easily lends itself to computerization. The experiment is simplicity itself and involves sand being poured onto a flat horizontal surface in a continuous stream. At some point the pile becomes as large as can be maintained following which any additional sand falls off the sides. At this stage, the pile is very sensitive to any kind of disturbance and is described by Bak as being *"critical"*—balanced precariously, yet stable. The observation regarded as crucial with respect to the complexity issue is the fact that such a system *"self-organizes"* to this critical state under any initial conditions and without any fine-tuning of the model. There is further speculation that this much sought after *self-organized criticality principle*—thought to be exhibited in non-living phenomena—"might be the underlying concept for temporal and spatial scaling in *dissipitive non-equilibrium systems*"[17]—a rather obscure term—whose only authentic example, in our view, is the LS. Thus, the attempt to link dissipative non-equilibrium systems to self-organized criticality, becomes a barely disguised attempt at forging a link between non-life and life itself. Until the Santa Fe initiative (and others, such as the Center for Complex Systems Research at the University of Illinois) came along, it was considered unnecessary to either implicate or invent any novel unification principles. But, the search for a solution to the SAb OoL mystery changed all that—for any such solution must entail the bridging of the logical and physical interfaces that separates life from non-life. And, researching complex systems would seem like a good place to begin. The bottom-up approach is typical of scientific methodology in such endeavors. "Bottom-up", as it applies to OoL entails the extrapolation in the direction of less-complex natural non-life phenomena toward the most complex of phenomena we call life. The hope is to gain an understanding of the plausible events leading up to a SAb OoL. At the end of the day we must consider the extent to which any comparison is justifiable between the principles that govern such simple physical phenomena (such as sandpiles) and those that might be implicated in the most complex of phenomena we recognize—biological life, the LS.

A measure of the importance attached to this effort at complexity unification can be judged by the impressive list of scientific luminaries that have pioneered this ambitious undertaking: Murray Gel-Mann, (co-discoverer of quarks of particle physics), Christopher Langton (artificial life researcher), W. Brian Arthur (nonlinear economist), and Stuart Kauffman (described as a leading thinker on self-organization and biological complexity) are all principals of the Santa Fe Institute. Their individual claims to fame within their respective fields of study are in large measure responsible for the widespread acclaim the institute has achieved. Couple this with the fact that the goal of this intellectual movement is to establish some understanding of fundamental principles that are thought to relate directly every phenomenon that could be described as complex, and it is no wonder that "complexity" had become one of the darling scientific movements of the 90's and continues in the new millenium.

Complexologists consider all the many forms of increasing complexity exhibited within the evolving LS as the emergent results of their still undiscovered universal principle which Stuart Kauffman refers to as *"self-organization"*. One of their goals is to define a meaningful principle of nature that will formalize the fundamental concepts of complexity theory to cover any and all complex phenomena—leading up to, of course, the enigmatic origin of life on our planet. In effect, the aim of complexity theory is to be able to adequately explain away any and all phenomena deemed to be more complex than simply the summation of their constituent parts. "Cells interact with cells to form organisms; organisms interact with organisms to form ecosystems, economics, societies"…is how Kauffman illustrates the phenomena of biological complexity. He then asks, "Where did this grand architecture come from?"[18] Well, one overwhelming fact cannot help but stare us in the face: all of the above cited examples, in reality, are derived from but a single system: the LS—and thus, their existence can be considered to be the products of that system alone. We would venture the speculative view that outside of the LS, there are no other comparable sources of complex phenomena to be found and that all genuinely complex phenomena that we label as such can be traced directly or indirectly to origins that derive only from within the system of bio-life on our planet. All other so-called complex phenomena that are not life-derived (such as sandpiles and the like) can be dismissed as the direct consequences of the 2nd law of thermodynamics. Perhaps we should clarify this declaration somewhat.

Self-Assembly As Complexity:

In order to buttress their premise of complexity as a natural phenomenon, complexologists have begun to classify and label all kinds of natural phenomena as examples of "self assembly". A *"theory of emergence"* has been formulated which essentially formalizes the concept of "the whole as being greater than the sum of its parts"—implying in the process that the whole exhibits more interesting patterns and structures that spontaneously *"emerge"* from the less interesting characteristics of individual component parts. Interestingly, emergence requires no code associated with lower-level components—a la von Neumann—that are supposed to spontaneously and inevitably lead to a higher level dynamic (such as and analogous to that which governs biology). It supposedly just happens—all by itself and no different in principle than in a host of non-life applications. Examples are offered: What is a raindrop, if not an example of the self-assembly of water molecules into a perfect lens-shaped object, the envy of any optical lens grinder? In no way can the spherical shape of the aggregate of molecules be suggested from an understanding of the characteristics of the individual molecules themselves. The liquid assumes this shape spontaneously as a result of the differential stability of its molecules at the liquid-air interface. The laws of thermodynamics intervene forcing the shape that maximizes energetic stability, by minimizing the area of the unstable surface.[19] The act of a multitude of water molecules forming into a single drop represents an emergent quality of all of the constituent water molecules that is considered to be unpredictable at the level of understanding of how a single water molecule behaves. While it is acknowledged that this type of self-assembly (known as "thermodynamic self-assembly") works only on the simplest and least complex of natural structures, like raindrops, this example is thought to convey in an elegant way the idea of emergence as a characteristic of complexity. Then, of course, at the other end of the complexity scale is the living organism, which is also cited as an example of the forces of self-assembly when it reproduces itself upon division. The important question to ask here is whether the self-assembly of such simple natural phenomena as raindrops and that exhibited by a living embryo are really comparable in any meaningful way? Can we really learn anything useful about the self-assembly of living cells from an understanding of the self-assembly of raindrops? For our understanding of how cells self-assemble to create organisms we defer to molecular biologists who have shed much light on how it's done—and it's complex indeed. Bridging the gap, in effect, is what complexologists at the Santa

Fe Institute, and elsewhere are really trying to do. Now, let's stand back and ask a provocative question: Is that not like comparing a stone rolling down a hill to a Ferrari rolling down a hill? Can we learn anything about the origin and operation of the exquisitely tuned sports car from the trivial example of the rolling stone? In truth, there is, indeed, an obvious common denominator—each is subject to the same forces of the universe they share (in this case the force of gravity is predominant). Similarly, raindrops and biological cells share the same universe and should be expected to be subject to the same physical laws at the microscopic level. But beyond that obvious observation, is the comparison any more meaningful? Can such comparisons ever be meaningful?

One important clue to an understanding of the fundamental difference between bio-life and all other natural phenomena may reside within the von Neumann concept of "coding" introduced above. It will be recalled that in natural phenomena typified by the sand pile and raindrop examples discussed, emergence requires no *code*—nor is one required—for lower-level parts (individual grains of sand and water molecules, respectively) to exhibit the inevitable higher level dynamic of the aggregate. In stark contrast, the kind of self-assembly that the living cell engages in is best described as *"coded self-assembly"*— in deference to the fact that the assembly instructions for life are, indeed, encoded within the genetic libraries of the system components (cells of organisms). And, we can logically extend the principle as it applies to the sports car example, in-as-much as detailed instructions are also required for its assembly and operation, but in this case, originating from the mind of the products of coded self-assembly— humans. No such examples of coded instruction have been found anywhere else in nature—outside of bio-life. Thus, the real challenge in understanding the origin of the unique kind of complexity exhibited within biological life is to determine the origin of the coded instructions that direct life processes. Find that, and you will unquestionably find as well the secret to the mystery of the OoL. That is the crux of the whole complexity issue! It is our view that—while in and of themselves interesting—neither grains of sand, nor raindrops nor rolling stones will have much to contribute toward an understanding of coded self-assembly (nor automotive design, for that matter). It is also our view that describing each as examples of "less" and "more" complexity respectively, in fact, obscures the very significant logical interfaces that separate these very different types of phenomena—coded self-assembly from the non-coded.

Thus, mainstream scientific interest in complexity theory is essentialy meant to advance the SAb agenda of unraveling the OoL mystery by acting as an intellectual bridge spanning the knowldge gap that separates our present understanding of the laws of nature from our total ignorance with respect to the the circumstances leading up to the appearance of the biological life phenomenon on our planet. If and when that link can establish itself, the complexity bridge can then feasibly serve as the sought-after validation for the SAb OoL option. But, until then and at the very least, the pursuit of an understanding of modalities associated with the concept of complexity could feasibly yield some clues to an understanding as well of the apparent trend toward increasing complexity as it appears within the operations of the biological LS and then, perhaps, to extrapolate that trend even beyond the confines of biology—to include the proto-chemical phases that supposedly preceded biology. Ultimately, the intent is to validate the processes that gave rise to a SAb OoL—that imagined spontaneous coming together of chemicals and their "complexification" into a self-replicating entity—processes that are thought to have both preceeded as well as precipitated the biological LS complexity phenomenon.

Thus, the search for some universal general principles of self-organization that could account for complexity and precipitate it ubiquitously, is really meant: 1] to explain the origin and functioning of the principles of biological evolution (a phenomenon that is evident only within the LS); 2] to validate the extrapolation of the premise of evolution to chemistry—a process referred to as "chemical evolution"; and 3] to relegate the phenomenon of biological evolution to the all encompassing evolution of the unfolding universe. It is significant that to date, hard evidence is completely lacking in any of these challenges. In effect, complexologists can only hope to accomplish this ambitious agenda by extending the phenomenon of biological evolution beyond its limited application to some universal all-encompassing imperative that surpasses biological life, in order to validate the SAb OoL option—as a case of "business-as-usual" in the natural universe. But, there are good and valid reasons to suggest that biological evolution—as it applies to an evolving LS—bears no relationship to natural non-life phenomenon in an evolving universe. The two kinds of evolution differ, in fact, at the level of thermodynamics.

Evolution...by any other name:

Another line of reasoning in the exercise attempting to connect the LS phenomenon to the natural universe—and thereby justify the concept of SAb—centers on the concept of evolution, as it applies to both. There is a ready temptation to link the two because both the LS and the universe exhibit change over time. However, there are fundamental differences in how the respective changes occur. And, while the LS a priori must adhere to the laws of nature of the universe within which it resides, over time, the dynamics of change as it applies within the LS is largely unpredictable. In contrast, change that occurs within the universe (with the exception of the LS) is essentially predictable, the universe unfolding in the only way it can—and according to the physical laws that define it.

The word 'Evolution' means: change over time. We are witness to two independent examples of change over time: 1] a significant single example of an *evolving biological LS* on some insignificant spec of a planet, within 2] an *evolving universe*. If we are ever going to fully appreciate how truly unique bio-life is, then it is important to understand the fundamental differences that separate these two time effective evolutionary phenomena—the evolution of bio-life, and the evolution of non-life systems. While it may seem that we are here arguing for the separation of the LS from the universe it inhabits (a preposterous proposition at the very least), let me assure the reader that our intellectual exercise is only meant to underscore how set apart the life phenomenon is from any other natural phenomena we are currently aware of—evolution being a case in point.

Biological Evolution: Biological evolution is more than the extinction of old species and the origin of new ones. While evidence of these kinds of results play an important role in the lifeform demographics of the LS, the nature of the underlying processes involved identify biological evolution as negatively entropic from the viewpoint of the 2nd law of thermodynamics. This occurs in both space and time:

Space: the system of bio-life increases in terms of biomass as more and more of the biosphere's inanimate material in the form of chemical compounds and elements is appropriated by the LS and integrated within biological space. In so doing, the inanimate material is upgraded from entropically low-grade chemicals into uniquely biological complex compositions—mainly proteins. When living things die, their components tend to revert back to simpler chemicals in the direction of increasing entropy and thermodynamic equilibrium, as prescribed by the 2nd law (to be discussed in greater detail). But, characteristically, biological materials are for the most part recycled back into the living state of other organisms before they can reach equilibrium, thus retaining some level of complexity and all the while avoiding the universal imperative of tending toward their respective equilibrium states, and, of course increased entropy.

Time: Not only does the LS biomass continue to increase—retaining and recycling older biological material while converting increasingly inanimate low grade chemical components into the highly complex LS—but, over time, generates as well more complex component organism designs (species) through evolution. All of this is accomplished by processes that can function seemingly against the gradients imposed by equilibrium thermodynamics and entropy—characteristics unique to the LS.

The Unfolding Universe—A Different Kind of Evolution:

All phenomena (with the possible singular exception of biology, for the moment) can be lumped together as the incremental unfolding of the evolving natural universe; a process described by the laws of thermodynamics as the ongoing spontaneous transformation from its state of disequilibrium, towards the inevitable equilibrium state—following which no further action is contemplated nor considered possible. Thus, the case can be made that the universe, in fact, becomes less complex with time as it spontaneously evolves in the direction of equilibrium and that its moment of maximum complexity and organization was at its origin—the Big Bang itself. Or, conversely the contrarian point of view defines the universe as moving in the opposite direction—from less to greater complexity over time—as the simplest constituents of matter within the homogeneous universe (following the Big Bang) aggregate into atoms and molecules from which more complex galaxies eventually form. Thus, the universe can be thought of as moving toward or away from its arbitrarily defined maximum state of complexity. Who is to judge? In fact, as regards the universe, no such judgment is required at all because one of the universe's own so-called laws of nature—the 2nd law of thermodynamics—addresses the issue directly and without confusion:

The universe unfolds as it evolves. The essential mechanisms of astrophysics are sufficiently defined such that the five evolutionary stages the universe is expected to pass through during its lifetime have been identified[20]: The Primordial Era: Dating from the Big Bang origin of the universe—the victory of matter over antimatter—to the generation of the light elements of the periodic table. The Stelliferous Era: Includes the present and characterized by the evolution of stars. The Degenerate Era: Dominated by brown dwarfs, dark matter and noted for the demise of biological life (as we know it). The Black Hole Era: A period when only radiation will permiate the universe. The Dark Era: A state that signals the termination of any possibility of further activity—an end state that probably will approximate any concept we may harbour as to the ultimate equilibrium state as postulated by the 2nd law of thermodynamics—the proverbial "Heat Death" of the universe. Whether the universe will be able to reconstruct itself at the end of this astrophysical journey or remain forevermore in cosmic limbo is anybody's guess. What cannot escape our attention as these progressive phases of the life of the universe play themselves out is the undeniable fact that these chronological stages—that define the evolution of the universe—tend to be progressively entropic—from greater energy to lesser energy and from greater states of order to lesser states of order. The chronological order in which they appear and the resultant phases that occur, down to the minutest detail are essentially preordained, if you will, no differently than what happens when a solid cube of ice is heated and melts—becoming liquid water in the process—on its journey to becoming gaseous water vapour. In a similar vain, the universe effectively adheres to a similar set of directives including, as stated, the 2nd law as it expands and inevitably passes through its various phases and changes of state. There are no surprises possible as the expansion of the universe proceeds in only a single direction from its Big Bang beginning through all of the stages of its existence on the road to its inevitable state of thermodynamic equilibrium—and we can say with some degree of confidence that if we could replay the tape, it would be a deja vue experience—an exact repetition of each of the predictable steps along the prcocession from the primordial era to the inevitable dark era. If the process of an unfolding universe can be characterized as emergent, any such emergence is entirely predictable as well as inevitable.

In total contrast, bio-life seems to evolve in the opposite direction as it expands. The history of the evolution of bio-life has been shown to be anything but deterministic as the LS proceeds over time from the simpler towards the more complex. Stephen Gould makes the point that if we could replay the tape of the evolution of life on our planet, we would enevitably witness a totally different set of results—because the results of biological evolution are considered to be an unpredictably complex and truly emergent quality—dependent on too many unreliable variables for the results to be anticipated in any way. Again, throughout these discussions, the nagging question is never far from the surface: how can it be that the LS can appear to be so different from all other natural phenomena, while at the same time residing in the only universe we know of and therefore must be subject to the same ubiquitous laws of nature of that universe? Logic would dictate there are only two possibilities: either the LS is, in fact, simply a natural phenomenon of our universe or—for it not to be—our understanding of the laws of nature require readjusting. We hope to demonstrate in the pages ahead that a modification of our understanding of the laws of nature is overdue.

Emergence—Two Kinds of Expectations:

What becomes apparent following the foregoing discussion is the undeniable fact that there appears to be important qualitative differences between an emergent unfolding universe (and/or any of its non-life subsystems) and an emergent evolving LS. If, as complexologists claim, all complex systems are the function of emergent qualities that themselves are a function of some universal rule of complexity, can there simultaneously be two kinds of emergence—one that is indeterministic and another deterministic—that can both qualify as deriving from the same rule? But, once we consider the idea that there could be different kinds of emergence—one deterministic and the other not—then we must also concede the possibility of different kinds of complexity; a prospect that can only throw into question the whole concept of complexity itself. For our purposes here, it suffices to draw attention to some of the mighty challenges that face any attempt to extrapolate the only truly complex phenomenon—that which we call life—from the inanimate universe, of which the LS forms a part.

Inevitable Emergence: Inevitable emergence refers to evolving systems that change in an inevitable way—where if the tape of the chronological history of the changes were to be replayed, it would retrace its steps precisely. This occurs in all systems that start out at their highest thermodynamic states of energy and order and proceed to unwind in the direction of increased entropy and thermodynamic equilibrium. In short, emergence according to the orthodox rules of thermodynamics is inevitable, and because it can be replayed in exactly the same chronological order—with the same results—is deterministic.

Fortuitous Emergence: As the term implies, fortuitous emergence refers to a system whose changes are logically unpredictable because they evolve in ways that are independent of one or more rules of thermodynamics. The only system, to our knowledge, that qualifies, of course, is the LS, which can be—and will be—shown to defy the traditional understanding of how evolving systems "should" behave. The simple fact that the living process, as exemplified by the function of every living organism, represents the avoidance of equilibrium on a continuous basis alone qualifies the LS as such a system. The additional fact that over time the form of the LS biomass represents the accumulation of more and more complex compounds incorporated within its evolving "value-added" lifeforms represents additional arguments in support of its decreasing entropy and thermodynamic independence. Thermodynamic independence renders the resultants of the emergence of such a system as fortuitous and indeterminate—neither inevitable nor predictable.

Emergence—inevitable or fortuitous, as the case may be—is directly linked to evolutionary change. A significant question as yet unanswered with respect to the evolution of the LS is: exactly when it began to occur. The answer, of course, is dependent upon how life originated in the first place and whether the processes of evolution could have been involved in the runup to the OoL event itself. For the moment, our interest is restricted to whether the one kind of evolution (biological evolution) can derive from the other (an evolving universe), and whether the one can be extrapolated in any way back to the other. As the differences in the emergent qualities of each suggest (the one being predictable and deterministic, while the other is the opposite)—as complex systems go, they indeed have nothing in common. As such, there is at present no logical way to simply extrapolate the OoL back to purely chemical beginnings. While chemistry is indeed the framework within which biology functions (an operational medium, if you will)—that is all it is. As stated above, what truly sets bio-life apart from its operational medium is its informational systems that permit that unique characteristic we have referred to as "coded self-assembly". This novelty, we suggest, is not a direct function of life's chemical medium but transcends any possible media as an independent informational entity and—as it will turn out—a necessary characteristic of any self-replicating "living" system. As such, the quest for the OoL should logically begin with a search for the origin of its inherent informational systems—assets in common with any other living system (if any others exist)—chemical or not.

There are compelling reasons to believe that the origin and existence of biological life on our planet is not chemistry as usual and that complexity theory as a route to an OoL explanation is grossly overrated. One of the roles for which the Rational Design Hypothesis (RDH) has been conceived is to investigate and demonstrate that dissenting point of view. The foregoing has laid the groundwork upon which we shall build as we continue in our quest to expose much of the mythology surrounding present SAb OoL endeavors. In fact, these efforts—at reconciling the forces of biological evolution with some universal principles of complexity that are thought to have preceded it—are not new. The fact is, that complexologists owe a debt of gratitude to a most unlikely individual, a theologian, whose historical insights into complexity and evolution could be said to have anticipated, if not directly contributed to, the inspiration for the establishment of the Santa Fe Institute and its objectives.

An Unlikely Pioneer:

From an historical perspective, I can think of no single individual thinker that better exemplifies the attempt to bridge the gap between religion and science in this century than Pierre Teilhard de Chardin, a French Roman Catholic priest. Born in May 1881, he became a Jesuit at the age of 18, but his parallel interest in science led him to develop a religiously oriented doctrine of cosmic evolution. A strong believer in the concept of biological evolution, he spent most of his life attempting to demonstrate that its acceptance does not necessarily imply a rejection of Christianity. Like many others before him, Teilhard paid the price for his insightful (and heretical) ideas. His superiors at the Institut Catholique in Paris where he was a lecturer rewarded his intellectual forays by removing him from his post and forbidding him to publish anything other than scientific studies. He spent the following 20 years pursuing paleontological research, which ironically included the discovery of that significant hominid fossil known as "Peking Man".

Teilhard obtained his original inspirations within the readings of Henri Bergson, the French philosopher who espoused a theory of knowledge in which intuition plays a central role[21]. Bergson invoked the concept of a vital ingredient within biological life—his "elan-vital"—which he argued permeated the living phenomenon, was essential for its existence, and accounted as well for biological evolution. Accordingly, he denied the possibility that non-living matter, devoid of that essential ingredient, could evolve, and characterized biological evolution as divergent, resulting in time in increasingly diverse life forms. Teilhard disagreed with both of Bergson's conclusions. Whereas, Bergson insisted that evolution is an exclusive phenomenon, restricted alone to elan-vital infused life, Teilhard, would have us extrapolate life backward in time to some non-biological (chemical phase) state where, he intuited, inanimate matter was subjected to an irreversible drift in the direction of increasingly complex organization that inevitably led towards life processes. He could thus be seen as one of the first modern proponents for the existence of a natural law of complexification—that of self-organization—that could account for the SAb of life. Significantly, he too, considered complexity as the natural product of some basic law of nature that applies to non-living matter long before the development of living things—continuing and extending, thread-like, through the LS—inevitably resulting in the ultimate emergence of humankind, with its capacity for self-conscious thought. By extension, he might have also included, as modern complexologists do, the emergence of economics, art and all the other cultural activities that the human mind individually and collectively engages in.

As such, one might think Teilhard would have fit in rather comfortably around the discussion tables at the Santa Fe Institute. One must wonder to what extent his ideas, directly or indirectly, served to inspire others, such as Per Bak's "self-organized criticality" concept, and ultimately the establishment of an institute devoted solely toward the discovery and formulation of natural laws responsible for complexity. Accordingly, it might indeed, be a fitting tribute to the memory of this Jesuit priest if his portrait were to adorn the entrance hall to the Santa Fe Institute in recognition of his pioneering insights that foreshadowed scientific interest in the field of complexity, together with the sacrifices he had to endure for expressing his novel ideas. Such a tribute would also be a good natured and humbling reminder to all those who pass through its gates of the fact that the search for a law of complexity (even if it was divinely inspired) began long before the Santa Fe Institute came into being—and by a theologian, no less. As we shall see a little later on, the RDH shares as well some of the sentiments of Teilhard, particularly with respect to his understanding that acceptance of evolution need not be seen as a threat to any religious beliefs, and particularly not to Creationism. It's all a question of perspective. However, the RDH will have reason to take exception with both Teilhard and SAb with respect to when evolution began. While both espouse a universal principle of complexity implying a prior evolutionary process responsible for the springing forth of Life from chemical aggregates, the RDH hopes to demonstrate convincingly that evolution is strictly a biological LS subsystem and is non-existent in the inanimate world (i.e., there is no such thing as chemical evolution). Furthermore, we are betting heavily against the existence of any rule or law of complexity under any circumstances—because none may be required to explain either the existence or the origin of life—and the 2nd Law of thermodynamics, as currently constituted, is sufficiently versatile to explain the "complex" workings of the inanimate universe.

As a passing additional thought, Teilhard considered that everything that arises must eventually converge. Perhaps his intuition took into account the implications of the second law of thermodynamics that implies that a system in dis-equilibrium must spontaneously move (converge, if you will) towards the equilibrium state. Thus, he developed the concept that the present state of humankind is by no means the end of its progression—that widely divergent human cultures were converging toward an "omega point", where consciousness can find a new unity. As part and parcel of the process, Teilhard viewed the superimposition of a growing worldwide complex of transportation and communication networks upon the biosphere as proof of an emerging collective human consciousness. He saw the final result of human evolution on this planet as the ultimate integration of personal consciousness within a "divine milieu", as he put it.

SAb Desperately In Need Of A Law Of Complexity:

Without question, research in complexity theory emanating from the Santa Fe Institute is serving as a positive counterpoint to the enormous difficulties presently being experienced within the various SAb attempts at an OoL solution. It is hoped that eventually insights derived from complexity theory might help in the quest to understand the enigmatic phenomenon of biological evolution and extend it to a chemical phase that is thought to have preceded it. Teilhard managed to integrate both by invoking the idea of a law of complexification that applied to matter long before it emerged as life, and continuing incessantly thereafter. His approach might be considered consistent with a theological perspective that tends to see everything within a seamless agenda proceeding according to a single root cause. Biologists have the advantage of being able to treat phenomena separately and then join them later if, and to the extent that, they can be correlated. Thus it is that Daniel McShea, a paleontologist at the University of Michigan carried out a study to measure complexity by examining the vertebrae and spinal columns of 30 modern animals.[22] His findings revealed that there was no significant increase or decrease in vertebral complexity within ancestral lines. Where there were changes over time among the samples measured, he concluded (inconclusively) that the descendants were just as likely to be less complex as more complex than their ancestors. And, the bottom line, in my view after all is said and done, is the admission, at the beginning of his paper, that although there is a sense among biologists that morphological complexity within LS species increases over time, the very idea of complexity is difficult to define and measure.

Thus, not surprisingly, complexity—according to some skeptics—exists, like beauty in the eyes of the beholder. The problem with the whole notion begins with the term "complexity" itself, and how it is defined. For those who keep track of such things, at least 31 definitions have been proposed, many of which fail to adequately distinguish the field from the closely related issue referred to as "chaos". In fact, the most touted definition places complexity "at the edge of chaos" with truly complex phenomena appearing at some arbitrarily defined border between the two extremes of *rigid order* and *randomness*. The contention of the RDH is that the logical interface between these two extremes describes as well the phenomenological interface separating bio-Life from inanimate matter. The former—*rigid order*— parallels the idea of *coded self-assembly* uniquely characteristic of bio-Life. The latter—*randomness*— efficiently describes the nature of the chemical reactions in which inanimate matter can engage. These two extremes are indeed separated by the life–nonlife interface. The problem that cries out for an explanation is how this interface might have been bridged some 3.8 billion years ago when life is thought to have first appeared on our planet. As we shall come to appreciate, the mystery of the OoL reduces to an understanding of the quantitative and qualitative characteristics of this life-nonlife interface and whether that interface can logicaly be bridged by natural processes, i.e., without any outside intervention.

Perhaps the most interesting aspect of the study of complexity and the one that relates most directly to OoL has to do with those efforts to study complex life systems using the computational might of the computer. This subfield of complexity studies referred to as *"artificial life"* or AL uses self-replicating computer programs as analogs of living organisms that are subjected to computerized analogs of fitness criteria and environmental pressures. The drive towards increased AL computational capacity is fast becoming, according to practitioners, an important research tool in the study of the evolution of biological life. In the same way that artificial intelligence researchers use computers in the hope of understanding how the mind works, AL hopes to bring the same powerful tools towards greater understanding of a broad range of biological phenomena, including, of course, evolution and how life might have spontaneously self-generated.

In the inaugural issue of the journal devoted to the field of AL study, Christopher Langton offered the hope that AL will teach us much about biology that could not occur by studying the natural products alone. He proposed that these same efforts will ultimately reach beyond biology into unnamed realms but which must include human culture and technology in an extended view of nature. Langton's particular concept known as "strong A-life" considers that computerized organisms, under certain conditions, could be considered living entities. This speaks directly to the premise held by complexologists to the effect that there are simple sets of mathematical rules that give rise to complicated patterns—bio-life included. This reasoning is extended to the conclusion that simple rules can explain many of the complicated phenomena in the universe. The computer is seen as the tool that can uncover these rules.

This seductive argument is not without its detractors—who feel that there are definite limitations inherent in mathematical models of natural systems. They contend that only closed systems can be verified using pure mathematics and logic. Because so-called natural systems, as they see it, are by nature "open", our knowledge of them, of necessity, must be partial and approximate. These are essentially the warnings of philosopher Naomi Oreskes to complexologists: to realize the extent of the limitations inherent in the tasks they have set out for themselves. These same limitations are also seen to underscore why biology has resisted mathematicization to date. At the same time, let us not simply ignore the obvious fact that biological systems are the most complicated in terms of the shear number of dependent and independent variables involved. Even under closed system conditions, (experimental closed biospheres have been constructed) the shear quantity of unknown variables involved in the miriad feedback control systems both at the macroscopic and microscopic levels of the basic biological cell alone would seem to obviate any possibility of accurate computerization for the forseeable future. Nevertheless, I believe it will be possible to develop a complete description of the workings of biology and that ultimately, increased computer technological capabilities will be sufficient to permit the analog replication of biology in cyberspace.

While I may have little to add with respect to the prospects of the eventual emergence of some unified theory of complexity, my skeptical mind can't help feeling that the whole movement to direct such a search has come about largely in support of the SAb of life on our planet—a neo Darwinist attempt, if you will. The emphasis on AL models of computerized life forms attests to this very fact. Supporters of the SAb hypothesis for OoL have the most to gain if a unified theory of complexity, no matter how vague, would emerge from the multidisciplined approaches pursued at the Santa Fe institute, or elsewhere—one that could serve as a convenient prop upon which they could lean. In this regard, SAb can draw encouragement from the views of Stuart Kauffman, described as one of the most ambitious artificial lifers. He has spent considerable time and effort attempting to show that Darwinian theory alone cannot account for the origin and evolution of life. His computer simulations have led him to conclude that a system of simple chemicals may, at an unspecified point, reach a state of self-organized criticality, at which time it could undergo a dramatic transition defined as "*autocatalysis*", circumstances that in the distant past, may have led to the SAb of biological life here on earth. (These ideas parallel

Per Bak's concepts of "self-organized criticality" developed doing studies on sandpiles.) Kauffman goes further by suggesting that both the OoL and its evolution processes were inevitable and almost certainly exists elsewhere in the universe.[23]

Too Many Solutions To Just A Single Problem:

As previously stated, our intent here is not to cover each and every effort being waged in the SAb war on the OoL mystery. Other excellent reviews of the state of the art of SAb are readily available in-as-much as this is a hot topic (and seemingly a never ending one). Our purposes are simply to describe the state of SAb at present in general terms and to provide an appreciation of the many possible scenarios SAb supporters envisage to account for it. And this, rather than argue in favor of SAb, could be considered to have the opposite effect, and indeed represents a kind of dilemma for SAb. Let's face it; with that many radically different scenarios to account for a single phenomenon, in this case SAb—they can't all be right, (and following the logic of Crutchfield above, maybe none of them are). If this last phrase has a familiar ring to it, it's because it's been used to describe the similar situation in which religion, in general, finds itself. There too, with so many theologies to choose from, similarly—they can't all be right, (and therefore maybe none are). Each and every SAb scenario put forth by a researcher represents an individual who is convinced that SAb could not have occurred in all the other ways described by everybody else. In addition, each in turn provides reasons why everybody else's SAb solution does not and will not work. The quantity, quality and variety that constitutes that body of dissenting arguments ironicaly amounts to a virtual condemnation of the idea of SAb by the very practitioners that claim to support that bottom up approach. Supporters find themselves caught between the proverbial "rock and a hard place". While SAb remains a compelling OoL option on psychological grounds (despite immense logistical difficulties, it appears to be the easiest to justify considering the current state of scientific knowledge), there remains the underlying conviction that the biological mechanisms of the simplest of life forms are just too complicated to permit a SAb origin of the LS phenomenon. The skeptics among those who take an interest in these matters and who appreciate full well the contradictions they face have begun looking for answers elsewhere—and for good reason.

Look To NASA, When All Else Fails:

In 1992, NASA took the decision to inaugurate a research group in the field of *exobiology*, the study of the search for life on other planets. Designated as a NASA Specialized Center of Research and Training (NSCORT), the center comprises five of the principal investigators in origin of life studies: Gustav Arrhenius, Jeffrey Bada, Gerald Joyce, Stanley Miller and Leslie Orgel. While emanating from different scientific disciplines, four of the five essentially represent different aspects of the same option: abiogenesis, or SAb. (Gustav Arrhenius happens to be the grandson of Svante Arrhenius—primary originator and promoter of the third option—Panspermia—to be discussed later. Bada's researching of the extraterrestrial origin of organic material on the primitive earth might be considered outside of a strict abiogenetic interpretation but organics themselves are still a long way from life.) Unquestionably, this SAb "dream team" and their associates are expected to prove the abiogenesis paradigm, not only in the traditional way in the laboratory, but by implication, should evidence of biological Life be found extraterrestrially. Essentially, the effort to nail down the chemical soup hypothesis will henceforth comprise a two-pronged approach: a) research to understand the nuts and bolts of biological self-replication in the laboratory, and b) searching for evidence of life beyond the confines of the planet Earth in order to demonstrate that abiogenesis has been proven to have occurred elsewhere and therefore must have originated in the same way here. If, at the same time, the search for evidence of life can spark the imaginations of those in charge of funding for NASA's space program, so be it. Thus, the agendas of a number of interest groups are served under the exobiology umbrella including those searching validation for the SAb OoL. While the bringing together of such a brain trust to the task of understanding the creation of biological life under laboratory conditions, must be applauded, I seriously question (for reasons that have already been put forward as well as others that will become evident) whether NASA and its SAb partners will actually get to gain any ultimate tangible satisfaction from the research. What if abiogenesis is not the way life originated here? And if life, indeed, turns out to be an engineered phenomenon, perhaps the inclusion of an engineering presence on the dream team might have been advisable? Somehow I have a sneaking suspicion that because the Santa Fe Institute has not as yet been able to pull off their mandate (find a principle of complexity to account for SAb) that now it is the turn of the abiogenesists in NASA to take a concerted crack at it, albeit in a somewhat surreptitious way. It is interesting to encounter a description of the progress that this virtual center for the origin of life is making. It portrays the group as having published "a bevy of high-profile papers and thrown fuel on a number of long-smoldering debates" and "they are pushing the limits of problems that are of high quality". That is, in effect, a nice way of saying: "We really are just getting to know the extent of the difficulties we are getting ourselves into".

More recently, NASA has established its Astrobiology Institute in its quest to further an understanding how life may exist throughout the universe. An important component in this pursuit is the funding of organized programs such as that undertaken by biologist Harold Morowitz and geophysicist Robert Hazen who together have organized a multidiscipline approach to tackling the OoL question. In keeping with the current popular trend in OoL studies, much of their attention is being directed at hydrothermal vents at the ocean bottom. This would seen to be a natural approach for studies in exobiology inasmuch as while few places outside of our planet would have experienced sunlit aqueous environments, it is though that more would likely have evidenced geothermal conditions somewhat analogous to the high temperatures and high pressures of hydrothermal vents. Laboratory replications of vent conditions are being explored by Jay Brandes at the Canegie Institute reminiscent of the Stanley Miller experiments of the 1950's. And so the quest continues.

Despite some impressive advances in the understanding of life processes, we can gain some insight into the challenges chemists and biologists face when we consider the fact that just trying to produce in the lab synthetic enzymes that catalyze reactions—for which no natural enzyme exists—has to date proved an evasive goal[24]. Gerald Joyce expressed it as well as anyone could when he surmised that science is constantly moving closer to a plausible explanation, even though it may not be able to unravel the precise origin of life. Our position, in response, would be:

"Science will unquestionably one day determine how to engineer life in the test tube. That, indeed may be precisely how our own bio-Life on earth originated."

In the next chapter, we will add more fuel to the debate as we continue to illustrate the uncertainties common to all the SAb scenarios. While we have engaged in some such discussions in this chapter, the following controversies will involve more substantial issues that go to the very heart of any and all SAb themes. In my mind, they are impressive in terms of both diversity as well as strength of argument. In the end, it may be the inspiration of the 13th century philosopher, William of Occam that might well determine which OoL scenario appears to have the best chance for success. He is credited with the maxim: "Entities are not to be multiplied without necessity". The implication here is that if a scientific study can be interpreted without assuming this or that hypothetical entity, there is no ground for assuming it. In the broader aspects of OoL solutions, "Occam's razor"—as this principle in logical analysis has come to be known—may well serve as a kind of litmus test in determining which OoL option has the best chance of success.

---

[1] The Chemistry of Life: p 128; Martin Olomucki

[2] Nature: Feb 3 1994 p409

[3] Scientific American: Feb 91; p 117; John Horgan [140]

[4] Time Magazine: October 11 1993; p43 [141]

[5] Sc Am: July 94; p48; Julius Rebek, Jr. [138]

[6] Sc Amer: May 1983, p 45

[7] Theory of Self-Reproducing Automata: J von Neumann

[8] From the strictly technical standpoint, von Neumann's automata are not accurate models of living things (e.g., they lack such things as a minimum of fault tolerance and their evolution are considered to be governed by too-rigid determinism).

[9] What Is Life? E Schrodinger [The World of Math p 973]

[10] Paradigms Lost: J Casti; p106

[11] Paradigms Lost: J Casti; p98

[12] Science; 12 Feb 1993; p 920; (referred to in Sc 22Dec95 p1925)

[13] The Seven Clues To Life: p6; A G Cairns-Smith

[14] Discover: November 1992; p78 [135]

[15] The Chemistry of Life: p 128; Martin Olomucki

[16] Scientific American: June 95; p104 etc From Complexity to Perplexity by John Horgan

[17] Self-Organizing Systems: e-print / E.H.Decker, Dept of Biology, U. New Mexico

[18] At Home In The Universe: Stuart Kauffman; c:1995

[19] Sc Am: p 148; Sep 1995

[20] The Five Stages of the Universe: F Adams and G Laughlin; Free Press, 1999

[21] New Grolier Electronic Encyclopedia (1991)

[22] BioScience: June 93; p 415

[23] Evolution: T Dobzhansky et al; W H Freeman, San Francisco, '77 [Complexity Journ Oct 96, p22]

[24] Science: 19Mar93; p 1699

3. The Case Against Spontaneous Abiogenesis

*"The important thing in science is not so much to obtain new facts as to
discover new ways of thinking about them."*
—Sir William Bragg (1862–1942), Physicist

Introduction:

In the last chapter we delineated a variety of suggested scenarios and models involving a variety of disciplines—all attempting to account for the SAb OoL paradigm (technically known as *"abiogenesis"*) on the planet earth close to 4 billion years ago. These were discussed together with the obstacles that stand in the way of their feasibility and acceptance. In addition to the issues previously addressed, any SAb scenario offered as a viable solution to the OoL mystery must provide satisfactory answers to a list of tough questions—questions that focus on the complicated facts and realities of the Life phenomenon as it differs from all other known phenomena—as well as how the LS might have achieved its present state from such humble abiogenetic beginnings.

Is Biochemistry Simply An Extrapolation From Chemistry?

If life began from inanimate chemicals, the implication is that biochemistry (the chemistry of life) is an extension of chemistry. This implies that the interface between inanimate matter and the protomolecules that SAb claims preceded cellular life is continuous, seamless and transparent. That is to say, if life derives from ordinary chemicals under the influence of natural forces—as SAb postulates— then the living chemistry of biology could also be extrapolated or traced back to non-living chemistry and should be at best nothing more than just a special kind of chemistry. This is the essence of the "Belfast Address" (1874) delivered by John Tyndall, a British physicist and contemporary of Darwin.[1] He argued that since living things can be reduced from the organic to the inorganic, the reversal of the process should be conceivable; that it was just the special arrangement of inanimate matter in living bodies, which led to the phenomenon of life. This position was echoed by a host of late 19th—early 20th century writers including T. H. Huxley, E. A. Schafer, and of course Darwin himself.[2] Their efforts, based on the simplistic nature of their understanding, would effectively set the agenda of the SAb paradigm that would continue still today. This, despite the fact that in their day they were totally ignorant of the fundamental differences between inanimate and living matter, and between ordinary chemistry and the directed chemistry that characterizes biological biochemistry. Interestingly, some would still argue that there is no difference—that there is only one kind of chemistry involved in both animate life and inanimate non-life. Martin Olomucki, French chemist in close contact with biological issues, contends that: "When we attempt to define life, or living, we immediately come up against a fundamental and apparently irreducible paradox: living organisms are composed of inanimate molecules[3]." We would question whether this is indeed a paradox at all, or whether it only becomes one when considered from the "one kind of chemistry" point of view of SAb. The weakness of Olomicki's position becomes obvious if we try to use his same logic to establish a paradox within the reality that a 747 jet plane is composed of inanimate metal, plastic and wire and that everything reduces to ordinary atoms and molecules. Does that in any way diminish the fact that the 747 originated by design, which defined its form, function and design intent? If not, then why should we be surprised that everything—including living things are composed of the same molecules under the influence of the same laws of nature as everything else in our universe? The whole is indeed greater than the sum of its parts—whether it be a 747 or a living organism.

In order to get a handle on this issue, it is essential that we examine the nature or characteristics of both inanimate chemistry and biochemistry to determine their differences and whether a seamless transition can really exist between the two? While in the previous chapter we dealt with the SAb concept of "complexity" as the proposed source of biological evolution and the SAb OoL, here we shall deal with the characteristics of the actual interface separating biological life from inanimate chemistry. Before we are through, the facts will show that the chemistry of biology is "*directed chemistry*"—totally controlled from within an "intelligent environment"—and not a simple extrapolation of anything. This conclusion goes to the very heart of any definition of biological life. In fact, the difficult question: "How do we define life?" essentially boils down to: "How is life different from non-Life?" This is a preferred and easier question for the simple reason that the basic building blocks of both living matter and non-living matter—atoms and molecules—employ the same cardinal and universal rules of physics and chemistry that permit the molecular combinations that constitute matter. However, the randomness of chemical reactions in nature contrasts sharply with the multiple levels of directed complexity achieved within the cellular production facilities that form biological systems, and that eventually culminate in the form, function and self-replication phenomena characteristic of bio-life on this planet.

Biological chemistry ultimately involves a hierarchy of four components intimately tied together that make it work:

1] the same matter and energy considerations that derive from physics and chemistry—plus:

2] the informational unit (von Neumann's tape) that codes for detailed instructions and controls the production of biological products—plus:

3] the complex energy conversion plant that harnesses the energy from the sun or other sources and meters out packets of chemical energy as needed to power all of the many sub-systems that comprise the living process—culminating in:

4] the cellular form and function of the assembly of Life.

As we can see, chemistry comprises just one of the four components, the basic matter—the "nuts and bolts" of the system, if you will. The other three essential components of life comprise the kinds of differences that readily strain the comparisons between the living and non-living states. Add to this impressive list the unique ability of the system, as a whole, to adapt to long-term changes in external conditions, and one begins to appreciate the problem with which we are dealing. It is verily impossible to envisage, for example, how the informational unit and energy conversion complex could derive from inanimate chemistry and come together precisely at the beginning of life. This may be somewhat less of a problem from the energy point of view because there were any number of energy sources available from the primordial environment—heat and chemical as well as solar energy—that could have fueled a simple life form. Still, at the origin, any energy conversion entity would have had to be a very complicated bit of chemical machinery. As regards the molecular encoded information unit ubiquitous throughout the cellular LS, there exists no counterpart in the inanimate world. Its existence—found only within the protective environment of the cell—is really what sets apart Life from non-life—controlling all aspects of the form and function of the life process as opposed to the randomness characteristic of inanimate matter. Add to that the distinct ability of living biological entities to call upon themselves to self-replicate, and the dichotomy becomes complete. Now SAb has a set of magnificent dilemmas with which to deal.

As stated above, while both chemistry and biochemistry use the same building block atoms characteristic of all matter—interacting according to the universal laws of nature to accomplish the same kind of chemical bonding at the atomic level—it will be seen that it is the "intelligent control" aspect of biological "bio" chemistry at the molecular level, operating according to its unique "form and function", that truly separates the two. A brief description of each will highlight the radical [this is not too exaggerated a term] differences between the interactions that spontaneously and randomly occur in the inanimate world of chemistry as it stands, as opposed to the exquisitely controlled cellular environment that characterizes the living world of biochemistry. Let's examine these differences in some detail.

The Chemistry of Non-Life:[4]

Every atom of every element in the periodic table is assigned a valence [combining affinity for other atoms]. This, together with the distance between adjacent atoms, the energy needed to break the bond connecting them, and the angle between any two bonds formed, determines the architecture of any molecule. The above rules pretty well determine the combination limits that control the chemistry of all matter. When two atoms approach close enough such that their outermost electrons assume a new distribution in space, a valence bond is then said to exist uniting the two atoms. Quantum mechanics further describes and elucidates this dynamic bond formation pattern in terms of, both the negatively charged electrons, as well as the positively charged nuclei. Except for the rare gases [such as helium and neon], free elemental atoms are the exception in nature while molecular aggregates formed by the spontaneous bonding through valence forces are prevalent. Many molecules of common compounds such as water, sugar, alcohol, and paper (carbohydrates) are pretty stable under standard (ambient) conditions, however, they are not necessarily in their states of maximum stability (lowest energy state that could be attained). To achieve greater stability, an investment in *"activation energy"* is required. Let's illustrate by analogy:

Imagine ordinary chemical reactions to be compared to a "shotgun". The shotgun operates by applying finger pressure on the trigger. This is equivalent to applying the activation energy necessary to begin a chemical reaction. Without the introduction of this initial energy to weaken the electron bonding in the outer shells of the potentially reacting compounds, no chemical reaction can take place. That's why paper does not spontaneously ignite. It takes the activation energy supplied by a match, or other heat source, to weaken the bonds of adjacent paper (carbon) atoms. Only then, can those atoms combine chemically with the oxygen in the air. Once the reaction begins, however, the process itself provides additional energy in the form of heat given off, to continue the operation within the carbon molecules immediately adjacent to the areas already reacting. With the introduction of the necessary activation energy to the reacting elements, the chemical reaction begins randomly and will be self—sustaining until all the materials are consumed, or one of the essential components has been used up. Often tremendous heat is produced (e.g.: burning), which raises the temperature of the products of reaction dramatically. The chemical reactions will go spontaneously in the direction that will produce a net liberation of energy. However, many different kinds of intermediate products may be created and destroyed in the reaction environment, as products are repeatedly and uncontrollably subjected to exothermic heating. Since activation energy is transmitted randomly from molecule to molecule, a highly heterogeneous mixture of reaction products may ensue in the course of the blind collisions that occur between the resulting molecules. The speed of the reaction is uncontrolled (subject to a number of variables) and analogous to the explosive reaction of a shotgun being fired. Several examples illustrate the principles involved:

Non-Living Chemical Activity:

1] Ordinary Table Salt:

Sodium (Na), a highly volatile metal, and Chlorine (Cl), a poisonous gas, combine in each other's presence to produce Sodium Chloride—ordinary table salt:

$$\text{Na} + \text{Cl} + \textbf{Reaction Energy} \longrightarrow \textbf{NaCl} + \textbf{Heat Energy}$$

2] Water:

Two atoms each of the volatile gases, hydrogen (H_2) and oxygen (O_2) combine when heated to produce one of the most stable compounds—water.

$$2\text{H} + \text{O}_2 + \textbf{Reaction Energy} \longrightarrow \textbf{H}_2\textbf{O} + \textbf{Heat Energy}$$

3] <u>Carbon dioxide:</u>

Carbon (C), a solid and oxygen (O_2), a gas, combine (when heated) to form carbon dioxide, a gas.

$$C + O_2 + \text{Reaction Energy} \longrightarrow CO_2 + \text{Heat Energy}$$

In these three simple examples, atoms of basic elements are sharing valence electrons in such a way that the resulting compound to the right exhibits chemical equilibrium and stability. Again, in all cases, reaction energy (in the form of heat, for example) is required to break or weaken the valence bonds of the elemental molecules on the left hand side of the chemical equations. Once this occurs, the exploding reactions can only proceed to the right producing new compounds, and at the same time liberating much more energy than the reaction energies needed to initiate the reactions. The resulting compounds will represent a more stable state—stable that is, until external energy is reintroduced, as mentioned above, to agitate and then weaken and break down the bonds holding together the diverse atoms within the compound molecule. Then, new chemical compositions can occur, as the individual atoms are freed up, and can randomly seek new bonding partners with which to form other such compounds.

Energy considerations alone do not determine the outcome of a chemical reaction in the inanimate world. The resulting gain in randomness or entropy (the measure of orderliness) is an important determining factor. In the chemical equations above, for example, if we add to each side the appropriate energies, then there is nothing that indicates why the reactions cannot, in theory, move as easily from right to left as from left to right. Equations, by definition, are expressions of equality. In other words, what prevents us from removing the arrow symbol and replacing it with an equal sign? However, it would appear that the reaction direction is predisposed toward that side of the equation (in this case the right) characterized by a state of greater equilibrium, increased disorder of its constituent component atoms (also described as lower "information" content) and increased entropy (to be discussed in greater detail later on).

Chemistry involves the spontaneous interaction of atoms and energy for the breaking and reformation of chemical bonds, resulting in chemical compound molecules. Before the OoL, and the eventual evolution of talented human chemists who could intervene in complex ways, most ordinary chemical reactions could come about only through random collisions. Only a small number of these have sufficient energy or proper orientation to produce chemical change. When change does occur, the new molecule becomes, in effect, the smallest individual unit having all the physical and chemical properties associated with its particular chemical compound. All things being equal (energy wise), most molecules will tend to dissociate into their simpler atomic components—characterized by greater disorder over time in response to the rules of equilibrium thermodynamics. When all is said and done, all that results from chemistry is inanimate matter, devoid of both "form" and "function". Biological Life, as it will become apparent, not only does <u>not</u> begin where chemistry leaves off but, in fact, represents multiple levels of organized complexity that is totally lacking in any other known phenomenon in the universe. Let's take a closer look.

The Shotgun and the Clock:

Biology is controlled and intelligent chemistry—and not simply a more complicated chemistry. While inevitably biology avails itself of the same laws of nature as chemistry—ionic and covalent bonding etc.—this would seem to be the end of the similarities. There are unmistakable and recognizable controlling mechanisms within life that direct the creation of 3-dimensional protein structures from the building blocks (amino acids) of chemistry. Proteins are organized to function in complex but coordinated ways within the living cell. There is nothing left to random chance here. To make the comparison between random chemistry and biology more understandable, we have, above, likened chemistry to an uncontrolled "shotgun". In stark contrast, the controlled biochemistry of biology can be compared to a finely designed "clock".

The biochemistry of life requires the controlled coordination of many different kinds of reactions—a great many of them happening simultaneously—within the confines of the controlled cellular environment where the business of life is carried out. The products of biochemical reactions are generally proteins, which provide structural and other biochemical elements within the living organism. And. all of the reactions take place within the temperature range of liquid water. This fact represents a radical departure from chemistry as usual. Instead of the highly variable reaction energies required to initiate chemical reactions in inanimate chemistry, biology creates and utilizes protein enzyme catalysts—themselves products of the cellular environment. Enzymes control carefully the three dimension orientations of the participant molecules as well as the speeds of the resultant reactions—all of which take place at the ambient temperature of the cellular environment. No runaway temperature extremes here. This unique ability to control both reaction temperature and speed permits serial operations, which ultimately yield more proteins—the fundamental biological products manufactured by and within the cell. Proteins are produced when specified amino acids are placed in a specific order and connected end to end, like beads on a string. The process ends with the folding of the linear *"polypeptide chain"*, into its three dimensional shape. Only then, does it assume its role as a protein, having both chemical and three-dimensional structural properties.

It is essential to bear in mind that all such transactions can only occur within the controlled and constant ambiance of the cell's interior, protected from the unpredictable variable conditions of the external environment only by the external cellular membrane envelope. The energy used in the majority of such reactions derives originally from the sun via photosynthesis. It is carefully metered out locally, and as needed, in discrete packets of energy. The stored chemical energy within a cell is released under extremely controlled circumstances, much as the escapement mechanism feeds the movement in a finely adjusted clock. All the reactions must be monitored and regulated from beginning to end in order to achieve what has to be described as an unbelievably complex symphony of controlled productive biochemical activity, within the miniaturized environment of the cell. And, all of this occurs with minimal energy loss and, over time, seemingly counter to the entropy rules imposed by the 2nd law of thermodynamics as they concern orderliness, information, and equilibrium. One cannot simply ignore the fact (although many mainstream scientists continue to do so) that the products of biological chemistry produced by living organisms from inanimate matter invariably have greater informational content (and complexity) than when they began. Just as interesting is the fact that all biological activity can take place only within a cell's internal protective environment, where the operations that comprise the living processes seem to defy any tendency toward the equilibrium state.

The effect of "increased complexity" within bio-life is compounded considerably within a multicelled organism. The selective assembly of more and more cells (creating conglomerate entities of even greater informational content) of varying specialties within such a unified multicellular strategic partnership demands the addition of complicated communication systems that permits individual cells to effectively pursue their appointed roles within the joint venture. As well, as an organism grows it incorporates and organizes within itself, through its controlled biochemical activity, more and more of the inanimate raw materials from the external environment. In other words, biological chemistry involves taking low-level inanimate raw compounds and elements from the external environment, and transforming them into the higher order organized vital cellular structures of living things. As a result, over time, the information content of the matter bound up within the system of bio-life on the planet has increased exponentially. Moreover, that increase is in direct proportion to the increase in the number of living cells continually added to the total biomass of the planet. We know that over time, the aggregate reproduction of more and more living cells outpaces losses due to extinctions and the demise of individual organisms. Thus, the inescapable conclusion is that the LS manages, not only to increase its presence on the planet, but is also directly responsible for the increases, as well. That responsibility extends to both the quantity and quality of the information content of the planetary matter it binds. Again, this phenomenon—exclusive to bio-life—is regarded by some as an unexplained paradox, contrary to the acknowledged norms of how matter and energy are supposed to function. This has created somewhat of an embarrassment for thermodynamics scientists who seem to be divided on how to interpret the 2nd law of thermodynamics such that it can logically include the LS. This issue is of critical importance within the context of how life seems to be in a class by itself, as phenomena go. We shall return to the crucial question of 2nd law "entropy"—with respect to living biological systems—a little later on in this chapter, and again in great detail in Chapter 11 where we shall discuss the energy aspects of bio-life. For now, a comparison between the reactions above that occur in inanimate matter and the primary energy reaction within living things will further highlight how radically different the one is from the other:

Photosynthesis—The Engine That Drives Life:

4] Photosynthesis   A biological reaction that characterizes the
                                      chemistry of living matter:

$$CO_2 + H_2O + \text{Photon (Solar) Energy} \longrightarrow CH_4 + O_2{}^{\wedge}$$

Carbon dioxide and water combine under the influence of the energy in sunlight (photons) to yield a carbohydrate and free oxygen. This reaction is the familiar formula representing the photosynthesis reaction, which is the fundamental first tier in the food chain upon which all life interdepends. The above reaction illuminates and crystallizes another fundamental difference between living and non-living things.

Photosynthesis is the engine that drives all of life's complex processes. At first glance, this equation, familiar to all high school biology students, looks deceptively comparable to the non-biological examples 1 through 3 cited above. After all, in both cases, in living as well as non-living chemical reactions, we can assume that the atoms of the elements themselves have no knowledge of whether they are part of chemistry or biochemistry and must behave exactly the same (according to the same laws of nature) regardless of the end products. But, in fact—here the comparison ends. The first set of non-biological chemical reactions can occur in nature spontaneously. That is, once the right elemental atoms are within each other's sphere of influence and can "mix", then any suitable source of input reaction energy will cause the reaction to proceed to the right with the expected unrestrained results. Not so in photosynthesis.

What is not shown in the classic photosynthesis equation is the "engine" that drives this reaction. While the equation, indeed, represents accurately the input and output products involved, it fails to convey any idea as to the complex machinery required to harness the sun's energies in the process, and without which the reaction cannot occur. Ordinary chemical reactions can occur spontaneously wherever, and whenever, the appropriate elements and reaction energies come together. Not so in photosynthesis or any other naturally occurring biological reactions. In fact, the reaction temperatures required to instigate chemical reactions and the extreme temperatures created by the heat typically given off exothermically would absolutely destroy the delicate biological machinery that comprises living organisms. As often stated, with few exceptions, biological reactions must occur at temperatures of liquid water: generally between 0 and 100 deg C.

So, you can take all the carbon dioxide you wish, and mix it with water (bartenders call it soda water), and let the sun shine on this mixture forever, and it will just sit there. You will not even begin to achieve the chemical reaction that is represented by the photosynthesis equation above. Photosynthesis can only occur when the constituent elements—the CO_2 and H_2O and the sun's energy—are processed within the complex machinery contained only in plant cells (photoplankton in the sea and plant leaves on land) and some special ancient bacteria (cyanobacteria). Without that machinery, there is no photosynthesis, arguably the single most important fueling process for all living things. For, without photosynthesis, you have no primary production of the food energy that supports the whole food chain upon which the entire system of life depends. Therein lies another exquisite dilemma. Without photosynthesis (or its equivalent), you have no living things. Without living things, you have no photosynthesis. The dilemma is not so much in terms of which came first, photosynthesis or life. The problem is: how do you get the two together—the complex machinery of photosynthesis within its biological environment? Moreover, photosynthesis is also the ultimate source of organic carbon compounds, the bottom-line building blocks of the biological LS. Remarkably, photosynthesis is single-handedly responsible for creating and maintaining the continual supply of oxygen in the atmosphere.[5]

Thus, photosynthesis is more than just a chemical equation. It comprises, as well, the biological machinery that controls and permits the chemistry to occur, within the organic building blocks it itself provides, and, as such, constitutes the "engine of life". This is no idle metaphor. Without it, carbohydrates and "carbon-based life" cannot exist. Photosynthesis is the energy conversion engine that generates the energy required to fuel all of life's processes. Furthermore, its very complexities are typical of the many thousands of kinds of such bio-chemical phenomena that comprise the life functions within biology. Finally, photosynthesis: one more phenomenological interface that separates life from non-life.

The DNA Informational Tape—Like Beads on a String:

While DNA can be said to be a molecule made up of ordinary atoms, there is nothing ordinary about it. Nothing like it exists in inanimate chemistry nor should anything like it be expected. DNA, as it relates to life, is nothing short of a medium of information, within which is encoded all the plans and instructions every living organism requires to implement both its form and function. The genetic information in DNA serves a dual purpose: an organism's instructions for self-assembly, and its repair manual. As such, its chemical and physical stability is essential in order to maintain the integrity of its information.

While we have become accustomed to media sound bites that variously describe DNA in terms of inheritable genetic disorders—or as a space age replacement for forensic fingerprints—there is always a sense that the concept of information stored in a tiny molecule is more metaphor than reality. In fact, such is not the case. Any description of DNA as a set of instructions, that brings to mind a kind of list of written directives to be found in some repair manual, in fact, hits the mark rather well. Written in the medium of the DNA molecule, an organism's genetic library is nothing less than a series of coded recipes. The language comprises chemical symbols that instruct the machinery of the cell exactly in what order to place amino acids (ingredients)—like beads on a string—in order to achieve a particular protein, one out of many thousands of such recipes. The proteins in turn play diverse roles in the makeup and functioning of the living cell. The information encoded in DNA is completely separate from the actual chemical composition of the amino acids in question. A methodically composed coding system, appropriately called the "genetic code" is the universally applied set of genetic language rules the cellular machinery "knows how" to read and interpret—resulting in the ultimate expression of genetic instructions (genes) into the physical structures organisms are composed of. How the genetic instructions written in the medium of DNA, came into being, and became part of the biological system of Life on our planet, remains one huge mystery, but one thing shall become clear as we proceed: This extraordinary information system, and its ability to store, control and process data within its biochemical medium, could not have had a non-informational chemical basis for its origin, any more than could the origin of parchment play the decisive role in producing the information contained in the American Constitution. Rather, the LS uses the medium of chemistry (its DNA molecules) in which to encode its vast instructional library, as well as the rules that allow it to do so—just one essential sub-system out of many that comprise this unlikely system we call biological Life.

Vive La Difference:

Our challenge in these pages is to determine whether the fundamental differences that separate chemical processes and biochemical ones are sufficient to preclude the possibility that the one could have spontaneously arisen from the other. It is important to remember that while all of chemistry works at the atomic level, biological reactions occur essentially at the molecular level of organic compounds under the rigid control of complex biological machines within the biological cell. Thus, it is hard to imagine how the one (inanimate chemistry) might have initiated and transformed into the other (biological life), even given the huge time spans SAb adherents rely on to qualify for it to have taken place. Even as researchers in the field grope for possible initiation scenarios, there is a growing appreciation that the OoL occurred much sooner after the origin of the planet than previously thought, drastically reducing the available time for the initiation and consolidation of abiogenetic processes into the biological primary design platform that defines all of life on the planet.

Evolution: Where Did It Come From and When?

The LS depends on evolution for the following:

a) to introduce mutations (variability) into the "*genotype*" (genetic makeup) and encourage changes to "*phenotypes*" (*new species*); and

b) to allow "natural selection", "adaptation" and other so-called mechanisms of evolution to work?

A) THE EVOLUTION OF EVOLUTION PROBLEM:

When exactly did the phenomenon of evolution begin? Would it have had to be there just before the first living organism came into being—during some chemical phase? Cairns-Smith makes the point[6] strongly that it would have had to be there during his "crystal phase" of life, before biology took over. If that were the case then is evolution there all the while, like some universal law of nature, selectively waiting for sufficiently complex combinations of chemicals, crystals or whatever, to come into being before being invoked? How does this fit in with what we know about chemistry? And, if evolution is, indeed, a universal characteristic of the chemical world, then should we not see many examples, both in artificial chemistry in the laboratory, as well as in the wild, of the spontaneous abiogenesis of complex chemical entities from less sophisticated chemical components?

B) MUTATIONS:

It is universally agreed, that, after the first organism (some self-replicating manifestation) came into being, evolution would have had to be there immediately in order to "plot" (modify) the course of future survival. Thus, the very first species of organisms would have had to have changes to their genetic instructions introduced simply to get the evolutionary processes going. Now, we know the problems talented molecular biologists are having trying to manipulate and help start such a process under laboratory conditions. If a progenitor self-replicating molecule, against great odds, somehow did indeed manage to self-generate spontaneously, could it really be expected to survive further spontaneous changes to its primitive genetic instructions that spontaneous mutations would introduce? Remember, a SAb OoL option implies that there was only one species of proto-organism alive at the beginning, and not too many of those. And this first organism would have had only a precious few (proto-)genes, representing a tight genetic makeup. Can one really imagine any changes to this first genome, whatever its makeup, that would have been, not only benign or neutral, but actually an improvement? It's almost like hitting the jackpot on a slot machine and then expecting a jackpot with every new try. No room for losers here! This now gives rise to the next question.

c) Natural Selection:

Natural selection is how evolutionary biologists traditionally describe the selective survival, from large populations of many diverse species, of only those organisms that are either lucky enough or otherwise sufficiently "fit" to produce viable offspring. Those offspring organisms, in turn, must survive, again, long enough to reproduce, in order to pass on to their own offspring their particular mix of genes. And, this is the point. While it might seem that it is individual organisms that are the object of the natural selection process, in fact, it is the genes of the reproducing survivors that are ultimately being selected and passed on, generation after generation. The evolutionary processes work as a result of two distinct features and requirements: First, a sufficient variety of species genotypes (genetic make-ups) must be out there in order to occupy a sufficient number of geographically separated environmental niches as a hedge and insurance against catastrophic events that, otherwise, could possibly cause the total annihilation of life on the planet; and second, sufficiently large populations of organisms in each extant species in order to satisfy the statistical distribution aspects of evolution upon which the natural selection process can be applied. The large population imperative is crucial for evolution just to work at any level (as we shall demonstrate later in detail), in order for a species to have many possible opportunities for adaptation to unpredictable long-term future changes in environmental conditions. This fact alone may turn out to be the Achilles heal of any SAb hypothesis. Because, inherent in any SAb scenario for the OoL is the inevitable premise of a single initiating self-replicating organism—alone in an unforgiving chemical environment—thereby obviating the possibility of any kind of even minimal support population that could serve in a food chain capacity, or within which the selective principals of evolution could apply. Today, we are all aware of the fact that the smaller the population of a species, the greater the probability that the species will not be able to keep pace with the long term direction or severity of environmental changes and consequently, the greater the probability of its extinction. (The fact that human activities have the effect of speeding up drastically changes to habitat conditions certainly exacerbates the dilemma). That is the essence of evolution, and ultimately, the survival of life on the planet. Produce large varieties of different organisms compatible with the large spectrum of environmental conditions they must endure, so that some lucky ones with the "right" genes will be selected (survive long enough to reproduce) to pass these on. Thus, future generations of species are continually tested for their ability to withstand environmental changes, over great lengths of time. But, at the very beginning of a SAb OoL, there could be no such populations of varied organisms within the first self-replicating species, if we can call it that. Thus, there must have been tremendous odds against the survival of any change to genotype or phenotype, for that matter. If the first occurrence of a spontaneously abiogenerated self-replicating entity is considered an extremely unlikely long shot, imagine how the unlikelihood of survival of that entity is acutely compounded with the necessity to introduce the mechanisms of genetic change through "blind" evolution.

Under these circumstances, it's just impossible to imagine how a single species that presumably occupied a single locality (where life presumably spontaneously self-generated) on a hostile planet some 3.8 billion years ago could have survived long enough to parent the rest of life on this planet without the benefits of the complex mechanisms of evolution described above (large populations of slightly varied organisms, already in place, for natural selection to work). Ask yourself: how could natural selection work only partially? Wouldn't it tend to cull out all changes caused by mutations that were not neutral and benign? And, how could any such changes be neutral? Within a homogeneous small population of pretty well identical organisms—whose genome would probably have consisted only of a small number of sufficient and necessary genes for survival—how could such an organism living just on the edge of survival have survived chance changes to a limited number of crucial genetic instructions; and survive long enough to pass on those changes to its offspring? And, since no large populations would have existed at the time, wouldn't the primary forces of evolution—mutations—then have had the opposite effect of not encouraging the production of new designs—like evolution is supposed to work—but rather tending to stop life, there and then, in its tracks?

Just to put the whole question of sufficient and necessary genome sizes in perspective, consider that the smallest genome for a self-replicating organism known to be alive on the planet today comprises no less than 580 kilobases (580 thousand nucleotide base-pairs). Scientists are presently studying this bacterial species called "Mycoplasma genitalium" in the search for what might represent the minimum functional gene set for a living organism[7]. This represents one of the first complete genome sequences of a bacterium to be published, providing a virtual physical map of the genetic information encoded within its DNA. Typically, it has been revealed that a bacterium invests 10% of its DNA toward energy metabolism; 17% toward the interpretation of DNA into proteins; 12% toward transport; and 8% toward cell envelope proteins. What we are trying to convey is the immense complexity gap that separates the very simplest living entities from even the most complex of chemical products. That complexity gap can be defined specifically in terms of applied information: living things require it in abundance, while in non-living things, it is simply non-existent.

This is typical of the problems faced by SAb: How do you get from the very beginning: informationless chemicals, to the first living, functioning organism, loaded with information and the infrastructure to do all of the processing? Even if you solve that problem and manage to reach a stage where you have a small population of nearly identical organisms concentrated in one spot on the hostile planet's surface, then how do you get to a point where the evolutionary forces of species attribute distribution and selection play a positive role in helping direct the future survival of the system itself? It essentially boils down to: how do you get from a few identical individuals comprising a single species lifeform with identical information libraries, to large enough populations of slightly different individuals having sufficiently different genetic libraries, so that evolution can go from having an initially negative effect to one that is positive and responsible for the future history of Life's survival. SAb, for its part, seems to ignore these kinds of questions and adopts a somewhat stoic stance: "Look", they seem to be saying, "The fact is that Life exists today, therefore, it must have survived all of those nasty problems. It had a lot of time to work these things out." We insist that supporters of SAb cannot continue to ignore and avoid, but must deal with these issues, as they place in question—at the most basic logical level—the very premise of SAb. We shall return to this most fascinating aspect of LS survival later on, as it impacts significantly on the conclusions of our thesis. For now, suffice it to raise and demonstrate the problem, that while species adaptation is crucial for the long term survival of the system of Life, the way its mechanisms operate would have had the totally opposite effect on any kind of originating self-replicators, and most likely would have decimated any self-originating life form right from the start.

Against The Forces of Entropy:

How did the very first organism get a "jump-start" and establish a self-organizing complexity gradient, contrary to the *"second law of thermodynamics"*? We are talking about a phenomenon that had to have begun at the moment of that very first self-generation event. The above dilemma has some serious implications. No matter how, exactly, you answer the above question, any SAb OoL scenario implies that there are unknown forces in chemistry that can act in opposition to, arguably, one of the most consistent laws of the universe—the 2nd law of thermodynamics—commonly referred to as "the 2nd law of entropy". No, we are not trying to put words in the mouth of SAb proponents. Rather, we are provocatively describing the implications inherent within any SAb hypothesis that sees all of the levels of complexity intrinsic to biological activity as a seamless extrapolation—and transparent extension, of pre-Life "chemical-soup" activity—whose nature would have been devoid of such complexities.

The 2nd law of thermodynamics is the same law that effectively put an end to the idea of the perpetual motion machine. It states that no closed system can operate at 100% efficiency because, in any energy conversion process, you always lose some energy that cannot be recovered. That being the case, any machine (one designed by humans, for example) that runs or moves, unless it is refueled and maintained, must eventually "run down" as it gives up a part of its energy to unrecoverable losses (friction, for example), and its parts wear out. That—in a nutshell—is the essence of the second law. In mechanical systems, this energy loss is represented by the added input energy needed to overcome the negative forces of friction and as such represents a continuous liability in the energy audit of the process. The measure of this energy loss has been termed *entropy*. But, as implied above, entropy has an additional component associated with, but separate from, simple energy calculations. Invariably, systems also tend over time to become less orderly (as parts wear out), which is also associated with, but in addition to, entropy energy losses. The net result of this associated effect is that systems tend, as well, toward greater disorganization.

In closed systems—whether chemical or mechanical—activity must move towards, what is referred to as, an "equilibrium state". Once reached, the equilibrium state represents the most stable matter-energy configuration and no further activity can take place. Conversely, until the equilibrium state is achieved, all systems must spontaneously move in that direction, no matter how long it takes. This is as true for man-made machines as it is for galaxies in our universe. Just as machines run down, so too is it considered that the universe shall eventually do likewise. The equilibrium state of the universe has even been given its own name: the "Heat Death" of the universe, representing the ultimate condition whereby all of its energy will have been rendered, literally, "useless". The point in all of this is that if, indeed, biology is an extension of chemistry, then the entropy characteristics of each, anywhere in the universe, must be identical. As far as chemistry is concerned, an example will serve to describe how the 2nd law of entropy applies.

When you raise the temperature of solid carbon in the presence of oxygen, according to the chemical equation above, gaseous CO results, plus a quantity of heat is given up. The transformation of a solid into a gas represents a change in the organization of the constituent atoms from a more orderly configuration (the solid state) to one that is less so (the gaseous state). In practical terms, this loss of order represents a real loss of information, in the sense that, whereby the solid state fixes the position of each of its atoms, the gaseous state permits atoms to occupy no fixed position, allowing each to continually change its position and direction of motion randomly—which qualifies as a reduction in the information we can have about any given atom's position and direction. The loss of information between the two states represents a gain in the "informational" aspect of entropy. But, at the same time, some of the heat given off, and unrecoverable for any further use, represents an irretrievable loss of energy and qualifies as well as a gain in the "energy" aspect of *entropy*. Thus, it has always been found that an increase in the entropy of a system results in both a loss in useful energy, together with a loss in the organizational information of the system. It is as if both aspects of entropy—energy and information—while not formally bound together within the mathematical expressions that describe entropy (the math only deals with energy), are nevertheless intrinsically entangled for all intent and purposes. You never find the one without the other. And, they always move in the same directions: an increase in the one is always matched by an increase in the other.

In special cases, and for limited amounts of time, it is possible for local conditions to allow for a temporary reversal of the direction entropy takes. The implication is that under these special conditions the incessant random forces that tend to undo organization and create increased chaos in the natural world can be reversed so long as the net result within the universe as a whole is maintained—that is, that the total entropy, or disorder, universe-wide is positive. Thus, in theory, it is conceivable that under local and limited conditions with sufficient energy input, chemicals, within a *Primordial Soup Theory* could aggregate into more complex molecular compounds (implying negative entropy) that could hypothetically serve as the progenitors of life.

The fact is that intuitively, even if local conditions allow for some temporary reversal of the natural tendency towards greater chaos and disorder, the prospect of such an occurrence perpetuating itself, throughout the complex process of setting up the business of life is a hard one to swallow. All the more so, because back 3.8 billion years ago when this was supposed to be happening, the environment was introducing too many conditions, as well as external forces that would have tended to destroy complexity and promote the tendency towards increased disorder (never mind allowing it to be maintained). Also, back then, "*anaerobic metabolism*" was the rule of the day in the absence of atmospheric or dissolved oxygen. Anaerobic metabolism (the fueling of life processes by fermentation like processes) requires 18 times more fuel energy than does aerobic based metabolism, and thus, the energy losses due to entropy within the LS would probably have been that much greater than they are today with a consequential increase in overall entropy as well.

Yet, here we have the phenomenon of bio-life, and its tendency toward greater organization, which seems to operate in a curiously contrarian fashion. Some biologists have been inclined to think that the LS seems to be bucking the entropy trend and defying the second law. This gives rise to the question of entropy, or rather missing entropy, and how it impacts on SAb. In this there is no doubt, in virtue of the undeniable fact that the LS continually becomes more complex with time—both quantitatively and quantitatively—and has done so throughout its history. As a result, the implied negative entropy question has dogged biology for some time. Some energy audit studies on biological samples have been undertaken, resulting in the conclusion by the researchers involved, that life indeed does seem to obey the second law requirements. But, as we shall see, energy audits tell only part of the entropy story.

When von Neumann put forth his self-replicator model—predicated on coded self-assembly—the whole premise presupposed the existence of the machine in question. SAb does not have that advantage. The bottom line question becomes: How could a SAb chemical precursor of biological life—if there were such a thing—get its "jump start" from scratch into existence with the built in ability for coded self-assembly—the whole against the forces of entropy?

If It Happened Once . . . :

Between 1957 and 1990 alone, The American Chemical Society's Chemical Abstract Service, has registered within its computerized database some 10 million new chemicals. The ten-millionth chemical to be placed in its computerized registry (for the curious among you) was of biological origin and described as: "an intermediate product in a series of chemical reactions leading to the synthesis of a natural occurring chemical that helps regulate cellular processes in animals and plants". Every year, the ACS registers an additional 600,000 or so chemicals, most of which are mentioned only once in scientific literature. That's a lot of chemistry being carried out in the many scientific labs all over the globe. The introduction of this bit of chemical trivia is meant to underscore the fact that scientists certainly have a lot of experience and knowledge in their understanding of chemistry, biochemistry, and biological reactions: With all this know-how, scientists should be able to enlighten us with respect to the following questions:

1] If life SAb'ed from simple chemicals 3.8 billion years ago, do we find any kind of solid evidence to support some kind of analogous natural self-organizing behavior in chemistry, that could possibly lead to a life-like process?

2] If chemical self-organization were commonplace, shouldn't we continue to see different varieties of such self-organizing activities, including, perhaps, different kinds of self-replication initiating mechanisms, within strictly inanimate chemical environments, in evidence today?

3] Shouldn't we find evidence on the planet of isolated pockets of other kinds of biology, using perhaps a different combination of amino acids, and not just the same twenty (out of a possible 100's) our biological format uses universally, to produce the polypeptide chains that fold into proteins? In other words, shouldn't we find evidence of some kind of competing biological or quasi-biological system occurring naturally in the wild?

The fact is, that we do not see evidence of any of the above. Nor is there any evidence of any kind of related self-organizing activity among ordinary chemicals. However, the whole idea behind SAb is that these kinds of independent phenomena are supposed to be natural in the wild and without which the "spontaneity" within SAb would seem to ring hollow. Because—if these cannot be shown to exist today, neither in the wild nor in the research lab—chances are they don't exist and perhaps never existed. These kinds of discussions should trigger some sobering reconsiderations of the premise of SAb.

More Issues:

How does the SAb OoL Model respond to the following negative indications?

1) The likelihood that the destructive processes rather than the synthesizing ones would have dominated the hostile prebiotic environment thereby preventing proto-life chemical organization;

2) The short time period following the formation of the planet for the appearance of the first life forms (though to be less than a billion years)—the implication being that the minimum conditions that might permit the precursors of biological life to self-organize had not as yet had sufficient time to establish themselves on the planet in order to permit a SAb lifeform to self—generate;

3) There is no geological or geochemical evidence for a hydrocarbon rich primordial soup—maybe there was no "chemical soup" hook for the theory of the same name to hang its hat on;

4) There is a huge difference between contrived, expertly controlled experiments carried out in a well equipped laboratory and what happens when chemicals (not biochemicals) are left to themselves in the wild; i.e., all of the ingenious lab experiments that hope to manipulate artificially prepared biochemicals and the like, in order to try and replicate how life may have spontaneously self-generated, represent very little of what might have happened all by itself naturally. What they might, in fact, legitimately resemble are the initial invested efforts on the part of a possible genetic engineer designer of the LS (within the context of the RDH) when the design of the biological life format, of which we are a part, was being first worked out. Who knows—one day human biological designers may themselves discover the trick of jump-starting biological life and may even learn how to modify such a design. Towards that effort, molecular biologists have already begun to understand how to manipulate parts of the working system using techniques we have come to call *"genetic engineering"*. According to our Rational Design Hypothesis, other talented genetic engineers, elsewhere in the galaxy may have beaten them to it.

In addition to the above problems facing SAb, we believe the following issues have not been properly addressed and should form part of the debate.

Life and the Marriage of Power and Information:

Let's assume that Life, however it may have abiogenetically self-generated, got going. Now, what would have come first: DNA or Photosynthesis? How did these two crucial components (two of many) come together? The first biological organism had to have had incorporated within it some sort of sophisticated system for converting outside energy into the kind that could be used to fuel its metabolic processes. Whether that be photosynthesis of one kind or another, or some other mechanism, based on an alternate energy source, it is clear that the energy conversion engine that drives life has to be complicated. And the same thing can be said of the information library, the genetic code and the cellular ribosomal machinery for the translation and implementation of genetic instructions.

This power plant of life serves a dual purpose, not only producing the energy to fuel life, but also converting free carbon and other crucial elements into the raw materials from which all living things are derived. Remember, the first organisms would have had to produce their own food, as there was nothing else alive (no food chain) at the time. Thus, photosynthesis, or its equivalent, had to be there, in some form or other even before the instructions for life (DNA) could be put to work. To rephrase the dilemma: It can be safely assumed that prior to the SAb origin of life, there had to have been available, and in place, both an operational power plant, as well as a mechanism of instruction for directing the activities of a proto-organism and its eventual replication. It's not simply a question of "which came first?". Both the power plant and the instructional genetic unit, no matter how simple they might have been, had to be available at the same time and fuse within a functioning organism (albeit a simple kind). Is it reasonable to assume that such an engine as complex as photosynthesis or a reasonable facsimile, simply self-generated on its own and stood around waiting for an instructional body to but it to use? Moreover, if it evolved from a simpler mechanism, would not that mechanism have had to be complicated as well? Even present day archaebacteria contain a genetic library comprising over two thousand genes, according to Carl Woese. Biology, indeed, is complicated stuff!

Trouble At The "Bottom—Up":

Tough issues indeed, but take away the assumption that Life spontaneously self—generated and the dilemmas melt away. The fact remains, that despite all that is known about how life works, science has not come close to producing a contrived, truly self-replicating molecule in the lab. Thus, without laboratory evidence that would show us that biology could, in fact, evolve from chemistry under artificially contrived conditions, the idea of an all natural SAb must remain just that—an idea, and to many, an unconvincing one.

As stated, abiogenetic SAb does have its "big name" detractors. Fred Hoyle, the same British astronomer who inadvertently coined the phrase "Big Bang" to describe the origin of the universe, has also contributed what is probably the most graphic and derogatory description of chemical soup SAb to date. In 1983 he compared the likelihood of a spontaneous self-generation origin of life to the self-assembly of a 747 jetliner "by a tornado whirling through a junkyard", perhaps also referring to the 'junkyard mentality' of scientists who favor a terrestrial primordial junkyard soup as the site for the OoL[8]. Then there is Ilia Prigogine, whose description and research of what he termed "dissipative structures" earned him the Nobel Prize for chemistry. Of particular interest here, is his inclusion of certain reactions in biochemistry that increase in complexity rather than decrease, and his conclusion that these reactions proceed contrary to the entropy provisions of the 2nd law of thermodynamics. We shall have more to discuss on this vital question a little later on.

Thus, it would seem that until it can be proven that: first, life can be artificially produced in the laboratory test tube, and then: second, life can self-generate naturally in the wild; no abundance of self-generation theories will suffice. Making it happen is the "sine qua non" of SAb. Without a doubt the challenge to produce Life in a test tube is more complicated than the biochemical nuts and bolts of it (which are well known) would suggest. The scientific search is presently confined to using what is known about molecular biology and genetics in order to create the conditions that could give rise to a self-replicating molecule. From that first step, they would still have a long way to go to replicating cellular activity. However, producing a self—replicating molecule, in and of itself, would comprise the necessary initial stage to satisfy the essential requirement for life. Only then, would the important questions concerning the spontaneous establishment, survival and thriving of the fledgling beginnings of life, discussed above, really come into play. Artificially produced self-replication, no matter how it occurs, is the essential first step to the validation of any spontaneous abiogenetic hypothesis for the origin of life. This is a *bottom-up* approach to the problem.

It has become apparent (if only by examining the results) that so far, researchers' efforts have had little success in coaxing out significant answers as to Life's origin on our planet. The self-generation apologists, if I may call them that, claim with much justification, that even the simplest bacterial organism is just too complicated, and that much work has still to be done in order to get a true handle on a solution to the origin problem. We could not agree more. However, as we have indicated, it is not only the sparsety of laboratory results that lies at the heart of the problems facing the numerous self-generation theories. But more importantly, self-generationists often fail to take into account the monumental paradoxical problems that lie at the heart of any abiogenetic solution. A number of these have been discussed above. These issues, in effect, place in doubt the very logic of the premise of self-generation.

In truth, it is only SAb that must deal with these problems because they all deal with the hurdles inherent in the transition from non-living chemicals into the initial proto-molecules that would have given rise to living biology. Once it got going (biological life), no matter which scientific OoL scenario you prefer, the fact is that we are all, essentially, on the same path of evolution to the present. The major disagreement among OoL theorists involves the origin event itself. The fact that we can specify an approximate date when life first appeared on this planet, and the equally obvious fact that there exists only a limited number of logically possible ways for it to have occurred—simply means that we have to raise all the issues, sort them through, and try to home in on the most likely candidate scenario that presents the most likely OoL explanation. Obviously, all the other problems faced by SAb will have to be confronted by any other pretender scenario, to the extent that these problems remain relevant origin of life issues. The fact is, that only SAb has to deal with the actual transition from chemistry to biology. Panspermia (and directed Panspermia) and Rational Design both obviate that requirement in virtue of their claim that the seeds of life (whatever their composition) were self-contained upon arrival on the planet. Directed Panspermia and Rational Design further stipulate that these were contrived prior to arrival. For them, the interface between OoL on the planet, and what preceded that singularity, concerns the logistics of arrival and acclimatization only, and not the coming into being of the seeds of the phenomenon.

While at first glance, the idea of SAb appears to be the least complicated, because of the fact that it requires no explanation for any outside intervention, it is actually turning out to be the most complicated, because any explanations of the physical conditions required for it to have come into being have become much too convoluted and difficult to explain logically. On the other hand, the Rational Design Hypothesis does require a leap of the imagination and confidence that the "N", in astronomer Frank Drake's formula (the number of possible intelligent alien civilizations in our galaxy) is greater than one (>1), in order to qualify the existence of the "designer". As we shall see later this will be more than adequately balanced by the fact that there are compelling reasons for pursuing state-of-the-art high tech SETI (Search for Extra-Terrestrial Intelligence) searches of the heavens, and more importantly, by the fact the Rational Design Hypothesis is *testable*. That fact alone, when you think about it, even obviates having to deal directly with the issue of "N" above. The real importance of our RDH is in its remarkable position of being able to sweep away a host of logistical problems, as delineated above, that seem to overwhelm the SAb option.

Additional Nagging Questions:

Any OoL theory should be required to explain—according to its model characteristics—the following peculiarities and paradoxes that pertain to the LS:

1) AMINO ACIDS:

Why are only 20 Amino Acids utilized to form the constituent building blocks of LS proteins out of the possible hundreds or thousands? SAb would have us believe that the twenty were simply chosen in some kind of natural selection elimination process at the very OoL. This might sound reasonable if we could find some obscure isolated species, or groups of species anywhere on the planet, where the same process of natural selection had selected a different compliment of amino acids. To date none has been found. It's as though the exclusive twenty amino acid group upon which all of life's varied structures within the millions of species are based, were hand picked as some sufficient and necessary set, and all the other possibilities shut out. Surely—if evolution was truly the open phenomenon researchers traditionally accept it to be—shouldn't we be able to detect in some obscure hiding place, far removed from other habitats in some remote part of the globe, some variant group of species; or at least some single creature within which evolution has seen fit to expand—or even vary—the pallet of amino acids (within the kingdom of Archea bacteria, for instance)?

2) CHIRALITY:

How to explain only left-handed proteins and only right handed nucleic acids? Louis Pasteur was among the first to demonstrate that molecules come in two geometric configurations, each—designated left-handed (L) and right-handed (D)—a mirror image of the other. The fact is that only *L-amino acids* are encoded into proteins and only *D-sugars* form the backbones of DNA and RNA, whereas the laboratory synthesis of these chemicals yields *racemic mixtures* (equal quantities of L and D). While left and right-handed versions of a compound have identical chemical properties, each is constrained in the kinds of molecules it can combine with, because of its 3-D geometry. Normally, in any naturally derived mix of *"chiral"* organic molecules (molecules that exhibit asymmetric carbon atoms), there is an approximately equivalent quantity of left and right handed mirror image versions such that proper combinations can combine to produce a resulting compound in a chemical reaction. The LS has locked-in an exclusive preference for only left-handed proteins, and only right handed nucleic acids. There is no deviation from this format anywhere in the LS. In fact, you might even conclude that, if Miller-style experiments prove anything, it is the glaring anomaly between the chiral evenhandedness of both left and right-handed molecules in natural chemical production, in contrast to the deviation from chiral orthodoxy evident in LS biological molecular production and utilization. The fact is that all bio-molecules that possess a chiral or asymmetric carbon have a rigid stereochemical molecular architecture.

The question in the minds of scientists is how and when did this homo-chiral characteristic of life originate—before, during, or after the OoL on the planet? At an American conference called to discuss these issues, (The Origin of Homochirality in Life"[9] held February 1995 in Santa Monica, Cal), it became apparent that there was no generally accepted explanation for the phenomenon. Some consider homochirality as the inevitable result of universal physical processes at a fundamental level, while others consider it a necessity for both the OoL, as well as its very existence. Still others see homochirality as a consequence of life, an effect rather than a contributory cause…Stanley Miller, of "Urey-Miller-experiments" fame was a contributor at the conference and, delivered a talk entitled "Homochirality was not required for the origin of life". No doubt his position took into account the phenomenon of "spontaneous racemization", a natural reaction that tends to convert any enantiomeric (non-racemic) mixture of chemicals back into a racemic one. This would appear to be just one more example of the 2nd law of thermodynamics at play; the tendency for systems to tend from order to disorder—from non-racemic to racemic. The rate at which this occurs is temperature dependent and has been calculated. All "Stanley Miller" simulation style experiments yield equivalent quantities of "left" and "right" handed chiral molecules; they were totally racemic, as one would certainly expect of any naturally derived chemical. Miller further contends that the OoL was synonymous with the origin of evolution. The implication for both positions becomes: since the influence of the forces of evolution were non-existent and therefore unnecessary before the OoL, homochirality was unnecessary as well, and only appeared later, once the forces of evolution were unleashed upon the LS sometime after its origin. Homochirality, in his view, is a consequence of the processes of evolution, both of which can now be argued to have been non-existent before the OoL. We are not unmindful that his position dovetails well with the results of the experiments that made Miller famous.

Accordingly, true to SAb dogma, a believer once again falls back on the classic SAb story line and prime argument that intimates that once evolution began, like some magic bullet, it can be relied upon to answer any question and account for any LS peculiarity, including chirality. But, as is typical of such intellectual gymnastics, in ridding himself of one problem, Miller ends up creating a larger one in its stead. For, the fact is, that there is a greater price to pay—as the consequence of this position—for the all-important notion of "chemical evolution" which many Darwinists rely upon to account for the chemical genesis phase that is thought to have preceded the biological phase of the LS. If evolution only began with the origin of biological Life—a position we wholeheartedly share with Miller, because in our view, there was no chemical phase—then what other forces (if not evolution) could account for the fine-tuning and survival of the "chemical progenitor" phase of life—a very necessary SAb concept— that must have preceded the "carbon-based" biological takeover that would have occurred much later? Mainstream chemical-soup proponents like to point to the vast amounts of time that evolution would have had to work its magic upon the chemically active chemical-soup of the primordial seas, out of which a self—replicating molecular mix is thought to have spontaneously arisen. Miller's conservative Darwinist position, appears to be a condemnation of the very idea of an evolution-like phenomenon during the chemical phase that would have "selected" for survival the chemical-soup progenitor products that could—after further evolution—result in an abiogenetic origin of biological Life on our planet. If evolution only began (according to Miller), at the OoL (biological phase) in order to account for the racemic characteristic of naturally occurring organic molecules—as compared to the chiral characteristics of biological structures—then it must have been non-existent during those many millions of years when—according to SAb orthodoxy—primordial chemical-soup was all that existed. And, how does this position effect the notion of the highly sought after "law of complexity"? Is it not considered as the probable basis for the chemical evolution phase of the OoL, required to bridge the interfaces separating animate life from non-life? Does the complexity idea now logically get thrown out with chemical evolution? And, as a final consequence, wouldn't SAb—under this scenario—be left defenseless, and reduced to just another example of the impossible violation of the 2nd law of thermodynamics discussed above—no different from the impossibility of perpetual motion machines?

At present, the only strength of SAb resides within the invocation of the argument of the existence of some as yet undiscovered organizing forces of complexity (a la "Santa Fe Institute") that might, both account for evolution, and also qualify or explain away any such apparent 2nd law violation(s). Now, we may well ask the question: "Why would Stanley Miller—a strong proponent of SAb—risk ceding this important SAb cornerstone "pre-biotic evolution" just in order to offer up an explanation for the differences in chiral properties between Life and non-life chemicals? Thus, we can speculate about Miller's logic—which may indeed follow along the lines of:

a) The primordial chemicals responsible for the run-up to a SAb "chemical-soup" OoL were similar to the organics produced spontaneously in Urey-Miller style experiments.

b) Urey-Miller experiments yielded only racemic mixtures of chiral molecules.

c) Therefore, homo-chiral molecules must not have been necessary at the origin of life.

d) But the key molecules of biological Life display homo-chiral characteristics.

e) Therefore, the homo-chiral character of biological life must be the result of the influences of evolution.

f) Therefore, in order to be consistent, the forces responsible for evolution must, as well, have only come into play after the OoL event.

Accordingly, neither homochirality, nor the influence of evolution responsible for it, could have existed during the chemical phase of life (prior to biological Life). This is in sharp contrast to the mainstream SAb position that invokes the forces of chemical evolution as the prime mover responsible for shaping the chemical phase of a SAb OoL until the biological phase took over.

In sharp contrast, a designer OoL model need simply state that the racemization characteristics were built into the original design platform of the LS, and that evolution would have had nothing to do with it. Biologists are aware of the fact that spontaneous racemization continues even in modern organisms that must deal with its detrimental effect on protein and enzyme structure and function. The point is, that homochirality operates against the gradient of spontaneous racemization—forces that had to have existed whenever it was introduced. In this respect, spontaneous racemization seems to be a direct consequence of the second law of thermodynamics dealing with entropy, as natural systems, over time, tend towards greater disorder and randomness. Homo-chirality would seem to represent one more example of LS biology's unique ability to thwart the rules that consistently apply to non-living chemistry. To account for the origins of these contradictions would seem to require some "jump-start" mechanisms that could account for the breaching of a very real—if invisible—interface that separates the two. This paradox only exists if, as SAb tends to do, we continue to equate the two kinds of chemistry—inanimate and living—as one and the same. On the other hand, these same logistical problems melt away, if we acknowledge that the controlled complex chemistry of Life does not operate the same as ordinary chemistry, but comprises a sophisticated and directed brand of chemistry, subject to its very own special rules and operating parameters within the protective confines of the living cell. Then, of course, we must confront the origin of this special kind of chemistry, and seriously consider the possibility it had to be of a contrived origin. For, it is only then, that the anomalies ever present within the LS (such as Homochirality)—and the tendency toward increased complexity—begin to make any sense.

Besides constituting a curious dilemma for SAb, the chirality issue (as well as the 20 amino acid issue above) raises some interesting suspicions, concerning the form and function of the LS, that always seems to be described in terms of "not knowing" in which direction its evolution is heading. If, indeed, evolution and natural selection were as directionless as they are constantly claimed to be—a "blind watchmaker", as Richard Dawkins has coined it[*], then these kinds of issues seem to throw into doubt exactly the degree of "blindness" in a process that seems to have precise notions of what it will allow and what it won't, which rules of nature it adheres to, and which it seems to ignore. The important significance of the above as important contradictions to the ideas of SAb simply cannot be ignored.

But, all is not doom and gloom when it comes to the chirality issue. Robert Hazen and Glen Goodfriend of George Washington University offer a somewhat tenuous solution to the chiral selection problem. They reasoned that some natural process would have been required to separate and concentrate left and right handed amino acids—a feat that would essentially bridge as well the interface separating the chemical and biological phases of abiogenetic OoL. Their experiment involved immersing a crystal of calcite in a dilute solution of chiral aspartic acid and discovering that left and right-handed molecules adsorbed "preferentially" on different faces of the crystal. Calcite happens to be a non-centric mineral— displaying pairs of crystal surfaces that have mirror characteristics and thus can separate and concentrate the L and D amino acid components. Importantly, calcite was prevalent during the Archaean Era when the OoL is thought to have occurred. The next challenge in their research will be to explore the possible role of calcite in the formation of amino acid chains.[10]

3) SEX:

Why was Sex invented? What was wrong with asexual cloning? It lasted for 2 billion years before sex came out of the closet, as it were. Cloning is less complicated and considerably more economical. Was sexual reproduction introduced as an expensive but efficient method of *"error correction"* for genetic libraries, or in order to introduce vastly increased *"variability"* within species attributes? That debate aside, (we shall have much to say, later on, about the primary purpose for the introduction of sex, and the debate currently raging among evolutionary biologists) the gnawing question is "How would, and how could, evolution create such a revolutionary alteration within a procedure so basic as reproduction? The issue we are raising here is that something as fundamental for the survival of the LS as reproduction would seem not to be a mechanism that would endure significant tinkering. Thus, the introduction of sex represents not only a vast increase in the order of magnitude of biological complexity within the LS, but represents, as well, the kind of watershed event in its history, the significance of which must bear heavily on the issues we are discussing. As it turns out, the debate alluded to above (error correction vs. variability) is relevant whether one considers the introduction of sex to be derived from the forces of evolution, as SAb would contend, or by design, as our RDH contends. After all, both schools of thought are convinced that sex does serve some purpose. The major difference between the two is that SAb must deal with the question of the evolution of sex: How it could possibly have come about and become consolidated within species. We hope to demonstrate that sex, from a design hypothesis perspective, is simply a sub-system of the design (no different, in that respect from evolution) and programmed to come into play when certain pre-conditions (both externally within the biosphere and internally within the LS itself) had been met and after a menu of system priorities had been achieved. We will argue the case in the pages ahead.

4) EVOLUTION:

Once biological life got started, how could it survive long enough until the mechanisms of evolution: mutations and natural selection could come into play in order to protect it from changing external conditions and natural disasters? At the beginning, according to SAb, there would have been only one kind of proto-organism. It would have had to take a long and indeterminate amount of time before the effects of evolution (chance mutations filtered by natural selection) could diversify the fledgling species sufficiently to offer insurance against extinction of the single entity that then comprised the total system. This is a major problem SAb must address because typically, at the OoL, it hypothecates a single self-replicating phenomenon as the initial biological canvas upon which all of the brush strokes of evolution would eventually culminate in vast populations of diverse species occupying innumerable habitats.

Both SAb as well as RDH rely upon the forces of evolution for all "changes" to LS component species and organisms over time. The difference between the two involves when evolution could have begun to do what it does. Because SAb considers the LS phenomenon to have begun somewhere and some time during some initial chemical phase, then it has to invoke evolution from that time forward. This, in order to account for the deviation from normal inanimate chemistry towards the state of increased complexity that would have been required to account for that self-replicating chemical entity that would eventually evolve, in turn, into the biological LS. How else can they explain the OoL from chemistry unless some natural and fundamental dynamic influence—such as evolution—was already in place? That influence becomes as well a constant that would follow the LS phenomenon from its chemical phase all the way through to its biological phase.

The RDH, on the other hand, acknowledges no inanimate chemical phase of Life. It considers the LS to have been designed directly from its chemical nuts and bolts and jump started into operation. Furthermore, as we shall demonstrate, evolution is a statistical phenomenon, cannot, and could not function unless and until a sufficient population of genotype variations (within any given species) is established. Thus, the concept of evolution will be shown to be inoperable under the SAb defining conditions—that of a single initiating species of identical self-replicators. Without that distribution of genotype variables within a population, evolution—relying absolutely upon statistical principles—simply could not operate. This will be discussed in greater detail later on. Again, such logistical problems are totally nonexistent within our RDH.

Time—Of The Essence:

Probably the most appealing argument in favor of the SAb OoL option is the contention that the precursor protochemicals had vast amounts of time in which to develop—within the chemical soup of the planetary aqueous environment—and, in turn, evolve into the cellular phenomenon of biological life. The standard caveat defers to: "Given enough time, all kinds of things can happen!" The question then becomes: how much time was needed, and was the sufficient and necessary time available? This becomes critical in the light of new findings by a multinational group of scientists headed by Gustaf Arrhenius to the effect that life may have originated some 350 million years earlier than previously believed—at around 3.85 billion years ago. Couple this with a recent study, based on the distribution of craters on the moon suggesting that a rain of meteors smashing into the early earth some 3.8 million years ago may have been intense enough to destroy any life that may have existed on the planet.[11] The implication is that there may not have been a sufficient window of time between the end of the bombardment and the earliest evidence of life for all of the steps that would be involved in SAb to take place. According to John Hayes, Woods Hole Oceanographic Institute, the new findings seem to suggest that biochemical processes "developed with breathtaking rapidity after the last large impact". But, the time frame for the development of the chemical processes that gave rise to the essential enzymes, proteins, and genetic codes is considered to run into the many hundreds of millions of years. This represents a very genuine problem for any chemical soup theory.

While it may be too early to draw definitive conclusions with regard to the glaring contradictions between the time available and the time required for abiogenetic processes to proceed to biological fruition, one thing is certain: SAb supporters can no longer glibly defer to open ended time frames to qualify the development of the many levels of chemical and biological complexity separating life from its inanimate environment. They are now going to have to think carefully about the consequences of these findings for any abiogenetic hypothesis that is time dependent.

There are two interesting footnotes to the report:

1] the first is the reaction of Stanley Miller whose pioneering experiments in the 50's, you will recall, single-handedly boosted the fortunes of the abiogenesis paradigm. "There is nothing to rule out a quick beginning of life" was his reported response. "Life may have arisen in, say, 10 million years, or less". These kinds of reactions, in my view, cannot help but damage the credibility of SAb, as they tend to undermine the ultimate "insurance policy" upon which abiogenesis could always depend to fall back on: an infinite amount of time for all kinds of self—organization to happen; critical time which, in turn, could produce the coded self-assembling logical phenomenon we call biological life. Indeed, when push comes to shove, the one ingredient any abiogenesis hypothesis must rely on—in copious amounts—is that of time. Take that away, and all bets are off.

2] the second is the curious fact that the international team that reported the discovery was headed by none other than the grandson of Svante Arrhenius, the renowned Swedish scientist whose work contributed much of the basis of modern chemistry in the last century. The curious aspect concerns the fact that Svante is also remembered for his belief that life originated somewhere other than the planet earth. He is also considered the father of the Panspermia concept, which forms the substance of the 3rd OoL option to be discussed in the next chapter.

Both of the above footnotes share a common thread that reveals a not unusual phenomenon within the scientific milieu. The thread in question concerns the appearance of vested interest in the outcome of scientific research. In the first case above and elsewhere in this chapter, Stanley Miller is seen to interpret the results in such a way as not to diminish in any way the importance he places on his own Miller-Urey primordial soup experiments carried out some five decades earlier that boosted SAb as the prime scientific OoL candidate. (You will recall that he did the same with respect to the issue of homochirality a few pages back.) In the second case, we have a grandson scientist heading up a scientific effort that has the effect of interpreting identical results in support of a totally different hypothesis contributed by his grandfather some two generations earlier. I don't for a moment question the legitimacy of the varied interpretations each of the parties assigns to the research reported above. What seems almost eerie is the blatant potential for conflict of interest within the interpretive judgment process. Any judge within our legal system would be morally required to resign from a case in which he might be seen to have a vested interest in the outcome. Apparently, in the court of scientific evidence, it is fair game for the participants to act in all capacities simultaneously—claimant, witness, and judge—all the while never having to proclaim impartiality in their deliberations. Of course, the peer review process is relied upon to sort these things out. As a follower and supporter of the philosophy of science, I have come to consider some of its limitations within the same context as democracy. Winston Churchill said it best: "Democracy is the worst system of government except for all of the rest." Perhaps the same sentiments could apply with respect to scientific peer review.

Conclusions:

In effect, spontaneous self-generation hypotheses (SAb) suffer from the inability to demonstrate definitive results, either in vitro or in the wild. The problems inherent within SAb (many of which seem to be conveniently ignored) seem to cry out that the OoL simply couldn't have happened that way; that there are just too many logistical complications to account for how biochemistry could have evolved naturally from non-living chemistry. We have touched on a few in this chapter. There are many more we shall deal with as we proceed. The bottom line becomes clear: the logistical interface that separates inanimate ordinary chemistry from the biochemistry of bio-life is not only real, but loaded with too many obstacles for any kind of linear and transparent extrapolation from the one to the other.

Some scientists regard the OoL on our planet as the natural result of self-organizing chemical reactions, a universal attribute of the natural world, and others as an extremely rare chance occurrence and one of those longshots that only exist at the extreme edge of the probability curve of possibilities. It is distinctly possible that it is neither of these, but a bit of both. It's all a question of context, upon which we shall elaborate as we proceed.

In this chapter we have made the argument that the SAb of the LS on our planet was highly unlikely. And, in truth, most proponents of an abiogenetic OoL understand full well the dilemmas and the problems that continue to plague any such hypotheses. Still, for many, the chemical-soup hypothesis seems to offer the best OoL option out of the small group of what we all consider to be really "lousy" choices, and for logical reasons. Still, SAb has a distinct advantage in that, despite all of the acknowledged difficulties, it simply relies on nothing more than the "natural forces and phenomena" of the host planet for the origin and existence of Life. It relies on no external intervention of any kind. In stark contrast, a design hypothesis assumes a diametrically opposite posture. It has the advantage of being able to sweep away so many of the burdens that plague an understanding of an abiogenetic event, but must explain in a logically satisfactory manner that single supporting pedestal upon which the whole premises rests. The single question primordial chemical-soup supporters ask of any design hypothesis (rational or religious) is: "How do you explain the existence of the designer? Is the designer simply an almighty "God"? If so, the discussion comes to an abrupt end since religion is considered to be unscientific and the two just don't mix. With respect to a rational design, the question becomes: Are you simply postulating a designer that had to have been the product of some other planet's earlier spontaneous abiogenesis?" If so, aren't you back to square one?

In answer, let me turn the questions back by asking some provocative ones of my own: "Why is the origin of the designer question really relevant?" I would continue: "If convincing and incontrovertible evidence of design can be demonstrated, then would that not constitute sufficient and necessary support for the designer option?" And, once you were convinced that the conditions for positive proof of design had been met, then all of us could begin to contemplate together the question of the design source and the nature of the designer. "Thus, the only responsibility required of the RDH—which also constitutes a minimum level of scientific relevancy—is to describe a controlled scientific experiment that could test for proof of design; is it not?" And finally: "Under these conditions, has not the question of the designer become, for all intents and purposes, totally irrelevant?" The idea here is that we don't necessarily have to have a direct understanding of all of the circumstances surrounding the OoL on our planet in order to be able to grasp some of the significant aspects of its presence, including whether the legitimate conclusion can be drawn that it is, indeed, a product of design. I would ask you to ponder these ideas as we pursue the mystery of the origin and existence of bio-life here on our planet.

---

[*]Actually a metaphor borrowed from an earlier Englishman, William Paley, who argued that a universe exhibiting design must have a Designer, much as a watch implies a watchmaker.

[1]Encyclopedia Brittanica, Electronic Edition (10)

[2]Life in the Universe: Norton Books; p 23

[3]The Chemistry of Life: M. Olomucki; p 123

[4]Brittanica Great Ideas Today—1967; p 198; Theodore Puck

[5]Grolier Electronic Encyclopedia

[6]The Seven Clues to Life; p 2; G. Cairnes-Smith

[7]Nature: Nov 16, 96; p236

[8]Life in the Universe; Norton Books; p31 (F Jackson & P Moore)

[9]Nature: Apr 13, 95; p 594

[10]Proceedings of the National Academy of Sciences: May 2001

[11]New York Times Article: Nov 7, 1996, p A30

4. The Other "Origin of Life" Options

"A great many people think they are thinking when they are merely rearranging their prejudices."

—William James (1842–1910), Philosopher

The "3rd" Option—Panspermia: Seeds From Outer Space

Perhaps, then, if the early Earth was hostile to the formation of organic materials—those containing carbon compounds—they arrived here from outer space. Variations on the theme range from "*lithopanspermia*", supported in the 19th century by the likes of Lord Kelvin and Helmholtz:—life arrived on earth aboard meteorites and comets; to "*radiopanspermia*", proposed by Svante Arrhenius:—the germs of life are propelled through the universe (space) by radiation pressure. In 1986, spacecraft observations of Halley's comet confirmed that it was comprised fully one-third of organic compounds. While interesting, the question remains as to whether sufficient organic material could survive the impact temperatures in order to contribute to the OoL. But, the fact is that over fifty kinds of small organic molecules have been found floating in the great clouds of gas and dust scattered throughout the galaxy.[1] Included are such chemically reactive molecules as hydrogen cyanide (HCN) and formaldehyde (HCHO), and it is considered that the small molecules that form the basis of life could have been synthesized from just such kinds of space matter.

Previously, we indicated that some of the essential chemical elements, required for biological life to exist, must have derived from the explosion of a first generation star—a supernova. Thus, life, as we know it, could not have arisen shortly after the Big Bang. The elements needed simply did not exist. It has been calculated that a period of the order of several billion years had to have elapsed before enough large stars exploded, spewing out in the process the atoms needed for biological, or for that matter, organic life-forming material to exist. Then you would have to factor in any additional amount of time that would have been required for the formation of the biological material that forms the object of a Panspermia hypothesis. One wonders whether there would have been enough time, then, to have this material wander through space, and somehow be lucky enough to find, no less land, on such an hospitable planet as the earth at least some 3.8 billion or so years ago. A most likely scenario, of course, would be for any such life forms to have spontaneously abiogenerated from within our solar system—in some analogous fashion to SAb here on earth. The argument would proceed along the lines of: Abiogenesis could not have taken place under the extant conditions of the planet and therefore it must have occurred somewhere in outer space where conditions might have been more promising. Jeffrey Bada, Scripps Research Institute, and a former graduate student of Stanley Miller contends, that if significant amounts of organic molecules arrived 4 billion years ago from space, then it could be reasonably expected that the supply would continue, if even at a reduced rate, until the recent past. However, the result of his research to date suggests that extraterrestrial organics would not have played an important role in the early Earth.[2]

Panspermia, the idea that life was created beyond the confines of the earth—possibly on some other life-bearing planets in the galaxy—and that some kind of material that served as the seeds of life reached earth from outer space, was first suggested by Nobel laureate Swedish chemist Svante Arrhenius in 1908. According to his thesis, the forces that could have propelled this material across the vast distances between the source planets and our own were the pressures of stellar radiation. One such spore might have eventually landed on our planet to serve as source for all of life as we know it today. The modern day proponents of this concept regard this hypothesis as a way to overcome what they obviously believe to be the enormous difficulties and challenges posed by any kind of earth-based abiogenetic hypothesis (SAb). Panspermia simply ignores the proto-molecular developmental stage essential to any SAb hypothesis for the OoL process, and overcomes the problem by proposing that the elements of life, wherever and however they were derived, somehow arrived in our neighborhood from outer space, and served as the seeds from which the life phenomenon took hold on the planet some 3 to 4 billion years ago. That accomplished, they figure that evolution and time took care of the rest.

Adherents to the ideas of Panspermia, a camp vigorously supported by cosmologist Fred Hoyle and collaborator N. C. Wickramasinghe[3], get additional encouragement from the fact that amino acids, hydrocarbons and other molecules involved in life processes have routinely been discovered in a class of meteorites known as *carbonaceous chondrites* that continually bombard the earth. One such meteorite broke up over Murchison, Australia in September 1969. The fragments were analyzed and found to contain both amino and nucleic acids—considered the building blocks of life. The fact that the analysis was performed by Dr. Cyril Ponnamperuma, an expert in the field of abiogenic synthesis of organic compounds, lent much needed credence to the findings. Based on these kinds of information, Hoyle and Wickramasinghe have enunciated their controversial views in their 1978 book, *Lifecloud*, wherein they proposed that life originated, not on our planet, but in space. They have even come to the conclusion, after studying the absorption spectra of interstellar material, that in addition to numerous kinds of organic molecules, large molecules such as starch and cellulose and even living bacteria are present in space[4]. In a more controversial but related vein, Hoyle has suggested that comets may likewise be a source of many of the viruses and bacteria blamed for the disease epidemics (such as the flu) in humans. Some scientists have concluded that a thin shell of ice could protect such space bound cells, even against radiation, until they had a chance, somehow, to descend onto the earth's surface. However, there is no evidence to date of any meteorite integrated spores or other biological configurations that might serve as an actual basis for a self-replicating entity. Thus, in contrast to the theories supporting the SAb of Life within 'primordial soups' on the surface of planets, Hoyle and company prefer the interstellar dust clouds as the venue where the transformations from inanimate chemistry take place, with comets (formed of these kinds of materials) providing the suitable environment for the elaboration, protection and transportation of the resulting seeds of Life in space. Just to cap the theory, Hoyle has added the additional ingredient of "some kind of intelligence of a directive nature" to the requirement mix for the process of development to occur—without specifying precisely what he has in mind. This last concept fits in rather well with our Rational Design Hypothesis. But, in sharp contrast with Hoyle et al, we will spell out exactly what we have in mind.

The bottom line proof for the validity of the panspermia hypothesis would be the discovery of such "seeds of life" and the verification of their having arrived on the planet from beyond the earth. Nothing else could validate the theory. And no experiment is conceivable that could bypass this imperative. Supporters must simply wait and search until such positive evidence arrives. The current state of this OoL option can be summarized according to how one critic put it: "It seems to us that, on the basis of current information and results, the "bacteria in space" hypothesis is difficult to defend, but at the same time it has not been shown with certainty to be wrong, and it is not a totally unwarranted speculation".

Problems With Panspermia:

1] If any seeds of life that could validate the PS hypothesis were derived from complex protomolecules—and of a purely chemical origin—then some of the same logical and physical problems that plague SAb would apply here as well.

2] If the progenators of life on earth were actual biological seeds or spores, then we have merely delayed asking the question: what is the possible source of such interesting material—accidental (SAb from somewhere else) or designed (RDH from elsewhere)?

3] Why don't we find evidence of some kind of such complex biological material similar to spores or whatever from outer space? At present, the best we can detect are organic chemicals that are a long way from crossing the demarcation line that separates life from chemistry. This kind of encouragement, that PS seems to rely on, falls woefully short of the kind of evidence proponents are seeking, and without which PS remains a dead issue. The recent discovery of possible evidence of past life on Mars provides no help here.

4] But, the main reason the Panspermia Theory has been generally discredited lies in the low mathematical probability, that even one such spore could have arrived in the manner described, on our planet during the entire history of the universe[5]. Add to this the likely perishability through solar radiation, and the cold and vacuum of space, of any microorganisms of the type we know today and we gain an appreciation why this theory gets low marks from the scientific community.

5] Even if against all odds, some viable spore or seed survived its mysterious voyage through space and managed to find itself on the planet Earth's surface, the likelihood of any single organism event initiating the whole process of biological life on the planet will be shown, in the pages ahead, to be a next-to-impossible proposition. Evolution, in order to function, requires populations of organisms—a single organism won't do. As discussed in the last chapter, this same principle applies as well to SAb and will constitute a cornerstone in the invalidation of any such "singularity event" startup hypothesis.

The real significance of PS, in our view, is the fact that such noted scientists as Hoyle and Wickramasinghe have seen fit to propose an alternative to the SAb option. In the absence of any hard evidence in support of PS, there is only one conclusion that can be drawn: the problems associated with any SAb OoL option are sufficiently overwhelming to require alternative, even if less than ideal, solutions. As such PS, with all of its obvious shortcomings, qualifies in their view.

The "4th" Option—Directed Panspermia: A New Twist

First suggested by Leslie Orgel and Francis Crick in an article published in 1973 and subsequently elaborated on in a "scientific book for lay readers"[6], this idea put a twist on the premise of Panspermia by injecting the additional idea that bacteria were in fact launched into space on some kind of unmanned spacecraft, by intelligent beings from a higher civilization, from somewhere else in space, and purposely sent in our direction. Their theory was inspired by two facts, as they see it:

1] the uniformity of the genetic code, and
2] the age of the universe.

The age of the universe appears to be more than twice the age of the Earth, allowing for sufficient time, according to them, for life to have evolved twice: once by the intelligent directors of Directed Panspermia (DP) somewhere else, presumably in our galaxy, and then, a second time for life here on Earth. The Rational Design Hypothesis welcomes this bit of speculation, as it conveniently suggests ideas that are still considered by some to exist somewhat outside of the realm of serious scientific consideration. And in truth, at first glance some of the details of DPS do evoke a kind of "smug" first reaction. In the book version, Crick argues that the Earth has been under continuous observation by intelligent and benevolent extraterrestrials that, at an appropriate moment, launched the germs of life (a variety of microorganisms) toward our planet. But, rather than simplifying the problem, additional questions and conditions must be overcome to validate this as a viable model for the OoL on the planet such as compatibility problems with the planet's existent geology, climate and chemistry; additional problems with survivability, thrivability, mutability. Then again, how do you go and prove such an idea? Finally, there is no suggestion that the seed organisms might have been genetically engineered, or created in vitro by extraterrestrials. Neither do they proffer any motivation for such a contrived OoL on our planet—for which the "directors" of Directed Panspermia presumably went to a lot of trouble to execute. Then, of course, one must deal with the stickler question: If DPS relies on a previous life form to validate the OoL on earth, have they not merely postponed having to deal with the larger OoL question; i.e., how did the life form that preceded all others originate? In truth, this is an issue that the Rational Design hypothesis, the 5th option, must contend with—and we will.

PS, DPS and Thirty Million Year Old Bacteria:

In an article in the *New York Times*, Malcolm W. Browne reported that a prominent molecular biologist had succeeded in restoring to life bacteria that had remained dormant in the stomachs of ancient bees embedded and locked away in tropical amber for 30 million years. The report suggested that confirmation of this event would "force scientists to reexamine long-held notions about the temporal limits of life". The fact that the scientist—professor Raul Cano of California Polytechnic State University—has admitted to reviving more than 100 types of such ancient bacterial organisms would seem to relegate the story beyond science fiction status. But, the prospect of reviving a life form that would have had to overcome the effects of starvation, extremes of temperature, chemical attack, oxidation and assaults by microorganisms and enzymes during its limited lifetime and then overcoming the ravages of eons of time as well is indeed reminiscent of the most imaginative fiction. Almost to compound further the trail of imagination, if that was all it was, is the news that Cano has founded a commercial enterprise to exploit the production of pharmaceutical products, including new antibiotics that can be derived from these and other ancient organisms. The announced hope is to harness the potential effectiveness of ancient bacterial antibiotics that had disappeared eons ago, but that might be extracted from revived ancient bacteria in order to combat today's pathogenic variants. Countering all this good stuff are the skeptics who contend that Cano's ancient bacteria are nothing more than modern contamination. You might say that for the moment, the doubters are content to equate Cano's revelations to the science fantasy writings of Michael Crichton as exemplified in—*Jurassic Park*.

But, our interest is more than just the curiosity of the reported account. Within this tale lies the potential to overcome one of the key problems pestering both Panspermia and Directed Panspermia— that of the survival of the seeds of life of a journey through both space and time to provoke the OoL on the planet. It speaks directly to the major obstacles of transport survival over an indeterminate period of time, and thus gains relevance within the context of our proceedings herein. But this minor victory, if it could be described as such, will not prove consequential in the long run. For both Panspermia hypotheses, when all is said and done, cannot circumvent the logistical pitfalls they face in common with SAb.

Additional Problems:

1] atmospheric entry (heat and impact)—even meteorites have a hellish problem with this;
2] compatibility with the chemistry and conditions of the biosphere of planet Earth at the time of entry (would it have to have been just a marvelous coincidence);
3] odds against survival of such event singularities over both short and long term;
4] how could evolution have gotten started? (This is a critical question that concerns all OoL scenarios and will be dealt with in depth later).

In a disclaimer type of statement made some time after its introduction, and probably in response to the snickers and criticism these ideas engendered at the time, one of the authors described his view of DPS as "rather detached" and that the object of the book was—not to solve the problem of life's origins, but to convey some idea of the many kinds of science involved in the problem, ranging from cosmology and astronomy to biology and chemistry. But, from our point of view, DPS has in a sense, removed the stigma associated with the idea of a biological life form having been designed elsewhere and transplanted to the earth planet—an idea that forms an important cornerstone within the 5th option—the Rational Design Hypothesis (RDH) we shall be investigating. This, particularly in view of the fact that the notion originated from no less than the co-discoverer of the double helix architecture of DNA in 1953—Nobel Laureate Francis Crick, and that DNA could arguably be called your basic "self-generation molecule". He might have added, but didn't, that one of the main reasons for coming up with the DPS scenario in the first place was perhaps to offer some alternative to the difficulties (and low probability) inherent in any SAb solution to OoL. It would not be a surprise if the original Panspermia hypothesis of Svante Arrhenius was resurrected and concocted in its present forms (PS and DPS) for precisely the same reasons—as desperation alternatives—after so many years of probing SAb with little to show for the efforts.

CONCLUSIONS:

As stated, the only possible way of overcoming all the obstacles posed by any SAb OoL option is to eliminate those obstacles entirely. Others have found that this can be accomplished by simply resorting to the other logical options—PS and DPS—discussed in this chapter, each of which manages to avoid some of the pitfalls inherent within the SAb option, but can't seem to sidestep giving rise to some significant others. Both Panspermia and Design hypotheses accomplish the task of bridging the imposing gaps between non-living chemistry and the very much alive biology—what we refer to as the "chemistry-to-biology interface problem". However, both PS and DPS suffer, as we will later see, from the same problems as SAb with respect to evolution, in addition to the logistical problems particular to their genre. The extent that the RDH overcomes these same impediments will determine in grand measure its own validity within the OoL mystery game.

While there may be some similarities between DPS and our RDH, the differences are sufficiently stark. Firstly, DPS simply suggests that the origin of the life form (bacteria is suggested) that gave rise to life on our planet originated elsewhere, without any consideration of either design or purpose. The implementation of un-"manned" spacecraft as a transport vehicle, in order to overcome the PS problems of survival during a long and unprotected journey through space raises some interesting complications of its own. For example, how could the shippers guarantee that their precious cargo of microorganisms would necessarily end up on any particular planet (the hospitable one) within the ecosphere of our solar system, even given that this solar system was the intended destination? Was it just luck that the transport system happened to drop off their microscopic passengers on planet Earth, or were all the other planets in our solar system equal candidates for such specimens? If that were the case, shouldn't we find evidence of life in these other locations?

The RDH, on the other hand specifies a second transport option that would eliminate these problems entirely. It suggests the delivery of the specimens of living space cargo using "manned" space vehicles. This would permit greater discrimination as to the ultimate destination—even to the point of actually choosing a suitable planet within a "well-positioned" star-planetary system. The goal would have been to choose one that would serve as a hospitable refuge where the deposited system of life forms could become "fine-tuned" in order to survive, thrive, and perform its long-term mission function. Thus, while the implication within DPS is that the establishment of the LS on our planet was an exercise devoid of practical motive other than the deliberate transport of primitive life forms to outer space, and their subsequent arrival on the planet 3.8 billion years ago—and possibly by accident—the RDH takes the diametrically opposite position in this respect. It specifies purpose and a large measure of planning to the whole operation—through both the genetic engineering of the life form candidates for the seeding of a planet, their fine-tuning, and even the quantity of such transplanted life forms sufficient and necessary in order for the statistical imperatives of evolution to begin operation immediately. Also, purpose is implied within the RDH with respect to a specific choice of destination both in terms of star system (our own solar system) and hospitable planet (the Earth). In truth, all that DPS accomplishes is the removal of the SAb random initiating process on the planet, and replacing it by a ready-made life form artificially transported from elsewhere—really uninspiring. They don't deal with the initial OoL question at all. William of Occam would have a field day with this one!

The "1st" Option—Creationism: An Historical Legacy

Creationism is in a class by itself. Its methodology is essentially a remnant from a time that preceded science in the study of cause and effect. Its distinct advantage would seem to lie in its premise that all effects can be ascribed to a single causative agent. But, over time—as scientific investigation has provided more and more knowledge of the workings of the universe—creationists always seem to be playing catch-up in their attempts to reconcile their essentially static views of reality with the ever-changing modern face of that reality. But, creationism (the product of theology) serves our purpose in that it supports a "design" OoL option and therefore some of its arguments in opposition to SAb might prove useful. More recently, creationism has been adopting an "if you can't fight them—join them" posture by enlisting sympathetic members of the scientific community to espouse and argue their opposition to SAb. A prime target has always been the notion of Darwinian evolution, which creationists have always regarded as the principle threat to creationist dogma, and upon which SAb hangs its collective hat.

Design by way of "creation" completes the circle within which any OoL hypothesis must of necessity find itself. The primary redeeming feature of creationism—if indeed one is required to be recognized—resides in the inevitable reality that while science may be able to shed light on universal processes, its efforts to unveil ultimate secrets may indeed always remain limited. Since the primary cause of the origin of the universe itself may forever remain beyond scientific grasp, it would not come as a surprise if the same might also be thought of the difficult OoL question. If that remains the case, then over time, the reliance on creationist theological underpinnings for primary cause arguments (with respect to both the universe and life) may achieve some measure of permanency, even among some scientists. In sharp contrast to creationist design, the focus of rational design—as espoused within the RDH—constrains itself to the OoL mystery alone, whose solution relies purely on the incontrovertible evidence of design—an attribute incorporated within all designed systems.

The Anthropic Cosmological Principle (ACP):

Somewhere in between these two conflicting positions—science and creationism—the Anthropic Cosmological Principle (ACP) has emerged as some sort of logistical compromise. While ACP methodology appears to be scientific, its core logic is reminiscent of theology. Imbedded in the "Anthropic Cosmological Principal"—developed by Brandon Carter and others—is the notion that the laws of nature and the conditions that initiated our universe are finely tuned *to allow for the development of intelligent life*. The implication in the ACP is that we may be in some freak universe—self-selected from innumerable others—in order to make our existence, or a reasonable facsimile, not only possible, but also pretty well mandatory. This somehow dovetails with the principles of "quantum reality" where the crucial act of observation on the part of an observer is supposed to cause the collapse of the "quantum wave function" associated with the phenomenon being observed. Until that occurs, according to theory, the very idea of reality is thrown into question. The ACP is unique in the way its mode of reasoning differs remarkably from the deductive mode that has traditionally characterized scientific thinking. However, it is reasoned that because the deductive method cannot readily be employed in determining the origin of the cosmos, therefore, the ACP may be the only way to circumvent that logical impasse. Even though it is inspired by the seemingly uncanny relationships that exist between diverse mathematical constants that define reality in our universe, the ACP kind of argument has an unmistakable theological bent to it and thus avoids any kind of logical refutation. It also may, in reality, rely heavily on what we might normally define as 'coincidence', but, which the ACP interprets as "inevitability". Let's face it: any universe that gives rise to intelligent life must be a special kind of place to begin with. But to postulate that the effect (intelligent biological life) might constitute the cause in and of itself (the inevitabile birth of our kind of universe) would seem to be putting the cart before the horse. Unquestionably, the bottom line reasoning behind the ACP is the refusal on the part of its supporters to conceive of a universe forever empty of intelligent life. Thus, the reasoning is reversed and it is considered by ACP adherents—not that: "the human species is a biological adaptation to the universe", but—the reverse—that: "the universe is specifically adapted for the existence of intelligent humans". While the ACP may seem to be a realistic attempt to rationalize the existence of both our universe and our place in it, we shall have occasion later on to test its tenuous logic. In my view, when confronted by more scientific cosmological argument, it falls short.

However, as stated, the design paradigm includes more than religious creationism or anthropic cosmology. It includes as well the premise that bio-life on earth could have originated as a rationally designed (engineered) and custom-made system, deliberately transported to our planet and properly installed—in order to achieve specific goal(s). The **Rational Design Hypothesis (RDH)** represents our distinct contribution to the debate and constitutes a fifth option for consideration.

Introducing The "5th" OPTION—The Rational Design Hypothesis:

You might say that the Rational Design (RDH) hypothesis fits in between the fourth option— Directed Panspermia and the 1st—Creationism, and would seem to complete the circle of options. Both Panspermia and Rational Design are scientifically inspired concepts and consider the essence of life on earth to have had extraterrestrial origins. In addition, both consider evolution as necessary in allowing life to take hold on the planet to become the ubiquitous phenomenon we observe today. On the other hand, both Rational Design and Creationism postulate that life is a designed system with a purpose (neither Panspermia nor Directed Panspermia make any such claim). Creationists believe, however, that all living things were placed here in their present form and that life as we know it is a uniquely earthly phenomenon, created under divine supervision and authority. In stark contrast, the Rational Design hypothesis assumes that biological life is anything but unique, not divinely inspired and totally mechanistic in nature, i.e. biological life, as we know it, is a system of "von Neumann-like "self-replicating" machines" that has interesting evolution capabilities. As such:

> The RDH option utilizes a "systems engineering" approach to search for clues that point to Life on earth as: 1) being the product of intelligent design intent and 2) introduced on our planet by an intelligent agent in order to serve a specific purpose (a quality typical of all designed systems) and to accomplish its specific design mission.

The Rational Design Hypothesis was inspired mainly by a process of elimination. It remained, after a thorough review of the extant OoL literature—as the only logical choice left to pursue following the rational assessment that led to the elimination of all the other options as viable choices. It began as a reluctant avenue of investigation but, strange as these kinds of studies often turn out, it ended up as a convincing alternative to the weaknesses apparent within all the other OoL options. When it became evident that the traditional investigative tools and bottom-up approach that had been brought to bear in the investigation of the SAb option were essentially leading nowhere, the very notion of SAb itself became suspect. This inevitably opened the door for the search for other logical considerations. The only untried idea at the time was "rational design". Once the idea of the logic of a design option began to take hold, it became obvious that design engineering methods were as relevant to LS analysis as biochemistry—much in the same way that artistic technique is just as relevant to the analysis of a Rodin sculpture as a chemist's knowledge of modeling clays. That's because the LS constitutes a cohesive interactive operating system—considerably more complex than merely the sum of its constituent parts.

But, the real impetus for pursuing the Rational Design option came upon the realization that the RDH was indeed _testable_. Of all the options up for consideration, it is the only OoL option that could possibly make this claim. The reason becomes obvious when you consider that if the LS was indeed the product of design intent then, like all other designed systems (of human origin, for example), there should be apparent somewhere within the design incontrovertible evidence to support that fact or—as in the case of the LS—knowledge of where that evidence should be found and/or how we can test for it.

The RDH considers the likelihood that biological life was:

a)   Designed, and

b)   Expressly placed on the planet Earth by intelligent extraterrestrial agents close to 4 billion years ago in order to achieve:

c)   A specific purpose or Design Intent. It suggests as well, that:

d)   Our solar system was chosen for its particular location within the galaxy as one of numerous such venues where similar bio-life systems could have been "emplanted" in order to serve a common "design intent" and useful purpose.

The above statements come with the proverbial "good news and bad news" follow-up. The good news is that of all the OoL hypotheses listed above, the RDH, as stated, is the only one that is testable. The only truly bad news is that we may never get to know the source of the design [the intelligent designer]. For our purposes the designer source is, in fact, not really all that critical. Remember, all we really want to determine is the empirical evidence of design—if indeed it exists—that biological Life originated by purposeful design, and then possibly, the intended use of that design. If the RDH can accomplish these limited but reasonable goals, it will indeed have achieved much. As for the problem of the designer, let's deal with the issue in the following way:

PHILOSOPHICAL CONSIDERATIONS:

It has been stipulated above that this is a scientific inquiry in the sense that "rational design" is distinct from creationist philosophy. As such, before we proceed, we must attend to some important issues that might tend to cloud this point.

Now, a unique problem arises when we consider a design-based theory of the origin of life. When considering a SAb theory, for example, we begin with and rely on nothing more than the accepted and established laws of physics and chemistry as they pertain to our physical universe—such being the criteria for any scientific theory, valid or not. What can be disturbing about a design-based theory is that it invokes ideas that seemingly lie outside this criterion. With so much attention being paid to SAb theories and little else, we see among the scientific community a complete disinterest in the idea of life as a designed system for only one reason: it seems to be unscientific. More to the point, it smacks too much of religious creationism which, of course, is for all intent and purposes scientific heresy.

Ironically, it is the advent of the numerous *SETI* projects, supported by megafunded government and private sector grants that is providing some compelling and fundamental reasons for the scientific community to re-evaluate this negative position with respect to any kind of design OoL scenario. SETI essentially reflects an underlying belief—one shared by many scientists—in the possible existence within our universe of a rational intelligence other than our own. It is that same intelligence—if indeed it exists—that can go a long way in validating a rational design hypothesis. While the discovery of alien intelligence, in and of itself, does not represent some absolute decisive factor necessary to validate a rational design OoL hypothesis, SETI scientific initiatives most certainly do allow us to rationalize the existence of a prior design intelligence—one that must precede any kind of design.

SETI—The Search For Extraterrestrial Intelligence:

The search for alien intelligence has had a noble historic tradition since man first trained his unaided eyes skyward and wondered if we were alone in the universe. In modern times, such efforts have turned to the sophisticated technologies of radio telescopy to expand considerably the breadth and scope of our exploration of the far reaches of outer space. The central figure in humankind's technological search for ETI—extraterrestrial intelligence—is the same individual who began the first such efforts in 1959 at the National Radio Observatory in Green Bank, West Virginia with "Project Ozma". This initial two-month endeavor consisted of listening for signals from two nearby "sun-like" stars. Today's efforts could accomplish the same work in a fraction of a second as computerized radio telescopes scan a million or more stars at a time, at distances in excess of a thousand light years from Earth[7]. Why, some may inquire, would we want to engage in expensive searches for distant extraterrestrial intelligence when there are so many more pressing issues we face considerably closer to home? After all, how many people truly believe that there are beings out there that might be able to compete with human intelligence? Well, the answer to this particular question might surprise you.

In the preface to his book: *Is Anyone Out There?* Frank Drake—that central figure referred to above—would have us believe that 99.9 percent of his scientific colleagues believe that other intelligent life forms do exist. Not only that, he adds: "and furthermore that there may be large populations of them throughout our galaxy and beyond". If this truly represents the consensus of our professional scientists, then how far removed from this view could the rest of us be? Thus, it is not surprising that from modest beginnings, Frank Drake has seen his pet project, SETI—the Search for Extra-Terrestrial Intelligence—expand over the years to encompass a $100 million dollar commitment from NASA "making the work a priority for the space agency and guaranteeing that coveted telescope time will be devoted to the search". As things turned out, this optimistic bit of news has been tempered as the United States Congress in 1993 saw fit to cut back on the committed funds. However, other project SETI's, as they have come to be known, are continuing anyway under private funding. Projects such as the Phoenix program and the ambitious project "BETA", operated by the Harvard-Smithsonian Center for Astrophysics, have joined the list of searches to prove the "principle of mediocrity (PoM)" as it bears on the existence of other life forms and possibly intelligent ones, in our galaxy. BETA (Billion-channel Extra-Terrestrial Assay), directed by Harvard Physicist Paul Horowitz, comprises an 84-foot diameter dish-shaped radio telescope antenna that is entirely automated, as it searches the heavens for intelligent messages from space. Each circular sweep of the heavens captures radio emissions reaching Earth in the frequency range of 1400 to 1720 megahertz. Every two seconds, a CD Rom's worth of digitized data is read into a supercomputer able to sort and discard any cosmic radio noise. (This ambitious program is a far cry from Project Sentinel headed by Horowitz in the early 1980's limited to 131,000 channels centered on hydrogen's 1420 mh band.) When, and if, the automated equipment detects signals that are non-random and meet some critical tests for artificiality, the program will rescan that portion of the sky for a repeat performance before sounding an alarm that will alert the scientists that indeed, "the extraterrestrial phone is ringing". Unquestionably, their first job will be to double-check the equipment (to eliminate the possibility of earthly spurious signals and naturally occurring energy emissions from outer space) and examine the recorded event. The aim of all this, of course, is to find out whether some other intelligent life form has discovered how to transmit radio waves and if so, has chosen to do so. The hoped for bottom line will be the discovery that we indeed are not alone in the galaxy (or the universe) and, as a result, humankind will then have to "humbly" acknowledge that it has entered a new age. While the odds of finding a positive result are unknown, only a positive result would prove anything. And just because the "phone" didn't ring today, doesn't mean there is no one out there or that it won't ring tomorrow. But, the very act of searching the heavens for intelligent neighbors must be seen, in and of itself, as a radical cultural departure for humanity. It truly represents the acknowledgment of a new collective mindset that bears significantly upon the exercise in which we are presently engaged. And anyone with a computer can get in on the act by registering to participate in the 'SETI@ home' sky survey. The data collected is analyzed using distributed computing with the help of hundreds of thousands of home computers connected to the survey through the Internet.

Part of the process of treading new pathways in the pursuit of extraterrestrial intelligence involves rational efforts to determine the feasibility associated with these imaginative and less conservative scientific endeavors. Included are the exercises that look into the likelihood and probability of the existence of extraterrestrial intelligent civilizations, and if so, the likelyhood of establishing communication with them. Probably the most famous of these efforts has culminated in a reknown equation referred to, not surprisingly, as the "*Drake Equation*".

The Drake Equation—A Dream Formula:

Frank Drake will long be remembered as the scientist who gave substance to all the dreams of science fiction writers world-wide, by enunciating an equation that takes into account all of the known variables associated with the likelihood of the existence of smart neighbors both willing and able to transmit and receive signals from somewhere in our Milkyway Galaxy. In so doing, Drake propelled the SETI idea beyond the fringes of science fiction and into the spotlight of many of our collective mainstream dreams. In this respect, the Drake formula tells more about us than it does about that which we are seeking. It shouts loudly, but in a clear voice, that there is indeed a way to describe, in a rational and quantitative way, humankind's yearning to know whether we humans are the only practitioners of our kind of intelligence and, as well, whether we are destined to remain alone within the vastness of our galaxy. Let's examine the formula that Frank Drake presented at a 1961 conference on the possibility of extraterrestrial life, and see what all the excitement is about.

The Drake Formula: $N = R \cdot f_p \cdot n_e \cdot f_l \cdot f_i \cdot f_c \cdot L$

where,

N = the number of detectable communicating civilizations in space.

R = the rate of formation of stars in our galaxy; (ranges from 1 to 10 per year)

f_p = the fraction of stars that form planetary systems; (ranges anywhere from 1% to 100%)

n_e = the number of planets hospitable to life; (perhaps 10 percent)

f_l = the number of planets where life actually occurs; (ranges from a few to everywhere it can)

f_i = the number of planets where life evolves into intelligent beings; (from very low to very often)

f_c = the fraction of planets with intelligent creatures capable of interstellar communications; (no real consensus here—no one really knows what some intelligent alien race might be capable of, or might want to do).

L = the average lifetime of such a civilization after it develops advanced technology; (anybody's guess within a range of 1000 to 1 billion years).

A cursory examination of the impressive form of the equation reveals both its elegance and at the same time its naiveté. Scientists are noted for their ability to make educated guesses in order to fill in quantitative measures where actual measurements are unavailable or unsubstantiated. The above equation strains the credibility of the process considering that the value of not a single variable can be estimated with any kind of certainty. Compound this fact with the reality that each variable represents a single probability factor out of the total of seven, all of which must be multiplied together in order to come out with the total probability "N"—that a detectable civilization exists somewhere out in space. The recent discovery in October of 1995 at the Geneva Observatory in Switzerland of evidence of a planet circling the star 51 Pegasis some 45 light years away from us in the constellation Pegasus caused great excitement within the scientific community as it was the first such confirmation of a planetary system other than our own. While the fact that the planet surface temperature in the thousands of degrees would negate the existence there of biological life as we know it, still the implication cannot be ignored—that such planetary systems may be much more common than has been thought in the past. As if to confirm that hypothesis, several months later in February of 1996, two more such examples—a planet circling the star 70 Virginis in the constellation Virgo, and one orbiting 47 Ursae Majoris in the Big Dipper were discovered by San Francisco State University astronomers. The prospect that both of these are sufficiently moderate in temperature to permit the existence of liquid water has ignited a frenetic search for other planetary systems in the heavens. To aid in the search, NASA is allocating several hundred million dollars over the next few years to the "Origins" program to locate and possibly photograph Earthlike planets orbiting neighboring stars. With respect to the Drake formula, these discoveries unquestionably impact upon the significance of the independent variable—f_p. But, even if we could nail down a solid approximation of any one of the Drake formula variables, there are another six to go.

If the essence of the equation were to determine a simple and precise mathematical solution, then indeed we would have cause to be concerned. The range of values for N, after all, produce a result somewhere between 100 and 100 million possibilities—hardly an exercise in robust accuracy. However, perspective indeed is the name of the game when considering the Drake Equation. What is actually sought here is not precision but a sense of reality. It is unimportant exactly how many ETI civilizations may be out there. In fact, just a simple N being shown to be greater than "one" would be significant depending on the degree of confidence and credibility backing the figure. The Drake Equation is not meant to solve an engineering problem—it is only intended to provide a sense of whether "anyone else could be out there". In fact, we can consider the Drake formula as a kind of reality check with respect to the prospects of discovering life elsewhere in our neighborhood.

It is in this respect that the equation represents an exercise both in human arrogance as well as futility; while at the same time demonstrating an expression of the highest order of optimism of which human nature is capable. For, in the absence of the slightest shred of anything remotely called evidence, Frank Drake—wearing, I suspect, more his poet hat than that of scientist—has created an expression that should prove, more than in any other way I can imagine, that scientists can indeed have an artistic soul. And in so doing, he has demonstrated a side of science that belies the cold and hard images often popularized as responsible for all of the imagined and real ills of our world. The Drake formula, when all is said and done, solves nothing in the real world, but has the effect of giving us hope and pause to consider each factor nested within it. And as we ponder each element of consideration, we cannot but marvel at the fact that our own LS has itself had to endure or overcome each of these same tenuous obstacles just in order to be able to consider those same possibilities in others. Thus, regardless of what your personal views are regarding the likelihood of SETI success, what makes this formula exceedingly relevant—as far as Frank Drake (and the rest of his fellow human beings) is concerned—is the fact that each phenomenon represented by the factors nested within it is an event that, as he reminds us, "has already taken place at least once". Thus, we really didn't need Frank Drake's equation to calculate the outside limit of $N = 1$ (ourselves). On the other hand in the absence of a positive SETI response, there is absolutely no way to fix even an approximate value in our minds of the extent, or indeed whether, N is greater than one? And that fact represents the limiting significance of the "N" factor and of the Drake formula itself. Still, the Drake Equation is significant simply by its very existence, expanding the limits of human inquiry, human culture, and human hopes and dreams as well.

The BETA project, and others of its kind, represents a global scientific effort to find evidence of extra terrestrial intelligence. It is understood that if and when such evidence emerges, there is a great likelihood that we will be confronting proof of a lifeform whose intelligence greatly exceeds our own; intelligence for whom, for example, the challenge of creating a biological life system—such as that found on the planet earth—could conceivably have been met. (Can we assume that at some point, molecular biologists here on earth will finally work out a scheme for artificially producing self-replicating biological molecules from inanimate chemicals in the test-tube?). There is no way to confuse designer-type genetic engineering with some happenstance spontaneous self-generation abiogenetic event occurring within the primordial chemical soup of our planet. In effect, this is the entire message of our thesis, which we will be repeating again and again, that: while the planet earth is an hospitable place for a biological life-system to thrive—for a number of good and valid reasons (some of which have already been discussed)—it is not the place where that same life-system could have abiogenetically originated. And, furthermore, biological life—wherever it may be found—could not be the result of SAb. Additionally, we hope to demonstrate that the origin of biological life is, of necessity, contrived.

It is important to realize that the immense amount of support, effort, and money invested in SETI-like projects indicates a specific as well as recent change in attitude held not only by the scientists involved, but as well by the scientific community and society at large: that given the fact that the technology is now available, it is both reasonable (more so than not) and cost effective to conduct such a search for the existence of extraterrestrial intelligence. So, what was once the science fiction notion of "aliens in space" has become a valid, and hopefully provable scientific idea. As well, supporters of Directed Panspermia can relax a bit more with this knowledge that they are not alone in raising the prospect of "extra terrestrial intelligence (ETI)" within a scientific framework. And, of course, the same reasoning can extend in support of the existence of an ETI designer within our Rational Design Hypothesis.

Thus, and most importantly from our point of view, is the fact that the SETI initiative has served additionally as the inspiration to pursue the RDH line of inquiry using a novel Systems Engineering approach. SETI and like scientific programs also serve to validate our Rational Design Hypothesis in the following way:

> *If SETI is a logical and practical scientific experiment with an open-ended time line (no end in sight until positive results are achieved) then the possible consequences of a positive result [N>1] are fair game for both scientific speculation and investigation.*

We would argue that insofar as the above relates to OoL theories, the Rational Design Hypothesis dovetails perfectly with SETI. This will become obvious as we proceed with our exercise. While to date, no evidence of extraterrestrial intelligence has been detected, recent discoveries of telltale signs of possible evidence of life of a more mundane character, within extraterrestrial material from our immediate planetary neighborhood, has sparked the imagination of the scientific world.

Design/Designer Dichotomy:

The RDH, as stated, fits neatly in the large gap between Directed Panspermia and Creationism. As such—and because it does represent a radical departure from the more mainstream SAb—we shall attempt to take the greatest care in preserving the scientific foundation and underpinnings of our investigative approach to the study of OoL. As regards the question of the designer: for the time being, we will have to content ourselves with the logical certainty that any designer of the biological system we call Life on the planet earth would, of necessity, have had to have been foreign to the planet, i.e.; of extraterrestrial origin. This is about as far as we can proceed with the question for now. However, we can raise the question as to whether it really is necessary to deal with the issue at all? Let me elaborate.

If a hypothetical caveman arose one morning to find at the entrance to his abode a modern object—say a coffee mug—what would be his reaction? Once he got over his initial surprise, his innate curiosity might impel him to take the unfamiliar object in his hands and try to fathom what it was and how it got there. After a while, boredom or the need to attend to his agenda (find food and water) might overcome his curiosity and he might set the object aside. Upon his return, and to his surprise, he might find the mug full of rain water that had accumulated in his absence. Eventually, we can imagine a glint in his eye and his delight at the realization that the cup could serve as a practical container to hold drinking water. The net consequence: the primitive investigation has resulted in the determination of a possible purpose for the designed object. Over time, our hypothetical object could quite possibly become revered within the clan as some sacred object. And, eventually, clan descendants might themselves discover the art of clay fabrication and thus establish with a measure of expertise that their ancient object was, indeed, an artifact and the result of design intent. But, in fact, the question of the designer—while interesting to contemplate—need never cross one's mind. It really makes no difference whether the provenance of the mug is known or not. The designed object and the source of its design remain two separate and totally independent issues. And that is our point. (N.B.: Having provided the above disclaimer in order to justify the logical separation between that which is the product of design and the causative designer-producer, be assured that we do address the "origin-of-the-designer" issue in detail later on. It was deemed premature at this particular juncture in our inquiry.)

We, in proposing the RDH, find ourselves in a similar situation to that of our hypothetical antecedent. Our goal is to determine what Life is doing here on the planet (possibly by design intent) and how it got here (the Origin of Life). As regards the designer or the design source, we are prepared to put aside this issue as irrelevant to our quest; it is of curious interest but unessential in the pursuit of our goal. We, in effect, separate the concepts of design and designer. Our focused goal is to examine the object of interest—the LS—and by analyzing it's many qualities and aspects determine whether, indeed, we can find clear evidence of a contrived derivation. As part and parcel of the process we hope to also uncover clear evidence that could shed light on what may have been the design intent. The extant system is all we have to go on; for all we know the designer may be long gone without any intention of returning to see the results of his/her handiwork, or how successfully the design worked out. However, having stated the case, this won't prevent us from speculating about the designer later on—within the context of the design intent of the system.

The Rational Design Hypothesis—An Occam's Razor of Sorts:

Possibly the most important implication of the RDH is that it does serve to eliminate some very sticky dilemmas that will always plague SAb. Among the issues the RDH will resolve in the following pages are the following:

1] It solves the problem of when and how evolution began;

2] It solves the sticky statistical problem of how an initial SAb lifeform could have overcome the immense (and intolerable) odds against survival in a harsh and changing environment that would have been faced by a single defenseless 'species'—all, as we shall see—without the benefit of the fully operational forces of evolution; this is a problem faced by both SAb and PS.

3] It solves the problem of when and how it was possible for 'photosynthesis'—the engine of life and 'DNA'—the informational library, to come together within the protective environment of the cell;

4] It answers the curious 'exclusive twenty-only amino acid' question;

5] It solves the 'negative entropy' problem. (The LS was placed here already primed for action and operational.)

6] It solves the curious 'chirality' problem (why only left-handed proteins and right handed nucleic acids);

7] It provides a definitive answer to the 'origin of SEX' debate—a focal issue of great importance;

8] It provides a solution to the Intron—'*junk DNA*' problem that still confounds molecular biologists;

9] The *Rational Design Hhypothesis* can be '***tested***'!

Where Do We Go From Here:

Our discussions so far have considered some of the complex issues any OoL scenario must address and the problems associated with the different options advanced to date. We are offerring as our own contribution to the debate—the Rational Design Hypothesis—The 5th OPTION, which we are confident will go a long way toward remedying the apparent weaknesses evident among the other OoL options. In order to do so, we shall be engaging some novel intellectual tools in the investigation of life—the LS—in order to fully exploit the implications within the RDH. Towards this end, the next few chapters will comprise a thorough study of the LS from a novel perspective, which will allow us to address all the many issue and debates—some of which have been alluded to above. All the while, we shall never lose sight of our objective—namely, to offer a viable and provable solution to the mystery of the OoL.

We begin by defining our operational goals and validating the methodology we shall bring to the task. Then we proceed headlong into an original analysis of all the essential characteristics of the LS from a "systems engineering (SE)" perspective—one that is fully compatible with the Rational Design Hypothesis we are investigating. Eventually, the essentials of the RDH emerge which we then test against the crucial questions that demand comprehensive answers and that any OoL option must confront. Now that I have whetted your appetite and teased your curiosity, let us pursue what promises to be an exciting and interesting quest: nothing less than a systematic and logical solution to the mystery of the origin of life.

---

[1] Life Itself: Francis Crick p34

[2] Science: 22 Dec 1995 p1926

[3] Lifecloud: The Origin of Life in the Universe (1979): F.Hoyle & N C Wiskramsinghe

[4] Life in the Universe: F. Jackson, P. Moore p29

[5] Paradigms Lost: J. Casti p116

[6] What Mad Pursuit: F. Crick p148

[7] Is Anyone Out There?: F Drake and D Sobel p xii

5. A Systems Engineering Approach

"Systems thinking is a discipline for seeing wholes. It is a framework for seeing interrelationships rather than things, for seeing patterns of change rather than static "snapshots'...And systems thinking is a sensibility— for the subtle interconnectedness that gives living systems their unique character."

—Peter Senge (1947–), Systems Theorist

The following chapters describe the logical levels of activity that characterize the Living System (LS). We shall treat the LS as a comprehensive and interactive system and then separate that system into a set of logical operational levels and components. This will enable us to bring to bear "Systems Engineering (SE)" procedures in order to try to understand what the different parts of the system are contributing to the operation of the system as a whole. By examining the various structures of the subsystems that comprise the LS, we hope to be able to fathom the overall form and function of the system itself, and then hopefully be in a position to try and determine whether we can recognize what it is that this system is actually doing. Only then will we be able to logically consider an actual and particular use or purpose the LS could possibly serve. If this lofty goal can be achieved, with any luck, we could then find ourselves in the interesting position of trying to identify the design intent of the system and the actual purpose being exploited, i.e. the raison d'être of the LS. Finally, at the end-game stage of our analysis, we may even be able to suggest how we can verify any such proposition, and make predictions on where the proof of such purpose may be found. And, of course, any test we can formulate for purposeful design, will not only be a test of whether biological Life on our planet is a product of design or not, but also effectively serve as the sufficient and necessary test criterion for OoL by design, as well. This Euclidean-like approach, in a nutshell, will serve as our logic agenda in order to pursue our quest to establish the merits of The 5th OPTION: the Rational Design Hypothesis.

Systems Engineering Basic Concepts:

There are distinctions between some of the ideas expressed above that should be made clear. The dictionary provides the formal definitions of some of these terms:

Form: (Philos)	(n) The structure, pattern organization or essential nature of anything; the outward appearance of something as distinguished from the substance of which it is made.
Function:	(n) The acts or operations expected of a person or thing. (v) To perform a specified action or activity in an indicated way.
Use:	(n) The act or practice of putting something into action or service. (v) to cause to function.
Design:	(n) A method devised for making or doing something or attaining an end.
Intent:	(n) What one proposes to accomplish or do. In addition,
Design Intent:	Engineers use the expression "design-intent" to express the idea of "a set of goals intended to be achieved by a designer as reflected within a design".

Take an internal combustion engine, for example. An examination of its various parts or components, and studying the way they are physically connected, will provide information as to its physical make up—what we refer to as its **"*form*"** or structure (you might say that "structure" is the engineering equivalent of "form"). A three-dimensional model or two-dimensional drawing is an efficient way to depict the physical form of a machine or system. Further analysis into how the engine converts gasoline fuel energy at the input into rotational mechanical energy will yield the operating principles, or how it *functions*. A schematic diagram can serve to clarify function. Then further analysis of the particular system under study, such as its output capacity, and how its mechanical energy is harnessed—whether to power an electric generator or a water pump, for example—will determine it's general or generic purpose or *use*. Very often, the actual or particular circumstances under which the function is utilized may demand modifications to the physical form of the system particular to the requirements or specifications of the end user, which will in turn be reflected within the overall system **"*design intent*"**. Thus, in our above example, the engine in question may actually drive an emergency electric generator, be packaged in a water proof housing for outdoor use and with a noise eliminating exhaust muffler to ensure quiet operation.

Thus, any SE analysis distinguishes between structure, function, use and design intent. Normally, any design involves an evaluation to identify desired objectives and to determine procedures for efficiently attaining them, as reflected in the design intent. Only then, is an attempt made to build the system that will accomplish all of the goals deemed important.

In our exercise, we shall be doing systems engineering in "reverse". Since we are considering the LS as a functioning system in place, our objective, as stated, will be to analyze the form and function of individual subsystems in order to:

1] try to identify overall LS objectives, (as distinguished from form and function);
2] try to recognize what generic use the LS as a whole can possibly serve, and finally;

3] try to determine what particular purpose the LS was designed to achieve, as reflected in its design intent.

Now, while our object system for study, the LS, is a singular phenomenon and the only one (to our knowledge) in existence, our SE approach will hopefully enable us to identify generic principles at work and then possibly evoke suggestions of particular goals and design intent. This is what our SE analysis of the LS is all about. In addition, the results of that study will constitute an integral part of the Rational Design Hypothesis we are investigating for the OoL on the planet Earth.

Validation of the "Life System" Concept:

The term "life" is an umbrella concept—one that covers many diverse but unrelated events that living things do, no matter where it might be found. For our purposes, life means the LS—that specific universally cohesive system of living things found on our planet and the only such system we know exists. Using the SE approach affords a broad arena of investigation on many different kinds of levels—from the macro to the molecular, and from the information to the energy levels—all in the quest to fathom what indeed it is the LS, as a whole, is doing. Supporters of SAb regard life as some universal attribute of planetary biospheres where conditions allow and thus might take exception to the system concept on general principle. However, the validity of the concept of "biological Life—the system" can be argued from the SAb point of view, as follows:

1] If life self-generated from the bottom-up (a basic tenet of SAb), and therefore,

2] the whole present day infrastructure of interactive life is an evolutionary outgrowth of that initial state, then

3] the total LS of today represents an equal level of homogeneity as that at its inception close to 4 billion years ago—the only fundamental difference being the number of LS participants—all of which constitute part of a single whole (now as then). The interactivity of the food chain attests to this fact. Therefore,

4] all of life today represents a single organized integrated whole made up of diverse but interrelated and interdependent parts, (acting and reacting with and within the external biosphere). This, in effect meets our definition of a "system".

The only questions that may remain relate to the degree of the relationships between different species and organisms that make up the system such as—but not limited to—questions relating to the LS family tree through its evolutionary past to the present. However, a unified system it is, in both space and time—all component organisms stemming from a common originating source at the OoL—and we shall deal with it as such.

The Top Down Approach:

There is a seductive temptation to try and analyze and study the LS using the same mental approach engineers use to design and create complex systems, because it does "appear to be" the ultimately engineered system (and, after all, we are trying to explain the "Design" option). I am not oblivious to the fact that this same "system" argument has been used by theologians throughout history to validate religious dogma and the like, but, in contrast we shall be invoking the idea of system design without any preconception of its validity, nor of the outcome of this kind of unconventional inquiry into what the LS is about. All we really are looking to accomplish is to set in motion an unconventional method of inquiry and to try and determine whether it can yield worthwhile results relevant to our exercise.

Historically, the study of Life, by those curious enough to engage in such pursuits, consisted exclusively in what can be referred to as a "top down approach". By that, I mean looking at the phenomenon of life from the big-picture point of view (also a system-wide approach). While the many kinds of organisms—plants and animals—have been recognized as being different from each other, there has never been a sense that all living things were not part of a greater whole and inseparable from their earth habitat. And regardless of whether one adopts a "mechanistic" point of view—the philosophical doctrine that conceives of the continuity of nature in terms of the universality of purely mechanical principles—or the "vitalist" position—that regards living things as a distinct domain in nature—living things do behave differently from the non-living and constitute parts of an interactive organization that we shall continue to refer to as the life system or LS. Thus, while acknowledging the many facets of living things, and the many different ways organisms carry on their respective lives, it has always been accepted that every living thing has its appointed place within the continuous tapestry of action and interaction that is the system of life on our planet. There is apparent an all-persuasive unity throughout the diversity that characterizes this ubiquitous phenomenon of biological life on our planet (We shall ignore, for the moment, any unique role that may be ascribed to the human species by some egocentric schools of thought).

In short, the top-down approach begins with the observer's own senses: sight, hearing, touch, taste, and sense of smell (and perhaps some others too subtle and less understood). After all, these were the original instruments of observation for experiencing as well as studying life, and the conclusions they led to then, and still lead to today is that, indeed, life on this planet behaves as an exquisite, if sometimes mysterious system. And, over time, as humanity's ingenuity afforded it more sophisticated equipment with which to extend the senses—in order to better understand the life phenomenon—that fact became ever more apparent. We have come to understand that the distinctions between species represent only minor differences in degree and that the unity of life extends from the top, right down to the molecular biological level. Over time, we have come to realize that there is something quite special about a system that is so diverse in it's components and levels of complexity, and so tenacious in it's abilities to thrive and survive over eons of geological time.

The Life System (LS)—More A Definition Than Metaphor:

The point is, that the description of Life as a system better meets the requirements of a "definition" than it does "metaphor", and indeed, the system approach has been the intuitive way we have learned so much about its different aspects. Man has traditionally learned how to study all kinds of complex phenomena by treating them as systems. By breaking up a complex system into a set of concepts or component parts that work together, each can be isolated and explored independently. So it has been in our learning about life. Science has effectively taken the system, biological life, and broken it down into myriad parts and functions and has developed whole disciplines many of which dwell on a single aspect of the system—the most complex of any on the planet. But having made the point, we shall still be ever mindful of the fact that in referring to life as a system, the word 'system' automatically reflects the idea of "purpose" and "design"—two very human concepts being applied to a phenomenon of non-human origin. These are concepts, which, at the onset of our SE investigation, we consciously wish to avoid. Let me explain:

The whole field of Systems Engineering attests to the way we think, deal with, and design complex systems that perform according to a "design Intent". The very human techniques of Systems Engineering (SE), however, also represent a powerful intellectual tool in the organization and analysis of complex systems (whether man-made or otherwise). It is only for that reason alone that we shall be using these tools in a novel application toward the understanding of what life is, and what it is doing. That novel application is to view the system of life—potentially and hypothetically—as a designed system, but without assuming it to be so. We shall be placing ourselves in a very delicate situation here. We must remember that it is only at the end of the exercise, after we let the chips fall where they may, that we will be in a position to draw any logical conclusions with respect to the validity of any such design intent and consequently a design hypothesis for the OoL. Only then will the SE analysis constitute an integral part of the validation process for the Rational Design Hypothesis for the OoL.

It is definitely conceivable that scientists on our own planet will one-day be able to literally "create" biological life in a laboratory.[1] In fact, there are primitive efforts already being made along these lines[1]. And, if we can conceive of the eventuality of human genetic engineers creating a biological "life-like" system in the laboratory, it would follow that any other highly intelligent life form (learned in the ways of biology) would be capable of doing the same. But, in conceding the above possibility, and fully aware of the importance that SAb places in artificially creating living entities from chemicals, we shall repeat our previously expressed word of caution: Intelligent human molecular biologists and biochemists contriving the conditions in order to coax life-like activity from a test tube full of chemicals bears little relationship to the SAb of the phenomenon. The operative modifier in the expression "SAb" is the word "spontaneous" and we have already spelled out some compelling arguments that support our contention that even if a self replicating molecular entity could somehow emanate naturally from the chemical soup of the oceans, the lack of the necessary conditions for the thriving, evolution and taking root on the planet of such a single accidental occurrence would most probably doom such an incident to failure. The RDH was conceived in order to remedy these kinds of problems—a goal achieved by eliminating them altogether. The invocation of a SE approach forms an integral part of the RDH solution to the mystery of the OoL on our planet.

We proceed with the understanding that the invocation of an implied designer in virtue of the SE exercise that we shall engage in lies well within the accepted bounds of science, because that concept (the designer of the LS) need consist of only the following two things:

1] a high level of technology (that which would conceivably allow for the design of a biological life system), and

2] the nature of the design intelligence being extraterrestrial (allowing an ET source to have designed the life system that exists on Earth).

Thus, if the scientific community can accept the possibility of the existence of, and search for, intelligent ET's using SETI technologies, and if they can also accept the idea that given enough intelligence/knowledge we humans may one day be able to create the necessary biological conditions and jump start a self-replicating "living" entity in a laboratory test tube ourselves, then the idea of a highly intelligent extraterrestrial designer of our life system capable of that same achievement becomes a logical extension and consequently, a valid scientific possibility. Add to this the fact that Directed Panspermia posits the seeding of the primeval planet with the help of some directed intelligence (a theory supported by Nobel laureate Francis Crick, no less), together with the megabucks support for SETI efforts and the realization sinks in (if it has not done so already): that our Rational Design Hypothesis is in good and valued company as regards the logical validity of ETI—which in turn validates as well the designer concept for the RDH that both allows for and makes possible the OoL on our planet.

It is in this new spirit, using the novel SE analytical approach, that we shall explore the merits of the 5th OPTION—that which we have defined as the "Rational Design Hypothesis". This distinctive approach will afford us the opportunity to put ourselves in the shoes of a would-be *"designer"* and then ask the question:

"What would I (the designer) have had in mind (design Intent) to have designed this system (we call "biological life") and implant it on a curious little planet within a seemingly mediocre solar system in a far-flung region of the Milky Way galaxy?

Again, it is essential to stress that we shall make no assumptions that the outcome of our inquiry will validate this controversial approach. But, at the very least, we can expect that a SE analysis might yield ideas that will permit us to see biological life on our planet from a new perspective and perhaps help to contribute to our greater understanding of this ubiquitous LS phenomenon, of which humanity forms an integral part.

Take It From The Top!

The bottom-up "chemical soup" SAb supporters have reduced biological life to its basic constituent chemical elements, believing any apparent complexity beyond the first chemical replicators, such as biological cellular life, to be a later phenomenological characteristic explainable by processes grouped under the all inclusive umbrella called evolution.

The RDH considers that life cannot be reduced to any simpler level than the basic cell. This comes as no surprise when you consider that—as investigators of a "top-down" design concept of OoL—we find ourselves able to extrapolate biological life only as far back as its minimum biological 'quantum' level of order and complexity—the biological cell. This can almost be considered as a given within any design hypothesis in consideration of the fact that the only evidence of the existence of life activity is exclusively cellular (we see absolutely no evidence of chemical life-like activity outside of the confines of the cell), and that, in fact, upon reflection, only the cellular entity could be expected to possess and protect all of the genetic information, data and energy processing mechanisms, reproductive strategies, and the feedback control mechanisms that tie these all together, and without which biological life cannot exist. Thus, however primitive the first lifeform on the planet might have been, it would have had to have comprised that certain minimum level of form and function that could constitute a least possible state of biological complexity—but that could also serve to insulate, protect and separate the operating system of life from the ever-present destructive external forces of nature. These would tend to reduce and destroy any such state of order and complexity, were it not for that all-important physical separation of the living phenomenon within the cell from the universally chaotic and harmful forces external to it. Thus, our RDH considers evolution—its mechanisms for adaptability and change—to be part and parcel of the cellular phenomenon and not merely an external causative agent instrumental in the creation and shaping of the biological cell. RDH also considers the simplest basic cellular machine, as comprising the sufficient and necessary minimum design features for biological life activity to be possible. We have defined this entity as the "primary design platform" of life (PdP)—comprising the following primary subsystems and all housed within the artificially maintained environment within the cellular plasma membrane:

1] an originating genetic library encoded in the chemical medium of DNA;
2] the form and function of the genetic code;
3] protein production mechanisms;
4] metabolic processes;
5] the fundamental biological energy conversion procedures;
6] essential reproductive strategies;
7] the mechanisms of biological evolution responsible for species adaptability to changing external biosphere conditions.

These primary design system features would be considered relatively constant and outside of the influences of evolution. The only aspects of the system that are permitted to evolve are the secondary attributes of species physical manifestation that must accommodate the external biosphere. And since all evolutionary changes must begin with changes to information written in the genetic libraries of individual organisms that can be passed on to future generations, it is understood that any such information dealing with implementation of the above list of so-called primary attributes would be locked in, so to speak and error corrected of any spontaneous mutations. These and other aspects of the LS shall be analyzed in detail within our SE analysis in order to fully understand what the LS truly represents, and consequently to better appreciate why it is that any SAb hypothesis is a troublesome notion.

Three Little Questions:

In adopting a *"top-down"* systems approach to the analysis of life, we are afforded some intellectual luxuries and bonuses that might not be available otherwise. Because the study of systems in general comprises a not unusual activity for the human mind, we shall have available to us some powerful tried and true systems engineering exploratory techniques, which we can bring to bear on our subject. We will forget for the moment that life is a unique system, in that it is the only one on the planet (besides the laws of nature) whose origins are devoid of the intervention of man. We will then have the opportunity, to ask the same sorts of questions we would of any man-made system, if only to examine the life phenomenon in this novel way.

The first task for any inquiry of this kind is to pose the right questions. There are three basic lines of inquiry we want to explore.

1) *What 'is' the system we call Life—What is its form and function?*

2) *What does the LS 'do' : What are its a) generic purpose, and b) specific use—that might reflect a notable design intent? And finally,*

3) *What is the 'origin' of the LS phenomenon?*

If—in the course of our investigations of questions 1 and 2—we can find incontrovertible evidence anywhere within the LS of "design intent", then the RDH would consider that the fundamental aspect of question 3 would be resolved. While the above statement would appear to be self evident, how to go about proving that some aspect or feature is indeed evidence of design and not some naturally occurring attribute is, on the surface, not an easy task. Creationists of many persuasions have used ingenious, if intuitive, arguments in pursuit of this very goal over many centuries, without being able to advance their cause against a growing scientific skepticism. Thus, we can fully expect the burden of proof to be an onerous one, before any evidence can be accepted. In fact, in the light of the history of human culture and the many spurious allegations made in support of unsubstantiable religious claims of all kinds, any such alleged proof of design would really have to be logically self-evident before one would expect it to be taken seriously—particularly when we are talking about the origin of the most significant phenomenon we can ponder—that of Life. Consequently, we understand perfectly well that the tenets of the RDH could only be validated if proof offered in evidence can logically only lead to a single conclusion: that the system of biological life on our planet had to have been contrived. That achieved, we might then consider that the system was placed here to accomplish some particular mission—depending upon the nature of the proof presented and whether the evidence points in that direction. The assurance we are providing here is that we shall be ever mindful of our intellectual responsibilities throughout this endeavor. On the other hand, we are insisting—and shall continue to insist—that the playing field remain a level one and that supporters of opposing ideas be just as prepared to own up to their own responsibilities of proof. Having established the agenda of intellectual responsibility let's proceed with our exercise.

Questions 1) and 2) are generic in that we could ask them of any system, man-made or not. The last one is particular to the LS for obvious reasons and represents the heart of the LS mystery. Obviously, the first two of the above questions could only be put because of our novel SE approach. This is what I meant when I referred to "intellectual luxury" above. Because life behaves like a system, we will use SE techniques of inquiry, all the while ignoring for the moment, the philosophical implications. As it turns out, these three questions will be shown to be at the heart of any serious attempt to deal with the origin of the system of life here on the planet earth (For obvious reasons, the more traditional approach has limited itself to simply the question of how life got a foothold on our planet some 3.8 billion years ago, and consequently doesn't even consider the other two basic questions as relevant). Now, it doesn't take much in the way of deliberation to realize that any positive answers we get to the first question will bear significantly on how we see the second question above. We can all relate to the experience of wondering what some device or other "does" until we are told what it "is". Then its purpose may become obvious. If our SE analysis of the LS can yield answers to the first two questions, the last one, hopefully, may just fall into place. There is also a very practical reason for assuming the three questions above rather than concentrate only on the object of inquiry—how life got here. Let's face it—there is no direct nor indirect evidence dating back some 3.8 billion years to the time that we suspect life originated on our planet. Thus, neither is there direct evidence of how life got here. This fact alone has plagued all efforts to come up with a plausible solution to the OoL mystery. All we can actually study and observe from the available evidence make up the substance of the first two questions.

Scientists continue to make impressive progress in their comprehension of the complex principles that underlie the phenomenon of biological life—both in the wild as well as in the laboratory. In addition, the same can be said with respect to the dynamic behavior of the LS over time (its evolution). That's what we have to go on. With the exception of the fossil record and the geological record, both of which are uneven and sketchy, our best bet to understand how life got here is to understand what it truly is and what it is actually doing here. These are attainable goals, if only because there exists so much current data on life from the myriad scientific disciplines that deal with every aspect of it—from biochemistry to all of the molecular biology fields, genetics, anthropology, medicine, botany, zoology, genetic engineering, ecology and the environment, just to mention a few. All of these represent a small sampling of the information on the life sciences that literally fills whole libraries devoted to the study of all aspects of biological life and what it does. Thus, just the act of invoking a SE viewpoint has yielded us the dividends that attend that approach. We have been able to expand our inquiry from one question, for which no direct evidence seems to exist, to three related questions, two of which can be studied in detail. Thus, our initial contribution to this process of discovery is a relatively easy one: simply to ask the right questions. As we shall come to realize, the information containing the answers is all there—waiting for anyone interested and willing to look.

Our ambitious task will now be to take what is known about life and try to piece together diverse aspects of this complicated system in such a way as to be able to see the system in a new light. This is analogous to putting together a jigsaw puzzle of many pieces, each of which has exactly the same shape. Until now, it has always been assumed that there was only one proper way to assemble the pieces to produce the predictable picture, although that effort seems to have failed to date. We are, in effect, trying to take the same pieces of the puzzle of life and reassemble them in a new way such that the resulting image, while new and different, will, nevertheless, be a valid representation of the life-portrait we are seeking. The resultant model that emerges will hopefully yield new revelations about the realities of the LS. This kind of exploration shall require some powerful organizational tools, which fortunately are readily available. Treating life as a system will allow us to bring to bear the effective mechanisms of

SE in our study and analysis. However, this approach is not without controversy.

Reverse Engineering—A Logical Catalytic Approach:

We will be using the powerful techniques of systems engineering in the study of the LS as a *"catalytic agent"*, if you will, in order to get close to what is happening without it actually taking part in or influencing the net results. These, normally used to put together a system, will be used in reverse—to break down the LS into its varied components—in order to better comprehend the many facets and characteristics the LS exhibits. In short, we will use any method that will help to delineate, illuminate and organize the information of interest in order that we gain a true understanding of what is happening within the LS. Once this is accomplished we will be in a position to decide what parts of the system are telling us something important and what parts are functional details; which parts must have been there from the beginning and which parts are "Johnny come lately" and the results of subsequent evolution. This, in essence, is what we have done in the next few chapters. By meticulously analyzing the LS from many different levels and diverse vantage points we have been able to distill the juices of the phenomenon into its very essence. In the process, we have been able to construct a new model of reality as it relates to life on our planet with some startling implications.

Systems Engineering (SE) Principles and How It Works:

The first step in this process of inquiry is to describe what Systems Engineering (SE) is all about, and how we can avail ourselves of it's methodology. In general, SE is the application of engineering skills to the design and creation of complex systems. A system is a set of concepts and sub-units that must be integrated and coordinated in order to function together and accomplish a desired mission. As the name implies, "systems engineering" focuses primarily on the total system, it's coordination and implementation. The basic concepts are not new and have been in use on the planet ever since humans had to develop elaborate methods of coordination and control in order to manage the construction of complicated projects—the pyramids of Egypt and Roman aqueducts, for example. The importance of the concepts, however, was not recognized until after the Second World War with the impressive increase in the complexities of modern weapons of war. The design of the Polaris missile system, for example, required not only the construction of the missile itself, with it's propulsion, guidance and warhead components, but, as well, the whole infrastructure comprising specialized submarines to transport and launch the missiles, and of course, the communications and tracking networks to ensure that the missiles arrive on target and fulfill their design intent.

Because of the need for sophisticated engineering techniques to coordinate all aspects of the design and implementation of such complex systems, the ideas behind systems engineering became formalized into the following set of steps:

1) The Problem Statement: is the reason for the whole enterprise to begin with. It describes the mission the design is meant to accomplish and is kept readily in mind throughout the engineering process.

It is reflected within the design intent of the system (steps 2 to 6) and is the basis for determining the objectives and the alternatives that will be considered.

2) *Identification of Objectives:* Often, the problem statement will require that a number of objectives be met. For example, the problem statement: "Design a Transportation System for Passengers" must include among its objectives provisions for a] passenger safety, b] comfort, c] pleasant ambiance, and d] cost limits. These are the sufficient and necessary design objectives for the function of the system as a whole.

3) *Examination of Alternatives:* is the creative process involved in the generation, selection and study of the choices available in order to come up with the most effective and cost efficient methods to meet the objectives. This involves piecing together the different blocks of the system from the (several or many) possible choices—not unlike assembling the pieces of a puzzle. However, the form and structure are kept somewhat fluid as—more often than not—there is more than one solution to achieve a successful function.

4) *Analysis of the Alternatives:* alternatives are analyzed in detail to predict how they would perform in their environment under design conditions and how well they meet the design objectives. One of the important considerations at this stage is the avoidance of *"suboptimization"*. This may occur if individual components of the system are independently optimized without regard to the effects such might have on the interaction with, and function of, the rest of the system. In other words, the separate optimization of each individual part or sub-system may not necessarily lead to an optimal design of the total system. The over-improvement of the performance of one part of the system may in fact worsen the overall system performance.

5) *Selection of Alternatives:* Once the basic system design has been selected, it must be defined and analyzed in sufficient detail to provide instructions for its construction. Then a management system is put in place to ensure that all the necessary construction activities are time-phased and coordinated.

6) *System Creation:* The system is put together, and

7) *System Operation:* is affected.

From the above it becomes obvious that the more complicated the mission, the more complex the solution will be. At present, we already have a good intuitive sense of LS form and functional complexity; no other system in our experience even comes close. The LS is a complete system already in operation. In effect, steps 6 and 7 are already completed and available to be explored. Our task will be to analyze the operating system in order to determine if the rest of the systems engineering processes apply and whether we can ultimately infer step 2. That accomplished, we shall hopefully be in a position to venture an educated guess at the mission statement (step 1). We will try not to make any hasty assumptions as to the relevance of what we may find. Rather, in the end, we will let the exercise speak for itself.

Recap of What We Are Trying To Do:

Engineers design systems from the *top down*. That is to say, we start from a desired result—the *Design Intent* or problem statement. Then we draw block diagrams that represent and unite the different components required to work together to produce the required result. Each component in turn may comprise sub-components. A block diagram may show the direction of flow of information and materials and energies of the system as well as any feedback control mechanisms that ensure the Design will work as intended. Engineering involves making choices of materials and components such that there may be numerous ways of fitting together components as well as different ways to accomplish the design. For example, iron can be produced from iron ore using fossil fuels as the heat source or electricity. The end result will still be iron. However, the plant layout and system operating instructions will be different. We shall be exploring the LS in an analogous way—as we would any other human designed system. The advantage of using this kind of analysis (the SE approach to the study of life) is in its ability to reduce the object of analysis into its operating levels and components. We can then assign the relative importance of the constituent parts. In a steady procession, we hope to strip away the minor players and highlight the essential features that define what is really going on beneath the surface. By looking carefully at how these components function we hope to determine, not only their roles within the system, but why they are a necessary part of the system, the extent of their importance, and, as a result, perhaps gain a better understanding of what the system as a whole is meant to do. We shall try to bring the above principles to the study of life as a system, in the quest for new insights and evidence which will eventually lead us, to the answers to the three fundamental questions we ask of life, and finally, to the solution to the OoL mystery, which, of course, is our primary challenge. Our SE approach will serve as the *"intellectual catalyst"* that will permit us to study the system of bio-life from the top down. Once the exercise is complete, we shall examine the results for insights they afford into a comprehensive understanding of the LS—and for their consequences with respect to validating (or invalidating) any of the OoL options we have examined.

---

[1] Given a complete understanding of the mechanisms involved, living organisms could be created simply through the proper assemblage of the necessary constituent parts, introducing some fundamental feedback control mechanisms, and then giving the process a suitable "jump-start".

[2] Playing God: The Making of Artificial Life—Discover, Aug 92, p 36 [90]

6. Bio-Life: A System of Functional Levels

*"....man will occasionally stumble over the truth, but usually manages to
pick himself up, walk over or around it, and carry on."*
—Winston Churchill (1874–1965)

Our aim in the next few chapters is to get comfortable thinking of Life as a possibly designed system (without assuming it to be)—as we apply the SE tools of analysis to the study of bio-life. To do so will require a very special mindset. Let me explain:

We spend our lives growing, learning and planning—all the while searching for a sense of purpose. Yet, irrespective of one's cultural background and upbringing, our attitudes have been carved to reflect a bottom line belief that there are some mysteries that must forever remain so. We humans are probably the only species aware of the fact that we don't live forever and we spend an inordinate amount of time in virtual denial of the issue. Of course, we have frequent personal reminders of the fragility and serenity of our existence. Still, we muddle through as best we can. How? By keeping busy staying alive and participating in the life processes shared by all other living things. Now I am asking you to place yourself outside the "LS-participant" mentality and join me in trying to figure out what the system, of which each one of us forms an integral part, effectively does. And, as if that were not enough, you are additionally being asked to put yourself in the shoes of the would-be designer of the system of Life and ask yourself the question: "What would I, as the designer of the life system, have had in mind to have designed it this way?" An interesting (and amusing) challenge, to say the least.

Remember, if the LS was indeed the product of design, then there is the likelihood that design choices would have been made (SE steps 3 to 5) that would reflect the intention of the designer—what engineers generally refer to as the "design intent". In addition, we shall be looking for system-wide imperatives, operating principles, and subsystems that unify and maintain organization throughout the far flung reaches of the LS across the planet, that may provide the clues we are seeking. In the final analysis, we shall be searching out any LS system attributes that betray possible proof of design in order to uncover the mystery of what the LS might have been designed for, and therefore, what it is doing and what purpose it serves.

A Little Background History:

Today, biology serves as an umbrella term comprising all of the life sciences, with increasing numbers of specialties that are indicative of the many traditional ways we have come to classify living things, their characteristics and behavior. Thus, zoology deals with animal life, botany with plant life, algology with algae, mycology with fungi, microbiology with microorganisms such as protozoa and bacteria, cytology with cells—just to name a few. The disparate nature of the various fields of study is in large measure indicative of the disorganized way in which the study of the system of life evolved. By the middle of the 19th century, the scientific study of biology had progressed to the understanding that living things were essentially related complex machines that had the unique ability to recreate themselves and most importantly, operated according to rules of logic. While this was not necessarily formalized as some kind of law, non-the-less biological processes were observed to operate according to the universal principles of logical cause and effect.

The study of genetics is a case in point. Gregor Mendel, an Austrian monk with a passion for plants and a propensity to tinker, crossed a green with a yellow pea plant and expected to get an equal number of yellow and green peas from the seeds produced. Or, alternatively, he expected greenish-yellow peas— a blending of the two. To his surprise, all the peas were yellow. Then he planted all the yellow peas, expecting yellow to produce yellow. This time, to his astonishment, there were some green peas among the yellow. His curiosity thus aroused, Mendel experimented seven years with all kinds of plants in his quest to understand the mystery of how a prominent plant characteristic could hide in one generation, only to reappear the next—as if it never left. It was in 1866 that Mendel formalized his discoveries in a hypothesis that stated essentially that hereditary factors (traits) of living things are quantized (come in separate packages) and behave in accordance with simple mathematical laws—they do not blend. While his great insight would remain misunderstood and ignored until the beginning of the 20th century he would be eventually vindicated. Today, no reference to the history of genetics would be complete without mention of the name Gregor Mendel.

Unbeknownst to Mendel, at about the same time, another amateur biologist was forging ahead with his own novel theory that would forever alter our understanding and appreciation of the fundamental forces that shape and forge the LS. The introduction by Charles Darwin of his "origin of species by natural selection" hypothesis in the mid 19th century defined his theory of evolution. Today—almost a century and a half later—not only the fossil record that paleontologists have assembled but the genetic record exposed by molecular biologists as well affirms some of the principles involved. Evolution, as it turns out, is the key to the long term adaptation and survival of the LS, and therefore within it's maze of influences should lie some important clues to LS design intent, if indeed the LS was a product of design.

Life Hierarchy:

a) THE TRADITIONAL APPROACH:

For the sake of scientific study, Life's organisms have traditionally been classified into a hierarchy of seven family groups referred to as taxa. They range from kingdom, phylum, class, order, family, genus and species. These arbitrary classifications overlap among certain species and are subject to change as the study of zoology, botany, and genetics advances over time. But, most importantly, this pyramidal classification serves to emphasize relationships among all life forms as comprising interrelated parts of a whole. It also is indicative of the fact that all differences between species are essentially considered to represent the branching effects—both vertically and horizontally—of evolution upon ancestral participants of the system.

More recently, ecologists have established organism categories and classifications according to how an organism functions in the environment. Thus, *autotrophs*, mainly green plants, are the "self-nourishers" in that they manufacture their own food from carbon dioxide, water, minerals and sunlight. *Heterotrophs* have no such capability and must acquire their food second hand. These, in turn are divided up into *herbivores*—the plant eaters, and *carnivores*—the animal eaters. The *omnivores* are sufficiently versatile to act as both. Then there are the *scavengers* that eat large dead organisms and the *decomposers*, such as bacteria and fungi that do the same microscopically. *Parasites* devour living things, but only a bit at a time.

Despite considerable efforts to classify cleanly the multitudes of life forms extant on the planet, these attempts continue to meet with mixed success as science continues to discover new evidence that tends to throw previously adopted classification schemes into disarray. Consider what was thought to be the simple and logical classification of living things into the plant and animal kingdoms. Dating back to the time of Linneus (1707-1778), this delineation of all living things into plant or animal category prevailed for more than a century. At first sight the distinctions between the two are obvious and numerous. In fact, however, at the cellular level, plants and animals have much in common. Then there is the problem of where to fit bacteria into the picture. Bacteria are of the order of a thousand times smaller than either plant or animal cells. This created headaches for evolutionary biologists—and for good reason. With improved microscopy came the realization that plant and animal cells have considerably more machinery and hardware in common that are missing entirely in bacteria. Most importantly, it was discovered that bacteria are missing the cell nucleus that is prominent in both plant and animal cells. Recent theory suggests that both plants and animals may have derived from a comparatively recent common ancestor, while the source of bacteria remains enigmatic.

b) PROKARYOTES AND EUKARIOTES:

On the heels of improved technology began a new form of classification at the microscopic level— the existence or lack of a nucleus within the cell. Those without a true cell nucleus (bacteria) became designated _prokaryotes_; and cells with a membrane-enclosed nucleus were termed _eukaryotes_. Plants and animals could now be lumped together as members of the eukaryote family. And, all bacteria were conveniently lumped together as the prokaryote family. It was neat and simple. But, just as biologists had become comfortable with this novel and updated classification, the waters became muddied again with new scientific revelations.

c) Archaebacteria:

If we want to get an idea of what some of the earliest biological organisms may have looked like, there is a relatively recently discovered (1970's) unicellular branch of life that might fill the bill. Termed *archaebacteria* by their discoverer—Carl Woese, a bacteriologist from the University of Illinois at Urbana—this microorganism branch of life—while still considered prokaryote—is thought to be as different from other bacteria as plants and animals were once considered different from each other. In effect, Woese successfully made the case that these enigmatic bacterial creatures comprise a new primary kingdom with a different status in the history and natural order of life. As a result, all other bacteria have now been designated *eubacteria*. Ancestral eubacteria are theorized to have evolved into all of the eukaryotic unicellular and multicellular plants and animals that today populate the planet.

Woese's genetic research into the genetic material (RNA) of these organisms has revealed that eubacteria could not have descended from archaebacteria. Further, chlorophyll based photosynthesis occurs only among eubacteria and may have developed universally and very early in their evolutionary history.[1] The archaebacteria, in contrast, use a novel mechanism to achieve photosynthesis (among those that do), and the mechanisms of capturing and transforming the sun's energy are entirely different. It is also interesting to note that both archae—and eu—bacteria contain among their ranks members that thrive in extremely hot environments, reminiscent of the conditions that existed early in the history of life. Both are thought to have been originally heat lovers and anaerobes (oxygen avoiders). This is the kind of primitive organism we could expect the old earth to have produced—according to Woese. As a recent update on the subject it was announced in September 1995, the discovery of two microbes in the hot springs of Yellowstone National Park whose gene sequences are sufficiently different from other archaeal species as to constitute, again another kingdom with the proposed name of *Korarchaeota*[2]. A computer-generated evolutionary tree based on their genetic variations suggest that they are the most primitive lifeforms yet discovered and possibly close relatives of the primordial archaea, and the closest yet discovered to what the common ancestor of all of life on the planet might have been like. Before we are through, however, we intend to put a somewhat different interpretation on their origins.

The above is representative of how biologists are continually called upon to update and modify how they organize their biology informational databases. They continue to depend upon the hierarchical approach as the way to appreciate the time effects of evolution insofar as older and fewer families of life have branched off into more numerous and complex groupings. In the past, it was the fossil finds of paleontologists that interpreted where in the hierarchy of life different species fit. Today—as in the case of archaebacteria—it is the molecular biologists, interpreting the information gleaned from the decoded language written in the nucleic acids of organisms (DNA and RNA) that are defining anew the relationships between species. From our own perspective, Woese's work with archaebacteria is significant in that we are no longer dependent only on paleontological microfossils for evidence that the basic biological mechanisms of all LS participants remains universally the same over time. Woese's investigations using comparative molecular biology informs us that the evidence lives in our mist—as the relatively unchanged "living fossils" within archea and eu bacteria. Despite apparent differences in some physical traits attributable to evolution, a comparison of the genetic information written in the universal language of DNA provides living proof that there is a continuity of universal biological principles, which has been maintained as a relative constant since the primordial era in which biological life originated on the planet. Its continued existence confirms that all creatures, regardless of size, shape or which family tree they come from are comprised of cell(s) which, despite differences, use the same basic genetic language mechanisms for encoding and reading the instructional genes located in their chromosomal DNA. The same can be said for the universality, both in space and time, with which organisms convert and use energy to drive their life processes. The inescapable conclusion is that the theme of life on the planet is indeed common and universal; a reminder that the life system on this planet is indeed a single system.

The history of archaebacteria represents an interesting mystery. Could these organisms be the relatively unchanged modern day descendants of some of the original biological seed stocks of the planet that never took off in the competition with some of the other originating life forms? In other words, are archaebacteria simply survivors of some of the more obscure varieties of original biological species that managed to adapt to the harsh environmental conditions they found within the biosphere but were destined to remain locked in, as it were, to those very restricted biomes? The implication is that other varieties by chance or talent, managed to evolve life forms that would become the ancestors of the prokaryotes and eukaryotes that have colonized the planet successfully. Archaebacteria would simply represent descendent varieties that stayed put where they were, remained apart, and managed to survive within their exclusive, if limited, diverse environmental niches. Which begs the question: "If archaebacteria are extant remnants of ancient life forms that have changed little from their inception dating back to the very beginning of life on the planet, and if life began as self-replicating protomolecules or other inorganic individuals, as SAb would have us believe, then would it not be reasonable to assume that remnants of those entities (protomolecules) as well should be found in and around the biosphere?" Wouldn't it be reasonable to assume that these precursors of life could carve out some safe, if obscure, (chemical) environmental niches of one kind or another, just like archaea, that could protect them from extinction? Why not? And, if that were indeed the case, then to borrow and paraphrase an Enrico Fermi quote (referring to extra-terrestrial visitors to our planet)—"so, where are they?" Well, maybe they never were! Perhaps the starting point for life on our planet was biology and not chemistry after all—something akin to archaebacteria, and eubacteria.

Getting Into The "Engineering" Frame Of Mind:

At the beginning of this chapter we referred to the traditional ways the knowledge of bio-life has been organized and to which we have become accustomed. This approach is fine if the aim is simply to reacquaint oneself with the kinds of information learned in school. Ours is a totally different kind of quest. We want to determine what features we can find in the LS that may betray its character as a designed system. Once these become apparent, (and if all goes well) then we will attempt to reverse-engineer the LS phenomenon in the hope of determining the system Design Intent, its purpose, and then hopefully it's origins. In order to do so, we will adopt a different kind of mindset—one that emphasizes the broad principles of applied science (engineering) as opposed to those of pure science. The first thing we have to do, right off the bat, is to get you to think like an engineer. How do engineers think differently from the rest of society, you ask? Well, you will recall the last chapter on Systems Engineering, item 3]— "Examination of Alternatives"—the statement referring to piecing together the different blocks of a designed system, etc. The engineering frame of mind would want to break down the LS into functional blocks and levels of activity, beginning at the top and working our way down through the system. This is also necessary for the sake of organization in order to keep track of the many pieces in the great puzzle that comprise the LS. Nevertheless, let's not dwell on the approach itself—the mindset and emphasis should become clear as we proceed. A most important item on our agenda will be the reorganization of the bio-life phenomenon along engineering lines—with emphasis on the relationship of the LS to the biosphere of the planet.

Life and The Planet—A Unique Partnership:

Life and the planet Earth today have been described as a single entity, a marriage of sorts. This concept has been formulated into an hypothesis referred to as the **Gaia Hypothesis**, (named appropriately for the ancient Greek goddess of the Earth), which views the planet earth as a self-regulating "organism"— a living entity if you will—that maintains the terrestrial and atmospheric conditions that make life possible. This idealistic notion was first described in 1969 by James Lovelock—following his studies of atmospheric gases—who suspected that living organisms had a greater effect on the atmosphere than was then recognized. The Gaia model has since been modified to reflect closer the concepts of *homeostasis* and the maintenance of equilibrium in biological systems, and extended somewhat to include as well the biosphere of the planet. The Gaia hypothesis, in effect, assesses the relationship between the planetary biosphere and the LS from a contemporary point of view. i.e.: the accumulated consequences of the interactions between the two over time, leading up to the almost symbiotic present relationship that Gaia describes. While the Gaia hypothesis is not the kind of falsifiable theory that can be emphatically proven (or disproved), it is regarded in certain quarters as an "innovative lens" through which to view the natural world. Gaia has inadvertently been given a boost in recent times by the planet wide aspects of ozone change studies and global warming. Lovelock has entered the OoL game and devised autocatalytic models involving non-equilibrium thermodynamics to justify how life could get jump started in seeming defiance of the 2nd law of thermodynamics dealing with entropy. Present efforts are aimed at determining the presence of feedback loops that could justify the existence of self-regulation. Gaia has also been cited in connection with the notion that living organisms are profoundly connected, as well, through the "theory of symbiogenesis" fostered by biologist, Lynn Margulis of the University of Massachusetts. Margulis has become closely identified with Lovelock with respect to Gaia; together they have proposed that the biosphere regulates the terrestrial and atmospheric conditions that make the planet habitable. They argue, for example, that global temperature is regulated thermostatically by the plankton of the seas; that glaciers are affected by the greenhouse gases released by soil based organisms; and that bacterial colonies in tidal mud flats help maintain ocean salinity within desirable limits. All of these relationships signify, according to Gaia, the interdependence of biosphere and life on the planet. They conclude that there is little probability of this occurring by chance. Many opponents of Gaia condemn the theory for its implications that somehow, natural phenomena have some kind of ultimate agenda. Darwinists, such as Richard Dawkins contend that the last thing bacteria have in mind when they produce gases is to benefit the world.[2] They would—according to Dawkins—do effectively better not to expend energy in the pursuit of "altruistic goals" that could be better served toward selfish survival ends elsewhere. While these kinds of debate continue, it is interesting to note that proponents of Gaia no longer claim that the earth acts purposefully—they are content to suggest that the living organisms of the planet maintain relatively constant surface conditions. We have our own take on the subject, not so much because of a direct interest in Gaia as such, but because the whole notion of the relationship between biosphere and life is fundamental to a number of questions we are concerned with in our search for the OoL.

While it is easy to demonstrate the interrelationship between planet and LS as it exists today, it is important to recall that when life originated on the planet, there was no such relationship. The biosphere conditions of the inanimate planet were the original set of conditions that the first self-replicating organisms had to contend with and accommodate. Having made the point, however, we cannot but acknowledge that the LS and its planetary habitat do represent two parts of a whole—not unlike partners in a relationship. Since they came together at the OoL, both biosphere and Life have been affected by the actions of each upon the other in an intricate "business-like" arrangement of give and take. But, the planet and its biosphere were here first and accordingly set the conditions of the contract with its dependent Life system, so to speak. The following parody is meant to put the relationship between the two partners in perspective.

When Life first appeared on the scene, some 3.8 billion years ago, it was as though in response to an advertisement for a "place to let" with certain conditions. The advertisement in the fictitious "Galactic Herald" might have read as follows:

New Planetary Habitat For Rent

Good neighborhood; Very roomy; Ideal location for biological life-forms; Needs considerable work; Presently heated and hot water supplied; Free rent and unlimited resources available for experienced do-it-yourselfers; Short or Long term tenant sought; List of present biosphere conditions available but subject to change; Rent at your own risk!"

At a meeting set up between the parties, the discussion might follow along these lines:

LEASING AGENT:

"Look! The planet is in the process of settling down. We think that the future holds a lot of promise. We're looking for an occupant that will treat the place like his or her very own. We don't expect you to pay any rent. In return, we do expect you to put in a lot of effort to develop the real estate into a decent habitat. Of course, we will supply everything you need. Just don't get too comfortable for too long— because we can't guarantee the permanence of any particular conditions. Don't worry—the important things you can be assured of—like the orbit and distance from the sun, liquid water and some 90 plus elemental raw materials which you can freely avail yourselves of. Risks?—of course there are risks, but that's life—isn't it?"

LS REPRESENTATIVE:

"I don't know. It sounds like an offer we can't refuse but the situation looks risky; what—with all that volcanic confusion and meteorite bombardments…. We're not even sure if we know how to get started, never mind getting used to the place. And what's this about ever changing conditions? That's going to take a lot of planning. What's that you say—we won't even be able to predict those changes? On the other hand, let's face it—it should only be tough at the beginning—once we get used to it, it shouldn't be too bad."

Leasing Agent: "Then we have a deal?"

LS Representative: "I guess so."

We have engaged in our little planetary soap opera in order to drive home the point: There are two distinct players in the game of life on the planet:

The Biosphere: provider of habitat premises, resources and continually changing conditions; and

The Life System: user-occupier that must respond and adapt accordingly to survive over eons of time.

But that's not all. The partnership we have described is, of necessity, a close one. It is a an exquisite "tango" of two partners—but it is the *biosphere that leads* and the *LS that follows*. The fact that the follower (LS) sometimes can influence the action of the leader (Biosphere) in no way changes the fundamental premise. In the process of give and take between these two elements, feedback mechanisms have developed over time between them, serving in a sense to reinforce the partnership arrangement that seems to be the inspiration behind the Gaia hypothesis. As the biosphere conditions change unpredictably, it is up to the LS to respond in kind and hang on tight, as it were. And, the glue that binds and dovetails the LS to the Biosphere is none other than all of the forces grouped under the heading: *Evolution*.

The Ties That Bind:

The forces responsible for the success of LS survival over billions of years is, of course evolution. As well, it is responsible for the many complex variations that the participants of life exhibit over time. The simple fact is that without evolutionary mechanisms, life on the planet could not have stood a chance. If the changes in the biosphere over time can be compared to the unpredictable changes in the curves and surface composition of a road on a pitch black night, then the forces of evolution could represent the fully automatic steering machinery of a metamorphic all terrain vehicle (representing the LS), navigating it forward no matter what the nature or direction of the external road ahead. In effect, "the Biosphere leads and the LS follows" is no idle metaphor. The paradox is that while evolution may be blind, in that neither it nor the LS it serves can have any way of predicting the road to survival ahead, nonetheless, it provides the LS the innate capability to follow that road regardless of the twists and turns, obstacles, or difficulties. Thus, evolution is responsible for not only the physiological and morphological changes to species over time, but the forces and influences that permit those changes. Evolution permits as well the participants of the LS to adapt to the ever-changing conditions of the biosphere—resulting in the thriving and survival of the LS as a whole. That being the case, we can readily conceive of evolution as an integral subsystem of the LS responsible for its long-term survival.

Question: What Exactly is the LS doing?

At first glance this might seem a strange question to ask! The first impression is to pause subjectively and wonder: I am alive, and part of this system we call Life. What am I doing? What is anybody doing and for that matter what does any living thing do? Of course, it is understood that the question refers not to the obvious—that you are presently reading this book or that you are simply engaged in your particular day-to-day life activity. While this turns out to be a most fundamental question of the LS, the answers of which hopefully may reveal themselves in the course of our analysis, it affords us an immediate opportunity to examine the logical intellectual tools of the engineering mindset we shall be bringing to bear on the whole exercise. Let's test these out immediately:

A Preliminary Assessment of Life Using The Systems Engineering Mindset:

Question: What do living things do?

Quick answer: At any given moment in time, what is life activity if not the enduring challenge to stay alive—to survive at all costs. That is what every living thing strives for and how it virtually spends all of its time: trying to stay out of the way of danger and acquire the resources it needs such as food and water. Yet despite all such efforts, it becomes brutally evident that no creature, large or small, ultimately succeeds at it. After a relatively short life span, the only tangible evidence any organism leaves behind of its existence is any offspring it may have produced during its brief allotted time as an LS participant. After that, it would seem that an organism—any individual organism—has no further value as such to the system. If it did, surely we would find evidence of perpetual organism life. Thus, it would seem that each one of us (every living organism) that comprises an integral part of the LS serves both a limited and similar role. The system, in effect, at any given moment in time embraces a large number of component organisms comprising many different physical species configurations that come into being as offspring and stick around long enough to produce offspring of their own before unceremoniously exiting the universe. This is a simplistic description of the LS from a common sense, top-down, engineering point of view. It's a "what-you-see-is-what-you-get" kind of assessment. It is a first appraisal of a sophisticated system of parts gleaned from a cursory surface examination of the phenomenon. It takes no account of the time effective influences of evolution, nor of what it is that organisms pass on to their offspring. Descriptions of these and other form and functional aspects of the LS shall have to await the more in-depth analyses ahead that probe beneath its surface. It also points up the fact that there are many ways to describe what goes on in the LS. What we have described above is just one, based on casual observation of the common fate of individual organisms, regardless of whether it be a simple bacterium or a complex multicelled primate. Our description has the advantage of being a universal principle, operating system wide throughout the LS and, therefore, will prove to be relevant to our proceedings that follow.

Also, what we have demonstrated above is the subtle difference between the strictly scientific mindset and that of engineering. That is the extent to which that elusive intuitive commodity called "common sense" is involved. Now, scientists have learned to distrust any arguments that base their appeal strictly upon a belief in common sense. The implication is that science can only trust hard and proven facts, even when the empirical evidence goes against our common sense experience. On the other hand, engineering—the application of science for pragmatic purposes, by reason of its very nature, employs healthy doses of positive common sense in order to begin the process of imaginative technological synthesis that leads to practical design results. And, the reverse engineering exercise we shall be engaged in—that hopefully will reveal the mysteries of life—is counted on to benefit from it as well. Accordingly, the engineering mindset is permitting us some latitude, within its methods of inquiry that, strictly speaking, might be considered less acceptable within the orthodox scientific approach. In the end, it is acknowledged that we shall be forced to let the facts speak for themselves. But at this stage of the game, it will be our intuition that will guide us in which direction to pursue those facts, and then permit us to draw preliminary conclusions. As such, the engineering common sense approach, by its very nature, contains a measure of increased flexibility that will hopefully allow us to break out of the limited paradigmatic restrictions that have stifled the debate on the OoL to date. However, as stated—in the end, regardless of the mental framework we utilize in our reasoning—the results and conclusions must stand on their merits.

It is within this context that we shall be seeking out basic attributes common to all living things (including ourselves), as bit players within the whole system, which ultimately must show up as the collective contribution each one makes to the system mission, whatever that may turn out to be. These are the kinds of phenomenological clues we shall be seeking in anticipation that they might illuminate some conclusive overall fundamental function or useful activity that the LS as a whole could be seen to be accomplishing. That is how the engineering mentality attempts to simplify and demystify the LS, something most of us might have previously considered to be too complicated a task.

The Operational Levels of Life:

Now, let's turn our attention to the physical structures and operational levels of the LS within its biosphere habitat in order to ascertain and understand how the LS works. A typical SE approach would break the LS and its planetary environment down into its various form and function levels much the same as we might do if we wanted to uncover the operational secrets involved in a classified and proprietary operating manufacturing facility. In our case, these will comprise the dynamic interacting levels of activity (not to be confused with the LS "Complexity versus Time" referred to above) that comprises the LS at any given moment in time—ranging from the big picture of Life and it's relationship to the Biosphere, down to the nuts and bolts of the LS at the molecular level. The Form and Functional Levels of the Life System are:

a) **The Macro Level**: Organisms and species operating within the planetary biosphere.

b) **The Micro Level**: The Cell—basic unit of Life and its molecular machinery.

We shall be examining the system of Life at each of the above levels, respectively, with a view to determining: The form, function and contribution of constituent parts and any resultant systems engineering conclusions (results of SE analysis). In addition, our SE exploration shall seek out for special concern some of the system wide aspects of the LS, which we shall treat as discrete phenomena and/or logical sub-systems. These include:

c) **Evolution Mechanisms**: Responsible for the adaptive phenomenon of the LS over time.

d) **Energy Conversion Systems**: The engines that drive biology.

e) **Information Systems**: The form and function of the information encoded in the chemical media of nucleic acids—DNA and RNA and the genetic code that mediates between genotype (genetic information library) and phenotype (physical expression of genetic information).

By the time we are through we hope that our SE analysis of the form and function of LS operation will yield its design intent capabilities (if any). We hope to then address the fundamental question of what generic purpose the LS can be used for. We will then be in a position to contemplate the actual purposeful mission and use of such a designed system (the reason it was designed and placed in operation here on our planet and what it does). At that point we should hope to understand where we can look for the sought after "holy grail" of our exercise: the incontrovertible evidence of OoL by design. Fun indeed! Let's move right along.

---

[1]Blueprints: Eddy & Johanson; p308

[2]New York Times Magazine Article: Jan 14 1996; p21

7. The Macro Level of Bio-Life

"Nothing has such power to broaden the mind as the ability to investigate systematically and truly all that comes under your observation in life."
—Marcus Aurelius (121–180 AD), Roman Emporor

The Big Picture:

The macro (-scopic) level of life represents all of the complex relationships among LS member organisms together with their interactions with the biosphere—the physical environment of the planet. It is the level of *species and organisms*—the fundamental units of the interactive system of Life—and where the LS interfaces with the environment. It is the "big picture" level at which we can observe how different forms of living things behave and interact, and indeed, it is the level at which we humans and all the other co-inhabitants of our planet have experienced the phenomenon of life. As well, it is the sensory level from which we can observe the LS in operation and hopefully gain the knowledge of what the LS is and our place in it. It is also the level of organism life, death, and continuity (reproduction).

From the organization of the LS point of view, we can describe the macro level of the LS in terms of different species and the diverse activities of their member organisms on the planet. At this point, we shall only deal with LS activities at a given moment in LS time. That is, for now we will ignore the dynamics of the system represented by time-effective evolutionary forces that occur over many generations in real time and concentrate instead on the LS dynamics as they occur in any given instant in time (a single vertical slice of Life at a single moment in time, such as the present).

Organisms:

Organisms are the basic units of the LS at the macro level. They come in different sizes—from single celled microorganisms to immense structures embodying thousands of billions of individual cells in a complex, cooperative venture. And, even cooperation among cells comes in many forms, including not only the cellular specialization that gives rise to the organs and tissues of multicellular organisms, but even all of the organism specializations that lead to modifications within the individuals of a species that make up complex insect colonies (workers and breeders among ants, termites etc.), and the complex symbiotic and parasitic relationships that exist between different species. The many ways that cells and combinations of cells are dependent on others in the interactive venture of life survival muddies the true interpretation of the concept of "organism". Are termite, ant, and beehive colonies single organisms composed of many specialized sub-organisms? Can we conceive of pheromones, which act as chemical messengers that convey information from one member of a colony to another as biochemical analogs of hormones, which convey information to different segments of an integral multicelled organism? In the honeybee, the single queen in the hive secretes the pheromone, oxodecenoic acid, which is passed through the colony by food sharing, thereby signaling to all that the queen is present. Deprived of that substance, the workers proceed to build queen cells and feed the young larvae special salivary secretions referred to as "royal jelly", in order to provoke specialized biological activity to produce more queens.[1] Other pheromones can act as alarm substances and as other behavioral modifiers in many ways similar in results to that occurring in integral organisms. In a different kind of example, a recently discovered aspen tree "colony" in New Jersey comprising many thousands of trees is actually considered to be a single organism—touted as the largest organism ever discovered. As we have come to expect, the varieties of form and function of living things defies simple classifications and can only be fully appreciated when all of their function levels are understood. Ironically, such an understanding reveals the startling truth that despite the appearance of phenomenally complex diversity among individual organisms and species, the fact remains that any differences in their physical form are at best superficial—because they are all composed of combinations of cells that all function essentially the same way. Thus, at present (the macro level) we shall concern ourselves with those aspects of organisms (regardless of physical size or makeup) that relate to how they interface with the external environment. (Later in the section dealing with the micro level of the LS, we shall concern ourselves with the common internal aspects of cellular life.)

The classical definition of life at the Macro level describes the activities that organisms—the member components of species—engage in, in terms of metabolism, growth, reproduction, self repair and the like. Non-living things can have some of these properties (crystals grow and reproduce in a way) but fall short of inclusion in the LS. For most of us, life (the basic umbrella term for living organisms) is one of those phenomena that fall within that class of ideas that are hard to define, but "we can recognize it when we see it". Strange animals and plants all have those life-like characteristics we are all familiar with. Exotic birds, fish, insects and trees pose no problem in our recognizing that they are indeed alive and share with us the resources of the planet. Mosses, fungi and even bacteria (which nobody has seen with the naked eye), all have that unmistakable quality of being a part of biological life—busy growing and surviving. You might even say that being alive ourselves pretty well makes experts of all of us when it comes to recognizing other living things. If it moves, eats, excretes, grows, reproduces, repairs itself, tastes good and satisfies hunger—then chances are that it is life in action. Even dead things have an unmistakable look about them that betrays the fact that while no longer engaging in the activities that living things do—they once did.

Probably the most important characteristic of all living things that make up the LS is the fact that the information necessary for the control and expression of each organism's physical structure, characteristics and behavior is contained within each individual (related to the concept of "coded self-assembly" referred to earlier). In other words, organisms are self-contained mechanisms that possess within their genetic libraries all the information necessary to carry on their life functions. Included are *genetic instructions* for self-repair, instructions for survival, internal biological housekeeping, and reproduction of new generations of the species. This is equally true for very complex multicellular plants and animals as well as the simplest (relatively) unicellular life forms. It is this self-contained information aspect of living things that truly sets life apart from the inanimate. Indeed, it is within the information libraries of living things where we hope to find the hidden secrets that will reveal the very essence of the LS and its origins. We shall examine this informational aspect in detail later.

At this point in our SE analysis, we wish to home in on some basic principles that apply to all organisms in order to achieve a sense as to what it is exactly that organisms accomplish and how they go about it.

Biological Feedback and Comfort Levels:

Feedback controls are implicated in innumerable ways within the LS form and function at the micro level of the LS. They control biological functions at the very basic primary design platform level of life (to be discussed in Chapter 10) that permits internal cellular operation. We can also see all kinds of examples of feedback control at the macro level of the LS—where organisms interface with the external conditions of their habitat environment. For example, the input signal that is interpreted by an organism as "hunger" will continue to increase until it "satisfies" its discomfort by feeding and the sensation disappears. The term "satisfies" accurately describes how the feedback control systems involved operate—as a dichotomy—on two distinct but parallel levels, each of which must be attended to. The one unconscious and purely mechanical, results from a set of predetermined logistical settings concerned with a low-fuel condition at the primary design level of biology. This, in turn, serves as the stimulus for the conscious perception of the discomfort recognized as pangs of hunger at the cognitive level. The organism can make a variety of choices, depending upon past experience and opportunity, as to how it will best go about reducing its hunger state to zero at the level of cognition, while simultaneously (and unknowingly) reducing the organism energy level feedback signal error to zero at the purely mechanical level. This example point up the fascinating dichotomy that exists between an organism's physical requirements, and how they translate into "perception" thereby encouraging appropriate action to satisfy "needs"—both physical and cognitive. These two very diverse but parallel operating forces that drive all organisms, are bound together to achieve different "needs"—but identical results. The organism as intelligent biological machine needs a continual source of energy to power its life processes. On the other hand, the only information an organism need "know" is that when it "feels" hunger, it is time to feed. Thus, the energy requirements for the continual operation of organism biological form and function are unknowingly attained through feedback control mechanisms whereby error signals are perceived cognitively as pain or discomfort. What is not appreciated is why this dichotomy should exist in the first place. We understand that the first part of the above statement is the operative one (organism needs energy) and that the second part is the subjective interpretation that serves simply as a means to an end. This interface that separates biological system external requirements from corresponding cognitive understanding that leads to appropriate organism behavior really defines a major difference between a biological organism and a non-biological machine. But, again, why should this be? Why should living things engage in two distinct kinds of activity: the autonomous actions of which an organism is totally unaware, as well as all of the levels of awareness that permits an organism to control its actions in the field—the latter, solely in order to satisfy the former which in turn ellicits a feedback to the latter, signalling a job well done? In fact the answer may well define the essential difference between an organism and machine.

Machines Have Purpose; Organisms Have Goals:

It is generally easy to ascribe a purpose to a machine—its purpose usually can be defined by observing its operation which in turn reflects the intentional goal of its designer. That is, the use to which a human-designed machine is put, is intimately tied to its operation. When it is operating, it's designers goal becomes evident. And over the life of a machine, its design value is generally commensurate with the number of hours it has operated. The same cannot be said of biological organisms. Organisms do function machine-like, in their capacity as active biological machines, but in sharp contrast, any purpose they may have cannot be immediately ascribed by watching them function. Their value does not seem to be intrinsically tied to their operation. What, indeed, does an organism achieve during its lifetime—a steady and seemingly repetitive agenda of action and interaction with the biosphere and other organisms? And, whatever the answer, does that purpose cease once the organism dies? When an organism reproduces offspring during its brief life-span can the mere act of reproducion in some way represent its purpose? While these kinds of ideas appear to address phylosophical rather than pragmatic issues, it is interesting to consider that, with the exception of humans, no organism can really be aware of cause and effect linking mating and the production of offspring. Probably no more than its awareness as to why it needs to feed. Dichotomies abound everywhere we look within the LS.

Thus, while we can ascribe to a machine a legitimate purpose as perceived within its operating results, we cannot do the same with respect to biological machines called organisms. An organism's day-to-day operation reveals virtually nothing in the way of purpose to the decerning eye. The only corresponding descriptive term we can ascribe to individual living organisms are "goals". Look at any organism, regardless of species and the goals are always the same: nourishment, avoidance of danger, and mating. Corresponding to these cognitive activities are the mechanistic needs: energy, safety and reproduction. No matter how you describe them—whether cognitive goals or mechanistic needs—these serve the short-term interests and requirements of every organism. Because organisms have no long term interests because they have no long term, they must, in fact, logically serve the long-term interests of the overall system we have designated as the LS—whatever they may happen to be.

Conscious Awareness—The Ultimate Extension of Feedback:

If organisms have goals, then the results must be defined in terms of achievement. And if we can identify short and long-term goals, then we can define short and long-term achievements as well. The goals of nourishment and safety are continuing short term organism goals, while the goal of reproduction could be considered long term in the sense that an organism must reach maturity of one kind or another for the goal to become part of its life agenda. And, in order for an organism to achieve its goal of reproduction, it must compete with others just in order to stay alive long enough—by avoiding danger from predation, while fulfilling its resource requirements. Perhaps it is within these differences that we can ultimately determine the need for the evolutionary development of conscious awareness as a kind of goal oriented survival strategy, by separating the autonomous biological subsystem functions and needs from the motivational strategies that consciousness contributes to personal safety and survival. Perhaps it is the faculty of conscious awareness that adds a whole new dimension of "feedback" as it manifests itself within the learning phenomenon. What is learning if not the filing in memory for future use of successful tactics and strategies of the past for helping an organism stay alive. In humans, learning amounts to retention in memory of concepts that mirror reality. The extent of learning success is measured by how little is the difference (error difference) between what is recalled from memory and the data placed into memory. In other words, the object in learning is to reduce to zero that difference—between data input in learning and data retrieval through the remembering process and then applying again the recalled information in similar or novel situations. As always, all such activity, controlled exquisitely by all kinds of open and closed control systems—using more or less complex central nervous systems—have a single goal at the organism level: to stay alive long enough to reproduce offspring.

The LS—A System of Paradoxes:

a) Survival Instinct vs Death

Organisms, the individual members of a species, are the cogs in the wheel of life. They come into this world in only one way—as the offspring of parent organisms. From the first moment of its existence, an organism takes its place as a member of its species of like organisms, among which it shares an environmental habitat. Not only must it share that habitat, but every organism must, as well, compete with others to survive within it. Survival means having access to water and food, avoiding disease and predation, and in general, being lucky. "What does luck have to do with it, you ask?" "Plenty"! Besides being lucky enough to satisfy the above menu of major considerations, survival involves as well avoidance of catastrophic events that can anytime occur to an organism directly or to its environment. Flooding or lack of rainfall, excessive heat or cold, forest fires (if applicable), volcanic activity, etc., all can spell doom for an individual organism and indeed all the organisms in the affected habitat if such conditions lie outside of the sufficient and necessary living condition parameters essential for survival.

But, as we all know, the LS is more than just a collection of individual organisms or a collection of species surviving and just doing their own thing. In fact, doing their own thing involves contact and interaction with a lot of others that are also doing the same thing—and that thing is survival. You might even conclude that the strongest influence that seems to guide individual organisms is that all-pervasive effort to keep going and to stay alive—an endeavor commonly and appropriately termed, the "*survival instinct*". Toward this effort, all organisms seem to be occupied by the same obsessions—to avoid danger, acquire nourishment and eventually to reproduce and reproduce and reproduce. Yet, with all this preoccupation with survival, the paradox is that no single organism has ever succeeded at it. "*To live is to die!*" would seem to be the motto of the LS as it applies to its individual participants. In addition, it can probably be safely stated that with the exception of humans, no other organism is aware of its certain demise. Yet ironically, the fate of the LS system itself seems to be totally unaffected as a consequence by the certain demise of its constituents.

If the LS was truly the product of design intent, and indeed we are studying it in this way (without necessarily assuming it to be so), then we cannot simply ignore such an all-persuasive paradox described above. If all organisms are "obsessed" with survival at all costs, then shouldn't that be an important design feature? On the other hand, death is the rule and, similarly, must be an important design feature? What is really happening here?

b) Immortality—A Question of Suboptimization:

Perhaps now is the time, early in our exploration, to refer back to item No 4 in the set of SE steps listed in chapter 5. Step 4 deals with "*Analysis of alternatives*" and indicates the desirability of the "*avoidance of suboptimization*". As stated, suboptimization may occur if individual components of a system are independently optimized without regard to the effects that might have on the interaction with the rest of the system. It goes on to explain that the separate optimization of a sub-system may not necessarily lead to an optimal design of the total system. What does that have to do with this, you may ask?

Well, the subsystem, which is the subject of our paradox, is the organism and the paradox we are trying to resolve is it's striving to survive and it's certainty not to succeed. Optimization of organism success, for what it strives for throughout its brief life would imply, in this case, organisms that lived forever. Surely, the system could accommodate such an organism immortality feature if it was considered desirable from the overall system point of view. By that I mean, if immortality were to contribute to the greater efficiency in achieving the design goals of the LS, then surely it would be there—either by evolution or design. Similarly, the fact that immortality does not exist among life's component organisms might well represent a clue as to LS imperatives. In principal, there are no compelling technical reasons that would stand in the way of a genetically programmed organism immortality provision within the LS design structure. From a technical design aspect, all that would be required would be to expand organism maintenance and repair subsystems to include the elimination of the causes of aging, for example, thereby perpetually maintaining the system integrity of biological housekeeping and restoration. In addition, restricting food chain activity exclusively to the consumption of photosynthesizers could further enhance individual organism survival, obviating the LS paradigm of competition for energy resources among participants. Eliminating the food chain altogether and equipping each organism with photosynthesizing energy conversion abilities would be another possible solution, although the argument could be made that such a design feature would subject the LS to an exclusionary "over-reliance" on the sun as energy source. But then again, it could well be that the concept of organism immortality is, in fact, incompatible with overall system design intent and could constitute a classical case of sub-optimization—something to be avoided at all costs. Thus, we must conclude that from a SE viewpoint, optimal organism life spans are limited by design.

The other side of the paradox involves the need to survive. The question is: to survive what? Well, probably the only important milestone achieved in the life of all organisms (spanning birth and death) is participation in the reproduction of new generations of offspring. Then what does an organism have to look forward to? Nothing, except it's inevitable demise. Let's put this in SE terms:

Organisms are programmed to be preoccupied with survival until they have reproduced and passed on their genes to their offspring. That's all they do. After a certain optimum period of time, during which it can be reasonably assumed that a successful organism has had sufficient opportunity to reproduce any number of times, the organism's demise is scheduled (programmed) within the system. This can occur, for example, as a timed weakening of it's survival skills and physical condition (the aging process) to encourage it to fall prey to either predation or disease following which it can be recycled within the food chain. Finally, if all else fails, death claims the organism from within. We call it dying of old age. Rest assured, this kind of peaceful death is a rarity outside of the human species. (Statistics could probably support the case that it is indeed a rarity even within the human species.) From a design point of view, we can describe the survival limits imposed on all organisms as an exercise in suboptimization prevention. Imposing immortality on organisms might entail the sub-optimization of one component (the individual organism) at the expense of the overall system design intent. The system objective would seem to be that a sufficient number of organisms do survive long enough to have offspring. In retrospect, this is obvious; otherwise, the LS would quickly grind to a halt. As a consequence, the assurance of the survival of most organisms, at least until they have reproduced offspring, would seem to be an operational imperative of the LS.

c) Reproduction—No Two Identical:

Each individual member of a species comprises the same form and functions (morphology) as every other member, however no two organisms of the same species are identical. Is this another example of an LS paradox? Well, not exactly. The differences between organisms of the same species account, in large part, for the success of the LS in adapting, surviving and thriving over the billions of years since it's origin on the planet. The survival of any variations among offspring ultimately allows for the testing of novel inherited traits, whose future survival will depend on the extent they confer increased reproductive success on their owners. Through a continual process of trait selection and amplification among organisms and their offspring species are able to adapt to unpredictable long-term (and to a lesser extent—short-term) changes in the biosphere. That is what evolution is all about.

In asexual reproduction, as occurs in cloning, each individual organism represents a unique opportunity for a _chance genetic mutation_ (change) to occur within it's DNA library, within its lifetime, that may or may not confer a physical trait that can be tested and _selected for_ (survive) by being passed on to the offspring of future generations. In sexually reproducing organisms, genetic variability is introduced in offspring by both mutations, as well as a process called _genetic recombination_. In both instances, each resultant organism represents a unique statistical event with varying opportunities for survival long enough to reproduce. Reproduction by an organism means, in effect, to confer upon it's offspring in the next generation the traits represented by the unique mix of genetic material residing within it—including any genetic changes brought about by mutation and/or genetic recombination within its lifetime. Thus, no two organisms on the planet have exactly the same genetic instructions. Not even parent and offspring.

A case can be made that cloning—reproduction without the sexual combination of the genes of two organisms of the same species—confers an identical set of genes upon the daughter organism. However, the shear quantity of bits of coded information involved that must be copied during an organism's lifespan does auger for the introduction, within the lifetime of such organisms, of some calculable mutation change (the number is immaterial for this discussion) that may be passed on to offspring. For that to occur, it is essential that the expressed information containing the mutation be helpful or at least benign (not detrimental) to the physiology of the owner. Think about it. What are the odds that a chance and arbitrary change in the instructional blueprints for the construction of a complex machine will actually be beneficial to the way that machine will function in the real world? In the case of living organisms, we might want to state the question this way: What are the odds that a chance change occurring to the genetic informational blueprints of an organism will not prevent it from achieving life as a physical organism in the first place or not allow it to survive long enough to reproduce, and thusly, pass on it's unique genetic mix to the next generation? Hopefully, in the process, any such change(s) would confer upon its owner organism and future generations some advantage. However, remember, the organism has to reproduce if the advantage is to become a legacy and passed on. And, after all is said and done, the change must be compatible with the future direction of external biosphere conditions in order for that change to survive future genetic copying. It is considered that most mutations, being chance alterations to the genetic instructions, are harmful and that only a very few, in fact, do survive. In the next two chapters we shall have occasion to explore whether this bit of common sense logic indeed applies.

Thus, from a SE point of view, we can surmise, at this point in our inquiry, why it is important for the LS to have large populations of diverse organisms. They can serve to:

1] Create a large enough surviving and varied genetic pool, in the informational domain, that occasionally, will produce novel and important species survival attributes in the physical domain; and

2] cover as much diverse biosphere geography as possible such that some LS member organisms and their offspring survive both:

a) long term, steady-state, slowly evolving, biosphere conditions, as well as

b) short term and localized catastrophic events that occasionally wreak havoc upon the planet.

D) SYSTEMS ENGINEERING CLUES:

Thus, to answer the question: "what is really happening here?" (put at the end of section "a" above):

Unbeknownst to the participants of life themselves, each individual organism is merely a dispensable component of a species and simply a disposable means to an end in the game of Life. Every organism only represents a single member of a large population, in the statistical sense, and only a single opportunity for change. Should an organism survive long enough to have offspring, only luck determines whether changes, introduced through the chance mutation or recombination of the genetic instructions for life, at the information level, will:

a) Be benign to the resultant physical organism itself and not hinder its own survival long enough to reproduce and/or;

b) Survive further mutation, be passed on to descendent generations, and be useful to future generations and have lasting survival benefit; or

c) Be destructive to the organism and an immediate failure, or

d) Be somewhere in between.

> *Author's Note: While it is to be expected that the SE approach to the analysis of life would invoke the kind of descriptive language more suitably applied to the study of human-designed systems, it's use here seems natural and not contrived in the least. Somehow, but not really surprisingly, our metaphors (and we have used quite a few) don't appear to be a strange application of language expression, nor out of context. That's because within the system of Life, there are indeed many instances giving the appearance of the "logic of design". Just the very idea that the LS involves coded information leading to self-assembly readily invokes mental images of design and production. However, while there may be something inherently intuitive in our metaphoric comfort level, there is no room for complacency. It is important that we remain cognizant of the special context within which we are operating.*

The Food Chain:

A) INTERACTION AND COMPATIBILITY:

Regardless on what branch of the LS family tree an organism (as represented by it's species) sits, it has been reasoned that if one reaches back far enough, there will be found a species of organisms that can be said to be the common ancestor of us all. Thus, it is not surprising that at the heart of the extant life system resides a ubiquitous measure of compatibility among all of the descendents of that putative founding species. It is precisely this inherent compatibility that permits the operation of the system-wide phenomenon known as the "food-chain"—a very non-exclusive club and web of dependency that all organisms of every species join as the price of admission into the LS. The food chain itself is a fundamental part of a concept referred to as the "energy pyramid" whose support base comprises the ultimate source of all but a minute fraction of the energy that drives the LS—the Sun. And of course the food chain begins with those organisms that can convert the suns energy into the kinds of biological energy that herbivores can consume and in turn become food for carnivores further up the chain. In fact, the term "food web" is probably more of an appropriate definition of what actually takes place as many species actually occupy more than one level of the energy pyramid. But, for our purposes, the food-chain notion vividly describes how living things depend on other living things for their sources of energy upon which the survival of all the participants of life rely.

The food chain probably represents the most significant measure of interaction between the many competing LS biological life-forms that come in contact with each other on the planet, as well as the most graphic evidence of the unity of all living things, past present and future. With few exceptions, organisms eat members of other species, but sometimes, even their own. What organisms acquire in the process is both sources of energy (stored within sugars and fats) as well as building block materials (essential amino acids). The process of digestion enables the consuming organism to break down the complex proteins of another organism into the less complex building block molecules that it can incorporate into its own compatible architectural fabric. In this way, nature continually cycles and recycles the essential elements of living things by re-incorporating them, within the LS in other, usually more complex organisms (further up the food chain). Then, when organisms reproduce, they effectively transfer some of this complex material forward in time to new generations. However, none of this energy and material cycling activity could take place unless all the participants—prey and predator, eater and "eatee"—had compatible operating systems and virtually identical metabolic systems. With few exceptions, the food chain parallels the vertical hierarchy of biological life as organisms that are more complex consume less complex living organisms on the ladder of life. The reverse seems to be true when it comes to recycling the remains of dead organisms. Then, scavengers—usually lower down on the life complexity scale—recycle valuable protein leftovers and clean up the environment in the process. Finally, the residue is left to insects, bacteria and fungi (decomposers)—which fill important roles in scavenging decaying biological matter and thus maintaining the delicate bio-chemical balance that exists in the biosphere—the physical environment supporting the LS on the planet.

B) SYSTEMS ENGINEERING CLUES:

From the SE point of view, the fact that all organisms in the LS have virtually the same metabolic operating systems, (the same biochemical functions) permits the transfer of biologically necessary (proteins and food energy) resources interactively across the system between habitats, species and generations. In addition, stabilization between the demand and supply sides of the system is maintained by redistribution through the food chain whenever and wherever excesses occurs, and overall system growth is affected accordingly. Any new expansion of the system, of course, is fueled by increased energy input from the sun, processed through the photosynthesizers at the bottom of the energy pyramid. Thus, the ebb and flow of biological resources remains in balance across the system—but always moving forward in time—as new offspring organisms replace past generations. This is all made possible as a direct result of the inherent universal compatibility within the LS as represented by the food chain. Of course, as the LS expands producing greater numbers of organisms in time, new and raw inanimate material from the external biosphere is increasingly processed and added to the universal LS infrastructure commonly referred to as the "planetary biomass".

We can view the foodchain as the distribution subsystem through which the LS re-assigns and re-distributes its basic materials (proteins and fuel energy) to different competing environmental niches throughout the system. If a species occupying a specific niche becomes too successful at survival and produces an oversupply of offspring there is always a danger that it may choke off it's own food supplies—at which point system intervention, directly and indirectly by means of disease and predation (as examples), transfers some of those biological resources to other needier organisms in other adjacent niches. Generally speaking, all proteins and carbohydrates can be digested (biologically broken down into simpler biological components) and used to rebuild and resupply other organisms within the system. Then, when an organism reproduces it takes the biological material from past living organisms (food) and uses those same building block resources to construct others (offspring) that will carry it forward into the future. In this way, through the feedback controls evident in the food chain, the interactive LS supplies, recycles and distributes the necessary energy and protein building blocks among its participant component organisms—from the past, to the present and into future.

Species:

a) The Basic Macro Group:

It is the last of the taxa categories—"species", that represents the basic "group" classification of life at the macro level of the LS. A species comprises an immense number of organisms that share common *genes*, (and therefore a common morphology or physical characteristics), a similar *environmental niche* (external habitat conditions) and can combine genetic information (if they have discovered sex) for the production of future generations. The species, in effect, characterizes a population of like individual organisms that carry on a common mission of living, reproducing and dying. Within the same geographic locality in the biosphere, many different kinds of species can display radically different and complex behavior patterns, propensities, and tolerances, which represent their own species-specific survival strategies. These are tailor made to correspond to the set of imposed external conditions that comprises each species particular environmental niche. Thus, there exists for every species a specific combination of physical characteristics that serves as its unique package of survival mechanisms that corresponds to its specific environmental niche conditions.

The collective success of the individual member organisms at reproducing future generations determines the survival success of any particular species. A cursory examination of Life in all the nooks and crannies of the planet reveals that each species appears to be carefully adapted within its *environmental niche.* Immense varieties of specialization and form are evident—from the simple single celled bacterium to the complex multicellular lifeforms, and from the microscopic to the elephantine. The first impression is irreconcilable diversity and unrelatedness between species. However, and it bears repeating, that upon closer examination it is revealed that all of life's variations are constructed on a common theme and survive and thrive in a complex web of interdependency. In addition, nearly all living things owe their existence to the Sun's energy, (converted by food plants through photosynthesis) which fuels the sustenance and interaction of life's constituent component organisms within the earth's *biosphere* or habitat for life. And, again, all living things derive their instructions for living from the universal DNA encoded information system. There are no exceptions. Nevertheless, while there appears to be a universal LS survival strategy imposed upon all species, each one is free to develop and refine its very own brand of operational tactics that it brings to the task.

Among the most curious tactical survival activities that diverse species engage in, is the interdependency characterized as *symbiosis*. This is the concept of two or more species whose needs are sometimes radically different, engaging in a living partnership whereby each supplies and receives a service or commodity essential for the survival of each of the partners. So it is that honeybees satisfy their quest for nectar while simultaneously fulfilling the vital transfer of genetic material in pollinating plants. Parasitic—host symbiosis, and feeding birds spreading plant seeds are examples of the intricate and delicate relationships that have evolved over time and that organisms share as they play their unique respective roles in the continuous fabric of life. The symbiotic relationships forged over time through the mechanisms of adaptive evolution form part and parcel of specie's environmental niche attributes, no different than does an aquatic specie's survival range of water temperature or salinity. The key to an understanding of the complex relationships between species survival tactics within the overall LS survival strategy is ultimately tied to an understanding of the dynamics relationships between a species form and function, its external biosphere environmental niche and the resultant forces of evolution it is subjected to. All of these issues form a part of the complex of ideas that gained prominence in the mid-19th century.

b) The Origin of Species:

Charles Darwin's fame rests upon his theory of biological evolution (unless otherwise stated, all references to evolution will explicitly mean 'biological' evolution) supported by the arguments contained in his "Origin of Species" published in 1859. The classic definition of evolution pertains to the "survival of the fittest" and the elimination of the unfit through a selective process referred to as <u>natural selection</u>. Implicit in the theory is the concept of inheritability of genetic variations within members of a species that provide the material for the selection process of natural selection to operate on. Some of Darwin's ideas concerning how heritable changes occurred or how they resulted in variations were incorrect. Explanations that are more precise would have to await the rediscovery, at the beginning of the 20th century, of the writings of Gregor Mendel, (the father of Genetics) on the principles of inheritance. However, the enormous evidence for the relationship between "natural selection" and variations in populations of organisms presented in Darwin's published work changed forever the way people thought about these issues and sparked a heated debate among the intellectuals of the mid 19th century, (that continues in some form even to this day) the likes of which had rarely been seen before or since. That the "theory of evolution" is less a theory in the hypothetical sense and more factual reflects the reality that: while not all the operative mechanisms are totally understood (nor agreed upon), the phenomenon itself is not the least in doubt within the broad scientific community.

In practice, many variables enter the equations of evolution. Our intention in the next few pages is to concentrate on the fact that *"nature"* works with many different species containing large numbers of organisms and has plenty of time to allow things to happen. And what is happening is that this combination seems to virtually guarantee that although evolution appears to be blind and unpredictable in terms of absolute results, it seems to single-handedly bear all of the responsibility for keeping the march of life in step with future changes to the biosphere environment. It has been doing so since the OoL for the past 3.8 billion years, more or less, and there is no reason to suspect that this state of affairs will change. This unpredictability of the future direction of biosphere conditions coupled with survival of the fittest (and of the fortunate), leads one to wonder how it is that the LS not only manages to survive as a whole, but truly thrives and expands its compliment of species over time—all seemingly without a game plan. Is this another one of those paradoxes that keeps cropping up as we journey along our SE investigative approach of the LS? One would think so from the descriptions that abound in the scientific literature of unpredictability of species evolution driven by the fickle engine of biosphere changes. Closer examination will reveal that there is no paradox in the facts of evolution; that if there appears to be a paradox, it exists only within how we generally tend to describe what is happening in evolution. Our particular approach shall be relying on the engineering mentality to help guide us in how to interpret the functioning of evolution.

Our first challenge is to try to understand what evolution seems to be trying to achieve before trying to understand how it goes about it. We can do this by examining what it is that evolution has accomplished in the past and can be assumed to be continuing at present. The quick and obvious answer is: "nothing less than <u>the survival of the LS over immense periods of time</u>". And, it does this by simply ensuring that sufficient numbers of member organisms reproduce offspring possessing within their genetic libraries sufficient versatility to ensure that their own future offspring will possess survival attributes as well. At first glance, it seems like a formidable challenge. But, careful observation reveals that the LS accomplishes what it does by simply making sure that somewhere, somehow, there are organisms of one form or another—of one species or another—that will have what it takes to survive long enough to reproduce future generations. Life just wants to go on. And, the solution to system survival would seem to lie within the numbers. Survival—whether of species or the system as a whole— is determined by the ability to maintain large populations of organisms within species, and large numbers of species within the LS as a whole. The next challenging question we want to ask is whether this survival success, over the life of the system (some 3.8 billion years and counting) represents merely chance and happenstance or whether survival represents an LS prime objective. Of course, the answer will ultimately be determined by which OoL option one adopts. But, investigating, as we are, the RDH option for the OoL, and using the SE approach in our inquiry, our question turns on whether survival can be seen as a quality imbedded within our proposed LS design intent. If so then we would expect to find mechanisms built into the system of Life that promote system survival success as a kind of prime objective to insure against system survival failure.

The next chapter will explore this seemingly "prime objective" as part of LS survival. We hope to demonstrate—as well as define—the statistical mechanisms that influence and—as it turns out—are at the very heart of this seemingly random process. In the light of our novel SE approach, we shall have occasion to reinterpret somewhat, the various relationships that exist between the different mechanisms that are considered within the LS evolution phenomenon. In the process we shall come to appreciate that, in reality, the LS leaves nothing, including the results of evolution (which translates into survival) to chance. As such, we will come to understand that the evolution capability can be considered to be nothing less than an essential LS survival sub-system and very much a part of its design intent.

c) Natural Selection—An Enigma:

The crucial dilemma that faces any design hypothesis would seem to lie within the purely statistical nature of heredity and the total unpredictability of the results. The dilemma is compounded by the fact that all the selection seems to be coming from the insensitive external environment and it's ability to virtually dictate the absolute conditions of survival within the confines of a species' attribute limits. One might well ask:

> "If the LS were indeed a product of design, should it not be able to determine it's own fate towards a goal that would be reflected within it's design intent?"

These kinds of issues alone may account for the reflex-like reaction of SAb proponents against any design concept—rational or otherwise. And, from the other side of the coin, you might even propose that the denial of natural selection, and indeed, of any aspects of evolution on the part of Creationists in general would seem to be the direct consequence of how they interpret the unpredictability of the results of evolution that would necessarily conflict in some irrevocable way with the basic tenets of religious creationist concepts. Acceptance of evolution and what it stands for would imply—especially to religionists—that the creator would seem to be having difficulty in knowing what results it was aiming for or in being able to predict the results emanating from its own design. Does this not leave the RDH designer option we are postulating in an equivalent logical quandary—the fact that the way the LS works mitigates against predictability of future results? Well, not necessarily so.

Remember our basic stated premise at the beginning of this exercise. We invoked the SE mindset and exploratory tools as a catalytic approach with no particular ax to grind. We agreed that if the results proved incompatible with reality, we would be prepared to pack up our intellectual tent and quietly steal away in the night. Have we reached that impasse? Obviously not. In fact our SE approach—meant to provide us with novel and useful intellectual tools to bring to bear on the analysis of the LS—will now be tested for it's ability to extricate us out of this potential intellectual jam. In fact, our whole exercise— and the Rational Design Hypothesis in particular—depend on it. How does the RDH—the product of the results of this SE analysis deal with this seemingly irreconcilable challenge? Well, it's really quite simple! It all depends on what we eventually conclude the real purpose of the LS to be.

d) Survival Through Change:

Let's recap somewhat: At any one instant in time, (the present, for example) virtually everywhere one looks in the environment, living things are apparent. According to evolutionary theory, different species reflect the different ways of accomplishing what is fundamentally the same thing: living and survival. Thus, any differences to be found among species phenotypes may be accounted for by how each has adapted to its individualized biosphere environmental niche together with any differences in strategies developed along the way that help achieve the universal mission of survival. Thus, it is universally accepted today that all the different species that make up the seven major taxonomic categories biologists use to classify life on the planet—kingdoms, phylii, classes, orders, families, genus and species—all are doing precisely the same thing: trying to compete and survive by doing their own thing. The ability to extract oxygen from water allows marine life to inhabit the oceans, seas, lakes and rivers. The ability of plants to create food from carbon dioxide, water and sunlight allows them to exhibit their particular lifestyles. The symbiotic relationships established between flowering plants and honeybees, for example, have allowed each to pursue life in their unique fashion. And so it goes with all the organisms on the planet.

A continuous genetic line can be traced from the earliest unicellular organisms to the myriadly complex examples evident in modern species. But, because so many extinctions have occurred in the process, it becomes evident, that later species simply represent the fruition of the potential inherent within the genetic makeup that must have been present within those earliest organisms from the very beginning. That potential became realized within the multitudes of species that developed along the way. Moreover, the increased complexity found in later species simply reflects the sophistication within the process whereby in time, more complex organisms arose in discreet (not necessarily incremental) steps from the less complex ones that preceded them. Yet, evolution is considered blind in that it responds to conditions over which it seemingly has no control—those of the biosphere. Therefore, there is no way for an outsider to predict the course of evolution nor the resulting species that are its products. We must then conclude that—from a design perspective—the LS uses species as a means to an end, and the only end possible under such restrictive circumstances is to "buy time". In other words, the only objective we can conceive of for the LS at the Macro Level is to develop both tactical and strategic defenses against total annihilation, much the same as pieces are deployed and sacrificed in the game of chess. The ultimate aim in the game of life, however, is to never run out of pieces. Nevertheless, the game of LS survival at first glance seems to be "stacked" against it. The rules appear to favor the opposition in the competition between the LS and the only set of constantly changing parameters that can thwart system survival— the external biosphere. The biosphere seems to have the advantage of making all of the offensive moves. The LS's obligation in the fray is to employ only defensive survival measures in response to continual external biosphere changes. But, the LS is not without powerful defenses—having the novel advantage of being able to muster new and novel replacement troops (organisms and species) to replace those caught off-guard and sacrificed (die off or become extinct) in the ongoing battle for LS survival.

Thus, each species represents a different LS survival strategy facing a unique combination of offensive biosphere conditions. By deploying enough tactical replacements, so the strategy goes, it is the hoped for expectation (by the LS good guys) that regardless of the opponent biosphere's aggressive moves, at least some of our players will survive. And, given enough time—and in this way—the LS refills it's ranks with newly created novel substitutions (newly evolved species) and redeploys, as it were, ever ready to respond to any biosphere challenges with newly invented survival strategies. Thus, organism survival leads to internal changes that are tested against continually changing external environment conditions—in a never-ending confrontation. In the process, the LS displays increased complexity over time. Within the SE context, we now want to explore in detail the relationship between "complexity" and "time" (long-term survival)—the two major considerations that characterize the LS—in order to try to fathom what the overall system objective might possibly be. Is "complexity" an end—in and of itself—or is "survival over time" the system prime objective? From the foregoing discussions, these would seem to be the only two logically possible choices.

The Two Major Axes of Life System Activity:

With the advent of the concepts implied by Darwinian evolution, the world of living things became unified in two essential axial directions, both of which can be considered as prevalent characteristics of the LS:

a) *Complexity* and b) *Time*

In fact, you could say that the complexity of the LS, in terms of number and variations of species, is a function of time and could (if we knew all the facts) be plotted on a graph to reflect complexity versus time since Life began 3.8 billion years ago until the present.

While time is continuous on the horizontal scale, any point on the hypothetical graph along that axis will represent a vertical slice on the complexity scale, much as a photograph represents reality at a given instant in time. However, the resulting graph, if it could be drawn, would be anything but linear. We know from the fossil record that, over time, evolution has seen fit to change the course of LS direction. Changes have been radical at times, but overall, and despite numerous setbacks, the trend has been towards greater variation and complexity, paralleling the adaptations to changing biosphere conditions succeeding generations of living things must accommodate to. Now, according to SAb dogma, we should also be able to extrapolate our curve of complexity versus time back to the origin of the LS to a single species entity of chemical origin. Extrapolating forward in time would be futile, in-as-much as nobody knows in which directions the future will take Life on the planet, nor what dangers lie ahead. We can be pretty certain that our sun, like all stars, will eventually burn itself out in the distant future, and cease to have a positive influence on LS survival. Whether intelligent life will be able to survive long enough for that eventuality to be of concern is, for the moment, a matter of idle (but, as we shall eventually see, not irrelevant) speculation. In any event, we can say with some justification that the uniqueness of the LS as a system lies within its dynamic characteristics in both time and space

From a SE point of view, we shall be examining both of these fundamental characteristics (time and complexity) to try and determine their real significance to the LS from a design point of view. By that, I mean to try and figure out whether permanence (and therefore time) can be considered a primary purpose of the system and whether complexity, or rather, increased complexity over time could have design significance. Put another way—from the System Design point of view:

COMPLEXITY:

Is it a prime function of the Life system that the system gains in complexity over time such that, for example, an intelligent organism such as (but not limited to) Homo Sapiens (humans) evolves? The Anthropic Cosmological Principle, you recall (Chapter 4), would have us believe so. Or,

TIME:

Is it an important design feature that the Life system be permanent on the planet from the time of its origin until the future demise of the planet (whenever that occurs)?

Life—A Tale of Two Possibilities:

A] COMPLEXITY:

Because evolution is blind and no prediction can be made as to which species or even family of species will be successful in propagating the information encoded in its DNA forward to future generations, the only logical conclusion we can draw is that 'increased complexity' itself is not, could not, and has never been the goal, if you will, of the LS.

Sure enough, the simplest organism must comprise a composition of biological mechanisms that constitute a sufficient and necessary minimum level of complexity at its root core. Without this, no self-replicating life form could exist. What is referred to here is that there is not, and in fact could not be, a complexity agenda within evolution because left on it's own, the LS is and must be susceptible to the random catastrophic events that have threatened in the past and continue to threaten the more complex life-forms that have evolved. Within our own experience, we know that the more complex a machine, the more things that can go wrong with it. This raises the question as to why life forms that are more complex should have evolved in the first place. Why develop life forms that are more complex when the case can be made that "simpler is better". One suggestion might be that perhaps the complexity strategy for organisms represents a decent investment in LS resources under steady state environmental conditions—those long stretches of time that separate catastrophic events within the biosphere. But, the more complex an organism is, the greater would seem to be it's sensitivity and vulnerability to environmental stress; the more that can go wrong and threaten organism survival. The evolution of complex organisms, then, would imply an expansion of the LS into greater areas of the biosphere by establishing novel environmental niches and accommodating more biosphere conditions. They are, in effect, a fruition of the built-in evolution potential of the LS, providing perhaps an incremental increase in LS survivability in some paranoid-like perseverance to that end.

It stands to reason, then, that the more niches carved out by emerging species within the large spectrum of biosphere attributes (conditions), the greater the likelihood that some niches will provide protection for their respective species during catastrophic events, that destroy others. Under relatively steady state (slowly evolving) biosphere conditions, we might expect that more species evolve and survive than become extinct. It serves as a period of entrenchment allowing species to fine tune their morphological attributes in closer synch with their external environmental niches while at the same time taking advantage of the opportunity of experimenting with novel changes—here and there within the species—that could serve future survival demands. Therefore, complexity can be viewed as the strategy the LS adopts during peaceful times—wherever they occur on the planet—between catastrophic events, both local and planet-wide—a time for LS evolutionary consolidation, as it were— in anticipation of massive culling of species and their organisms when the hard catastrophic times hit.

B) TIME:

The changing biosphere represents the dynamic environment that the LS members must continuously adapt to over time. At any given moment, the full spectrum of conditions in the biosphere can be represented by the niches, that species of one kind or other can occupy. The LS seems capable of filling many of these biosphere niche 'units', as it were, by producing corresponding niche specific species to fill those units, which, from the LS point of view, represent the full composition of all extant living things. Thus, as relatively slow (steady-state) changes to the biosphere occur (Climactic, geologic, atmospheric, aquatic, to name a few), the LS meets the challenge of system survival by:

1) availing some of its species units to become extinct when their niches disappear (niche conditions become extraordinarily altered faster than their species can adapt), and

2) adapting sufficient numbers of other species within the allowable time frames through the various processes of evolution—to fine-tune their attributes—in order to better accommodate future changes to their niche biosphere conditions.

In this way, the continuity of the system of life itself is assured. Thus, complexity and variation being totally unpredictable can be viewed simply as defensive consequences of the adaptive survival measures integral to the LS and need have no deeper significance. In other words, the system is programmed for survival—pure and simple—and, therefore, has no scheme to produce and entrench any particular kinds of species that do the surviving. Species development and adaptation occurs incessantly (if at different rates) across the complete spectrum of extant biological life forms according to no particular agenda. Their respective opportunities for survival depend only upon being able to match the specific sufficient and necessary survival conditions defined for individual species, to those species-specific niche conditions presented by and within the impartial biosphere.

Thus, it would seem that nothing in the LS is permanent, or even predictable, except its very survival in one form or another through the element of time and within the confines of its host planet biosphere. Through good times and bad, the LS has endured and can be counted on to continue to do so. Moreover, this would seem to be the point of it all—LS survival. The LS would appear to have no agenda—other than its own continued existence over immense periods of time. (We will deal with the "why" question later on.)

Survival Context at the Macro Level:

Thus, at the Macro Level of Life, "*survival*"—as they say—"is the only game in town"; survival of individual organisms; survival of species; and ultimately the survival of the LS itself. Within the LS, all component organisms and species are expendable and replaceable by other expendable players in the game of Life. It is estimated that presently, there are some two million different species alive that have been documented, and an unknown number that have escaped our attention to date. This number, large as it is, represents less than one tenth of 1 percent of the species that have come and gone in the history of the LS with an estimated 2 billion species having evolved in the past 600 million years alone. As stated, for the first two to three billion years our ancestors were merely microorganisms. Therefore we can conclude that the existence of the LS is significant—not so much in it's ability to create more complex organisms over time, all of which are temporary life forms, but rather,—in it's ability to survive the past 3.8 billion years through at least 5 great extinctions (and an unknown number of lesser ones) resulting from catastrophic events.

EXTINCTIONS HALL OF FAME: A STATEMENT OF SURVIVAL

Nothing seems to capture human interest or imagination more than the disclosure of record-breaking events. The subject of paleontology has its hall of fame of sorts when it comes to extinctions. There are five in particular that have achieved sufficient notoriety to make the grade. In reality, we define extinction as the demise of a particular species. The fact that many species happened to go extinct within a given frame of time would not ordinarily draw too much attention. It happens all the time. What sets these five extraordinary periods apart from the usual is the extent of the radical changes that occurred in the composition of the LS within a distinct and relatively short time frame. And to this day, the questions as to the how and the why of these events are still being asked. The bones of the fossil record, like the remnants of some universal terrestrial graveyard, are all that remain as indicators of extinct species that once thrived.

Probably the best-known mass extinction is the demise of the dinosaurs some 65 million years ago, at the end of the Cretaceous geologic period, and more precisely defined as the K-T boundary. Besides the interest and fascination children have with these bygone creatures, the true significance of this event lies in the probability that had it not occurred, it is arguable whether mammals would have achieved the world dominance we experience today. There is little question that the dinosaurs had already attained considerable sophistication with respect to variety of species and widespread planet entrenchment. Their impressive track record of diversity and survival over hundreds of millions of years prior to their untimely demise attests to both their endurance and eminence in the complex species category. In sharp contrast, by the time of their mass extinction, as far as is known, the only evidence of mammalian existence comprised a small shrew-like creature that might be considered merely an evolutionary experiment with questionable chance for improvement, no less survival. But then something truly extraordinary happened that altered the destinies of both mammal and dinosaur that exemplifies the stark reality of the importance of several rather obscure factors for the chances of emergence and survival of mammalian species—all seeming to involve nothing more than pure luck and chance: 1] being there in some form; and 2] extraordinary timing. According to the proposal contained in a controversial research article published in 1980 by L. W Alvarez et al, the K-T boundary extinction that led to the demise of the dinosaurs resulted from the collision of the earth with a giant asteroid or other extraterrestrial object with a strength of the order of 10,000 times the explosive power of the global nuclear arsenal. That cataclysmic event triggered instantaneous and long-term catastrophic changes to the habitat conditions that apparently no dinosaurs could endure. (An exception might comprise the ancestor of birds, which have been suggested as descended from a dinosaur species.) The Alvarez catastrophe hypothesis has also challenged one of the most respected theoretical doctrines of geology and evolutionary biology—"uniformitarianism"—championed by Charles Lyell and dating back to the 1830s. At the time, uniformitarianism replaced catastrophism and held that the history of the world has been shaped by slow moving processes and events such as geological erosion and the gradual replacement of one species with another. The discovery in the early 1990s of a giant crater hidden beneath the Yucatan Peninsula in Mexico lent considerable weight to the Alvarez hypothesis for the calamitous demise of the dinosaurs and has promoted research focusing on other such crises in our planet's history.

Whether the dinosaur demise was instantaneous (it had to be for those in the immediate area of impact) or over an indeterminate period of time, the net results were the same and complete. But, as devastating to the continued existence of dinosaurs this catastrophe was, this same event was all that was apparently needed to give the mammalian evolutionary experiment a chance to fill the biological "vacuum" within the biosphere thus created—which eventually led them to dominance over of the planet. To clarify, it is not as if the future success of mammals was or could have been predicted within the context of the eradication of the then dominant genus of species. Rather, the forced chance removal of dinosaurs opened a whole menu of evolutionary possibilities, within and available to, the then surviving species. Consequently, one such survivor—a mammal, albeit sparsely represented at the time—was sufficiently poised to exploit the new reality created by the extinction of, what was probably its greatest environmental competitor and threat. Obviously, our mammalian ancestor had already established environmental niche conditions that were sufficient to allow it to survive the same conditions that proved to be catastrophic and that led to the extinction of its major rivals. It is more than likely that many, if not most, of the mammals alive then also succumbed to the instantaneous stresses provoked by the violent event. Fortunately for us, some mammal did survive (that's why we are here) that could take advantage of and exploit the new conditions on the planet. Lest we forget, the catastrophe that did-in the dinosaurs also wiped out 38% of the genera of marine life, no doubt providing the survivors within that habitat spectrum similar opportunities to exploit.

The five great extinctions in the history of life on the planet have occurred, one each in the Ordivician,

Devonian, Permian, Triassic and, as stated above, Cretaceous periods—the largest and most devastating occurring at the end of the Permian. Collectively these extinctions are known, in paleontology circles as the "Big Five". It has been suggested[2] that mass extinctions occur with regular clock-like spacing in time as a result of periodic astronomical events that disturb comet orbits every 26 million years or so. If that be the case, then the LS has proven that it contains the sufficient and necessary strategies to ensure life system survival, even under the maximum stresses the biosphere becomes exposed to during these periodic events. Certainly, it can be expected that the periodic bombardment of our planet adheres to no such timetable and can occur at any time in between. Our goal here is not to reiterate the many accounts that describe these monumental events in the life of the LS but to present a realistic if graphic picture of the tenuous reality of long term survival for any particular form of biological life on our planet—in contrast to the success of the system as a whole. Again, survival of the LS on the planet is the only name of the game. And speaking of survival strategies now would seem to be as good a time as any to introduce a little "sex" into our proceedings.

Sex—Games Species Play:

A) UNIVERSAL AND EXPENSIVE:

Some two billions years after the LS was introduced to the planet, some strange things started to happen. Individuals of the same species started to exchange genetic material. They must have liked it because the practice caught on and radically changed the directions the LS would travel. Today, sexual reproduction is practiced universally throughout the LS—in plants, microorganisms and animals alike. It is estimated that fully 99.9% of higher organisms are presently sexual. The exceptions are a few species of fish, a type of salamander and several plants, including the common urban dwelling dandelion. But, liking something and being able to afford it are familiar enough issues in most of our daily comings and goings. And the introduction of "sex", as it came to be called, exacted a steep price within the economies of biological activity. Indeed, it's not only expensive biologically in terms of resources required directly and indirectly, but also considerably complicated from a logistics point of view. The fact is, as one researcher on the subject put it: "No organism in its right mind would opt for sex as a way to create offspring. It's too expensive". The cost in genetic material alone is incredible when one considers that any sexually reproducing organism discards fully half it's genes when it produces sex cells—eggs or sperm. Each consists of only one-half the chromosomes contained in the rest of the organism cells. The union of haploid (halved) egg and sperm following sexual union restores the diploid (paired) chromosome condition. In contrast, asexual organisms transmit all of their chromosomal genes to the next generation. Nevertheless, from our unique SE point of view, if it happened and seems to be important, then it could have design implications. The fact that sex began seriously some 2 billion years after life began and managed to totally displace—what at first sight appears to be—a much more efficient reproductive system poses some serious questions that require answers. Among these:

1] Could sex have evolved as some "lucky" strategic improvement in the LS or was it programmed by design to come into effect under certain conditions or after some 'time delay'?

2] If, indeed, sex was introduced as part of a design, then the important question is why? What system purpose could it serve?

By 'time delay', I don't want to imply that some kind of alarm clock had been ticking away in the genetic library of every living organism, ready to spring sex into action in the lucky generation when the alarm went off. The time delay could very well comprise, for example, some kind of genetic sequence that gets triggered following a particular genetic combination, whenever it might occur. In other words, the genetic program that would have triggered the sexual phenomenon among members of any given species might have existed within the genomes of the originating species dating back to the OoL 3.8 billion years ago, and programmed to function if and when certain conditions came about within the genetic library. It could be that in the case of the LS, that only happened 2 billion years after the OoL. How that might have occurred might be analogous to the timing mechanisms involved in "telemeres"—DNA sequences that limit the number of times a cell can replicate. There are other examples of biological timing mechanisms such as that involved in "*apoptosis*", or programmed cell death, an important mechanism involved in fetal development in animals.

As regards purpose, it has always been assumed that the aim of natural selection mechanisms of evolution was to reward those individuals who get the most copies of their genes into the next generation. If that were indeed the case, then sex would seem to make little sense. Cloning is far more efficient in this regard—no investment in wasteful time pursuing mates for compulsory union with other organisms— time better spent in finding food and avoiding being eaten. Clones essentially split in two or bud to produce genetically identical copies. It's fast and efficient. In addition, probably the most negative aspect of sexual reproduction, as opposed to asexual reproduction, has to do with the taking of two perfectly good genomes of the parents and scrambling their genes. What are the chances that the result will indeed be an improvement? And, even if it were an improvement, the next time around—in the next generation—all that good genetic stuff could be totally undone. Considering the above, there has to be some compelling reasons to account for the replacement of asexual reproduction by a phenomenon such as sex that appears—on the surface at least—to be expensive, complicated and risky. The question of sex: "why did it evolve and what keeps it going?" has evoked a debate among scientists that proceeds along the following lines.

b) Genetic Variability Argument:

How does that old gag go? "Sex is good for one!....but, for two....?" Some thirty odd years ago, the question of the "reason for sex" was considered pretty well solved—it was said to be 'good for the species'. By ensuring that offspring were somewhat different from their parents, a species could improve it's chances of survival through environmental changes while at the same time gaining some advantage on rival organisms or predators. Thus, the mating of genetic material from two individuals to produce a third individual with a novel genetic combination would seem to have the advantage of providing the species with genetic variability. This also would have permitted sexual populations to evolve faster. Gene recombination through sex produces diversity and diversity is considered to be the fuel of evolution. This, in short, is the main 'variability' argument for the introduction of sex as a replacement for cloning. However, there are several problems associated with this kind of reasoning which we shall raise shortly.

c] DNA Error Correction Argument:

Other scientists support the idea that: "Sex is an ideal way for the repair of defective DNA". They concede that once sex got going—for this reason alone—in time it also contributed the variability advantage, which—in the view of some researchers—became as important and beneficial to the LS. This kind of co-evolution of additional benefits beyond the initial advantage and reason for the development and establishment of new species attributes seems to be common enough. In this vein, they argue that variability is not why sex began in the first place. The reshuffling of the genes from two organisms originated, accordingly, as a repair strategy for damaged chromosomes and variation, as stated, is nothing more than a secondary, if important, effect of sex. In asexual organisms, mutations are automatically copied and passed on to future generations. This is important as a mechanism to promote evolution. But, over time—the argument goes—the damage to genes due to mutations accumulates, which could ultimately lead to species extinction if left unchecked. Thus, we might view an error correction algorithm, provided by sexual reproduction, as a modus operandi to limit the damage to an organism's genes as a result of mutations, but at the same time providing a new and different strategy to help evolution: the shuffling of the genes of two unique individuals of a species through sex.

Richard Michod, professor of ecology and evolutionary biology at University of Arizona makes the argument for DNA repair this way: Since DNA is a way of conveying information, perhaps sex was initially a way for getting the message straight—it might be about error correction, not variation.[3] In experiments with bacteria, he effectively demonstrated the principle of sex-for-DNA repair. These minute organisms, in a process referred to as transformation could incorporate within their genetic DNA bits of extraneous DNA from their internal cytoplasm environment. It is believed that this spare DNA is used to repair environmental damage caused by excessive oxygen or ultraviolet light. The evidence lies in the fact that damaged bacteria use more DNA than undamaged bacteria. In addition, repaired bacteria reproduce better. Sexual reproduction cleans the gene pool because bad mutations are not automatically forwarded to offspring—some are, but not all. The main obstacle, in this error correction scenario to account for the introduction of sex, is the question of mutation frequency. If mutations don't happen all that often, the urgency of error correction may be sufficiently small and questionable. Daniel Shoen, botanist at McGill University in Montreal has been studying the rate of mutations in plants and is the first to show that the mutation rate is sufficiently high to make the theory of error correction credible. Nevertheless, I believe there is another even more compelling reason for coming down on the side of error correction as the prime incentive for the introduction of sexual reproduction. More of this later.

d) SE Implications of Sex:

From a SE point of view, and particularly if you accept the premise discussed above that survival 'time' and not 'complexity' is the prime LS imperative, then which of the two makes more sense. The question becomes: Which sexual reproduction function—variability or error-correction—best serves the LS as an essential asset in support of the LS survival 'time' imperative? Also, in order to narrow down the field further, we may ask: Of the two choices, which could possibly be considered as a built-in LS design feature? Without hesitation we can affirm that variability doesn't stand a chance considering that for two and a half billion years, LS survival did rather well asexually. The system expanded and thrived without sex. As such, from a 'time' perspective, variability had little to offer, because the system was ostensibly meeting all of its external challenges—those imposed by the external biosphere. In fact, the only dangers the LS faced were wholly internally derived—dangers that could conceivably degrade the system as a whole over time. And, within the cell itself, the only conceivably vulnerable candidate for scrutiny would have to be the information data bases upon which all of biogenesis depends. All biological processes depend on the faithful encoding and decoding of genetic data; this is universal throughout the LS, both then and now. As such—under an LS open-ended 'time' imperative—a glaring endemic system weakness involves the unavoidable introduction of base-pair mutations—random errors to the informational databases. Unchecked, the accumulation of such genetic anomalies could jeopardize all species and the LS itself. Thus, the only logical conclusion, from both SE vantage points is that the primary function of sex falls with the 'error-correction' option. DNA error correction is a necessity for long-term LS survival and error correction subsystems would, of necessity, have been incorporated within an LS design framework under the Rational Design Hypothesis. Ergo, sex = error-correction!

E) ADDITIONAL CONSIDERATIONS:

I have come to believe that the primary importance of maintaining the integrity of information encoded in DNA makes absolute the necessity for the inclusion of error correction mechanisms as a design feature of the LS. Furthermore, the precision with which the error correction function is carried out within the sexual reproduction scheme provides a compelling reason for the inclusion of sex—as expensive as it may be biologically—as being both sufficient and necessary as the error-corrective reproductive strategy in LS design. I would even suggest that the genetic schematics for sexual reproduction could have been programmed to come into effect at some particular stage in the LS history on the planet and its introduction can be considered to be a turning point in that history. From a design-intent vantage point, the strategy makes a lot of sense:

Consider, if you will, that for the first half of the history of life on the planet, the LS priority must have been the rapid spread of organisms and species throughout the planet during a time when biosphere conditions were known to be extreme. Thus, during this formative phase, the LS global strategy would have emphasized the priority of "rapid expansion" that would generate enough unicellular organisms for the necessary acclimatization of the LS to its new planetary habitat. Eventually the LS became entrenched following a process of elimination that saw some of the diverse varieties—out of the spectrum of originating implanted species—selected for by the prevailing biosphere conditions. Nevertheless, a price had to be paid for such a rapid expansion, and that price was the accumulation over time of genome errors that would have threatened the genetic integrity of all extant species. At some point, then, the

LS priorities must have shifted away from rapidly expanding populations of relatively few species to the imperative of cutting down and correcting the inevitable harmful and potentially catastrophic genetic errors accumulating within the genomes of proliferating species—after countless generations of cloning. Thus, error correction would afford the LS a way of eliminating the risks similar to sexual inbreeding, by introducing a way to compare two different sets of genetic instructions for errors and restoring the integrity of the species genome in future generations. It is important to note that this error correction benefit to the LS afforded by sex would have been felt immediately after it began. That is to say, that no long term acclimatization period would have been required for the error correcting system to work properly—the actual beneficial results of restoring information integrity would be seen virtually instantaneously, following its introduction. The reason becomes obvious when we realize that error correction refers directly to the information contents within the DNA of an organism and of the quality and integrity of that information as it relates to its ultimate expression in organism morphology. And, since an organism's physiology is a direct consequence of the expression of its genes, any change in the DNA brought about by any means—including beneficial error correction—would immediately be expressed in the same generation. In other words, the sexual mixing of two genomes (one from each parent) and the scrutiny and implementation of the included error correction algorithms to produce an improved error free set of genetic instructions in the offspring, would confer and result in an immediate improvement in offspring morphology. Error correction means instant results.

While sexual reproduction could also serve to introduce increased variability within the genome it could really only express itself after many trials and tribulations and after many generations as a proliferation of new and divergent species. Variability results from the taking of two genomes and mixing the combination of genes—some from one parent and some from the other—thereby doubling the possibility of genetic variation per gene. Thus, even if the number of chance mutations is minimal, as they must be to insure continued genome integrity, still the laws of probability ensure that genomic variability is ubiquitous throughout the species. But most significantly, variability ultimately must express itself within the context of species modification, and change, eventually resulting in totally new directions of complexity and adaptation. Once this new reproductive format became standard on the planet, species variability and complexity could proceed in greater novel directions. Until then, the LS would remain characterized as an overabundance of relatively few member species on the planet, occupying a limited number of environmental niches. This would be the conditions of life on the planet as a result of the members of a species reproducing by cloning (copying) exactly the DNA comprising their genome at the time of reproduction. The only changes responsible for variability that an organism could pass on to its offspring through cloning would be those acquired during its brief lifetime through chance mutations. Standard reasoning considers that most of these could be expected to be deleterious to the offspring. Thus, it is to be expected that many failures of survival should be the rule, with few genetic changes becoming expressed as improvements to the species design with respect to survival. Therefore, relatively little change to species morphology could be expected by way of natural selection. Perhaps this could account for the fact that during the first 2 plus billion years following the OoL on the planet, the only life forms were unicellular organisms—possibly not much different from the originating biological organisms that existed at the OoL event itself.

Thus, because of the difference in the time elements involved (error correction is instantaneous, variability takes many generations of time), for that reason alone, it would seem that sex would have originally been introduced and maintained to rectify the important and dangerous problem concerning genetic information integrity—that only error correction mechanisms could remedy. And, from a purely Darwinist point of view, because any benefits deriving from variability would have involved a long term settling in period, it most probably would have been selected against simply on the basis of too great a biological expense yielding too little benefit. But, the vast investment in complexity and biological budgetary resources required to implement error correction in the short term has paid off handsomely in the form of long-term variability dividends that ultimately proved as valuable for LS survival.

From the SAb OoL vantage point, the co-evolution of error correction and variability afforded by sexual reproduction some time later—while constituting a most fortuitous event—would have been totally coincidental. Another important issue to consider is how could such a system (sexual reproduction) get started. Again, we are facing an issue that parallels the negative entropy "jump-start" question (to be explored in detail later). Let's say that sex originated through some chancy exchange of genetic material between members of the same species somewhere within the LS and that it provided an improved offspring organism. Good! But, why should this become ubiquitous throughout the system? We are not talking about the gradual evolution of some new genetic trait within a species here. We are dealing with a more complex way of doing probably the most complex function of Life—that of self-replication; not simply more complex but, in fact, more complex by several orders of magnitude. This would not be such a serious problem if sex had always been there from the beginning. However, billions of years later? Could one take this point to the extreme and compare the mystery of the introduction of sex into the LS with the mystery of the OoL itself on the planet? Maybe not, but the origin-of-sex issue is sufficiently important that it can't be readily swept under the SAb rug with a shrug of the shoulders. We can't simply wish the question away by speculating that: while clones are excellent colonizers because they reproduce quickly and accurately—that they become unable to meet the demands of stable ecosystems where life teems with organisms and species in fierce competition. Not after billions of years! So where does that leave us? Back to design!

The introduction of sex only makes sense within the context of design. And that leaves us squarely in the camp of error correction—with the benefits of future variability as a bonus. We will have reason to return to this issue later. It turns out that sex is a cornerstone in the edifice we are building and we will pick up where we are leaving off further down the road in our exercise. Seen from the RDH point of view, if sex was actually a programmed design feature, then perhaps the added benefits conferred later on by variability would have been calculated in as part of the design equation, making the expense and complication of sex worth the investment in biological resources and programmed to take effect when conditions demanded. But, regardless of which OoL hypothesis one adopts the introduction of sex simply and only for the sake of future variability, really does not make much sense. Think about it: for the first several billion years, life had obviously achieved sufficient, if limited, variability to have survived rather nicely. The additional variability afforded the LS by the introduction of sex under the circumstances of that kind of history might be considered perhaps "too little, too late" to be considered a crucial addition.

Conclusions from the "Macro" Perspective:

Each organism of every species that is alive today or has ever lived has played as significant and as essential a roll as any and every other organism of any species, whether that species is still in existence or has become extinct. The fact is that each is a unique combination of inheritable attributes among a large population of organisms containing diverse inheritable attributes. As such, each can be considered to be a distinct statistical event among a large population of such events, past and present. (I know that certain members of my own species may take exception to this statement upon philosophical or ideological grounds, but I am just as convinced it stands on it's merits). The LS at any given moment in time comprises the distributions of all of the organisms that make up the survivor species engaged in the living process. Each species, in turn, is characterized by the genetic information that defines its genotype together with its physical expression in the form of the biological attributes that define its species phenotype. Thus, survivorship rewards the physical ability of an organism and its offspring to cope with all of their external biosphere conditions and challenges, by preserving their genes responsible for that ability within the overall species gene pool. It is from within these ever-changing genetic databases that the future composition of the system, as represented by species attributes, is sculpted to mirror the changing shape of matching biosphere attributes.

As things seem to be moving, man's precarious intervention in the natural order of biosphere change may indeed trigger the next mass extinctions on the planet resulting in new directions for evolution to take the LS. The compelling question is whether the LS will, indeed, be able to continue to withstand the unprecedented mischief we are unleashing upon the life sustaining biosphere. I have no doubt it can. Major changes of a polluting nature have happened before. Let's not forget that midway in the history of the LS photosynthesizing species began flooding the atmosphere with, what was then, the most poisonous of gaseous by-products—oxygen. Many anaerobic species that could not adjust succumbed to the crisis and became extinct. The system not only managed to adapt and survive, but also thrived as the new oxygen atmosphere triggered the evolution of more complex life forms that in turn eventually gave rise to multicellular animal and plant species. Surely, the LS system can accommodate some contemporary global warming caused by an overabundance of gases such as CO_2 (the greenhouse effect); or the demise of the rain forests (ecological damage); or the increased artificial mutations potentially critical to higher life forms caused by ultraviolet radiation (destruction of the ozone layer). Even artificial cataclysmic events (nuclear conflagration) will fail, I am certain, to extinguish the system itself. How higher life forms such as the human species fare in the future is another matter entirely. From an LS perspective: even though great harm may accrue to so-called higher life-forms—including humans—because of the destruction of those parts of the biosphere they depend on for survival—as long as there will be LS participants that have carved some safe niche somewhere in the global biosphere (at the bottom of the oceans, for example), the LS will endure. Ironically, the most potent example of such survival is our own—the survival of our insignificant mammal ancestor in the midst of the wholesale destruction of the dinosaurs 65 million years ago. Judging from the tenacity that the LS has exhibited over it's immense history and the colossal challenges it has faced and overcome to date—from within and without the planet—can anyone seriously doubt that the system will survive the excesses of even it's most intelligent species? Since it is humankind that is sowing all these potentially catastrophic possibilities, the demise of higher life on the planet—a prediction often voiced by those sounding the "Earth-Watch" alarm—might actually provide the biosphere with a much-needed respite. Such a catastrophe for our own species could, in fact, represent an idyllic opportunity for the planetary biosphere to regenerate itself undisturbed so that, possibly, another intelligent species might one day arise—one that might be more appreciative of—and responsive to—the precarious nature of the LS-biosphere relationship and take better care. It would, indeed, turn out to be the greatest of ironies—and a kind of poetic justice as well (with no one around to appreciate)—if the demise of humanity by its own hand of excess and indifference results in just the kind of stress reduction and much needed remedial rest to the global environment essential for its restoration—allowing it to continue to foster and serve future less self-destructive species, as well as the design intent survival mission of the LS.

Will humanity survive? Before we are through, this burning question will be at the top of the list of consequences predicted by the new model of reality defined within the Rational Design Hypothesis we are engaged in molding. But, for the moment, lets take a closer look at the group of strategies and tactics employed within the LS: mechanisms responsible for its survival through adaptation over billions of years, and that which allows it to continually defy time—collectively referred to as "evolution".

---

[1] Insects: Behaviour,: Insect Societies—1996 Encycl. Britannica Electronic Edition
[2] Extinction: Bad Genes or Bad Luck:David Raup—p65
[3] Discover: Jun 1992, p36, JoAnn C. Gutin

8. Evolution: Defying Time

*"I am inclined to look at everything as resulting from designed laws, with
the details, whether good or bad, left to the working out of what we may
call chance."*

—Charles Darwin (May 22, 1860)

The Politics of Evolution—Revisited:

Evolution is the embodiment of all the influences that bear on the adaptation, survivability and thriving of life (in all it's manifestations) over the great period of time since its origin until the present (some 3.8 billion years at last count). Obviously, to grasp how the forces grouped under this rubric called "evolution" function is to understand one of the most important features of the LS, and one that has come to epitomize for many the very differences between biology and chemistry—between the living and the inanimate.

Curiously enough, evolution—the principle itself, has been embraced wholeheartedly by virtually the whole of the scientific community, while remaining virtually ignored, if not outrightly denied, by those of a creationist persuasion. This is a mystery for many abiogenesists (believers in the chemical soup hypothesis) who find it hard to fathom the refusal of many adherents of religion to embrace evolution and abiogenesis itself, for that matter. The question we can ask is whether such apparent obstinacy—in the light of all of the scientific research establishing firmly evolution's effects—can only be rationalized as some unexplained combination of naiveté and stubbornness. The fact remains that what we are dealing with here is, more than simply a denial of unproved principles, but, as well, an important aspect of basic human nature. Let me explain:

When Darwin unleashed his theories in 1859 upon, what had to be considered, a "creationist" world (in the western world, at least), he upset a lot of people (as well as religious institutions)—all of whom had a life-long vested interest in the creationist paradigm, (as propounded within Natural Theology). As such, it was no surprise that he encountered a lot of opposition. In fact, this is a gross understatement. Since that time, supporters of the Darwinian view have been faced with—not so much having to prove, but—trying to persuade and convince their skeptics, over and over again, of the logic of Darwin's case for evolution—based on the empirical evidence they have gathered. In truth, they have succeeded—more or less. Yet, still to this day, there are many who refuse to buy into evolution, no matter how convincing the scientific case for it is put. Can this simply be explained away as blatant religious zeal on the part of the holdouts? And, if that be the case, how do you explain why it is that science—with all of its successes at explaining reality and controlling our environment—cannot make a dent in the intellectual armor of a large segment of the human population when it comes to making the case for evolution? The answer to this question is not as illusive as we imagine. If one thinks about it, the creationists are really left with little choice.

The problem, as I see it, is the direct linkage that continues to exist between evolution, a theory that has plenty of evidence to back it up, and SAb, the "chemical soup" OoL theory on the planet, for which there is none. Unfortunately, science has entangled the two together to such an extent, that the one evokes the exclusive consideration of the other. But, as stated, while there is convincing evidence for evolution, there is precious little (hard evidence) for abiogenesis. Therein resides the "rub". If science could validate SAb as fact, then I would wager that large numbers within the creationist camp could be persuaded to abandon both their opposition to abiogenesis (again, assuming positive confirmation for it) and at the same time would be left no choice but to buy into evolution as well—as the operational mechanisms for the long term adaptation and survival of life.

I don't have to remind you that there is, at present, no compelling case for SAb. It is, itself, an umbrella term that encompasses a variety of spontaneous self-generation hypotheses—works in process, none of which seem compellingly promising to date. So, why should creationists abandon their beloved 'creationist' (the 1st OoL option) scenario? It's been handed down, in one form or another generation upon generation, for a couple of thousand years, and they are naturally reticent to abandon an integral part of their belief system—one that has stood them in good stead for so long. And, I trust they believe in creationism as strongly as Darwinists believe in evolution. Evolutionists 'may' also believe in abiogenesis, and with rational reasons to support that belief. But lets face it—they are only betting on it; that's all! And creationists are betting on their particular scenario for the origin of life; that's all. If either side gets to prove it's case (which seems highly unlikely), then it's safe to say that a lot of supporters of the one or the other will be changing their minds, as occurs in all other such similar debates. But, and this is my point, regardless of how one believes Life originated on this planet, it is at present logically possible to accept evolution without buying into abiogenesis nor any other OoL hypothesis—because evolution stands on its own, independent of how life originated!

Francis Crick, in his excellent *What Mad Pursuit* raises, as have others, the question as to why so many find "natural selection"—the dominant principle behind evolution introduced by Darwin—so hard to accept. He suggests that part of the problem may be the slowness of the effects of natural selection as to render it impossible to experience. More importantly from our perspective, Crick raises the contrast between the "highly organized and intricate results of the process—all the different living things we see around us—and the randomness at the heart of it". He goes on to point out that "this contrast is misleading since the process itself is far from random, because of the selective pressure of the environment", and, "The process itself, in effect, does not know where to go". He continues: "It is the 'environment' that provides the direction, and over the long run its effects are largely unpredictable in detail".[1] Here in a nutshell is the prevalent view of what evolution does and goes some way in explaining why it evokes so much confusion. However, I believe that the same phenomenon, evolution, can be explained in a way that leaves the basic principles intact while evoking a whole new philosophical point of view, one that could be acceptable even to creationists. I assure you that I am not the first to make this attempt. (You will recall that Teilhard de Chardin beat me to it in chapter 2.)

What You See Is What You Get?

Let me preface my explanation in the following way. The prevalent scientific bottom-up approach to the OoL lies at the heart of how evolution is perceived. And because abiogenetic SAb is considered a chance phenomenon produced by the chance association of raw chemicals under the influence of natural forces, the same thinking is easily extended to how the forces responsible for evolution are seen to come into play—by chance. While Crick does qualify the random aspect of evolution with the assertion that the environment exerts it's selective pressure—because the whole phenomenon of life and its origin is seen as the result of natural phenomena—no purposeful direction is evident nor could there be. He explains: "Yet organisms appear as if they had been designed to perform in an astonishingly efficient way and the human mind therefore finds it hard to accept that there need be no designer to achieve this." He adds: "The statistical aspects of the process and the vast numbers of possible organisms, far too many for all but a tiny fraction of them to have existed at all, are hard to grasp."[2] I can agree with this statement as far at it goes, even though at first glance it might appear to be an indictment of the very concept of design. For indeed, the possibilities within the results of the evolution process (organism phenotypes) do seem endless as well as transient—which makes the idea of a designer seem rather pointless. However if Crick means to convey the idea that evolution—the process of natural selection and the other mechanisms involved—works without the benefit nor need of controls that can confer some modicum of consistency of LS organization and direction, I would seriously question the underlying premises upon which such ideas are based.

The RDH acknowledges the fact that there are numerous independent elements that make evolution work, and that the resultant process seems, therefore, to be randomly variable in nature. Also, we can agree that both the LS and the biosphere contribute separately their influences and indeed it is the inanimate biosphere that effectively initiates the process by changing its conditions in unpredictable ways. But, this in no way invalidates the possibility that the controlling mechanisms of evolution derive *not* from the external biosphere but actually emanate from within the LS itself. And, if that be the case—then like so many other operational features built into the LS—there may indeed be included mechanisms that provide both the control and directions evolution is permitted to take. This notion is directly implied within the concept of species "adaptation". Also, despite any protestations modern day Darwinists may muster, there exists a primary organized uniform structure that pervades the whole LS—a "primary design platform of biology (PdP)"—which logically could not be subject to the influences of evolution and indeed seems to be immune to its effects. We are referring here to the maintenance of biological consistency at both macro and micro levels of the LS as evidenced even within species whose environmental niches have been isolated by geography and conditions from the rest of the LS for many millions of years. This suggestion flies in the face of SAb. As far as they are concerned, evolution has no constraints whatsoever. Yet the fact remains that there exists a universality and consistency within the foundations of biological life (the constant composition of the sufficient and necessary conditions upon which cellular life takes place) in all species and all habitats right across the planet. From a Rational Design hypothesis point of view: this ubiquitous biological uniformity suggests that it has been in place over billions of years and most likely since the OoL itself. and could, in theory, have been programmed to remain constant. As such, the RDH position would suggest the distinct possibility that this PdP of life possesses an immunity from evolution. We will in due course attempt to show this to be the case. But, this idea—that parts of LS could be immune to the influences of evolution—is considered heresy to Darwinists of all stripes, who contend that because there is no master plan guiding evolution, accordingly there should exist no such restrictions with respect to how and where evolution applies within biological life either. "If mutations to the genetic information of individual organisms is random and natural selection is free to select the gene pool, then no restrictions are possible!" would seem to be their rallying cry. And then, they would try to foist an additional detail that looms large within their particular choice for OoL. The SAb of the chemical precursors of biological life within a "chemical soup" depends entirely upon the premise that evolution predates biological life back to a time when it is considered that the first level of self replicating "life" was entirely chemical in nature, i.e.: SAb considers evolution to be responsible for the transformation of the first self-replicating complex chemical entities on our planet through all of the subsequent chemical phases eventually culminating in the first primitive biological lifeform. (Alexandr Oparin, Russian Biochemist and father of the modern theory of SAb implied as much in the 1920's). Accordingly, if there is a bottom-line primary organized structure within biology, its presence, they would argue, is the result of evolution and thus could not, itself, be immune from the influence of evolution by natural selection. Then, there are Darwinists who would argue that evolution goes back even further and attribute the very existence of life on our planet to some universal rule of complexity which is considered to have given rise to the self-organization of the first chemical precursors to life. In fact they consider evolution by natural selection to derive from such an as yet undiscovered rule of nature. As it turns out, it will be seen that while the term "natural selection" is meant to describe what is thought by Darwinists to be the prime mechanism of evolution— a blind selection process of inheritable species attributes—the term itself badly serves the cause of both understanding and explaining the operative principles that result in evolution. Evolution, we will show in due course, does not result because natural selection is 'natural', nor because it is 'selective'. These issues serve as a backdrop to the discussions and challenges we face in the pages to follow.

The Prime Cultural Challenge:

Certainly, it can be said that Crick's reasoning is relevant from the point of view of SAb and Panspermia, and, for that matter, any naturally occurring OoL viewpoint. And in that sense, his arguments follow logically from the originating premises. But, there is nothing 'a priori' in their content nor do these assertions stand alone on some esoteric or universally logical merit. In fact, looked at objectively, you could conclude that without the underpinning resulting from the intimate association of evolution with the abiogenetic approach to the OoL, these kinds of arguments are in themselves impotent and without basis. As it stands, they become, in effect, circular in their attempt to support themselves. "Life is a chance abiogenetic occurrence—the result of some naturally occurring process of random self-organizing chemical complexity"—the story goes. Therefore, "the forces of evolution that give the system of life direction must themselves be random and undirected", becomes the logical conclusion. And, "if the primary process provoking evolution is, in fact, the unpredictable chance mutations to the genetic libraries of individual organisms, followed by the so-called "natural selection" process that dictates which organisms (and therefore which genes) survive to future generations" the argument continues, then logically, and on both counts: "no purpose nor direction to life could be possible when its future direction (of form and function) is blind". As you can readily appreciate, the case all hinges on the starting premise (that life began by a chance SAb), which is still unproved—and therefore speculative to say the least. As usual in such debate, the conclusions can have no greater validity than the suppositions upon which they are based.

But these "defensive" statements of Crick represent an acknowledgment, in a certain sense, of a broad consensus among scientists that there are so many examples of LS functions that seem "a little too good to be true" and that are counter-intuitive to the SAb paradigm they have adopted. The appearance at this stage in its development of the LS to be a little "too perfect (and complex) to have arisen by chance alone" together with the scarcity of conclusive evidence, goes a long way in explaining why detractors of the "chemical soup" OoL scenario continue to be skeptical. It also explains why supporters are obliged to go to extraordinary lengths to explain away the apparent contradictions. The very language used to describe the results of evolution has tended to reinforce what Darwinists might describe as the stereotypical design mindset that accompanies how we naturally think about these issues. There is no shortage of examples within scientific writings on the workings of biological phenomena where the free and casual uses of design engineering 'cause and effect' correlations belie the bottom-up assumptions of SAb. Such metaphoric language tends to reinforce the intuitive feeling many of us have that says that there is indeed a design-like aspect to the form and function of life processes, yet all the while denying the imbedded implications because of the philosophical connotations which, heretofore, have seemed to be more theological than scientific. We aren't referring here to any religious or spiritual zeal that may inadvertently creep into some of their scientific thoughts on some rare occasions, but rather to the rational appreciation of the many ways and instances that so many aspects of the LS exhibit some characteristic "design" trait that seems to serve it's implied biological purpose so well. We are not using this as an argument to bolster our case, but rather raising what we consider a curious dichotomy—between the design metaphors used to describe life processes generally by practitioners of science, in stark contrast to how they actually perceive the LS itself, and promote its SAb origin, and evolution by natural selection. Unquestionably, the above deliniative remarks by Crick and similar ones by other scientists serve to acknowledge and highlight that dichotomous curiosity, but while they sound as though they are meant to inform the reader, in fact they are really meant to serve as a not too subtle intellectual warning—an admonishment, really—not to place any credence in one's own intuition with respect to the true nature of the LS. Because, the argument persists: "the LS itself is devoid of any possible purpose", and therefore the conclusion: "evolution is directionless and blind"—must hold, at all costs. This, of course, is the natural consequence of the "bottom-up" SAb approach to the OoL.

Thus, first and foremost, and as if to the rescue, the "bottom up" approach nearly succeeds at rationalizing away any possible credence in, or consideration of, the intuitively inspired design concept. And then, if that hasn't done it, the reminder of the randomness at the heart of the results of evolution would seem to dispel any lingering doubt. As it turns out, this kind of thinking has been self-serving for supporters of SAb and indeed has set apart the two major philosophical camps on the issue. Ultimately, our RDH would hope to satisfy the same concerns of the Darwinists, while at the same time breaking through the restrictive barricades of Darwinist orthodoxy in order to pursue the rationale of the "design" position. It really can be done without resorting to "smoke and mirrors", or an appeal to what one classical Darwinist has referred to as the "Argument from Personal Incredulity" (the premise that scientific principles are continually being challenged by unsophisticated skeptics of all stripes who habitually invoke claims of unbeleivability when faced with examples of complex phenomena that they are perceived to have not taken the trouble to properly investigate.) Indeed, our position parallels that of classical Darwinism, with three noteworthy exceptions:

First, because the RDH postulates a design OoL scenario, that position not only entitles it to view adaptive evolution and any other important features as part and parcel of the hypothesized design, but obliges it to consider any primary and system wide operational mechanisms of the LS, such as biological evolution, as not being a self-derived product of nature (i.e. not itself a product of natural forces).

Second, as the essential sub-system of the LS design responsible for long term survival through adaptation, the primary influence of evolution must be seen as being "controlled" and "driven" from within the system it serves, and not simply the application of some hypothesized universal laws of complexity and self-organization, nor the kinds of naturally occurring external influences implied by the term "natural selection".

Third, any designed biological Life system must, of necessity, maintain a structural and operational platform immune from any and all influences that could arise from its adaptive evolution sub-system (primary design platform of biology—PdP). That "primary" operational platform could be expected to serve as the permanent design base that preserves both the underlying intelligence of the system as well as all of the operational means for achieving the system design intent.

Our challenge in the deliberations ahead is to show these to be so. And, all it really takes, as we will demonstrate, is the simple extension of the developmentalist concept interpreted from within the RDH perspective. Perspective, indeed, is the watchword when it comes to evolution by natural selection, as the differences in perception between the SAb OoL paradigm and that of RDH provoke as well differences in the understanding of its role and operation.

Authors Of Their Own Misfortune:

But, the creationist camp, staunchly defending its distinctive brand of "design" ideology, doesn't help its own cause either. They seem unable to buy into any evolution argument for understandable but paradoxically invalid reasons. At first glance, creationist argument follows along the lines of the immutability premise—that all the different species of creatures alive today were intentionally created as God's handiwork in their present unchangeable form and as part of the great design of the universe. But, I suspect that they really got taken in by the limitations they appear to have placed on the broader design concept possibilities. They never really considered the possibilities discussed in the last chapter (Complexity vs Time LS agenda), nor, in all fairness, could they at the time in history when their positions were formulated. Intellectually, they were in no position to consider that the design intent of the designer need not necessarily be confined to the existence of the component creatures that make up the LS (complexity) but could, in fact, comprise the limited objective of the long-term survivability of the LS itself (time) upon the planet in order to achieve some specific other purpose. Had they, they then would have had to deal with the dilemma involving a major shift in understanding where humans fit in to the grand scheme of things—arguably the most important of theological considerations. Creationists, since Darwin's day have uncharacteristically accepted at face value the scientific arguments that relegate evolution, and all that it stands for to a class of unpredictable phenomena. Because the number and varieties of potential paths that evolution can direct the LS admittedly appear to be infinite, coupled with the fact that all but a minuscule number of species survive under such circumstances, their logical conclusions drawn from the Darwinian exercise become predictable: that the organisms that cover the planet, including humankind, according to Darwinian argument, must accordingly and logically be considered to be the consequential products of accidental chance alone. Therefore, any successful results of evolution must represent but single events out of countless possibilities. Even the Darwinists must reason that this is chancy stuff, indeed. And, since they, the creationists, cannot accept the unintentional aspect of life's origins as put forth by scientific SAb, neither can they be expected to see the point of evolution as it is defined (as purposeless, non-directed forces shaping a purposelessly derived life system). And, because science (Darwin et al) have beaten them to the punch at both defining evolution and fixing its association with a purposeless SAb'ed biological system of life, they have found themselves with no other choice but to deny the SAb inspired paradigm of evolution in toto as entirely incompatible with the concept of design–creation (and therefore, the product of a purposeful designer-creator). When the creationist understanding of the scientific position is considered as described above, one can fully appreciate that they, the creationists, really were left with no choice. "After all", the argument goes, "how could a chance mechanism of evolution direct unpredictably the formation of new species (transmutation) and still be compatible with a purposeful (all-knowing) designer-creator?" This, rather than postulating an alternative point of view to demonstrate how evolution, particularly within the concept of "adaptation", can indeed operate within the same prescripts of science, and still logically have a direction, or purpose according to some design intent. The historical intellectual climate, as well as the state of scientific knowledge, that ensued at the time evolutionary theory made it's mark provides the interesting and relevant context within which arguments on both sides of the debate were formulated.

They remain a legacy to this day. It also helps to remember that Darwin was the "new boy on the block", so to speak, and was in the position of having to defend his new ideas against the universally accepted religious paradigm of the day. No enviable task!

So, while, creationists hold to their views of "designer-purpose" that excludes evolution, and science tenaciously clings to "purposeless evolution" as it applies to the LS phenomenon of the chance OoL, the divisions on the issue between the two continue[3]. Are there any compelling reasons to assume that no change in this intellectual interface is possible? We hope to demonstrate that evolution is certainly not—as Darwinists would have you believe—the *"theory of everything"* with respect to the form, function and origin of Life. We shall make the case that the total reinterpretation of the role of evolution and the key principles of how it works resides within the developmentalist concept of "species adaptation", as envisaged by the RDH. The arguments we shall put forth could also go a long way toward reconciling the differences separating creationism and Darwinist abiogenesis.

In the pages that follow, we hope to demonstrate that evolution is undeserving of the kind of attention each side has accorded it.—that it is, in fact, simply a tool—only one of many incorporated within the LS—designed to facilitate the achievement of a rather complex design intent.

An Intellectual Middle Ground:

Let's return to Francis Crick who, together with Leslie Orgel, postulated the idea of "Directed Panspermia (DP)"—that the seeds of Life were intentionally directed here from outer space. While there are some suggestions that he appears to be hedging back from some of these ideas,[4] nonetheless, the consequences of the ideas expressed are important. In effect, DP encompasses two rather interesting and curious concepts, particularly so taking into account the stature of the scientists involved:

1] There must be technologically advanced intelligent extraterrestrial life somewhere out there that could do the "directing" referred to in "Directed" Panspermia, and;

2] Biological Life <u>could not</u> (according to them) have self-generated spontaneously here on the planet earth (in other words—it is not a chance bottom-up event explainable by the primordial conditions of our planet).

Both statements above serve to impact significantly upon the possibility that, life could very well have been a designed phenomenon. How does DP deal with evolution? Quite simply—in the traditional Darwinian way. But, considering that DP postulates an intelligent source for the origin of life on earth, perhaps Orgel and Crick should have considered the possibility that the "directors" that did the directing, might have had specific reason to genetically engineer that life form before sending it on it's journey through space expressly to our planet—in order to achieve some genuine purpose and usefulness. And perhaps again, the genetic engineering could have included the introduction of built-in strategies, such as the mechanisms of evolution, which could affect and control certain aspects of LS survival over time. Our point is that DP allows (does not exclude the possibility) that evolution itself could logically be thought of as a subsystem of a designed and genetically engineered system of life on our planet. In this respect, you might say that DP establishes the legitimate background for some of the ideas implied by the RDH. In fact, both RDH and DP highlight the idea, which is the purpose of this whole discussion—that a "Designer" model for the OoL is compatible with Darwinian natural selection and, therefore, evolution as well. All we have to consider is that "biological life" was engineered, if you will, with the built-in capacity to modify existing organism phenotypes, permitting future offspring to adapt continually over time in order to remain compatible with, and thrive within, a dynamic biosphere environmental framework over billions of years, i.e., *'adaptive evolution'*.

Systems Engineering Considerations in the Debate:

Theoretically speaking, let us imagine that a designer wished for whatever reason (we will explore that aspect in detail later) to create a versatile system that could:
a) perform a specific function (whatever that might be);
b) operate over a time frame in the billions of years, and
c) operate within an external environment that changed continuously under both:
    1) slow, long-term steady-state evolutionary conditions, as well as
    2) periodic short-term catastrophic revolutionary conditions.

Then, what better system, designed for survival, can one imagine than biological life on our planet? (Strictly speaking, this is not a fair question since our collective experience in these matters is understandably severely limited; nonetheless:) Seen in this light, we would expect, following careful analysis, to be able to recognize within such a system its basic autonomous building block or "primary design platform" (PdP). The PdP would reflect the minimal system components at the physical level coupled with the sufficient and necessary levels of operational complexity that support the design intent. The PdP would also be expected to incorporate within its form and function the kind of built-in flexibility and pliancy that would allow the system as a whole to be sufficiently adaptive to accommodate continually changing external conditions—in much the same way that LS lifeforms evolve and thrive. To lend legitimacy to this hypothetical exercise, imagine such a designed system comprising many different kinds of interacting self-replicating "von Neumann" replicator machines designed along a common plan and built up of similar building blocks—the mechanical equivalent of a PdP. The system might incorporate some innate ability to form cooperative unions among such autonomous units in order to overcome, as need be, changing external conditions that might present challenges to the survival of individual basic PdP units. Such cooperation might entail the incorporation of changes to operational instructions that promote the fabrication of superficial novel piece parts and operational mechanisms from a limited set of constructor building blocks (amino acids, in the case of the LS). Any modifications to macro form and function could be passed on to future generations of offspring—according to whether those modifications survive in response to further changes to the external environment. Further, imagine such a system that can efficiently scavenge resource piece parts and building block materials from less efficient and irreparable such machines in a massive and continuous recycling program geared toward the present and future expansion of machine production, both in terms of quantity and complexity of design. By now, the point has been made, and we need not dwell on the hypothetical any further.

We have drawn the above comparison between an hypothetical self-replicating system and its analog proposed by von Neumann simply in order to reflect upon what such generic systems have in common and in particular to extend the exercise to include our own LS. Effectively, this exercise is meant to inject a generic description of the LS. Of course, such a designer of Life on our planet would have used biochemical "wetware" building blocks instead of mechanical "hardware" units to produce the biological "von Neumann" machines we call organisms. But at the bottom of it all, that's all Life is: a biological primary design platform (PdP) capable of improvising useful but temporary add-on features (the basis of speciation) that permit the survival of the primary genetic library through reproduction and replication, one generation at a time. And, of course, if the designer chose not to stick around to monitor its "designed system", then the certain success (survival over an immense period time) of the system could only be assured if it had incorporated within it such an efficient "adaptive subsystem", with the built-in capability to respond to, and survive the ongoing environmental changes that a typical host planet can be expected to undergo. Remember, the designer could be assumed to have cognition of, and appreciate the evolving nature of, a "site planet" on which the LS is designed to operate, and would be expected to equip the system with appropriate countermeasures—the strategic subsystem we call "evolution". Thus, pursuing this line of reasoning, the idea of an LS designed for permanency on a planet becomes compatible with that of freedom of the basic system—the PdP—to respond in reactive but strategic ways to changes to the external conditions of the environment of its host planet. In principle, there is no logical inconsistency. How this is accomplished must indeed be a neat trick at both the micro and macro levels of the LS and undoubtedly involves complicated modes of problem solving. And, as von Neumann demonstrated long before the discovery of the role of DNA, at the heart of any such system must be an informational database—that serves the built-in system "intelligence". In the LS, the processing of information contained within the data bases encoded in cellular DNA serves two distinct essential purposes: a) maintaining the constant integrity of the PdP which embodies the design intent, and b) permitting limited alterations in the form of novel physiological addendums to operational units—what we call "evolved modifications". In both cases genetic information, serves as the raw information from which the blueprints, and operational and repair manuals of the LS are forged. Thus, the information encoded in DNA is implicated in any LS biological problem-solving exercises.

The Goal Is Adaptation—Evolution Is The Result:

The result of changes within genotypes that express themselves as—changes in phenotypes that survive to reproduce offspring—is the evolution of species. From the point of view of the RDH, this ongoing process is a complex strategy for achieving the design intent of LS survival over great periods of time. In order to achieve this strategy, embedded within the LS is a host of tactical measures that would make any developmentalist proud. In order to comprehend some of the intricacies involved, we begin by a schematic analysis of the chronological series of events that culminate in the resultant phenomenon of evolution. All changes in species phenotypes occur over time frames, not measured in days, weeks, or years, but in generations, because the generation is the time frame building block of biological change—

during which incremental changes in genotype information accumulate and are expressed as changes to the phenotypes of offspring. Thus, we begin with an organism that reproduces an offspring and examine the sequence of events from which changes to genotypes arise progressively.

Question: Where does the genotype of an organism's offspring actually originate?

Answer: It derives from the genotype originally inherited by the parent, plus any modifications introduced to that genetic library up to the time the resultant genetic information is expressed in the reproduction of any offspring.

But, that is not all, because it is known that before the reproductive process is allowed to proceed, an error correction procedure is implemented to clean up any accumulated errors that could prohibit the expression process from taking place. In fact, reproduction will not proceed until any and all genome errors due to DNA damage are detected and corrected. The exact nature of the errors involved is not at issue for the moment. Also, whatever other informational changes that occur during reproduction will again modify the genome inherited by the offspring compared with that contributed by the parent. Biological reproduction begins with a single cell that must be able to express its genetic instructions in order to create an organism that will have the capability of performing within its species habitat niche. Once this is achieved, the organism will attempt to survive within its environment by meeting all of the external biosphere conditions of climate, temperature, etc. imposed within the niche environment, as well as surviving the competition from fellow species members for necessary nutritional resources, and finally surviving predation from non-fellow species.

We know that nothing lives forever, so the meaning of organism survival is tempered by the universal system condition that it survive at least long enough to reproduce offspring, thereby passing on its own genes to the next future generation. But, what about these genes being passed on? Are they the same genes it has inherited? Not at all. The genome our subject offspring passes on to its own offspring has changed since it was inherited from its previous generation. In fact all kinds of chance mutations to the information in the genetic library have added changes in a somewhat random fashion that could represent a real danger to the reproduction of the next generation, depending upon how critical is the location in the genetic library where such changes occur. That is, if a change due to mutation occurs to a non-critical bit of DNA it might well be overlooked in the overall scheme of things. But, if a change occurs to a critical gene—one involved in a vital cellular function responsible, for example, for cellular energy conversion—then it could doom the offspring at the very start of life. Of course, sexual reproduction affords potential offspring a second set of genes from which to construct a complete working set of genetic instructions. Even so, and in accordance with our own experience with sophisticated and complicated systems, the more complex an organism and its reproductive processes are, the greater the opportunity for something to go wrong. In order to follow all of the changes to a species genome within a single generation (all of which are ultimately responsible for the evolution of species) requires us to take into account three succeeding generations—an offspring, the parent that came before and the parent that came before that. Let's represent the three generations involved as Gen 1, Gen 2, and Gen 3:

Table 8-1

Phenotype:>	^ Gen 1^	^ Gen 2 ^	^ Gen 3^
Genotype:>	G1 > M1 > <u>G1' > m1 ></u>G2 > M2 > <u>G2' > m2 ></u>G3 > M3 > G3'		
	^reproductive process^	^reproductive process^	

Our frame of reference must extend through three generations of a species in order to demonstrate all of the six possible sources of transformations a genome (DNA informational library) goes through as it transfers between an organism's parent and its own offspring, each one of which effects the results of evolution. The point is that the genome an organism is born with is not the same one it passes on to its offspring. There are four distinct transformations that occur between the genome an organism's parent inherits (G1) and the one received by its offspring (G3). We shall examine each type of transformation and show that, while mutations to DNA may occur in a somewhat random and unpredictable fashion, their expression in the genesis of a new physical organism are controlled from within the organism in order to accomplish one simple strategy—adaptation of phenotypes to changing external biosphere conditions. The goal, of course, is long term species survival, spanning as many generations as possible.

Mutations:

While mutations can occur in the DNA of any individual cells in multicellular organisms, only those that occur within the reproductive cells (sperm or egg) will be able to affect the information passed on to offspring. We have delineated above (Table 8-1) two different categories of mutations, labeled "M" and "m", according to when they occur in the life cycle of an organism, culminating in the reproduction of the next generation. As indicated, all organism mutations begin as changes to the genetic information in its genotype. Once the mutation is physically expressed within the phenotype, it can be described as a physical mutation and the organism itself as a mutant. In that respect, we can describe all surviving organisms as mutants, since they all contain mutations of one kind or another that make them different from their parents.

"M-type" mutations refer to all mutations to the genetic library of an organism (without regard for how they occur) that occur during its lifetime up to the time it reproduces offspring. All such changes to genetic information occur as a result of the physical manipulation of the chemical "letters" of the language in which genetic instructions are written in the chemical medium of DNA. Some changes can occur spontaneously when, for example, some high-energy particle at the atomic level strikes the chemical DNA information medium and alters the chemical composition of the information contained therein. This usually occurs at the individual "bit" information level, whereby individual letters of the genetic information are changed for others. That's the same as changing a letter in the English word from "s<u>t</u>op" to "s<u>h</u>op", or damaging the second letter altogether so that the instruction is no longer recognizable. These are the kinds of errors that can creep into a genome and because they are spontaneous and occur randomly, can be expected to be of negative consequence most of the time—but no problem if the physiology of the organism concerned can live (literally) with the error. Then, when the organism reproduces, such errors can be passed on to offspring, where they are tested against the reality of survival. These spontaneous mutations occur randomly and at rates that can be measured.

"m-type" mutations occur specifically during the reproductive process when a parent cell gives rise to a daughter cell. During reproduction, the genetic library of the parent must be replicated in toto (together with all of the M-type mutations acquired during its lifetime) in order to provide a full set of operating instructions that will control the life processes of the offspring. But, before the replication process is allowed to proceed, a full compliment of error correction procedures are brought into play in order to attempt to repair any and all accumulated damage to DNA. Specific enzymes such as DNA polymerase are specialized to effect such repairs. It is quite efficient at what it does. Yet, in a curious way, DNA polymerase is a little too good at what it does—because it is designed <u>not</u> to work at 100% efficiency. What is indeed curious is the fact that DNA polymerase allows, in the order of one mistake per one hundred million replicated base pairs (letters in the DNA alphabet)—just enough to provide sufficient and necessary change to genomes to permit evolution to occur at a "proper" pace. The fact is that without this steady, yet controlled, pace of mutation at the bit information level, there would be little for natural selection to select from. Other kinds of mutations that occur during the replication of the genetic library before being installed within the offspring concerns such information changes as additions and deletions of small and large sequences of DNA, as well as the repositioning of lengths of DNA in new positions and in reverse directions. While these mutations are themselves random as well, their significance is quite different in as much as it permits a certain level of "shuffling" (rather than damaging) of perfectly good genetic information, affording significant experimental variability between organisms of a species. Sexual reproduction increases dramatically this shuffling of genes using the information resources from the genetic libraries of both parents. Obviously, these kinds of changes can only occur at the replication stage just before being passed on to offspring otherwise they could severely impair an organism having to live with and accommodate such changes to its own genome. The same kinds of error correction mechanisms come into play when multicellular organisms replicate their own cells during embyogenesis, organism growth, and maturation. On the whole organisms can only survive if their DNA has been replicated accurately.

Both kinds of mutations to genetic information—M, and m, and their physical expression effect whether an organism's genome will ultimately contribute to the future survival of its species, or become a dead end as a result of its inability to meet the many challenges to survival. Thus, every organism begins with an altered genome it inherits and from which it's phenotype becomes expressed. This genome will undergo two levels of additional mutations plus error correction algorithms before being passed on to its own offspring in the next generation. Stated in mathematical form, if G1 is the base genome inherited by any organism from its parent, then the genome, G2, it passes on to its own offspring in the next generation can be described as:

$$G2 = G1 + M1 + m1 \qquad\qquad (8\text{-}1)$$

where:

M1 and **m1** are respectively mutations to genetic information acquired during the organism's lifetime until replication, and mutations directly associated with replication.

This is so for any generation and, therefore, we can produce a universal expression that will apply in any given generation as follows:

$$G_n = G_{(n-1)} + M_{(n-1)} + m_{(n-1)} \qquad (8\text{-}2)$$

where:

n = any given generation.

The above expression simply acknowledges that the genetic library inherited by every generation comprises that of the previous generation, together with both **M** and **m** kinds of mutation modifications. From this simple relationship describing the composition of any inherited genome, in terms of its previous generation, we can synthesize an expression that takes into account the fact that all member organisms of a species derive from a common origin—which we can refer to as the initial generation, "G_1". The exercise that follows will help to drive home some interesting characteristics of the evolutionary processes that mold and shape the composition of the LS. We continue the exercise by applying the above expression to the fifth generation (as an example) following the founding of a hypothetical species. Accordingly, if

$$G5 = G4 + M4 + m4 \qquad (8\text{-}3)$$

where,

$$G4 = G3 + M3 + m3 \qquad (8\text{-}4)$$

then, substituting (8-4) in (8-3),

$$G5 = (G3+M3+m3) + M4 + m4 \qquad (8\text{-}5) \text{ or,}$$

$$G5 = G3 + (M3+M4) + (m3+m4) \qquad (8\text{-}6)$$

Following through with the same logic, we can write the expression in terms of the first genome of the species:

$$G5 = G1 + (M1+...+M4) + (m1+...+m1) \qquad (8\text{-}7)$$

where,

G1 represents the genome of the founding organism for the species;

(M1+...+M4) and (m1+...+m4) represent all of the changes from mutations that have occurred during all of the succeeding generations leading up to G5.

We can generalize this expression for any generation of any species as follows:

$$G_n = G1 + [M1+M2+...+M(n\text{-}1)] + [m1+m2+...+m(n\text{-}1)] \qquad (8\text{-}8)$$

Now, the above expression describes the genome composition of any following generation in terms of the hypothetical first generation of that species. I use the term hypothetical because it is too much to hope that a single organism be singled out as the actual originator of a species. However, the principle remains valid with respect to any "founder" organisms of a species, regardless of how you pin it down.

The sequences "M1 + M2 +...." and "m1 + m2 +...." are meant to convey the fact that in any given generation, the resultant phenotype represents an accumulation of the effects of the sequential progression of changes to the ancestral genotype occurring over each preceding generation regardless of the consequential contribution of any specific generation. It's much the same as the multiple shuffling of a deck of cards, with each shuffle of the deck representing a phenotype generation, and the changes in the order of the cards representing changes in the information of the genotype. The final order of the cards is determined, not only by the number of times the deck is shuffled but by the accumulated contributions of each shuffle as well as the order of the shuffles. Each subsequent shuffle of the deck begins where the previous one ended. Remove any shuffle from the sequence, no matter how little change it has contributed and the outcome will be different. Even a shuffle comprising only the change of just a single card is passed along to effect future shuffles and in fact becomes amplified with each subsequent shuffle. Thus, both the sequence of change is as important as the quantity or the quality of changes in card shuffling or genetic mutations because every generation comprises the evolutionary base for each successive shuffle of the genetic information of every generation. That base consists of both the genotype and the phenotype wherein it resides. Of course, when it comes to evolution of species, only the survivors count. Along the path of evolution are strewn the remains of countless generations of organisms that get stopped in their tracks, the last generation failing—for whatever reasons—to pass on the genome so arduously accumulated over many generations to the next.

Now, what we want to do is extend the same principle all the way back to the first LS biological organism that is thought to have parented all of the rest: In other words, any generation of any species (**Gs**) comprises an initial genome, let's call it Go, that has existed since the beginning of biological time on this planet, and from which all species are descended, plus the accumulation of all "M" type mutations and all "m" type mutations leading up to its own generation, within its own species (those sequentially acquired during the lifetimes of the individual surviving generations and those sequentially added during all of the replication phases of reproduction). Thus,

$$Gs = Go + \text{sum of all (M's + m's)} \qquad (8\text{-}9)$$

Where, **Go** represents core genetic information;

sum of all (M's + m's) represents both additions and deletions to genetic information over generations.

Our aim in all of this is two-fold:

First is to portray the overt causes of genotype change as being diverse and unrelated mechanisms (M's and m's), and whose results both affect and are effected by the sequence in which they occur (**M1+M2+…. and m1+m2+….**). In the pages that follow we shall explore how they contribute to the adaptation of organisms to their environmental niches or habitats;

Second, is to try to establish the primary design platform (PdP) of biology, referred to earlier, that defines the sufficient and necessary set of biological form and function which serves as the original evolutionary base to which evolution appends add-on adaptive features, but that must itself remain immune from change. The search for the existence of such a PdP—which binds together the biological platform for cellular life—is an implied imperative within any design OoL hypothesis, because any designed system must operate in a consistent and constant manner throughout its operative framework. Thus, its identification within both the genomic as well as phenotypic biological states will help delineate more precisely the interface problem that exists between ordinary inanimate chemistry and the PdP meant to define the sufficient and necessary primary conditions for the existence and operation of the LS. Further, the discovery of the existence of such a PdP—one—that is ubiquitous throughout the LS, also implies its immunity from any and all forces of evolution that could diminish its integrity, i.e.: by definition, no PdP can continue to remain so and be subject to evolutionary change. And most importantly from our perspective, if we can identify the PdP as an untouchable state of biology that is immune from evolutionary change we will be able to argue that that same PdP could not logically be a product of evolution either (and consequently advance the validity of the RDH). The logic of the existence of such a PdP that would be constant and immune from the influences of evolution is quite simple: if you change the essence of what makes biology "tick" (its operational form and function) then apriori the processes of reproduction could be interrupted as well thereby preventing such changes from being passed on to the future through offspring. Thus, by definition, changes caused by any means— including mechanisms responsible for biological evolution—could not affect or have influence over the PdP level of biology without jeopardizing the survivability of the LS itself.

Primary Design Platform of The LS—Go:

The concept we are proposing is the existence of a PdP of the LS, which must be so unique as to require the constancy of both its form and function. As such it must be not only identifiable as ubiquitous throughout the LS across all species in biosphere space, but as well across the whole history of biological time. We can, in fact establish both:

1] BIOSPHERE SPACE:

It is not a difficult task to try and identify the primary biological design platform common to all living things within the LS, regardless of what environmental niche they occupy across the whole planetary biosphere. That platform is identifiable within the phenotypes of all organisms as the cellular entity of biology, with all of its biological machinery, genetic information library encoded in DNA and the metabolic pathways that power its varied activities. Ignore the details and all eukaryotic cells are the same regardless of which organism of which species—past, present or future, you choose. And because to our knowledge it is all the same everywhere we look throughout biosphere space, we can make a comfortable case that it is a truly universal aspect that exists across all LS species lines. As well, it *could not be* subject to evolutionary change at that primary level; it is only subject to adaptive evolution whose role is limited to the augmentation and modification of novel add-on features to the basic design platform. Thus, in one fell swoop evolution is reduced to an exploitative roll instrumental in expanding the LS spectrum of environmental niches its organisms can accommodate. Evolution is only responsible for species modification to the specific conditions of relevant habitats, while essentially leaving intact the "bottom-line" cellular form and function we describe as the PdP.

2] BIOLOGICAL TIME:

It is a more difficult challenge to try and pin down the constancy of a primary biological design platform, immune from evolution, dating back to the dawn of biological life on this planet. Here we cannot rely on phenotype fossil evidence but must resort to the logic inherent within the expression of genotype composition in terms of Go in the equations above. What is the true significance of Go in the exercise above? Is it not the basic genome that gets expressed as the basic physical form whose sufficiency and necessity permit the PdP of biology to function? The equations logically indicate that all evolved generations that come later can be expressed in terms of the expression of the first and primary genome, Go, plus the sequential accumulation of all the M and m types of modifications and mutations that provide novel add-on features. Since all mutations are added to Go to produce variations in future generations, Go becomes, by definition, not only the founding genome of all future genomes, but as well, the genome of the primary biological design platform. As such, we can propose that Go represents the genomic essence of biological form and function that cannot be further reduced. As to the nature and ubiquitous influence of Go within the LS we have only to refer to its phenotype counterpart, which we shall refer to as Po.

As stated above, in terms of changes that lead to new species, the M's are responsible for what happens (mutations) between the time an organism emerges and when it produces offspring as a mature adult, while the m's are responsible for what happens during the processes involved between the time mature adults conceive offspring and the emergence of that fully formed new offspring. But lest one comes away with the impression that the difference between M's and m's are in the timing—at what stage of organism life they occur—the facts speak a different story. There is a real difference between the two types of mutations. One is mechanical and the other is procedural. M's occur mainly as a result of modifications (usually damage) to DNA of the egg or sperm caused by external or chemical conditions. m's, on the other hand occur mainly due to well planned procedural mechanisms resulting from the melding of two parental genomes into one, as well as errors in procedure. Thus, procedural mechanisms involve the way in which the DNA is processed during meiotic replication (combined and sorted out between the parents and replication of the results) and not subject to error correction. Errors in procedure involve spontaneous changes to sequences of basepairs that represent damage and must be repaired before reproduction can proceed. How these are dealt with respectively determines, in the end, the viability of the organism being formed. But the constant factor in every instance of cellular life is the form and function of that primary design platform that both maintains the permanence of procedures, operations, and error correction mechanisms within all eukaryotic cellular entities and also permits the occasional inclusion of replication errors if they conform to the platform imperatives. This is the real stuff of survival and evolution. It all begins with the ubiquitous informational Go that controls the form and function of Po; information expressing itself.

Wherefore "M and m"s?

But, the significance of Go goes far beyond its status as the primary genotype design platform. The obvious question that comes to mind is: if all future genomes derive from add-on mutations to Go, whether, in fact, Go represents an evolutionary platform from which we can move only forward and not backward in time? In reality, the only evolution we are aware of has taken place within biological life forms (within living biology and not inanimate chemistry) and in particular as represented within the M's and m's of our equations above. Think about it. If Go represents a biological bottom line which cannot be reduced any further, and the only evolution we are aware of has come after Go, then it itself could not have been a product of evolution. All other genomes that have come after are represented within our equation as Go plus modifications arising from an accumulation of M's and m's. Thus, as stated, evolution is only concerned with M's and m's and not Go, which would appear—by definition, and for all intents and purposes—to be a constant. But, if G1 = Go +(Mo +mo), and (Mo and mo) represent the expression of add-ons and not simply changes to the primary design platform, where did they come from i.e., if the M's and m's represent changes that cannot effect Go because Go represents your bottom line constant design platform, what is the real significance of M and m? Could it be that the operational instructions that permitted the expression of M's and m's at the very beginning of biological life on the planet must have accompanied the Go information within the genetic library encoded in the DNA of the initial life form(s) introduced at the OoL on the planet?

Our goal in the next few pages will be to describe the evolutionary mechanisms of M and m and to show how their influences are exquisitely controlled from within the LS itself. No need to resort to some indefinable *rule of complexity* here. Evolution will be revealed for what it truly is: the accumulation of the results of permissible controlled changes to phenotypes, brought upon by occasional random changes to genotypes, and nothing more. Of course, the key to changes in species resides within the "selective survival" of genetic information (as a direct result of the survival of the organism phenotypes) that can be expressed in future generations. This, of course, refers to the key concept of Darwinism— *natural selection*. While it represents an important component of evolution—we will make the case that its overall influence within the evolution scheme of things is firmly held within the grasp of the LS. This requires neither sky-hooks to explain nor special rules of self-organization to conjure up. We will begin by examining the results of both kinds mutations—M and m, which invariably leads us to the concept referred to as "variability". It is within the variability of species attributes among species populations that resides the secret to adaptation and the long-term survival of the LS.

Environmental Initiative Challenge:

The many parameters of the planetary biosphere environment important to life continue to change over time. This is really an acknowledgment of the fact that the planet biosphere is not a static set of conditions. If it were, then we could seriously question any need or justification for the inclusion of the complex mechanisms that lead to evolution, within an LS design. The physical makeup of our planet has been changing ever since it coalesced from space matter and dust some 4 to 5 billion years ago. Eventually the benign conditions of the planetary biosphere were achieved, wherein life could exist, under relatively steady state conditions. (Steady state conditions refer to the relative calm that describes the planetary biosphere over time between periodic catastrophic events such as meteorite bombardments, widespread volcanic activity and the like that have the effect of making radical changes to both extensive and local habitat environments in very short periods of time.) Then, some 3.8 billion years ago, life appeared in some form within the harsh conditions of the biosphere, and managed to get a foothold. It had not only to endure those initial conditions but, as well, had to be able to extract from the planet the resources necessary for its sustenance and continued survival. And, as the planetary biosphere changed, so did the LS need to keep in step—always capable of overcoming the unpredictable and averting total annihilation. It had to have been a delicate balancing act, but life not only survived—it thrived. We want to know how this state of affairs could have possibly occurred. What were the sufficient and necessary initial conditions, within such a biological LS, that would have permitted it to do so?

Evolution—A Curious Duality:

We trust that we have arrived at that point in our deliberations where one can feel comfortable with the premise:

> *There is a logic that says that any self-replicating system (such as the LS) that can operate and survive both the relatively slow changes in steady state conditions as well as the totally unexpected catastrophic occurrences, over billions of years on a planet <u>could</u> have intentionally incorporated within it that distinct capability for adaptation. Also, logic dictates that from the very start, its form and function would have had to be compatible with its external biosphere and required to meet a number of critical operational and survival conditions. The net result is the survival and reproductive success of those individuals best adjusted to their environment—leading to the perpetuation of genetic qualities best suited to that particular environment.*

From the RDH point of view, being able to continue to meet those sufficient and necessary system survival conditions, in effect, <u>is</u> what evolution is all about. Additionally, for the RDH to have credibility, evolution must be seen as the designed and built-in survival capability of the LS in response to both the slow evolutionary (long term) changes to the steady state conditions of the planet from within and the revolutionary and catastrophic (short term) changes wrought upon the planet from both within and from without (e.g., volcanism, meteor impact). Thus, the RDH sees evolution strictly as an adaptive process, emanating and controlled from within the LS as a direct consequence of that built-in capability. While supporters of SAb agree with RDH with respect to the results of evolution, in contrast they view evolution as principally a natural selection process having roots in the self-organizing attributes and properties of the universe. This view follows directly because SAb views the OoL event as a natural process, and is therefore forced to seek the origin of the forces of evolution as part of the same natural law(s) of self-organization (as yet undiscovered) that they consider responsible for the OoL on the planet.

Thus, one thing becomes clear: depending upon how you view the OoL will determine, in large part, how you consider the forces that influence its survival. Again, SAb sees evolution as a phenomenon compatible with its fundamental premises: Life is a product of purposeless (natural) SAb and therefore evolution and natural selection are seen as reflecting that primary premise. In like manner, RDH postulates a purposeful-design model of the LS and therefore can be expected to consider evolution as anything but natural—an intentionally contrived design feature, necessarily fully compatible with a rational design approach. And, we did make the point above that there is no logical incompatibility with that view. Are we faced here with a paradox? Can the complex phenomena of evolution have a duality, somewhat analogous to the *wave/particle* duality reminiscent of atomic physics? Surely, regardless of how you view evolution, its source and operation must of necessity be independent of the points of view of those examining the phenomenon. What follows is the RDH case to advance the idea that evolution—far from being a natural phenomenon—is in fact exclusive to the LS and totally controlled from within the system; it is the adaptive sub-system of the LS.

How "Natural Adaptive Selection" Really Works:

In order to appreciate some of the fundamental principles at work here, we are going to have to resort to some extensive simplifications of what is acknowledged to be among the most complex, important, and misunderstood collection of phenomena responsible for the survival of the LS over a period of billions of years. The mechanisms of evolution are considered to operate on many levels—not all of which are altogether recognized—and of those that are, evolutionary biologists have yet to coalesce them into some concerted interpretation. Numerous schools of thought have developed over the years to account for both the causes as well as the consequences of evolution. In virtually all instances, natural selection, as introduced by Charles Darwin takes front stage. But natural selection itself has been partitioned into a variety of theoretical models that attempt to shed some light on the complications inherent in homing in on its true nature. For example:

1] *Normalizing* **Selection:** A selection process that counteracts the accumulation of hereditary diseases, malfunctions and weaknesses within populations of species;

2] *Heterotic Balancing* **Selection:** Considers a selective process that favors heterozygotes (organisms having different sets of genes for a specific trait) over homozygotes (organisms having identical sets of genes).

The above two processes concern evolution under sexual reproductive conditions and thus could only date from the time that sex came into being. Our concern here is to describe evolutionary processes that date back to the OoL on the planet—processes that could be considered within the context of a built-in subsystem that could be considered an integral part of a designed LS. The following could qualify:

3] *Diversifying or Disruptive* **Selection:** Some modeling of evolution processes make the simplifying assumption that the environment in which a population lives is uniform and that the selective advantages and disadvantages of different genotypes are independent of their frequencies in the population. However, the reality is inconsistent with this hypothesis in-as-much-as many species can and do subsist on a variety of different food sources, for example, and under diverse conditions (e.g., plants grow in different soils). Thus, there is a likelihood that some genotypes will be fitter in some environments than in others. Diversifying selection takes this into account by favoring different genotypes in different sub-environments or ecological niches.

4] *Directional* Selection: This scenario views natural selection in the context of responses of species populations to changes to environmental conditions over time in virtue of the diversity that exists within the distribution of variables within those populations that are responsible for species attributes.

This last model qualifies imminently well as the kind of evolutionary process that fits our design criteria. Not only does it produce the kinds of adaptive results that would be expected of a designed system primarily concerned with long-term survival, but—most importantly—its modalities and controls can be demonstrated to emanate from within the LS. Studies have shown that with increased genetic variation comes greater opportunity for evolution to occur. British geneticist R. A. Fisher verified mathematically his fundamental theorem of natural selection in 1930 such that: "The rate of increase in fitness of any organism at any time is equal to its genetic variance in fitness at that time."[5] This implies a direct correlation between the amount of genetic variation in a population and the rate of evolutionary change. But there is also a direct link between genetic variation within a population and its expression as variation of physical attributes within phenotypes. It is the phenotype, after all, that must interface with the external environment and survive long enough to reproduce offspring. Evolution occurs through a mutual process of mutation driven variability within genotypes and the survival through reproduction of some of those variations expressed within "more fit" phenotypes. When it comes to understanding the basic principles of evolution, the understanding of the relationship between variable genotype and variable phenotype is crucial.

We shall turn our attention to, and concentrate on, directional selection for these reasons, as well as the fact that it represents the kind of fundamental evolutionary process that can easily be imagined to have existed since the very beginning of life on the planet—in order to solve the most fundamental kinds of problems that could threaten LS continuity. Directional selection indeed provides modalities for life-system adaptation to continuous changes to external biosphere conditions. We shall explore it in detail for the insights it may offer into how the LS can control its evolutionary destiny with a single goal as its objective—system integrity and survival over planetary life-time scales. In addition, there are concepts described within "micro" and "macro" evolution (which themselves are umbrella terms) meant to cover a number of diverse mutation mechanisms operating on varying levels, that affect evolutionary trends, e.g. adaptive radiation—the evolution of an animal or plant group into a wide variety of types adapted to specialized modes of life. A prime example is the radiation of basal mammalian stock—beginning in the Tertiary period—into forms adapted to running, leaping, climbing, swimming, and flying. Important as well are the effects of mass extinctions. A variety of hypotheses have emerged in recent years implicating contrasting evolutionary trends. There is, for example, the "Red Queen hypothesis" that implies a slow gradualism to evolution, which like the Red Queen character in the Lewis Carroll novel, keeps running simply to stay in the same place. Then there is the "punctuated equilibrium" model introduced by Stephen J. Gould and Niles Eldridge that implies unexplained spurts in an unsteady progression that characterizes evolutionary history.

Another important model is the doctrine of "symbiogenesis" proposed by Lynn Margulis, as a prime engine of evolution. She suggests that mergers between species in a symbiotic relationship may contribute significantly to the creation of new species—every bit as much as random mutations. This has been suggested as an explanation of how mitochondria—which play a central role in the energy economy of the eukaryotic cell—may derive from a cyanobacterium that was engulfed by another cell and that later established a symbiotic relationship with it. Chloroplasts, present in some protists and all green plants (responsible for photosynthesis) are also considered by Margulis to be derived from once free-living microorganisms that have relinquished their independent existence in favour of a symbiotic partnership—upon which all eukaryotic cells have come to depend. In support of her ideas is the fact that both chloroplasts and mitochondria contain small fragments of DNA reminiscent of prokaryotic (bacterial) DNA. Besides providing a novel explanation of how mitochondria and chloroplasts may have originated, the real significance of Margulis' hypothesis resides in the premise that evolutionary change can come about as a direct result of the activities of phenotypes that don't directly involve reproductive success. Her proposal runs counter to Darwin's proposition that evolutionary change is a gradual incremental process of adaptation, arising principally from the effects of mutations to genotypes. The symbiogenesis model is not without problems, however. How, for example, would the genotype of a resultant organism actually accommodate such a symbiotic occurrence, i.e., how would an organism translate such a cozy (and unexpected) physiological event into the informational genetic instructions that would be required to replicate such a partnership from scratch in future generations through the reproductive process? Also, if this kind of specialized phenomenon could happen once, wouldn't it most likely be the kind of event that could recur, in all kinds of different formats and combinations among other unicellular organisms and bacteria. Thus, we can conceive of the spontaneous creation of all kinds of varieties of eukaryote-like cellular species containing innumerable symbiotic combinations and partnerships? This process would, in fact, constitute a typical situation for the invocation of the Principle of Mediocrity would it not? (e.g., if it happened once, in all likelihood it could be expected to repeat itself and exist elsewhere). The fact is that the form and function of the eukaryotic operational platform (what we refer to as its PdP) is pretty well universally constant and conserved. This unexpected reality could suggest that the exclusive existence of mitochondria or chloroplasts, respectively, within eukaryotic cells is both compatible and logically consistent more within the concept of design than chance. The RDH can readily accept the premise that the mitochondrial and chloroplast energy converters could have been genetically engineered into the eukaryotic PdP and designed to operate as semi-autonomous subsystems. Each could be independently programmed to operate under a variety of complex circumstances, under the control of their own DNA—particularly, for example, when the demands upon the central DNA informational library in the nucleus become excessive. In this way, the continuous production of all of the energy the cell could require for all of its activities is assured. Symbiotic relationships involve the retention of respective genetic libraries and probably independent and unsynchronized reproduction cycles. Unquestionably the many examples of such symbiotic relationships imply a synchronization of the evolution of the one with the other in order for both to benefit from the partnership. The same generality can probably be said about parasitism—whereby one member of the partnership benefits at the expense of the other. In the case of mitochondria and chloroplasts, however, it would seem that little evolution has taken place. We can make this statement in virtue of the apparent universal sameness of their form and function within all eukaryotic cells, regardless of species. We would suggest that the existence of a semi-autonomous chloroplast or mitochondria within the eukaryotic cell and the universality of their respective formats, represent additional arguments in favor of the RDH concept of the existence of a constant eukaryotic PdP concept—one immune to the influences of evolution. The RDH can thus accommodate the existence of mitochondrial and chloroplast DNA within their respective cellular sub-systems, together with the appropriate programation of the central genetic library of the cell to accept their presence. In our view, the only way to account for such accommodation that satisfies both the presence of a) the physical manifestation of these power plants within the eukaryotic PdP, together with b) the corresponding encoded information within the genetic library that can give it expression during organism reproduction processes—two very separate but necessary conditions—is the RDH design paradigm.

Our roll here is not to engage in an in-depth assessment of the ongoing discussions and debates being undertaken, but to try and discern an overview of fundamental principles that must control how diverse organisms can accommodate the changing conditions of the biosphere and how the long term survival of the LS, depends first and foremost upon strategies that emanate from the LS and not the biosphere, i.e.: what is really happening at the interface between the LS and the Biosphere. This, in our view, is where the real action of evolution is taking place. SAb proponents may call it Natural Selection. We prefer to call it: "*Adaptive Selection*" resulting from the phenomenon we call: "Species *Biosphere-Attribute* Anticipation". Whatever you may call it, all such adaptive changes begin with the accumulation of the mutations we have designated above as M's and m's, whatever their sources. Since neither complete nor acknowledged accounts of evolutionary mechanisms are available, we shall feel free to strip away some of the controversial complexities—both for the sake of clarity of function, and as well, to sidestep much of the confusion. We will make every effort at maintaining the fundamentals while concentrating on the influences and results. Incidentally, it is the same Lynn Margulis who was quoted in a New York Times Magazine article referring to how scientific attitudes change when "certain people die and differently behaving people take their place". In a similar vein—but ignoring the unpleasant connotations within the quotation—perhaps the time has indeed arrived when differently behaving people have begun to look at the OoL and its most important dynamic influence—evolution. That's what we are all about.

The Influence of Genetic Changes:

Genetic changes that are passed on from parent to offspring influence a number of areas of survival. We shall discuss three:

1] **Organism Function:** This refers to genetic changes expressed as alterations to the physical structures of an organism—beyond the PdP level as discussed above—that can effect its internal or external functions (such as changes in the composition of proteins that make up, for example, the physical composition of enzymes, cellular membranes or other anatomical structures). These genetic changes could well affect the ability of the organism to survive it's coming into being, in the first place and—this accomplished—function properly, in the second. The net result is to influence the competence of the organism both in terms of structure and function, and its ability to take its place as a fully operational organism within its species population. Then, of course, nothing is accomplished unless the resulting entity can maintain its organism integrity and survive long enough to reproduce, passing on its genes—including any genetic changes—to its offspring. Again, any chance changes to the PdP of any LS participant are disallowed and destined to fail.

2] **Tolerance of Biosphere Conditions:** This refers to an organism's survival capabilities within the range of external environmental conditions that constitute its species environmental niche. This is the stuff of **M**'s and **m**'s, expressed as changes to offspring phenotype that confer some survival advantage to external conditions. Local conditions such as extremes of temperature, water quality, availability of food, etc. impact on an organisms ability to survive long enough to pass on its genetic mix to the next generation, and the ability of future generations to adapt to incremental environmental changes over time. The long-term results of such adaptation have been refereed to above as "directional evolution".

3] **Organism Competitive Edge:** Also the consequences of **M**'s and **m**'s, this refers to genetic changes that may result in novel structures that affect the ability of organisms of one species to compete for survival with those of its own or other species within the same geographic habitat. Sharper claws, shape of beak, increased swiftness, endurance, and cunning are such examples in complex animals all of which result in varied organism fitness, allowing it to: a) defend against predation, b) acquire food [both attributes that confer fitness with respect to Food Chain activities], c) attract suitable mate if sexually active, and the like. Fitness ultimately depends upon an organism reproducing a new generation.

While any genetic change or combination thereof could affect more than one of the above categories, we have delineated the affects according to the consequences for the organism. In fact, the possible combinations of genetic change and expressed repercussions within the phenotypes of any given organism seem endless. Then, add myriad variable external local environmental factors that interplay with the results of genetic makeup, together with a heavy dose of "serendipity" and the presence or absence of adversity, and the possibilities for survival of any given organism (long enough to reproduce) become virtually unpredictable in the short term—but certain (death) in the long term. However, we are trying here to get a feel of how the selection process functions and must therefore try and narrow our sights to manageable limits—fundamental principles that can be easily examined and understood. One overriding and general principle becomes clear: the primary effect of selection and evolution involves the preservation and propagation forward in time of genetic changes that affect organism survival at its fundamental phenotype design level—those that express themselves as "tolerances to specific external biosphere niche conditions" (category No 2 above). Ultimately the results must express themselves as survival of variable offspring, so that logically, the effects of successful evolution (by definition) must reside wherever changes to organisms of species survive the processes of change and are inheritable. In principle, evolution represents only the results of survival of an organism and its offspring, regardless of the circumstances that lead to its success or failure. Thus, it is immaterial whether survival of any given organism in any given generation, long enough to reproduce, can be attributed specifically to its particular survival talents or to merely a measure of good fortune. Chances are survival requires good doses of each. The very fact that an organism survives long enough to reproduce implies, from the natural selection point of view the possession of that organism of that sufficient and necessary capacity to do so, defined as "fitness". Under the circumstances, survival success would seem to be its own (and seemingly only) reward. What becomes obvious—even at this stage of discussion—is the influence of population size on the ultimate outcome for evolution.

The Rules of Engagement:

In the pages ahead, we shall be exploring the relationship between biosphere and species in simple mechanistic terms, again, in order to describe fundamental principles only and within the SE context of the LS as a designed system. As such, we shall be developing new descriptions that are perhaps more compatible with engineering analogies than strictly biology. Just think in terms of the mechanical von Neumann machine parallel as a way of injecting objectivity in thinking about some of the ideas ahead. Again, what we are trying to do is to schematicize and simplify what we understand to be a much more complex set of factors and influences—in order to get across some of the basic issues of adaptive evolution.

The term "evolution" covers many complex and diverse phenomena; all influencing how species and their strategies for survival originate and how the commulative effects influence LS changes over time. It is a catch phrase covering not only the direct effects of a set of causative agents, but as well, the whole slew of emergent qualitative results that are ultimately its consequences. We are interested, not so much in the individual mechanisms and how each contributes to the phenomena, but rather we wish to home in on the broad principles that can be said to describe the essential survival problem posed by the physical environment to the organisms that make up the LS, and how the LS goes about solving it. In particular, it will be the phenomenon called "natural selection" that we shall be concentrating on because of the fact that the forces that do the "selecting" are generally seen to emanate strictly from external factors and as a result, seem as well, to be outside the control of the LS. It is this misconception in particular that we shall be attempting to remedy. For the moment we will ignore the actual mechanisms that give rise to genetic changes—these will be dealt with extensively later in the chapter entitled: The Information Level.

One of our prime goals will be to illuminate the important operating principles that have the effect of removing entirely the element of chance that seems to be universally associated with evolution (and which seems to be one of the strongest arguments in favor of SAb). Further, from a SE vantage point, our task will be to show that the principle operating mechanisms inherent in evolution are, in fact, design features purposely installed in the system and not merely self-evolved chance products of self-generation. We understand perfectly well and willingly accept the responsibility of demonstrating how evolution can be considered to be primarily a built-in developmental and adaptive feature of the hypothetical design postulated by the RDH. Our job will be, not only to show how it can be done but in the end, the extent to which we succeed will bear on the probability that the LS can, indeed, be logically considered to be the product of design intent. We have already set the stage with the establishment of the PdP of biology, represented by genotype, Go, and its basic cellular phenotype expression—the eukaryotic cell—common to all organisms (except bacteria) within the LS. Let us now proceed with a systems engineering analysis of the evolution phenomenon to determine how this basic phenotype PdP has been built upon—and the results fine tuned over and over again as variations among species—in response to external changes to survival conditions.

A Question of Survival:

At any given moment in time, the planet exhibits innumerable organisms—each doing it's own thing—within the framework of it's environmental habitat. An individual organism has to survive its birth and survive, as well, long enough to reproduce and thus pass along its genetic library of information to a future generation. In order to do so, that organism's genetic instructions for life must ensure that it's physical structure is compatible with, and able to thrive within, the larger environmental conditions— climate, environmental gases (oxygen, carbon dioxide, etc.), protection from hazardous radiation from space, as well as local habitat conditions such as ample food and water, ability to defend against predators, and availability of optimal reproductive conditions.

Any organism born within its environmental niche can be no stranger to that environment. Its compatibility within its habitat is taken for granted as though it were custom made for it. And in a large sense it is. True to form, each species, under normal steady state conditions (absence of catastrophic changes to its environmental niche), produces new generations that can span, in some cases, million of years with relatively little change in morphology (genetic expression) over such impressive periods of time. From generation to generation, on the surface at least, there is little to differentiate between descendent organisms and their antecedents—despite the greater or lesser genetic differences we know to exist between the members of the same species. But, we do know that over time, changes in the environment do take place both, at the local level of individual habitats, as well as on the planetary level as a whole. Some of these changes involve the physical climate and geology. Others involve local modifications to food supply and increased (or decreased) dangers from predators. The long term results of mutations to the genetic instructions encoded in an organism's DNA and the resultant physiological changes they cause, can produce anywhere from refinements to elegant features within a species—all the way to the branching off of the genetic line into totally new species and families of species. How then does evolution bridge the gap and enable organisms with a given set of attributes to change their offspring over time to exhibit a new and different set of attributes seemingly in synch with the changes in the exterior environment? To understand how that occurs is to understand the very essence of species survival over time as well as the progression of changes that takes place along the way and confirmed, more or less, by the fossil record. Thus, in order to truly appreciate how the forces inherent in evolution function, it is essential to understand the true nature of the relationship between biosphere and species. Again, at first glance, it all seems chancy and almost frivolous because of the endless and unpredictable possibilities. But there is an obvious sophistication in the way evolution works to preserve long-term

LS survival that seemingly leaves nothing to chance. We should expect nothing less from the Rational Design Hypothesis viewpoint.

Species and Environmental Niches:

A) THE BASIC QUANTA OF THE LS / BIOSPHERE RELATIONSHIP:

By definition, a species comprises a population of members, all with the same *morphology* (physical form), yet each a little different from its fellow organisms. This group lives and thrives and becomes specialized to a specific *environmental niche* within the biosphere that essentially comprises:

  • the spectrum of physical limits that a species must endure on the one hand, and,

  • the sufficient and necessary needs and requirements the species' organisms demand for their day-to-day survival on the other.

The limits and conditions referred to include, but are not limited to, climactic, geological, water and food availability, as well as the defense against and resistance to disease and predation, and subject to any symbiotic and parasitic relationships. Included as well, are any local geographic conditions, specific to the locality within which a species has access. This can vary anywhere from very small isolated niches where relatively new species have evolved to the total surface of the planet and beyond (orbiting space stations, for example) that the human species calls home.

Thus, each species represents, if you will, a particular solution to survival of the LS within a specific relatively limited spectrum of environmental conditions out of the totality of biosphere conditions available on the planet. And, that solution involves having within it's species *genotype* (genetic instructions encoded in it's DNA) all the information necessary to express in the *phenotype* (the physical expression of those instructions in each individual organism) the spectrum of *species attributes* that match precisely the present demands and challenges of its biosphere environmental niche, as represented by a specific spectrum of corresponding *biosphere attributes*. We can summarize the above as follows:

B) EVOLUTION, THE LS, AND THE BIOSPHERE:

Evolution thus attempts to match, over time, the contributions that the two partners—the <u>LS</u> and the <u>Biosphere</u>, each bring to the process. As stated above, these can be described as two sets of corresponding attributes or conditions, emanating from:

1) The LS:—represented by a multitude of species each of which exhibits a <u>*Set of Individual Species Attributes (SA's).*</u>

Commonly referred to as "traits", these are arrived at and shaped by individual chance changes to the genetic blueprints of large numbers of member organisms, some of which survive the so-called natural selection process to future generations. These interface with and are in response to:

2) The Planet Biosphere:—represented by an equal number of species occupied environmental niches at the local geographic level, each of which exhibit a corresponding species specific <u>*Set of Biosphere*</u>

Attributes (BA's) that define the external conditions that must be met by the occupant participants of life. These BA's are the result of both:

    a) steady state long-term biosphere changes (planetary and local), and

    b) catastrophic short-term events (large meteor bombardment, volcanic activity, etc.).

Many such portentous events (too many in number to be extraordinary) capable of causing mass organism death and species extinctions in the history of the planet are memorable, both in terms of their sweep and scope of devastation visited upon the LS species that existed at the time, as well as the permanent influences they have wielded upon the future direction of LS evolutionary development. Thus, many of the resultant innovations within the makeup of the LS, were precipitated by radical modifications to the living conditions of the species extant at the time; depreciating changes that irrevocably affected the biosphere attributes of the niches occupied by those species. Those changes would have occurred faster than a species population's ability to adapt and therefore leading to the mass extinctions of some, while possibly opening up new opportunities for others.

We can describe the above relationship of Biosphere and LS in terms of Survival:

c) THE ULTIMATE STRUGGLE FOR SURVIVAL:

Evolution is a phenomenon of survival on two levels:

1) _From the species point of view_—"survival" means:

    a] producing sufficient numbers of member organisms at any given moment in time that meet the sufficient and necessary conditions of the external environmental niche; and,

    b] implementing mechanisms for change over time enabling a species to accommodate the inevitable changes that occur to its external environment. Any species that cannot or does not continue to reconcile it's set of species attributes (SA's) with changes to its specific environmental niche biosphere attributes (BA's), resulting in failure, at some point in time, to reproduce offspring in sufficient numbers to maintain a population (for whatever reason) becomes, by definition, extinct.

2) _From the Life System point of view_—survival involves:

    a) meeting the challenge of providing a multitude of species, occupying a multitude of environmental niches, separated geographically across the planet, resulting in

    b) there always being some species players (organisms) alive over the short term that can give rise to and ensure the survival of some species or other over the long haul.

Think of multiple species as a form of redundancy—many LS components doing essentially the same job: surviving and therefore serving to perpetuate the survival of the LS. The ultimate aim is the continued and permanent presence and existence of biological life on the planet in the pursuit of a very specific goal arising from an equally specific purpose. As we shall demonstrate in due course, the goal of evolution is to buy time—billions of years of it—allowing the LS to carry out its purpose according to its design intent. And, the role of all of the mechanisms responsible for the adaptive capability of the system, the results of which we call evolution, is nothing more than the means to that end. This, in a nutshell, is the essence of the role of evolution as seen from the Rational Design Hypothesis perspective. It is important to emphasize the fact that the function of evolution is limited in scope to the continual adaptation of biological Life to the changing biosphere of the planet. Any attempt to expand or extrapolate that limited role—beyond biology to some chemical phase that SAb claims preceded biology, for example—will, in our view, continue to meet with failure.

Thus, to recap, in order to survive at least long enough to reproduce, living organisms must endure the sometimes-harsh conditions of the habitat on the one hand and acquire sufficient and necessary goods and conditions from it, on the other. And it can be said, that the large number of species in existence at any given moment in time, each possessing a set of specific SA's—corresponds to a matching number of environmental niche BA's, and is indicative of the scope of the global spectrum of environmental attributes existent within the planet's biosphere that are accommodated by living things. As well, such large populations of living things confirms the success of the LS in meeting the challenges of creating and filling as many niches as possible (that comprise only a minute fraction of the total environment potential), and thus spreading the LS risk of survival—a form of survival insurance, if you will—over the whole system. What generic or absolute purpose this system serves will occupy our thoughts a little later. For the moment, lets concentrate on the prime objective of system survival.

We have previously stated that the exact number of species is unknown but has been estimated at the conservative figure of the order of 13.6 million, out of which only about 1.7 million have been identified and described. Exactly how conservative can be judged by the calculations of some entomologists that have put the possible number of insect species alone at 50 million. Contrast this figure with the less than one million insects, more or less, currently identified. It is estimated as well, that some 2 billion species have evolved on the planet just within the last 600 million years and that 99.9% of all species that ever graced the planet have become extinct. It is chilling to consider that between one quarter to one half of those alive at present will probably follow the path to extinction within the next 30 years.

Thus, it would seem that different species occupying varied environmental niches represent the LS solution to survivability under many different conditions and the shear number of species represent an effective insurance policy on the part of the LS to virtually guarantee the survivability of some old species, some newer ones, but at the very least, the survivability of the system itself—which at any given moment comprises the totality of organisms that make up all the surviving species on the planet. As stated, the system has experienced at least 5 significant extinctions that during their respective eras have virtually wiped out an impressive number of species including whole families of species. The results have produced entirely new demographics of surviving life forms that would have been virtually unpredictable before. As a result, neither the demise of whole species nor that of whole families of species represents either failure or faltering of the system. It is rather indicative of the dynamics of the system at work—the changing composition and/or directions of the LS in adaptive response to the continuous and ongoing changes in direction of environmental conditions of the biosphere. It essentially works in the following way:

D) SPECIES—THE IDEAL SOLUTION FOR LS SURVIVAL:

Adaptive evolution can be seen as providing two primary ways to ensure survival of species over time. Both derive from the LS:

1) The first is through the phenomenon of large organism populations of many different species spread across the planet.

2) The second is through the phenomenon of mutations and other engines of genetic modification (M's and m's) operating within the genetic instructional libraries of individual organisms that produce the expression of unidentical offspring, possessing variations across the whole spectrum of species attributes.

In effect, the LS contains within itself the two essential raw ingredients that allow it to be studied using the universal rules of probability mathematics: 1) large populations of organisms, and 2) measurable variations within those organisms, of physical attributes responsible for survival.

Species and Their Biosphere Habitats:

The biosphere of the planet can be divided up and represented for the sake of simplicity, as a set of discrete geographic locations where local conditions apply:

1) *Biome*: refers to the largest geographic biotic unit.

2) *Habitat*: refers to any place where an organism or a community of organisms lives, and includes all living and nonliving factors or conditions of the surrounding environment. A host organism inhabited by parasites is considered to be as much a habitat as a terrestrial place such as a grove of trees or an aquatic locality such as a small pond.

3) *Biotope*: refers to the smallest topographic unit of a habitat with a characteristic uniformity of plant and animal species and environmental conditions (such as a sandy beach).

4) *Microhabitat*: is a term for the conditions and organisms in the immediate vicinity of a plant or animal. And, as the organisms get smaller and smaller, so do their habitats, as microorganisms inhabit microhabitats.

These biomes and habitats contain any number of biotopes where a number of different species coexist. Each discrete species is said to carve out it's particular environmental niche which defines all the conditions it's member organisms must meet and endure, on the one hand, and the resources they require for survival on the other. It doesn't make any difference how you divide it up, so long as we understand that within any given local geographic area, a set of conditions will prevail that will serve as environment and habitat where organisms live, and changes to which could effect their survival. And from the systems engineering point of view, a niche represents a distinct set of biosphere parameters represented by the physical conditions of the habitat of a particular species. Different species are a way for the LS to exploit on the one hand and accommodate on the other, a small fraction of the total spectrum of such parameters characterized by the planetary biosphere as a whole and represented by the many different habitats living things occupy. The quest for organism survival translates into species adaptation and ultimately the survival of the LS itself. We can quantify the relationship between LS species and the biosphere habitats they occupy as follows:

Table 8—1

	The LS	**The Biosphere**
1]	1 species =	1 environmental niche (a set of species-specific environmental conditions)
2]	Total LS Species =	Total niches occupied at any given time
3]	Total LS Species Potential =	Total Spectrum of Planetary Biosphere Conditions

In terms of measurable variables (attributes), we can express the above relationships as follows:

1] each *species attribute* (SA) corresponds to its measurable niche *biosphere attribute* (BA);

2] the total SA's of all species corresponds to the total of matching BA's;

3] the total potential SA's possible cannot exceed all of the possible BA's.

Thus, the millions of species inhabiting our planet at any given time occupy and, in a sense represent, through the biosphere niches they occupy, part of the broad spectrum of external habitable BA conditions that the biosphere offers. And, since those biosphere conditions are continually changing unpredictably, so must the SA's of species organisms keep pace and adapt or go extinct. Remember, any factor or group of factors acting concurrently (including Food Chain relationships, symbiosis, parasitism etc.) within a species environmental niche that can have an effect on the survival of that species will constitute an environmental niche BA.

We have now set the stage to pursue some novel lines of reasoning with respect to the dynamics at play within the "LS—Biosphere" relationship that exists at the macro level of life. Before we are through, we hope to make some convincing arguments in favor of a statement of evolution in terms of LS design intent that will place it in direct contradiction with the directionless, purposeless and ruthless consequences ascribed to "natural selection".

Species Attributes (SA's) and Biosphere Attributes (BA's):

We have delineated above the two functions of the "species-biosphere" equation. With respect to species, we have defined for each a set of discreet attributes we have labeled "Species Attributes" or SA's. These are the particular traits and survival properties possessed by each organism of a species that permits it to survive, on the one hand, and thrive, on the other, within its environmental niche. An environmental niche is said to be "carved out" by each species in acknowledgment of the fact that every niche, by definition, is specific to each species, and indeed, can be said to define the survival limits of any given species.

The other side of the equation—the biosphere—can be said to provide the resources and a set of external conditions we have labeled "Biosphere Attributes" or BA's that must be, not only met, but in fact, exceeded by the organisms of any species. This ability on the part of living things to accommodate external conditions and derive the necessary resources from the external environment is part and parcel of survival—both for individual organisms as well as the undivided species—in both the short and long term. Of course, in the case of individual organisms we refer to survival in terms of a single generation (at least long enough to reproduce), while in the case of species we would be referring to the long-term survival prospects before certain extinction (it's a fact: no species, however successful lasts forever).

At this point we should distinguish between SA's that relate: a) directly to species survival that emanate from the reactive adaptation to external biosphere conditions (BA's), and b) those that relate to the proactive development of particular physiological assets such as organs or functions.

The latter are essentially arbitrary, in the sense that they are unpredictable and their permanence is determined by how well they serve their client organisms. We would suggest that the "natural selection" concept applies exclusively to these kinds of arbitrary features and constitutes the operative "Use it or lose it" principle of biology. They seem to involve a high degree of biological experimentation and subject to "hit and miss". The evolution of complex organs, where every individual feature has to be precise and in place in order to function remains a mystery. While all SA's ultimately rely on the emergence of the aggregate expression of combination of groups of genes, J. B. Haldane makes the point: "For an evolutionary progress to take place in a highly specialized organ such as the human eye or hand a number of changes must take place simultaneously"[6]. The implication is that complex organs do not arise from gradual continuous morphological change but rather that a number of changes involving many genes must take place simultaneously resulting in the change from "one stable equilibrium to another". There is no disagreement here. However, it is important to acknowledge that there are two separate phenomena involved in any evolutionary change to a SA: the first involves changes to information in the genotype; the second involves how and when the change to information is expressed. There is reason to question whether these necessarily coincide i.e., whether changes to genetic information become immediately expressed as changes to phenotype in the following generation. We are not referring here to dominance or recessivity in alleles but to a more fundamental phenomenon that derives from the degeneracy of the genetic code. This issue will be discussed in detail later on.

In stark contrast, the former (reactive adaptation to external biosphere conditions) constitutes predictable, permanent, and essential SA's that must exceed the corresponding external BA conditions at all times. They relate to the sufficient and necessary conditions of survival of all living things within their respective environmental niches and as such constitute the critical endurance variables, which the fundamental mechanisms of evolution must address.

We can describe the environmental niche of a particular species, at any given moment in time, as a discreet set of BA's (out of the total BA's that potentially make up the total external biosphere) that dovetail and match a particular set of SA's which define that particular species. If we label each planetary Biosphere Attribute as BA1, BA2, BA3 and so on, then we might define the total spectrum of planetary Biosphere attributes at any given point in time, BAt—both actual and potential, in terms of a summation of all of the individual BA's....

$$BAt = BA1 + BA2 + BA3 + ... + BAn, \qquad\qquad (8\text{-}10) \qquad\qquad where,$$

BAn defines the nth **BA** out of a total of n different biosphere attributes or conditions that apply on the planet.

Then, we can expect that any given species will have to exhibit SA's within its organisms that need match only those BA's that correspond to it's specific environmental niche.

Caveat Lector [Let the reader beware]!

Our purpose in all of this is to emphasize how a set of a limited number of attributes of an individual species dovetails (as it must for survival) with a corresponding set of matching biosphere niche attributes. And, we can extend this premise to all the species that make up the LS at any given time. By labeling both the external biosphere parameters and the inheritable species traits that enable a species to accommodate those parameters—"attributes", we in no way attempt to limit the actual quality or complexity of the relationship between living things and their external conditions for survival. It is understood, for example, that many traits exhibited by organisms are the result of "emergent" qualities expressed by combinations of genetic instructions. In effect, what we are limiting are sights to and highlighting here is the interface that exists between living things and the external world in which they must persevere—by dividing up that interface into a number of discreet relationships, each characterized by a biosphere attribute (or external biosphere condition) that is matched closely by a species attribute (or survival ability). This delineation is important in order to appreciate that a species exists and survives by successfully adapting over time to complex combinations of those very external biosphere parameters, in an ongoing process belied by the slowness in time of the dynamics and the seemingly steady-state survey we short term viewers are afforded. The dovetailing of individual species attributes to corresponding individual external biosphere attributes will allow us to examine the mechanisms at work in natural selection and how species adapt to the changing external environment, one or more conditions at a time. The net result, over time, is seen to be the successful adaptation of some species and the failure of others that result in either survival or extinction. We want to better understand this process of short-term success and certain long-term failure, a paradox that inevitably ends in species extinction but certain survival of the LS. By quantifying this relationship, we hope to demonstrate the dynamics of this LS-Biosphere association and to see it for what it truly is: an LS adaptive survival mechanism. As such, it will come to be seen as an integral sub-system of the LS from the RDH perspective.

An Equivalency Principle of Evolution (EPE):

"*equivalence*" is a fundamental law of physics that equates gravity with inertia. Because these forces are of a similar nature and indistinguishable, they are considered to be experimentally equivalent. We can formalize a similar principle of equivalency with respect to the organism fitness aspect of evolution that can serve to illuminate more clearly the dynamics of adaptation operating between the external biosphere and the organisms that seek accommodation within changing biosphere conditions. In the case of adaptive evolution, we can visualize an analogous equivalency as follows:

> Increased offspring fitness depends only on how closely its spectrum of SA's are synchronized with the spectrum of BA's within its habitat environmental niche, regardless of how that is achieved.

The equivalency bears upon how the increased fitness is achieved. That can occur in two distinct ways, each of which we consider to be equivalent, from the evolutionary point of view:

1] increased organism fitness of offspring, due to inherited genetic changes. The SA's of a new generation dovetail more closely with the unchanged biosphere attributes (BA's) of its environmental habitat; and

2] increased organism fitness of offspring due only to changes in the biosphere attributes (BA's) that better dovetail with the spectrum of species attributes (SA's) that have remained unchanged.

The EPE highlights an important aspect of the dynamics of fitness and survival—how the changes in BA's that effect organism fitness occur. BA change can occur in two important and independent ways:

1] In Time: Incremental or drastic changes to BA(s) within a specific geographic habitat location over time, that effect the whole population of a reproducing species and,

2] In Space: Incremental or drastic changes to BA(s) due to the migration of all or part of a reproducing species to a new geographic habitat location having a different but more compatible set of biosphere conditions.

Indeed, many species have originated as a result of ancestral migration to new habitats. It must be noted that in practical terms, there is a huge difference in the operational effects of reproduction derived from migration to a new habitat. That difference results directly from the composition of the gene pool of the migrants. Change of geographic habitat by a limited number of breeding individuals (as small as a single pair) has the effect of defining the future offspring in terms of the limiting genetic composition of that migrant group. It can be imagined how this kind of genetic segregation "sampling" can serve as the founding generations of new species.

Thus, regardless of whether it is changes to the BA's of the external environmental niche that impact on a species fitness or whether it is the internal changes to species SA's brought about by mutations to the genotype, the effect is the same—a change in fitness due to a better or worse fit or accommodation of species SA's to niche BA's. The results are equivalent—change in fitness. The equivalency principle also serves to emphasize the fact that the LS is, indeed, an integral partner in the evolutionary process. We would contend that the exact extent of LS involvement and influence in the evolutionary process has not been adequately appreciated. We shall be attempting to redress this oversight in the pages that follow.

Action and Reaction—An Exercise In Survival:

As an example, let's take a small pond biotope inhabited by some hypothetical species. For convenience, let's arbitrarily label each individual external biosphere condition or attribute such as water temperature (BA1), water salinity (BA2), pH level (BA3), dissolved oxygen level (BA4),...., lowest ambient air temperature (BA8), highest ambient air temperature (BA9), food availability (BA10), ...BAn, out of a total of "n" such biosphere attributes (BA's) or conditions that impact on our species. Again, biosphere attributes within any given habitat must include the many complex relationships with other organisms within the same local physical habitat (including Food Chain relationships), each one of which and, combinations thereof, constituting an environmental niche condition and therefore an essential BA as far as the organisms of an affected species is concerned. Thus, if the lowest ambient air temperature of the environment niche, that a particular species will be exposed to and therefore must endure, is arbitrarily labeled "BA8", then the members of that species must possess a matching SA—"SA8" let's say, that allows it to meet or exceed the lowest temperature value BA8—just in order to survive. It is understood that any organism of our subject example species that cannot endure BA8 because it does not possess a corresponding SA8 whose low temperature tolerance value exceeds (is lower than) the actual external environmental low-temperature value that BA8 represents, will perish when that temperature occurs in the environment. To clarify the point, let's say that BA8—the coldest recorded air temperature at the extreme low end of the temperature range within our subject habitat during the last several seasons was +10 degrees C. Thus, the corresponding SA8 low survival temperature an organism must be able to endure would, of necessity, have to be the same +10 degrees C or less. Because no two organisms of a species have exactly the same SA8 low-temperature survival value, some having greater tolerance to cold then others, it is understood that during an extraordinary cold spell, when the BA8 record cold temperature is reached within the habitat, some organisms (maybe most) will be unable to survive the extreme cold. In this case, SA8 represents, for each organism of our imaginary subject species, the lowest temperature it can survive, and below which it will perish. Obviously, any organism that has a SA8 that extends well below 10 deg C (to 6 deg C, for example) will fare better than its cousin that barely survives with an SA8 of, let's say 9.5 deg C. Now, we are neglecting all of the factors that could be expected to have an affect on BA8 survival and are concerned only with the bottom-line ability. Such variables as duration of a cold spell or the effects of cold on resistance to disease or predation are neglected for the moment in order to describe the point and define the principles involved.

Thus, in like manner, each species comprises a set of SA's (that, in effect, define that species), many of which are linked to survival in a critical way, that match a specific set of BA's from the total BA's exhibited by the biosphere. Fig 8-A provides a graphic representation of the relationship between biosphere attributes and species attributes for any given species within its environmental niche.

Fig 8-A: Niche BA's Corresponding to a Single Specie's Set of SA's

Total Environmental Niche Spectrum		
BA's >	BA1_|_BA2_|_BA3_|_BA4_|_BA5_|_BA6_|_BA7_| .... |_ BAn	
SA's >	SA1 ^ SA2 ^ SA3 ^ SA4 ^ SA5 ^ SA6 ^ SA7 ^....^ SAn	
Total Spectrum of Matching Species Attributes		

Pretty well all BA's exhibit a range of values that change periodically (seasonally, daily etc.), having historically high and low values within a given increment in species time (we will adopt the average generation span of our subject species as that time increment). Within any generation, BA's such as temperature, rainfall, water salinity, acidity, food availability, threat of predation, etc. will exhibit respective periodic highs and lows. In all cases, survival of an individual organism will require a corresponding combination of SA's that will enable it to exceed somewhat these limits or it will perish. It is the commulative extent to which individual organisms of a species endure the external conditions of their environmental habitat (can match their SA's with the external BA's) long enough to reproduce offspring that will in the end determine, as well, the success or failure of the species to survive, in both the short and long run. Thus, to recapitulate, in order to survive within the habitat, any species has to have corresponding SA survival attributes that, in practice, will vary in measurable value over the whole population of its organisms, all of which must meet or exceed each corresponding biosphere attribute, whose nominal value will vary over periods of time.

Thus, in our example above, each organism must be able to tolerate the extreme low end (and high end as well) of the environmental temperature range in order to just survive. Failure to do so may prevent that organism from reproducing, if it has not already done so, and passing on its genes to future generations. Therefore, "survival of the fittest"—an expression both overused and much misunderstood—includes individual organisms surviving the extremes of temperature that the species environmental niche can be exposed to (together with all the other conditions they must contend with). This fact of life becomes readily apparent when, every now and then, as can be expected, the low end of the environment temperature scale, BA8, will achieve record cold for an undetermined duration, that will exceed the SA8 survival values of a number of member organisms of a species population and exact a heavier than usual toll of victims. This will have the effect of "filtering out" for survival, only those organisms whose species attribute (SA) survival value is sufficient to withstand the extreme cold temperature biosphere attribute (BA). Thus, we are exposed to the first determining criterion for continued species survival—the ability of a sufficient number of organisms to accommodate harsh environmental conditions that inevitably claim some. The second critical condition is reproduction of offspring by the survivors. For, when the survivors reproduce (those that do), it can be expected that their genomes will contain specific genetic information that will be expressed within the physiology's of their offspring as beneficial survival traits responsible for their own SA8 species attribute that permitted their forebears to survive the extremes of temperature as represented by biosphere attribute—BA8. In other words, most or some of their offspring, in turn, could be expected to inherit, to a greater or lesser degree, the increased genetic propensity for low temperature tolerance and survival as their parents, within the limits imposed by the rules of "population genetics", (including dominant and recessive gene considerations among sexually reproducing species). It is understood that tolerance to extreme cold within habitat conditions represents only a single species survival attribute—just one of the multitude of such attributes that the organisms that make up a species can be expected to have incorporated within their physiology in order to endure and survive. We can thus extend the same principle of organism survival to apply to any other SA, corresponding to an external BA. Thus, over time, by trial and error, through exposure to extreme and forever changing conditions and the dynamics of so-called natural selection, species are said to "carve out their environmental niche". But, there seems to be an ambiguity in the above statement that arises out of its contradiction with the accepted wisdom on the subject that must be addressed.

It is traditional for Darwinists and evolution scientists in general to define evolution as the product of a culling procedure that is initiated by natural selection processes independent of the lifeforms involved—their only role in the equation being either as survivors or victims. Thus, the expression "a species carving out its environmental niche" would seem to be missing the mark as it relates to the prime mechanism thought to be at the bottom of the phenomenon (natural selection), and would seem to be definitely outside of the control of the "carver". Under the circumstances, is the attribution of niche creation to the species participants of the LS simply a lapse in logic—an indiscreet oversight? Perhaps so. On the other hand, perhaps the language reflects a certain degree of acknowledgment (albeit somewhat subliminal) on the part of evolutionary biologists that the LS has a significant role to play in the "give and take" involved in the relationship between the LS and the biosphere, and indeed, as we shall demonstrate, the significance of that role cannot be overstated. Even so, I believe it would be considerably more accurate to describe the so-called "carving" procedure a species engages in as being— not so much a function of the natural selection process, but rather—a function of a species adaptation process, in virtue of the demographics of the genetic distribution of its survivor "carver" organisms. Thus, at any given moment in time, the gene pool of a species comprises, among other things, the direct consequence of the accommodation of its host organisms to specific external biosphere conditions (BA's). Further, it is the resultant composition of that gene pool that is responsible for the generation of future species populations whose organisms are (hopefully, for species survival) more finely tuned to the existing external conditions of the environment than their ancestors. It is this feedback control loop of "species gene-pool" modification according to changes to external biosphere conditions that in turn is responsible for the changing demographics of future generations and which comprises the niche carving process referred to. The continuity of the process, generation after generation, implies that the carving is forever ongoing and that a niche description represents only a single instance in the unfolding drama in the evolving life of any species.

Just so that we understand the difference: a species no more actively carves out an environmental niche than does it carve out its future evolutionary direction. If a species could indeed carve out a somewhat permanent environmental niche, it really wouldn't have to evolve, would it? In other words, the ability for a species to carve out its conditions of survival would imply an ability to alter the environment to suit its particular attributes. We know that not to be the case—or do we? The fact is that the members of a species produce offspring that either survive long enough to reproduce or do not. Those that can—and in fact do—reproduce, by virtue of that fact alone, can be said to be in synch with a discrete set of environmental conditions that evolutionary biologists define as its "environmental niche". According to our EPE principle described above, this can occur in either of two ways: biosphere attributes change to better accommodate the species attributes of certain segments of the population, or species SA's change and become closer synchronized with the corresponding environmental BA's. Abiogenetic SAb supporters stress the results—the survival of better-fit members of a species as the operative principle of evolution, utilizing the nebulous "natural selection" label to embrace both cause and effect. For our part, we are attempting to delineate the part each of the partners (LS and Biosphere) plays in the equation of evolutionary change, and in particular the important role assumed by the only party in the process that has a stake in the outcome—the LS. Essentially, the EPE describes the potential role of each, while declaring equivalent results, and thus provides a logical basis for considering the legitimacy of the role of one of the partners—that of the LS—in being able to intercede on its own behalf to guide and direct the outcome. This fact will become clear, as we shall demonstrate in the following exercise how a species effectively "molds" itself "reactively", through its population of organisms, over time, in order to accommodate its environmental niche requirements and conditions, rather than "actively" carving out anything from the environment itself. While this change in emphasis may appear to be trivial, I believe the implications for how we approach our understanding of the phenomenon are fundamental, and significant from our systems engineering exercise point of view. We will demonstrate convincingly that a species has built-in specific stratagems that enable it—not to control the future direction of its evolutionary development—but rather to respond positively and effectively to external biosphere changes over time in order for future generations to adapt and survive. The resultant offspring are different from their distant ancestors primarily to the extent that they can survive the present set of evolving external biosphere conditions, while their ancestors—given the opportunity to relive their lives under present conditions—would be unable to do so. Species that go extinct are expendable because, of the ability of the LS to produce shear numbers of novel species to ensure that the system itself survives—which, we maintain, is its only agenda. It is the production of varieties of phenotypes and not any predilection of phenotype design direction that allows the process of LS survival to work. And, this can only occur because of the "plasticity" inherent within phenotype adaptive design potential. We shall demonstrate that the fundamental evolutionary mechanisms are adaptive "reactive stratagems" emanating from within the nature of LS genetics and offspring survival, rather than from any type of unpredictable active biosphere dynamics, usually referred to as natural selection. In effect, what we are engaged in here, is not an attempt to deny "natural selection", but rather to reinterpret what it really stands for. The term itself is somewhat misleading to begin with, in that the concept of "natural" within natural selection implies that it is ubiquitous in nature with the further implication that the phenomenon the word is associated with has no restrictions to biology alone, but is somehow derived from the same natural laws that apply to the natural and inanimate world of chemicals. This implication clearly does not square with the facts, for the natural selection mechanism of biological evolution has no counterpart outside of biology. Furthermore, if the possibility exists that the OoL could have been the product of design, and therefore unnatural, then so too must we consider the phenomenon we call evolution in the same way. While the results of natural selection may appear to be unpredictable at the organism level, the results for the species involved are anything but. We shall demonstrate it to be a finely honed system built on an impeccably logical framework. We contend that the term "adaptive selection" more accurately describes what is happening in "natural selection", in virtue of the perspective that it is the LS that does the surviving (and "niche carving") and must bring to the task survival capabilities—among them SA's—in order to accommodate and match corresponding BA's. However, these mechanisms responsible for adaptation—or "self-evolution" of the LS, if you will—do have their limitations, which insufficiencies are responsible for the demise and ultimate extinction, in good time, of all species. However, as indicated, extinction of a species does not necessarily mean failure of its member organisms to contribute remarkably to the surviving genetic pool of future species. Lets us not forget that all future evolutionary experiments within the LS derive their genetic basis from antecedent species that went extinct only because an insufficient number of member organisms comprising their particular genetic makeup were able to accommodate further changes in their particular niche environment. Also, some members of the same species may have moved to other geographic habitats where they "lucked out", survived, and reproduced successfully, allowing for the survival of many of their 'species' genes in, perhaps, a new genetic package, within a more benign and advantageous environmental habitat. It can be easily envisaged how, a new set of environmental conditions, while conducive to a newcomer's survival, would at the same time make additional demands and pressures upon an alien phenotype. These new challenges to survival, coupled with the specific makeup of the alien gene pool could, in turn, alter dramatically the interface variables between SA's and BA's causing and promoting speciation among future offspring—genetic modifications leading to novel morphological changes in offspring that eventually result in entirely new species. Or, conversely, new habitats replace old ones within the same geography, thereby changing important BA's that members of a species must adapt to, and in time, turning into a new species in the process. Species extinction simply implies that a species no longer functions in its original form and may, in fact, have been replaced in its habitat by its altered descendants that curious future biologists can claim, in virtue of those changes, to constitute a separate species. It is only with the discovery of fossils that the actual distinction is made. Fossils of historically related organisms may merely indicate a snapshot moment at different times in the life history of the continuity that exists among species and belie the gradual changes that occur in between. Obviously all species alive today descended from others that today are said to be extinct. But, whether or not a former species gave rise to others or reached a dead end before becoming extinct is in reality a function of the survival of genetic compositions and their distributions within the LS and not in the least that of the biosphere. The biosphere is dumb and blind and has no knowledge of the LS. The LS, on the other hand, must not only anticipate the existence of biosphere constraints but also must react and respond in such ways as to maintain its continuity; virtually regardless of, and despite, the unpredictable directions biosphere conditions take. Let's get to the crux of the matter and demonstrate this to be so.

Species Attributes and Distribution Curves:

If we took a random sampling of one hundred ten year old boys living in your community and measured their heights, what kind of results would you expect? The first thing that might come to your mind might be that no two measurements would be exactly the same. We are not referring here to the limitations inherent in measurement techniques but to actual differences in height. Within our experience, we have come to appreciate the fact that when it comes to comparisons of any similar things, even the concept of identical must be taken within the general context that no two things are exactly the same. There will always be some measurable, if small, differences. But, the measurements of the heights of ten year olds leaves little to the imagination and their measured differences could best be visualized by plotting a simple graph, known as an "histogram" showing the distribution of height values. The resulting distribution graph (histogram) might appear similar to Fig 8-B.

The best way to visualize the range of height values is to "class" or quantify the individual measurements. We first determine a constant class interval or range—(in increments of one-half inch, for example) and count how many measurements of height fit into each such measurement interval. We would then plot the distribution in terms of number of boys per class vs. different height categories. Let's say, for example, that we separate the height measurements into eighteen class intervals, or categories of ascending height one-half inch apart between 50 and 59 inches. If the tallest and shortest measurements were 58 1/4 inches and 50 1/4 inches respectively, then we would have eighteen measurement classes between the shortest and tallest measurements. The idea is to obtain a distribution of the number of individuals in each ascending class. Our main point here is to convey the idea that any measurable biological variables of individuals of a species can be described by a similar graphic histogram frequency distribution representation that affords visual clarity to the observations, and the way the differences are distributed throughout the population of subjects. What becomes clear is the range or width of the distribution curve between the minimum and maximum measured values, and the fact that the graph rises to a maximum value somewhere in the middle of the distribution curve. It also affords an appreciation of the average measured value and the mean value. When the shape of such a distribution curve takes on a symmetrical bell shape, it is called a "normal" or Gaussian distribution, and commonly referred to as the familiar "Bell Curve" distribution. It doesn't always happen that way, particularly in small randomly measured samples. But, there is a meaningful rule called the "central limit theorem" that states that under general conditions, the larger the number of measured observations, the closer the distribution will resemble a normal, Bell-shaped curve. Most importantly, the mathematics of statistical analysis can be applied to the measured distribution of a small random sample from a population of individuals in order to determine—within specified confidence levels—the likely distribution of a specific species attribute (such as the heights of ten year old boys) throughout the population as a whole. The term "statistic" applies to the measurement of an attribute within a sample; the term "parameter" is the counterpart that relates to the population as a whole. Let's see how this distribution phenomenon can be applied to evolution and species survival.

Distribution analysis can be applied to any measurable parameter of organisms of a species including SA's, and more particularly to those of our interest—SA's that are directly related to species survival.

These include a variety of tolerances to external conditions (hot and cold temperatures, water salinity or pH values, etc.). Long-term steady state conditions in the planetary biosphere have a habit of changing gradually (temperature, atmospheric gas composition etc.) and not abruptly, and species must be able to accommodate and adapt to these changes over time. In order to do so, tolerances to these changing conditions must involve heritable variations that form a continuum (as do young boys' heights), much as Darwin thought, theoretically with no limit to the possible smallness of a variation within a large enough population. Again, if population size is large enough, the approximation of continuous distribution applies. It is these kinds of variations within a species that we shall be concentrating on in forming our evolution model.

Figure 8—B

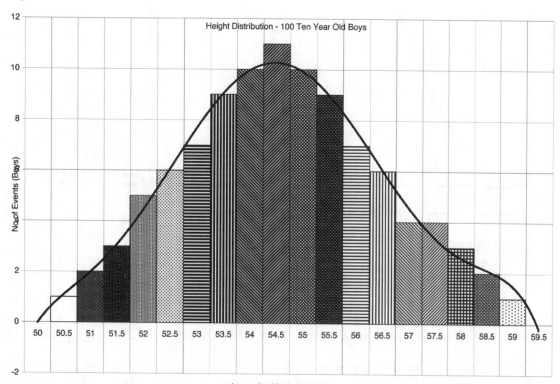

Figure 8—C: Steady State SA8 & BA8

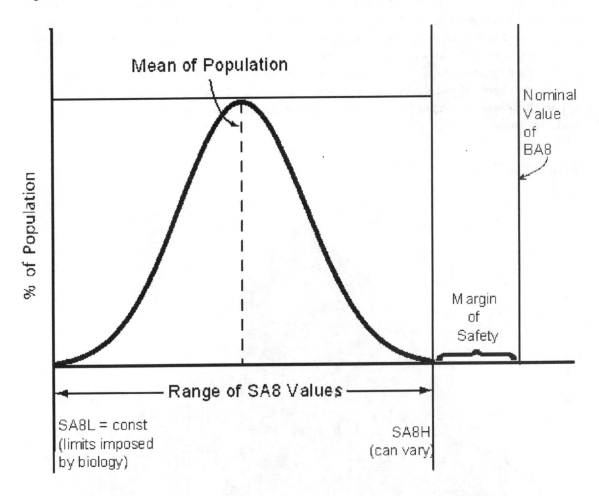

Populations, Variables, and Statistics:

When you deal with a species comprising a large population of organisms, each one of which exhibits a slightly different set of SA's that must meet or exceed a set of limiting BA's—in order to survive long enough to reproduce—you have on your hands an ideal statistical environment. If we humans ever thought that we invented the application of probability statistics, well, guess again. All we have really done is to formalize a mathematical phenomenon that has always been ubiquitous throughout the universe (and the LS)—no different in that respect from all the other so-called mathematical laws of nature. Thus, when we speak of species as "large populations" of organisms we are referring to organisms that are members of a *statistical population* as well. This is no accidental coincidence but, in fact, comprises a key LS element that permits evolution to operate. The statistical aspect arises from the unpredictability of where on the distribution curve of any species attribute, an organism's particular measured value (called an event) will occur.

To illustrate the statistical aspect of the phenomenon of evolution, let's return to our hypothetical species and the one biosphere attribute—that of low ambient temperature of an environmental niche (BA8) and it's corresponding species attribute—low temperature species tolerance limit (SA8). Again, we will neglect for the moment all other considerations that may mitigate the relationship between low environmental temperature and organism survival such as tolerance duration and other variables. We wish to simplify the issue merely to an organism's built-in ability to tolerate and survive a low temperature spell of unspecified duration and how, all other things being equal, this ability can vary throughout a population of organisms of a single species. In other words, every member of the species occupying our subject environmental niche and capable of interbreeding will have a unique individual measurable parameter value for its cold temperature tolerance limit *species attribute* which we have arbitrarily designated as SA8 (just as ten year old boys in a given population will register different heights). As stated above, this attribute is determined by a combination of undetermined variables, all of which contribute to the low temperature survival value that must exceed the lowest exposure environmental temperature we have arbitrarily designated BA8. We can assume that such a low temperature tolerance limit can be quantified into class intervals (as was done in our height measurement example above), in terms of degrees Celsius (or fractions thereof) for each organism of a species population much as we can measure other species attributes such as height, weight or other physical measurements. Now, in theory, we can prepare an imaginary histogram from an imaginary list of minimum temperature tolerance levels—including each member of our species population, plotted against the number of organisms (or better still, the percent of the population of organisms) within designated class intervals for the same maximum tolerance temperature attribute. I use the term imaginary to describe such a survival limit graph because we obviously cannot measure the minimum low temperature tolerance levels of individuals without freezing to death our hypothetical population of organisms in the process. But, if values of such an attribute parameter could be ascertained for every member of a species population within the habitat, the results could be expressed as a histogram of the number of members of the population in each class that exhibit a given low temperature tolerance limit. But, as mentioned above, there is a difference between a 100-member sample taken randomly from a large population and measurements taken from the total species population. When the number of organisms within a species is large, the resultant distribution curve can be considered the normal Bell-shaped distribution curve for statistical purposes. Thus, a plot of how SA8 values are distributed within the species population inevitably yields a distribution curve, which can well serve as the prime element among others that contribute to a robust mechanism of survival, and therefore evolution itself. The rest of evolution involves the source of such variations within populations and how they are controlled within tolerable limits, e.g.: mutations, and other factors and how they produce variations in a genotype that are translated into variations in the phenotype.

Species Populations and Continuous Distribution Curves:

The theory of statistics "is concerned with the mathematical description and analysis of observations that subsequently form the basis for prediction of the occurrence of events under given conditions". Thus, by studying the distribution of height measurements of a 100-member sample from a much larger population, statistics can provide an estimate of the probability of such a distribution within the population as a whole. Having achieved that estimate, it will further provide the level of confidence that any given sample size represents the characteristics of the population as a whole by stating what the probable error between the statistical measured sample and the population as a whole is likely to be. That is why statistics is such a valuable tool. But, when we talk about a species population within its environmental niche and the distribution of SA survival parameter values that can affect the entire population and future generations, we (and evolution) are not limited to samples; we are working with the whole breeding population that could typically run into the many millions, billions and beyond—each individual organism having a distinct measurement for any given survival SA. Thus, while humans wishing to gain knowledge of total population attribute measurements must, of necessity, resort to statistical mathematical sampling techniques as applied to a limited randomly selected sample of that population, it is understood that if you could measure the whole population instead of just a sample, you would obtain the true, actual picture of the distribution of any particular parameter measurement. It's a bit like a nation carrying out a periodic census of its entire population rather than just polling a small sample. In fact, because within a species we are dealing with what could be described as an infinite population (one large enough to be considered so), and because the parameter of interest can take on all possible values within some interval (known in the field as a continuous random variable or variate), we can reduce the class interval small enough such that our histogram becomes a continuous distribution curve (in practice, all measured variates are rounded off to the smallest unit of measurement). In other words, because the population is so large, and the measurable variate is continuous, we could reduce the size of the class interval as small as we wish and the resultant population distribution curve assumes a continuous shape rather than the discontinuous granular graph (as depicted in Fig 8–B) unavoidable with small samples. Under these conditions, the resulting population distribution curve for its low temperature tolerance parameter, SA8, should look something like Fig 8-C., where the horizontal axis represents the range of temperature values (SA8) and the vertical axis represents either population numbers or the percentage of the population. (Because the graph in Fig 8-C comprises the distribution curve for the population as a whole, it becomes more convenient to plot the graph in terms of the percentage of the population rather than actual numbers against various temperature values for cold temperature survival limit, SA8).

We will assume, for our plot of SA8 a normal distribution (symmetrical Bell-shape) approximation even though, as stated, total symmetry is neither inevitable nor necessary. By assuming this approximation for our SA8 vs. population curve, we are in a position to take advantage of the readily available mathematical tools that apply to such a graphic representation.

What we are seeking, after all, is an understanding of general principles that apply to continuously variable parameters within any populations and in particular how such principles can operate as effective mechanisms for LS species evolution (read: 'survival through adaptation'). The approximations we are assuming above are therefore both beneficial and valid. At the center of our idealized symmetrical distribution curve we would expect to find the nominal value (equal to the median, average and mean values) of low temperature parameter SA8, around which the survival temperature measurements of our species would be distributed. We will now see how the distribution curve graphically illustrates the true significance of what it means for a species to carve out its environmental niche. Because, what is being carved is really the shape of the distribution curve relative to two independent variables: the lowest value of biosphere ambient temperature BA8 within its normal range of values, and the distribution of SA8 survival temperature values corresponding to the biological considerations imposed by the species physiology. What becomes readily apparent is the fact that an environmental niche in fact is nothing more than a specific book of distribution curves for a whole variety of external BA conditions—with each emergent SA assuming a similar kind of distribution configuration for the organisms that make up a species. Thus, a niche is essentially seen to be carved, if you will, one attribute at a time—similar distribution curves existing for each important survival attribute—every one of which is critical for the survival of its species organisms. Thus, while an organism may occupy the safe middle ground of some attribute distribution curves, it may occupy the critical upper or lower portions of others. Now, it becomes obvious that to survive at all, an organism must continue to occupy the survival portion of any and all survival related attribute distribution curves. In Boolean logic terms, each critical SA represents an essential survival "AND" gate and an organism's survival consequently depends upon its ability to negotiate successfully every single such gate. The stage is now set to examine the dynamic relationship between a BA and its counterpart SA as represented by the continuous distribution of cold temperature survival values within a population (arbitrarily designated BA8 and SA8 for our purposes).

First and foremost, any margin that exists between the BA8 and SA8H (the highest survival temperature end of the distribution curve) values as depicted in Fig 8-C, comprises a "margin of safety" that insulates the whole population from any environmental stress accountable from that SA. Members of the population can go about their business of dealing with other external conditions without any concerns of cold temperature survival because of the existence of that margin. In fact, if the environmental temperature never changes, the actual shape of the SA8 distribution curve could in fact be just any single value (the trivial case of a vertical line graph), so long as BA8 remains higher than the species SA8. Then we could expect the graph to be extremely narrow and almost vertical as in Fig 8-D.

Fig 8—D: Single Value SA8

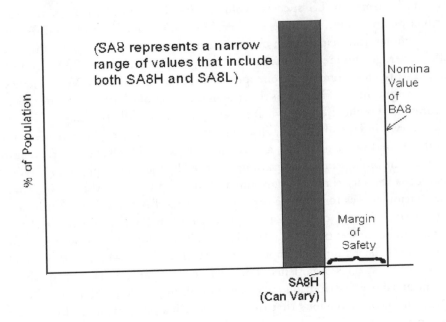

(SA8 represents a narrow range of values that include both SA8H and SA8L)

Nomina Value of BA8

Margin of Safety

SA8H (Can Vary)

% of Population

Fig 8—E: Steady SA8 / Moving BA8

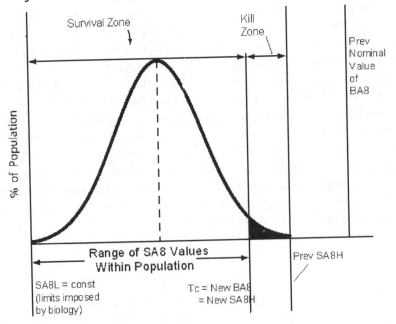

Survival Zone

Kill Zone

Prev Nominal Value of BA8

% of Population

Range of SA8 Values Within Population

SA8L = const
(limits imposed by biology)

Tc = New BA8
= New SA8H

Prev SA8H

In such an hypothetical case, SA8H, could effectively be equal to SA8L (the low end SA8 temperature survival value), so long as it remains lower than BA8. (The distribution curve under this hypothetical condition would reflect the extreme narrowing of the range of SA values that occurs in a variable population). We can even go further and extend the concept to all other BA-SA relationships and state that if the external biosphere conditions were constant across the whole of the planet in both space and time, there would be no pressure for a species to evolve at all, because all of the organisms of a species would come into this world ideally matched to their static environmental niche conditions, and therefore, there would be no changing external conditions to cause a differential survival rate that could effect the gene pool composition. This state of affairs would immediately place into question the very need for any sizable variation within a population. In fact we can claim advantages that an idealized species would have if under unchanging environmental BA's, every one of its member organisms had exactly the same mutation-free genetic library. Under such idealized conditions, the expression "don't fix it if it ain't broke" would apply eminently well. The ideal species (incidentally, there need only be a single species to meet the minimum conditions of LS survival) under such circumstances would intimately reflect the ideal set of constant biosphere conditions. All SA's would closely fit all relevant BA's, all "AND" gates would meld together—like notches in a key opening a lock, reflecting the most efficient prescription for LS survival. But, that is not the way our world functions.

Accordingly, it is precisely because all biosphere conditions are variable, over both the short and long term, that evolution mechanisms including SA distributions are required to come into play for successful species adaptation. As we shall see, the job of evolution is to ensure that over time, living things and their descendants negotiate successfully all of those commulative survival "AND" gates resulting in ultimate LS survival.

Distribution Curves and Evolution:

It is understood that at any given moment in time, all the members of a breeding population (species), as in our example, will have a BA8 value somewhere on the distribution curve, between SA8H(igh) and SA8L(ow)—the high and low temperature limits on the curve. A cursory examination of the distribution curve reveals the obvious fact that the majority of the population will have values that are closer to the average and mean values. This is reflected in the height and width of the central part of the distribution curve. As stated, it could also be the case that the distribution curve may not be an exact "Bell" shape but might be skewed in one direction or another, or even be "m" shaped and have two peaks instead of one because of some complex relationship with other contributing variable attributes or because of the existence of two or more distinct sub-population groups. Again, that is not the point. The important characteristic is the spread or width characteristics of the distribution of a species population (called the "standard deviation"), which functions as a safe zone with respect to a SA. The central principle here is that the actual distribution will span a range of values that will in effect provide most of our species population an effective survival hedge in response to any unexpected changes from the biosphere with respect to the value of "low environment temperature"—SA8. Let's elaborate.

The graph in Fig 8-C indicates the distribution of low temperature tolerances within a population of organisms at a given moment in time. Again, it is highly idealized and ignores the combination of other influences. We have also superimposed a range of values of BA8 centered about the nominal value that can be expected during a species-specific time span—let's say a single generation. Now we have a steady state situation, so long as the biosphere "behaves" itself and produces niche temperatures (and low BA8 temperatures in particular) that remain stable within the tolerance limits endurable by all the organisms represented by our distribution curve. Under these conditions, BA8 remains uncritical to the survival of our species, so long as our graphical representation indicates the distribution of SA8 low temperature tolerance values within the breeding population exceeding (lower than) that of BA8. In fact, there is even a considerable "margin of safety" that protects all the members of the population. And even if, from time to time, BA8 drops below the upper population SA8H temperature survival limit, only those organisms occupying the distribution curve close to SA8H will be affected, leaving the rest of the population relatively safe for now. But this instantaneous snapshot of reality represents an ideal steady state habitat condition that could change at any time. In fact, few conditions in the biosphere remain static and this fact translates into BA's that change, more or less, over time including the range of temperatures within environmental niches. So, it is conceivable that for any of a variety of reasons (e.g., if the planet happens to be going through a general cooling trend), the minimum temperatures can decrease over time in a large number of habitats. But, planetary changes such as warming or cooling periods don't happen overnight. They generally occur gradually, if continuously, and affect few individuals in any given generation. Over many generations, however, the cumulative effects can be dramatic. A cooling planetary trend can occur due to the cyclical nature and variation in the sun's activity, whereby the results translate into decreases in the heat radiation outward from its surface. Or, for example, increased and continuous volcanic activity could throw up an effective dust screen that could affect the average amount of sunshine reaching the planet surface over indeterminate periods of time. The resulting decrease in radiant energy in the infrared portion of the spectrum of energies that impinges on the earth's surface and converts into heat can translate into gradually cooler habitat ambient temperatures over time that can have dramatic consequences with respect to the SA8 low temperature tolerance attributes of many species. This can be expected to reflect itself in the BA8 temperature ranges experienced in the upper reaches of the oceans, lakes and rivers, as well as in the desserts and plains on land. The numerous "ice ages" in relatively recent geological history attest to these kinds of continuous changes to climates.

For our exemplary species within it's niche we can illustrate the change as a shift in the BA temperature range along the cold temperature axis towards the left as depicted in Fig 8-E. This trend may occur slowly (over many generations) or quickly. But it's effects will be immediately felt within the species by the demise of all population members whose SA8 temperature value falls to the right of BA8 value Tc—comprising the "kill zone" in the distribution curve. This is one "AND" gate they have failed to pass. Let's take a closer look at what happens as the BA8 temperature starts to fall. For the sake of the example, lets assume that it falls drastically in a single event, such that all members of the population that occupy the portion of the survival temperature distribution curve described as the kill zone, by definition, do not survive the drop in temperature. Two things will happen: 1) The population decreases by the amount represented by the area under the kill zone portion of the distribution curve; and 2) The distribution curve is no longer symmetrical with a sizable chunk of the breeding population annihilated. An important characteristic of the Bell curve distribution is that the increase in the casualty rate as BA temperature decreases is not linear—every additional degree decline in habitat temperature produces an accelerated rate of population decline. From the population genetics viewpoint the effect on the gene pool becomes increasingly dramatic in the effects on the next generation—the greater the number of resultant casualties leads to a quicker response genetically for adaptation. We can expect that the distribution curve returns to the normal shape quickly—within the next generation or two as more offspring inherit more beneficial genes (lower SA8 values). Of course those offspring unlucky enough to inherit genetic combinations that result in SA8 that is below the expected BA8 value will succumb during the first cold challenge. Eventually it is expected that the population distribution will result in an SA8 survival curve that reflects the new reality (lower average temperature tolerances) as the population numbers return to normal (Fig 8-F).

What becomes eminently clear is that those species members that comprise the left side of the population curve will be best fit to survive a cooling trend and thus better able to survive to reproduce offspring. As such, it will be their genes that will survive and gain influence within the species gene pool, including those genes influential in the specific organism morphology responsible for lower temperature tolerance, SA8. As the cooling trend intensifies itself over many generations, the genes that permit low temperature tolerance, (SA8 values on the left side of the distribution curve) will inevitably become more widespread throughout the surviving gene pool because those are the genes that will survive preferentially over those that lead to failure in the survival test of cold temperature tolerance. And it can be expected that the graph representing SA8 will creep slowly in the same leftward direction. In effect, what happens is that member organisms that cannot tolerate the new colder reality represented by lower temperatures will die out, together with their genetic dispositions. The genes of those organisms that do tolerate the new conditions survive and spread by a process of genetic diffusion through the offspring of surviving interbreeding members of the species population creating the corresponding shift leftward of the SA distribution graph. These effects are illustrated in Fig 8-F.

Eventually as the trend continues through many generations, as represented by further shifting of the BA temperature curve leftward on the graph, the distribution curve will continue to narrow accompanied by a reduction in the standard deviation because the low temperature limit is set by the biological limitations of species morphology. And finally, species extinction defines the condition whereby BA8 temperature declines below SA8L.

Fig 8—F: Dynamic Shifting of SA8 Distribution Curves

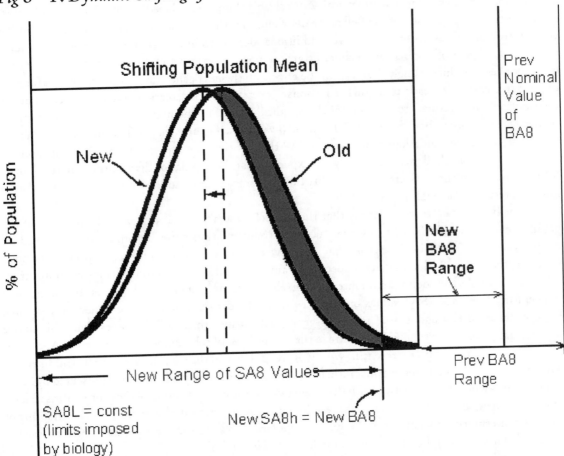

Consequences of Biosphere Attribute Changes:

It is the combination of the changing of a BA such as low temperature limits and the tolerance of some organisms and the intolerance of others to that change that results over time in:

a] direct primary changes in the corresponding SA within the gene pool of the species as reflected in the corresponding movement of the population distribution for that SA—together with:

b] secondary unnecessarily related changes to other SA distribution curves reflecting the newly emergent demographics of the gene pool—comprising as well any novel genetic contributions from the surviving members of the species reproductive population.

Naturally, in order to avoid total annihilation—leading eventually to extinction—it is reasonable to assume that changes must be introduced to the species genetic pool fast enough to enable a sufficient number of offspring to confront and survive environmental BA changes. But the question is when and how? Obviously, after the change to a biosphere attribute occurs it would seem to be too late to play catch up with respect to the corresponding SA in direct response to a change of an important environmental condition. Our SA population distribution curves address this issue directly. They elegantly illustrate the fact that accommodating changes to any SA in question are not, and need not be, introduced at all—because <u>they are there all the while</u>. And that is the point of this exercise. The ability of a species to respond to external environmental changes exists within the species-specific population distribution curves depicting SA values. Thus, change within a species to accommodate changes to biosphere conditions occur, not as a direct response to changes in the associated BA, but through the selective survival of beneficial genes—those belonging to surviving members of the statistical population of species organisms that happen to be at the favorable end of the <u>already existing</u> population distribution curve—corresponding to the changing BA in question.

There are other consequences of this phenomenon. For, just as important is the fact that when an organism survives preferentially as a result of successfully passing through a BA induced survival "AND" gate to reproduce—not only is the SA responsible for its survival reinforced within the population, so too do all its other genetic propensities, relevant to survival or not, that are passed along as well to future generations. In other words, while it takes only a change to a single BA to effect the survival of a large number of species organisms over time, the effects of such BA specific "culling" of unsuccessful organisms removes from the species genotype as well all of their potential genetic contributions. This inevitably results in both fortifying and/or removal within the surviving population of any number of genetic influences that had heretofore been part and parcel of the population gene pool. The direct consequences of this phenomenon are modifications as well to many other SA distribution curves, some of which are directly and indirectly linked to the SA under stress and others, simply in virtue of the redistribution that inevitably occurs through genetic diffusion, whenever changes occur that effect survival within species populations.

Thus, the LS "takes advantage of" both random genetic changes to produce novel variations within the individual member organisms of species that result in the essential distribution curves of SA's—together with large numbers of such organisms within the species population—in order to produce and maintain the necessary distribution range of survival SA's relative to any given corresponding BA attribute condition value. While there are many SA's—other than those responsible for survival—that develop at the same time, it is the survival specific SA's that generate wholesale gene pool modification that affect the resultant species genetic makeup at any given time. And of course, an SA that has no direct survival value today may end up having influence over some survival value in the future. And most importantly, at any given moment in time, the BA value for a particular "primary" attribute—such as low temperature tolerance—is always exceeded (on the side of safety) by the corresponding distribution of SA tolerance values within the population of species member organisms; that is essentially what survival is all about. But, (and this could have important bearing on both speciation and punctuated evolution) whenever a BA condition responsible for species survival begins to change relatively rapidly, the resultant population of survivors that pass through that particular "AND" gate filter represent not only the predictable statistical events on the distribution curve for the corresponding SA, but also the unpredictable statistical events of all the other distribution curves for SA's. These other SA distribution curves are now in a position to influence, more or less (depending on conditions) the future direction of species adaptation, with the potential of creating new survival opportunities for their organisms, both within the same habitat and/or neighboring habitats. The key evolution principle within the distribution curves of SA's is represented by the capability they bestow upon a species population for surviving the obstacle course of survival "AND" gates that define the niche BA's they must endure. Accordingly, all it takes in order to redefine the distribution curves of many other SA's is the dynamic movement of a single BA that places into stress the distribution curve of the corresponding SA. The consequences for species genomic composition are immense. The same can be said for the consequences for speciation, whether gradual and /or punctuated. But, the bottom line is: all of the SA distribution curves of all species are there all the while, awaiting a shift in their respective BA conditions. This anticipation on the part of LS species, and the ability of some species members to pass through all of their survival "AND" gates (all of their SA's are within the favorable range for survival) successfully and reproduce offspring is what allows species to change and adapt—resulting in ultimate LS survival.

Mutations, Tolerances and Natural Selection:

Once the value of a BA starts to move—incrementally and imperceptibly—and starts to affect the survival of some members of the population and their genes, it becomes obvious that, over time, the larger the SA range or width of the distribution curve for that particular SA, and the lower the slope of the curve, the greater the likelihood that more species members will survive, than if the distribution curve were narrow and steep. The size of the standard deviation—or width of the distribution curve (a measure of the probability of the SA value of any randomly selected member of the population)—becomes relevant particularly with respect to the rate of change of the BA over time. It is obvious that the faster the movement of the BA to the left, the greater the advantage of having a broad distribution curve—spanning a large range of survival values (particularly in the direction of safety)—in order for more members of the population to survive long enough to reproduce, thereby fortifying within the population the genetic information that directly affects the SA that is "under attack".

It is obviously too late for our imaginary species to try and adapt in hindsight and play catch up to the changes that are already taking place in the environment. Too late, that is, unless over a long period of time prior to the deleterious effects of BA8 and other environmental changes, subtle but consistent chance mutations and other changes have occurred in the punched tape like information contained in the DNA of a species' organisms. These changes, however they occur, are the source of variation of individual attribute values within the species population and the currency of SA distribution curves. And the larger the population, the more complete and continuous will be the distribution curve that describes the frequency of values for any given SA's among the population. Consequently, the larger the population, the more efficient will be the survival mechanisms built into the species that depend on the endurance of sufficient numbers of organisms. These survivors, then, will constitute the basis for reshaping the species genetic makeup in response to the newly emerging realities (changing BA's) of the external environment. In our example with low temperature tolerance, there will be some members of the species that will be better able to endure lower temperatures than most others, which translates into a lower personal SA value for that BA than most of the population. It is only when the biosphere condition for that SA changes, that a 'selection' process kicks in and has the effect of removing from the gene pool, selectively, individuals and their genes that represent failure to survive the changing corresponding biosphere condition. Natural selection essentially reflects the "pressure" exerted by the external environment upon the various traits of the organisms of a species. This translates directly into the reshaping of the gene pool with respect to the SA involved, the distribution curve for that SA, and for a host of other SA's that exhibit ranges of values. Just remember, however, that if the distribution curve of SA values did not exist in the first place, selection processes, natural or otherwise, would have nothing to select.

In effect, the full spectrum of species attributes represents the species-specific needs and sensitivities that accommodate and are accommodated by that species' environmental "niche". And these so-called niches effectively reflect the resultant species phenotype parameters shaped by the survival histories of the individual ancestral forebears of every species and whose individual genomes in turn were shaped and "carved" through countless survival trials of their own organisms' ancestors. A species effectively ends up, at any given time, with morphologies that are survival successful in virtue of their accommodation to a unique and limited sufficient and necessary set out of a large number of environmental conditions. Each species adopts a somewhat unique set of specific environmental conditions within which it will compete for survival in the local biosphere with all the other species. Then again, each member organism of a species, by virtue of it's unique composition of SA's characteristic of it's species will be competing with other members of its own species for the available resources and reproduction opportunities within the environmental niche—in other words, for its own survival as well as the survival of its genes. But, the fundamental basis upon which the whole system responsible for LS adaptation to changing external biosphere conditions depends, lies within the statistical nature of population genetics.

Morphology and Species Attributes:

When we refer to an SA trait such as temperature tolerance, what are we really referring to? After all, most genes are simply instructions for the production of proteins of one kind or another whose three dimensional architecture usually defines their function. So how can a gene affect low temperature tolerance? One way might be, for example, if in a complex organism, a combination of genes expresses itself as the protein production of a thicker coat of hair, feathers or other insulating material that has the effect of increasing the protective qualities at the organism exterior surface. Then, there would be a direct relationship between low temperature tolerance and insulation qualities of the protein external coat. Of course, such a feature could also translate into a lower high-temperature SA tolerance and an inability to radiate efficiently excess heat. Thus, the same genetic combination responsible for lower temperature tolerance could doom such an organism and it's future influence within the species gene pool if the temperature trend tends toward warming instead of cooling—unless efficient cooling mechanisms (such as perspiration) can co-evolve simultaneously and on time. But, the key issue here is the fact that successful morphology adaptation (that which avails its organisms physical survival) translates into successful future genomes (because survival translates into success in the reproduction of the genes responsible). And while it may appear that luck has a lot to do with the future direction in the evolution of species—and indeed it does to some extent for individual organisms, and the future prospects of their genes influencing the species gene pool—the LS is the only party in the LS-Biosphere arrangement that can and does assume the initiative in order to be able to adapt responsively. The point we are making is that the LS, in virtue of its spectrum of SA distribution curves—representing the expression of each species gene pool—comes prepared and indeed can be said to anticipate the challenges to its own survival. The fact that it remains successful (LS survival is alive and well), despite those challenges speaks for itself. The biosphere sets the external ambient conditions and the LS— through the survival and reproduction of individual fit organisms (whose SA compositions occupy any number of individual Bell shaped SA survival distribution curves)—continuously alters and shapes it's present composition in anticipation of future biosphere BA changes, in order to survive into the future. This kind of accommodation capability that the LS brings to its external biosphere conditions, indeed, can be said to have a kind of built-in foresight, in virtue of the ability to continuously reshape its SA distribution curves. In fact, for the most part, the shape of the distribution curve remains more or less constant while any given BA changes slowly. It just gets whittled away at one end and filled out at the other, as surviving members of a species at the lucky side of the Bell curve reproduce preferentially with similar others in a kind of random diffusion phenomenon among the survivors (analogous to the kinetic diffussion of a large population of molecules in a volume of gas). This dynamic process constantly— generation after generation—refines and retunes the shape of the distribution curves for any SA process, so that a species continues to "try" to maintain its variable distributions set while moving ever so steadily in the direction of safety (away from the moving BA). If it can—then good and well. If it can't—then simply enough, it goes extinct.

Just one more point—how does a species deal with a consistent drop in temperature as that temperature approaches criticality (point at which survival of the whole species is threatened)? Simply put, the species' descendants will survive only if it's genome can change sufficiently, over time, to produce morphological mechanisms and combinations thereof, that can protect future descendants from the effects of cold, in one form or another. Or, if members of the species happen to migrate, for any reason, to a different geographical location where external conditions are conducive to survival (SA's compatible with BA's). Perhaps that is how mammals evolved, developing both physical protective measures (hairy coats) as well as sophisticated heat generation and temperature control mechanisms that maintained crucial anatomical structures at requisite temperatures while ambient external temperatures plummeted. Part of that survival success may also be attributed to their mobility—enabling some to discover new and warmer habitats more congenial to their survival. Of course, the results of such survival opportunism eventually may express itself as new species. But, this highlights the point that life—the LS—is a continuum and that all life forms on the planet derive from a limited set of originating species.

Couple the above effect over many SA's having primary and secondary and probably many additional interrelationships and side effects and you have a statistical biological formula that translates into the many varieties of species that continually emerge. Because, in our example of low temperature tolerance, while the shift in the low temperature limit over time may have produced, for example, hairier species, the balance of the genetic library of these surviving individuals also contained other genes that would have changed and influenced other characteristics. These are essential to exert their influence over the continually changing landscape of the species gene pool, affecting any number of SA's in the process, and thus furthering, again, genetic variability. They, in turn, are expressed in the phenotypes of the members of the species population as new features that, over time, can alter in substantial ways the species and indeed lead to the creation of new ones. Thus the uniqueness that is every organism is more than just a cliché. But, as illustrated above, it takes large populations of such unique organisms to pull off LS long-term survival. The LS subsystem responsible is adaptive evolution.

We are now in a position to identify a variety of adaptation strategies at work in species populations in response to environmental pressures exerted upon SA distribution curves:

a) Directional adaptation: BA pressure is applied to one side of the SA distribution curve, thereby pushing it in the opposite side direction e.g., cold temperature BA (Figure 8-E).

b) Stabilizing adaptation: Pressure is applied simultaneously to both sides of the SA distribution curve.

c) Disruptive adaptation: Pressure is applied within the SA distribution curve—resulting in an "m" shape distribution curve—effectively producing sub-groups within a species.

d) Sexual adaptation: Reflects differences in SA's between males and females within a population, e.g., differences in physical size.

e) Artificial selection: Reflects the results of selective breeding carried out by external intelligent agents e.g., humans engaged in artificially selecting "desirable" traits within animals (pets, livestock, etc.) and plants (food, flowers, etc.). Artificial selection essentially obviates any suggestion of species adaptation. It effectively sidesteps and renders nil the built-in LS adaptive mechanisms for species survival described above.

Note: While the above categories of adaptive evolution reflect a distinctly RDH perspective, they do have corresponding counterparts within the sphere of natural selection evolution. This is to be expected inasmuch as the results from the point of view of evolution are identical i.e., evolution does, indeed, occur. Accordingly, both SAb and RDH must describe the same phenomenon—evolution—but differ in their unique respective perspectives.

While the Equivalency Principle of Evolution defines some of the degrees of freedom that evolution dynamics can assume—including the genetic founder effects due to migration of small numbers of individuals—within the grand scheme of things, adaptive evolution responsible for LS survival depends upon the collective accommodation of SA distribution curves to BA's, regardless of how that occurs within the LS. The statistical nature of SA variations within LS populations that permit preferential survival in the face of external environmental pressure in effect endow those populations with the ability to anticipate first, and only then adapt to, long term external change—which is primarily what evolution is all about.

---

[1]What Mad Pursuit: Francis Crick p. 30
[2]What Mad Pursuit: Francis Crick, p. 30
[3]Recent modifications to this perception and the "special" status accorded the human species within the system of Life, announced by the Catholic Church, really don't address the fundamental issues. Only when creationists learn to appreciate evolution in terms of its survival value for the system of Life instead of focusing on how it contributes to the complexity of individual species will they realize how truly compatible the concept of evolution is with design philosophy, including creationism.
[4]What Mad Pursuit, Francis Crick, p. 148
[5]Encyclopedia Britannica: Electronic Edition 1997
[6]Mathematics of Natural Selection: J.B.S. Haldane

9. Species Adaptation:
A Complex Exercise in Survival

"It is an error to imagine that evolution signifies a constant tendency to increased perfection. That process undoubtedly involves a constant remodelling of the organism in adaptation to new conditions; but it depends on the nature of those conditions whether the directions of the modifications effected shall be upward or downward."

Thomas H. Huxley (1825–1895), Zoologist

Survival Strategies and Tactics:

Following the discussions in the last chapter. we are now in position to discuss the probability that large populations of many diverse species (regardless of how they came into being) are tactical weapons in the battle for LS endurance and an integral part of the larger system strategy for survival under the radical and potentially catastrophic conditions common to any planetary biosphere. As such, and consistent with this logical position, any tendency toward species complexity would be—not an end in itself, but merely part of an imbedded capability that promotes LS survival over ions of time. (This ignores for the moment the very real design possibility of the existence of preinstalled evolution schematics within species genetic libraries; more of this later.) The expansion of life into many different species occupying a large variety of habitat conditions—by the common processes of chance mutations and the LS principle of anticipation of biosphere environmental change—is simply the continuation of the fundamental LS strategy to broaden the base of SA's within the broader spectrum of BA's. If survival over a period of billions of years, under the dynamic changes to the conditions of the planetary habitat is, indeed, the principle activity of the game of life, (including slow steady state as well as short term violent changes) then the safest and most efficient way to achieve this challenging and difficult goal would be to modularize the system. And that is exactly what different species represent—adaptive modules of the LS system. That was and continues to be the effective strategy for the LS—to overcome the periodic revolutionary and catastrophic events that have lead to mass extinctions, but leave the survival of the system intact. That means many different species (LS modules) occupying many different environmental niches and equipped to accomplish the same goal: survival—the LS mission (design intent).

Safety In Numbers—A Hedge Against Catastrophe:

At any given moment in time, the planetary environment represents the total extant pallet of BA's that both support and challenge living things on the one hand, and conditions species SA's must accommodate on the other. Over the several billions of years that life has existed on this planet, it would seem that no environmental habitat, however extreme, has been passed up as unsuitable for the tenuous existence of some modular lifeform (species) or other. Now, niches come and niches go, and so do their occupiers, if their descendent offspring cannot stay in step with the demise of their particular niche, and if any species cannot adapt its SA distribution curves to the BA conditions that are represented by the replacement. The expansion into new habitats of individual organisms and the subsequent permanent isolation from the rest of the population members permits novel changes to species to become established within a limited isolated group that, if they survive, ultimately earn the right to be labeled a distinct species on their own. The premise is simple: Isolate a unique mix of genes (that's what every organism in fact is), allow them to replicate and inbreed and what do you get—a (sub)species that eventually will no longer be able to breed with the descendants of the original parenting species. Just look at the world of insects.

When asked: what might be learned about a "Creator" by examining the world, J Haldane, the distinguished population geneticist, is reported to have responded: "an inordinate fondness for beetles". This renowned quote reflects the fact that there are classified in excess of 350,000 species of beetles. They range in size from 0.3 mm to 15 cm in length and their oldest fossils date from the Lower Permian (265 million years old). How did this come to be? It can probably be said with some confidence that most, if not all, of these are descended from a handful of (and perhaps only one) species. We can envisage the situation where some member organisms of the original species population became separated from the indigenous habitat and managed to settle elsewhere. The breakaway *founder group*, could then extend their particular genetic influence together with any genetic variations and deviations picked up along the way, while being able to survive and thrive under the new habitat conditions (sometimes extreme) of neighboring and progressively distant territories on the fringes of their species habitat. As a result, it could be expected that the distribution curves for the SA's of the new population would center somewhat differently than that in the original species niche population. But more importantly, the new habitat would represent a somewhat unique set of BA's—pressures that would bear upon the adaptive selection mechanisms of the descendants of the new arrivals. In time, this, as well as the process of new chance mutations in the growing and isolated population group, would allow the natural statistical processes to further alter the nominal values of SA's in order to stay in step and coincide with changes to the nominal values of the BA's in the new environment. Extend this scenario many times and over long periods of time and you soon begin to understand how it is that you can get hundreds of thousands of beetles and any other species, for that matter.

In like manner, life has expanded it's initial base of existence from a relative handful of primitive organisms (Self—generationists would insist on a single organism) through countless millions of intermediary species—to the present state of life comprising millions of uniquely qualified species inhabiting countless habitats across the whole planet. This reflects the almost limitless LS potential for versatility and pliancy allowing the LS to exploit as many opportunities as is possible within the extremes of conditions to be found on the planet. It also affords the LS the kind of insurance that virtually guarantees LS survival. The all important question in all of this is whether there is a minimum number of organisms and species required for these kind of evolutionary phenomena to work, acknowledging all the while that all the facts concerning exactly how species evolve are not known. In other words, from what we know and surmise about the statistical nature of evolution and how it has given rise to the multitudes of species adapting to changing biosphere conditions, can we assert with any real confidence that:

1] the more species and organisms that exist and interact within the LS, the greater the chance of evolution operating smoothly and efficiently, (according to the statistical population requisites as described previously); and

2] there is a critical number of organisms and species required just in order for evolution to function, and below which evolution ceases to function effectively, species tend more rapidly to become extinct, and below which the very survival of the LS could be considered to be problematic?

First and foremost, if evolution is, indeed, a parametric (trait) phenomenon involving the whole population of reproducing individuals, then it simply cannot work without a population of events to operate on. In order for the SA distribution mechanisms of evolution to work, large populations of organisms of any given species are necessary (to provide Bell curve-like distributions of attributes that can serve as BA buffers). As a consequence, the first assertion above would seem intuitively to be true. With respect to many organisms of many species occupying many niches, it's nice to have any number of surviving species in widely separated niches that can carry on the survival imperative of the LS—even while numerous others are continually failing to meet the challenge on their respective roads to extinction. If the system had but few species, we can easily envisage the case where coincidentally several biosphere conditions change simultaneously and eliminate entirely the niches of all of those few species resulting in the catastrophic complete obliteration of life on the planet. Within this context imagine, if you will, the risk to a single vulnerable species at the very beginning of an abiogenesis OoL. Is this a likely scenario for survival success at the OoL?

The second assertion above is somewhat more difficult to ponder and may in fact be impossible to quantify in any meaningful way. Another way of putting it would be: is there a sufficient and necessary number of organisms required simply to satisfy and initiate the SA distribution-dependent evolutionary processes and allow them to work effectively? Of necessity, this is a loaded question. It is loaded in the sense that it starkly places abiogenesis on the spot, inasmuch as SAb implies that at the very beginning there must have been only one species (or quasi-species) that began with a single simple self-replicating organism possessing only a primitive and "tight" genome. And, that is our point. Under SAb conditions, it is hard to imagine (no less fathom) a substitution for the population-dependent mechanisms described above that underpin evolution.

While we may not be able to put actual numbers to the question, we may be able to gain an insight into the problem by examining it from a relative point of view. And because evolution is a phenomenon that deals with large numbers of randomly active species and organisms (population events operating randomly within certain constraints or degrees of freedom) we may be able to borrow an idea that applies equally to population genetics, the Kinetic Theory of Gases and any other phenomenon dependent on the interaction of many participating agents.

Inverse Square Root of "n" (ISRN) Rule:

The ISRN is a statistical expression, used generally to describe the degree of inaccuracy to be expected in any physical law or phenomenon that apply to populations of events. In statistics, it is used to give an estimate of the effectiveness of a random sampling taken from a population—totally independent of the population size. Take Boyle's law concerning the behavior of a sample of gas, for example. Simply put, the law states: *At constant temperature (T), the volume (V) of an "ideal" sample gas is inversely proportional to its pressure (P). This statement can be written: PV = k, a constant or as it turns out, PV/T is a constant.*

Now in practice, there is no such thing as an ideal anything, no less so for a gas. In fact the behavior of any real gas will depend on its chemical composition and the actual test conditions, and as it turns out, the number of gas molecules in the test sample. So in effect, Boyle's Law, as it is written, is an idealized law and simply a good approximation of real gas behavior. Because a gas is comprised of individual gas molecules, that behave both independently and randomly, the question can be asked: will the law be able to describe equally the state of a liter of gas as opposed to a thimble full? Notice that nowhere in the Boyle's law formula does the quantity of individual gas molecules appear. Boyle's Law represents a simple relationship that makes no limitation on the sample size and, as stated, is meant to apply to an ideal gas assumed to comprise of a sufficient number of gas molecules for the law to apply. How many, and just as importantly, how does Boyle's law vary as the quantity of gas molecules varies? The ISRN rule defines the degree of inaccuracy of any statistical process (which is how gases are treated according to the Kinetic Theory of Gases) as a function of the number of events or members of the population in a defined population group. In our Boyle's law example, the total number of molecules in the sample being tested represents the population group. In evolution, the population group is the total number of organisms within any given evolving species, and on another level, the total number of species that make up the LS.

For our ideal gas example, if we were to confine "n" molecules of an ideal gas within a vessel of a given volume at a particular temperature, then the pressure exerted upon the vessel walls could be calculated using Boyle's law, but the degree of accuracy (and therefore effectiveness) of our calculation is determined by the ISRN rule. The reason for differences in accuracy, depending on the population size of the molecular particles involved, is due to the fact that each gas molecule behaves independently and is subject to the random motions caused by its heat energy according to the Kinetic Theory of gases.

Naturally it can be expected that the greater the number of participating gas molecules in the sample being tested, the closer it will behave as the ideal gas defined by Boyle's Law—as the accumulated contributions of individual molecules *"average out"*. Here's where the "inverse square root of n" rule comes in. It goes as follows:

> *The laws of physics and physical chemistry are inaccurate within a probable error of the order of <u>1 divided by the square root of n</u>, where "n" is the number of molecules that cooperate to bring about the law.*

Thus in our case above, it becomes evident that the effectiveness of our gas law, which treats the population of gas molecules as a statistical phenomenon, will indeed depend upon the population size of the molecules involved. Thus, if we had a sample of 1 million gas molecules, we could be confident that Boyle's Law was accurate within $1/Srt(10^6)$, or to 1 in a thousand. Thus, even though a million may seem to be a large number, an accuracy of 1 in a thousand is not "overwhelmingly good, if a thing claims the dignity of being a Law of Nature" as Erwin Schrodinger[1] so aptly put it. The same principle can be applied to the degree of confidence that the measurements of any limited sample represent a population as a whole.

"What does this have to do with evolution?" you may ask. Well, to the extent that evolution would seem to work better, the larger the population—we are trying to determine in relative terms, how much better? In effect, what the ISRN rule does is to provide a quantitative value of the degree of effectiveness (as opposed to accuracy), of the statistically dependent evolution mechanisms as a function of the population size. The reason it works the same for a whole population of organisms is because evolution involves not just a sampling from the population but involves the population as a whole—the whole population is the sample, if you will. There is precedence for the use of the ISRN rule in association with evolution. But first, a disclaimer:

I don't suggest for one moment that the ISRN rule can be used to determine the degree of effectiveness of anything that claims to be a "natural law of evolution" (as Boyle's Law is referred to as a law of nature). There are no precise laws of evolution that can give rise to numerical measurements or other exact relationships. It is not in this respect that the ISRN rule can be useful. But, the ISRN rule has been mentioned in connection with the estimate of mutation rates according to the "neutral theory of molecular evolution"—where it has been shown that the neutral mutation rate decreases as the population increases. The rate decrease referred to is proportional according to the ISRN rule[2]. I am not going to make sweeping generalities with respect to this interesting example. However, I will suggest that, perhaps in like manner, the ISRN rule is applicable as it conveys a measure of the change in the effectiveness of evolution mechanisms, that are dependent upon the cumulative effects of populations of randomly active individuals—as a function of population size. And it provides a proven principle that governs such phenomena over and above what our intuition may have to say about it. In fact, the ISRN rule implies a non-linear relationship between the size of populations and the effectiveness of results. Thus, the ISRN as it applies to the number of randomly acting organisms participating, as they do, in the survival over time of a species, would tend to exaggerate the effects of decreasing populations, as they get even smaller, as opposed to larger populations as they grow in number. For example, according to the

ISRN rule, the difference in the cumulative effects between a population of 10 thousand organisms and 100 organisms (1/100 and 1/10) would be the same as the difference between one million organisms and 10 thousand organisms, (1/1000 versus 1/100)—a single order of magnitude. The point here is that we are trying to evoke a measure of relative effectiveness of evolutionary phenomena upon the collective behavior of different orders of magnitude of populations of organisms, and in particular to gain an insight into the breakdown of this effectiveness as we approach smaller and smaller population sizes.

In the previous pages we have argued that the operative mechanisms of adaptive evolution can be considered to emanate from the LS and are directly a function of species population size as it reflects upon the statistical distribution of SA's. As such, like any other LS activity, evolution can be considered to be the commulative results of population statistics as applied to all the unique individual organisms that make up the LS and reproduce. But at some point—the mechanisms begin to break down exponentially (non-linearly) when a critical decrease in population size is reached. That is the significance of our introduction of the ISRN rule.

I believe the ISRN rule has relevancy to species evolution, which depends, as it does, primarily upon the population size of "n" similar but unidentical individuals, each having numerous degrees of freedom within environmental space, i.e., statistical events having uniquely measurable species attributes, many of which are responsible for survival. And that's exactly what organisms of life are. In fact, I would make the point that the ISRN rule has a crucial significance for the survival of the LS, and particular consequences for the OoL. In fact, it will be seen that the ISRN rule goes to the very heart of the "evolution of evolution" question and represents possibly a stunning indictment of SAb. It flies in the face of those who insist that the operating principles of evolution must have become operational prior to or simultaneously with the abiogenetic OoL, and that it is uniquely responsible for giving rise to populations of different kinds of replicating non-biological entities. The ISRN rule implies that the converse is true—that you need a population having a distribution of different individuals in place before you can have any kind of effective evolution. At the end of the day, the ISRN rule may indeed help us appreciate one of the most effective arguments against SAb and in favor of RDH—that evolution absolutely depends on a sufficient and necessary population of varied individuals for it to function at all.

Adaptive Survival—A Numbers Game:

The population size of a species bears an important relationship to the cumulative effects of the random behavior of the individual participants. The greater the population of a species, the better its chances of survival. We are witness to numerous examples of species teetering on the brink of extinction as determined by the decrease in breeding members over a period of time. The ISRN, as applied to the survival of the LS provides an ideal way of graphically portraying the importance of a large (and growing) population sample for the very functioning of evolution. But species population size is not the only population that evolution has to work with. Within the LS one finds a number of different populations of events that evolution can apply itself to, including:

1] the number of different species;

2] the number of organisms that make up individual species;

3] the number of genes within the genomes that express themselves in the phenotypes of individual species.

If we take all the mechanisms of evolution (expression of all of the M's and m's as they emanate from within the LS) and lump them together as the single phenomenon we call "Adaptive Survival", the ISRN rule could provide the relative effectiveness of LS survival as a function of the numbers (of species, organisms and genes, as the case may be) it has to work with within the respective populations. I believe this to be a fair, if simplified, representation, as it has been shown to apply equally well to any random sample of individual particles or events. Thus, it might apply as well to the ideal, if simplistic, portrayal of evolution at work in the past few pages. Accordingly, we can conceive of a lower limit, below which the mechanisms of evolution will act against a species; e.g., where the effects of random mutations that feed evolution could produce more failures than successes. While this number may be subject to a variety of indefinable variables and therefore not be easily calculable, the ISRN rule can provide a relative measure of the statistical differences between different values of "n". We also know, for example, that the more organisms you have, the more points on the distribution graph of SA's will be filled in, and in particular, the greater will be the number of organisms occupying the all important extremes of the SA distribution curve for any given corresponding BA. As well, the larger the number of organisms within a species, the greater the opportunity for the successful passage of some through all of the restrictive survival "AND" gates; obstacles that function as survival filters that environmental niche BA's represent.

There is one more largely unappreciated fundamental variable that must be taken into account within any consideration of population reproductive success—that of species organism population density dynamics within environmental space. Every organism has unique mobility characteristics within its environment that permit it access to other breeding organisms. Generally, we can approximate the mobility of any species organism within its environment as a circle of fixed radius. Effectively, the length of the radius would represent the greatest distance around a central point that an organism could be expected to traverse within its breeding life. This distance would depend upon both organism size, effectiveness of means of locomotion and species—specific territorial behavioral characteristics. Thus, in the simplest case, we might find a species whose organisms are free to roam anywhere within their radius of mobility. The chance of an encounter between two breeding individuals of the opposite sex would simply be proportional to the number of mobility circles of individuals that overlap. Wherever an overlap occurs would signify common territory where individual organisms paths could be expected to cross. On the other hand, strict territorial behaviour constraints on the part of a species might tend to minimize such encounters. Then, any real understanding of reproductive success must entail as well an appreciation of the more complex mating algorithms that apply on a case-by-case basis. Thus, population density considerations alone are insufficient to account for reproductive success. And changes in species behavior—however they evolve—can influence reproductive success and consequently the success of future species survival.

Population Size, Mutations: and Survival:

From the forgoing discussions, we can say with some confidence that both evolution and survival over the long term require sufficiently large populations of organisms; once population size decreases below some critical value, both are thrown into question while the probability of extinction increases. There is no surprise here. This would apply to organisms with respect to species and species, in turn, with respect to the LS in general. In this respect, the ISRN rule takes on a double significance—one for each of the above considerations. The ISRN rule simply provides a relative measure of efficiency, as a function of population size; a relative measure of safety for different value of "n" with respect to the numbers of organisms involved. And as we get down to low numbers, until you reach the trivial case scenario where n = 1—for the starting point of any SAb scenario—it becomes evident that the whole process, according to the ISRN rule, breaks down, and so too must SAb. In a reversal of the process, even if a SAb founder organism managed to increase its offspring at the very OoL, the non-linear ISRN rule sheds important light on the negative gradient dragging down the effectiveness of population growth on the continuity of the spread (standard deviation) of SA's and its corresponding negative effects on the diffusion dynamics of evolution.

Organism complexity enters the picture as well from the following perspective: the more complex an organism, the greater the number of SA's—many of which correspond to complex BA survival "AND" gates that must be met for species survival. Each value on every SA distribution curve of a species represents an individual event from the statistical point of view. Ultimately, species survival depends on the product of the survival probabilities for each sufficient and necessary BA condition required for evolution to work, and that's where the rub comes in. To arrive at a composite population size confidence factor for a species, you must, in principle, multiply the survival probability for each SA by each and every other crucial attribute survival probability. It becomes obvious that overall species survival probability decreases rapidly with an increase in the number of critical survival BA's, each with its own survival probability as it affects a population of organisms. Under such circumstances, it is essential that offspring reproduction numbers be sufficient to makeup for such losses plus an increase factor to stave off extinction. Under these assumptions and conditions, it becomes evident that truly large numbers of organisms may be required simply in order for adaptive survival evolution to work at all. The ISRN rule provides some comparative measure of the difficulties involved in smaller populations. Simply put, the power of evolution and the origin and survival of species is in the numbers._

In a twist of irony, the same kind of argument could be made with respect to the minimum number of genes that a primitive species must have in order for it's organisms to endure chance mutations. Above we have argued the disadvantages of organism complexity with respect to survival. Now, we make the argument that fewer genes in the genome of a (presumably) less complex organism would necessarily imply greater mortality levels for individual organisms so affected. A mutation within a small genome represents a larger percent change and correspondingly greater consequences for survival than in a larger genome; all the more reason to question the survival of a species where each gene would have to be considered vital to organism survival. It's hard to imagine neutral chance mutations in a primitive first generation SAb genome. Thus, even greater numbers of organisms would be required to satisfy both chance mutations (necessary for evolution to work) and the increased risks to basic survival of such mutations compared to species genomes having large numbers of genes. But, in the beginning of a SAb OoL, such could not be the case. A founder SAb genome of necessity would have integrated only the most primitive, sufficient, and necessary genetic information and would therefore remain—for all intent and purposes—fatally vulnerable to the minutest mutational change. But again, the common solution for survival of species as well as the LS itself resides in the numbers. The RDH indeed hypothesizes starting out with large numbers (organisms, species, and genes)—all of which would seem to guarantee survival success. SAb hypothesizes beginning with single individuals—the first organism, the first species and presumably the first gene. But then again, SAb has a lot of explaining to do.

Getting back to our original ISRN discussion, the important question is whether we can treat living organisms in the same way as gas molecules. Real gas molecules within an enclosed volume act in a random fashion according to their chemical characteristics, and energy content and the thermal agitation of "competing" neighboring molecules. We can argue that living organisms of a species are contained within the area and volume confines of "biosphere space" that comprises their environmental niche and behave according to their organism characteristics, individual energies and degrees of freedom—subject as well to the behavior of the other competing members of the habitat. The ISRN rule suggests that when it comes to evolving species, decreasing numbers lead to convergence and extinction, while increasing numbers tend toward divergence and expansion.

Back To Square One—The Beginnings of Life on the Planet:

If large populations of life's participants are indeed what drive the continuous distribution curve mechanisms of evolution and adaptive selection to work so well to ensure the survival of the LS, then what conclusions can we draw about the beginnings of the LS at the OoL? We know that most spontaneous changes to the genes in DNA cannot be but harmful and that it is only the advent of large numbers of organisms and a limited number of such changes that permit the system to work. There had to be in effect, at the beginning, a very careful balance between mutations and population size for evolution to work at all. This is further emphasized by the ISRN rule. When a species comprises multi-billions of members, we can expect that the statistical rules will effect a smooth and continuous application of the mechanisms of evolution as described above. Remember, evolution is concerned with survival of the system and not individual members. As long as only a few members (species or organisms) are at risk at any one time, the system functions exceedingly well. We know that every individual organism contains genetic variations some of which could in theory put it at risk and prevent it from producing offspring. And those members that undergo genetic changes are necessarily put at risk in order to generate variability, fill out SA distribution curves of sufficient standard deviation width, and permit the system as a whole to move forward and adapt to changes in the biosphere. But, at the beginning,—according to both SAb and Panspermia—there were no large populations or distribution curves (of species, organisms, or of genes)—in both cases there had to have been, by definition, a single species under the control of a simple and primitive set of genes. Our whole discussion above mitigates strongly against this likelihood.

The bottom line for any OoL scenario: the mandatory inclusion of the sufficient and necessary numbers of species, organisms and genes in order for the statistical operational imperative of evolution to work is compelling. Below the critical values for any of these factors would have represented a no-starter with respect to evolution and consequently a disastrous beginning that could not have gone far towards survival long-term. In addition, we should not underestimate the negative influence of the second law of thermodynamics with respect to the continuation of any kind of SAb entity (an important issue that will be discussed in depth). This alone would have prevented the proliferation of a singular self-replicating entity to the point where adaptive evolution could begin. Accordingly, under abiogenetic conditions, we might well expect that the OoL would have led, rather quickly to the DoL (demise of life). Interestingly, only the RDH can substantiate the deposition on the planet of sufficient and necessary populations of species, organisms and genetic complements to account for: 1) the jump-start of biological life on the planet and, 2) the operation of evolution from the word "go". In other words, the only way for that to have occurred is for the LS system—lock, stock, and barrel to have been implanted on the planet as fully equipped operational populations of varieties of unicellular species capable of accommodating the initial conditions of the lifeless planet and primed to modify and tailor those conditions to future LS needs. Because nothing could be left to chance, the RDH maintains that nothing was—all of the details had to be in place.

The LS-Planet Symbiosis—By Chance or Design?

Not only has life been affected by the dynamics of the conditions to be found here on earth, but living things have become so intimately involved with the planet over the past billions of years that it is difficult to imagine how the planet would appear today had life not exerted it's profound influences, modifications and alterations that are ubiquitously evident. (In fact, this statement is not entirely true. We have just to look at any of our planetary neighbors in our own solar system to gain an appreciation of what lifeless planets look like.) This symbiotic interactivity that characterizes the influences the planet and its host life system exert upon each other has even been given a human label: Gaia. This reflects, from our point of view, the possibility that within the LS design was provided the capability to alter the makeup of it's habitat planet such that over the billions of years, the Earth has become increasingly compatible and hospitable to it's host life-forms. In effect, the LS has long ago met the challenge of terraforming the planet in order for this to be so. The first 2 billion years of unicellular and asexual life forms would have served that purpose well. We can also ponder the prospect that the LS was designed with that specific capability.

How Far Have We Come?

In the light of our elementary exercise in distribution statistics above, together with all of the considerations that flow therefrom, can adaptive selection and all it entails now be seen as the fundamental and primary evolution subsystem emanating from the LS? Can we now relegate natural selection from the inanimate environment to an all important but secondary role of filtering out novel but non-essential add-on organism physiology? Can we now accept natural selection for what it truly is—not really a selective process at all but simply a descriptive metaphor that represents the fact that some organisms survive to reproduce and some fail to do so? On the other hand can we now appreciate the fact that the LS—because of its populations of organisms displaying continuous distributions of SA's—does indeed possess the defensive capabilities able to counter the results of spontaneous changes to BA's; LS initiatives that incorporate imaginative population-effective strategies to promote LS survival? Admittedly, we may be seen as distorting the strict definition of natural selection, but we are, after all, trying to make a point: that before natural selection could even begin to come into play, the LS had already engaged numerous strategies built upon the principle of large population SA distributions. Whenever natural selection imposes itself, the LS comes equipped—ready, willing and able—to respond by surviving the ever present challenges it represents—all the while building larger and more diverse, if unpredictable, populations to meet the unforeseeable challenges of the future. Thus, from a SE point of view, we can state with some assurance that:

1] the mechanisms of evolution and the anticipation of adaptive selection must be considered part of the LS Design in order to achieve its mission (we have shown this to be a distinct possibility); and

2] the goal of the LS obviously *cannot* be the creation of any particular physical life-form, or level of complexity (an intelligent species, for example), because we have seen that none of that can be certain to be permanent—never mind predictable. This squares with reality and supports the assertion we made to this effect earlier.

In theory, there would seem to be little problem in accepting the above propositions on the merits alone. However, it would help our efforts significantly if we could come up with a possible alternative purpose (other than physiological complexity) for a time effective LS. Rest assured we will a little later on in our exercise. The above arguments have implications that go beyond the immediate issues. They impact considerably on the premise that evolution is, in fact, not primarily a question of "selection", natural or otherwise, but rather one of "anticipation"? The biosphere conditions change without purpose but the LS responds in dynamic ways in order to "purposefully" survive those changes—both short term and long term. Thus, since the LS is the partner in the duo that has within it the strategic wherewithal to respond purposefully and accurately to any and all changes, no matter what—it is fair to conclude that evolution and any selection process are really a function of life itself—comprising the ability to survive by *anticipation*. I'm convinced that it is! Put another way, since it is the LS alone that will survive or not, depending upon it's ability to anticipate and respond to changes in the planet, doesn't that success— achieved some would argue—in contradiction to the Second Law of Thermodynamics (law of entropy), entitle what is commonly called "evolution by natural selection" to be reconsidered as such? Remember, the planet has nothing at stake in LS survival. There are enough lifeless planets and one more probably doesn't make much of a difference. They remain part of the unfolding universe, regardless of whether they support biological life or not. So while the planet Earth may be ideally suited to the support of such life it can safely be stated that it is the LS that has transformed the planet biosphere, adapting it to its own benefit—all the while self-adapting to the changes its own antecedent members are responsible for bringing about. The point is that it is the LS that has over time taken effective charge of steady state planet dynamics wherever biology exists—on the surface, in the atmosphere, in the oceans, seas and rivers. It would seem that the only challenges that can truly threaten the biological Life phenomenon on this planet are changes to fundamental planet characteristics that could cause the destruction of the total spectrum of BA's that presently accommodate the LS phenomenon. The LS seems to be able to anticipate and adjust to everything else.

Evolution is—"Species Biosphere Attribute Anticipation" (SBAA):

And, if that is the case, then the question becomes: "Anticipation of what?" Let's go back to our Bell curve distribution of SA values versus biosphere environmental temperature for our imaginary species. Fig 8-C really tells the whole story. If we assume for the moment that all other variables remain constant, then the truth is that our species can easily accommodate a change in temperature in any direction. There is no risk for the species. Even though the temperature change cannot be directly anticipated, the fact is that the species is ready and waiting for such a change. And the same can be said for any and every variable SA that comprises the attributes of our species. The distribution of variables within every species is meant to ensure that—not if, but when—a change in any direction comes for any particular variable BA, the species will accommodate the change by readjusting the distribution for that attribute within the population. Of course, there will be times when the changes in a number of BA's simultaneously will overwhelm a particular specie's ability to respond. In that case, that species may be doomed to extinction, unless some of its members have sought refuge in some other geographic safe haven environment. In addition, any novel tag-along attributes will naturally have to prove themselves as beneficial down the evolutionary line if they are to become entrenched. The same can be said for older and obsolete attributes. But the shear versatility imparted by the wide statistical distribution of many interrelated genetic influences within a large species population is the key to why evolution works. And the biosphere, or nature as it is referred to in "natural selection" has a diminutive role to play at best. The statistical distribution and how variability is achieved is strictly an internal LS phenomenon. While the biosphere does influence the changing of the position limits of individual SA distribution curves, the LS makes sure there are enough such curves within enough organisms within enough species that insure LS system survival through adaptation. When failure does occur, the result is the extinction of the effected species. But there are lots more where that came from. The LS seems to be saying to the external environment: "We accept the challenge—give us your best shot! Some of us will survive." To this end, the LS enlists the additional versatility of many species occupying habitats distantly removed from one another both geographically as well as strategically. Organisms that occupy the bottom reaches of the ocean and hydrothermal vents are far removed from the microbes, as well as insects that inhabit the topsoil universally around the globe. Each of these habitats and all the others in between represent the additional critical measures the LS enlists to take care of all emergencies and contingencies. The challenge is to create habitats and exploit environments that include many interfaces that can effectively shield and protect species from harmful biosphere conditions. Included are any additional and unnatural insults that human excesses can inflict upon the biosphere that can affect countless environmental niches occupied by countable endangered species. Thus, we can conclude that evolution may be reinterpreted from the LS design point of view as "Species Biosphere Attribute Anticipation" (SBAA) subject to Adaptive Selection—all emanating from the LS—rather than the traditional "natural selection" coined by Darwin.

I cannot overstate the fact that the above exercise represents an over-simplification of what is a most complex process involving many variables. But, having stated the obligatory caveat, I believe the principles have remained intact. It can safely be said that, even today, no one is aware of all the details and intricacies that the term evolution implies. But, I hope that we have demonstrated that the basic governing principles are simplicity itself. Now, the question is whether we can reinterpret evolution according to LS imperatives.

A New Interpretation?:

The Biosphere is inhabited by millions of different species of the LS. To the extent that no single organism occupies the complete biosphere—but rather a particular niche that represents a small spectrum of biosphere conditions—we can think of the biosphere as representing a myriad set of overlapping niches whose sum total is the biosphere. A niche within the biosphere, in turn, represents the limited sum total of external conditions that are sufficient and necessary for the survival of one species of organisms. It's like a hand and a glove: one niche—one species—one geographic area (limited or unlimited). Taken together, then, all the species that thrive in the earth's biosphere match the corresponding global biosphere attributes including those specific to particular geographic localities. And in the process, much overlapping occurs. Does the LS occupy every possible niche possibilities in the biosphere? Surely not. But from what we already know about the LS abilities to survive, and judging from the number of species we have been witness to—both present and past—we know that the LS is continually inventing for itself new organism models to occupy some of the infinite combinations of environmental niche possibilities.

Thus, many varied species represent the answer to the challenge of how a) the LS fills the biosphere with biological organisms of species covering most of the biosphere attributes, while each species alone need only endure one niche worth of the spectrum of biosphere conditions, and b) the LS survives under continuously changing biosphere conditions (both: slow & long term, and fast & catastrophic)—not by natural selection but by *Species Biosphere Attribute Anticipation* (SBAA) subject to *Adaptive Selection*.

Systems Engineering Perspective:

In systems engineering terms, we might state the situation as follows: The living biological system we call life has established myriad species occupying as many environmental niches, separated geographically across the whole globe—each species representing a population of statistical events exhibiting SA distribution curves for all ranges of BA's within its specific environmental niche. The LS has done so by expanding its initial and limited range of compatible niches, all the while allowing mutations to species genomes to establish evermore SAs to fill those niches. Today, some 3.8 billion years after the OoL, the LS continues to expand its species compliment—while possibly approaching the very outside limits of the full spectrum of biosphere environmental attributes that can be accommodated by living things—restricted only by the physical constraints imposed by LS biology (the temperature range of liquid water, for example). In the process the LS has terraformed the planet—altering and reshaping the planetary biosphere—and has accordingly enhanced it's abilities to maintain the sufficient and necessary statistical distribution of species attributes required to ensure the survival of component organisms and therefore of the LS according to its design intent. As well, it has in place a very efficient multiple species strategy to overcome the possibility of total LS destruction that could accrue as a result of the occasional cataclysmic events visited upon the planet by excessive volcanism, meteorite impact and the like—by varying the distribution of species both structurally and geographically across the planetary biosphere. Question: Is this state of affairs compatible with a SAb scenario for the OoL?

Implications For SAb:

The consequences for the concept of evolution under the above idealized conditions are laid bare. No longer is it necessary—nor even logical—to propose that evolution may be part of the natural order of the universe—some self organizing mechanism associated with some unrecognized law of complexity. What we have demonstrated in Ch 8 is that if you remove the need of the offspring organisms of life to adapt to changing conditions over time by postulating unchanging external conditions, you can safely remove the concept of evolution from biological life, without threatening its existence. But, having done so, you have also removed any possibility of explaining the origin of such an LS by any abiogenetic process. Any and all SAb OoL hypotheses hang all of their collective hats on the magical influence of evolution to validate their scenarios. And then, as part of the mental calisthenics, they are forced to postulate (within an intellectual exercise that can only be described as some outrageous leap of faith) that there exists this nebulous unseen law of complexity simply to validate the unique organizing and adaptive qualities of the LS—all attributed to evolution. Just remove the need of evolution from the LS (as might well be under constant environmental conditions) and in that same stroke you remove as well the need to validate evolution as some natural principle—applicable to a chemical soup mix of proto-life molecules. Remove evolution from the equation, and the need to validate a rule of self-organization, or of complexity evaporates completely into this air.

To further hammer home the point, doesn't the scenario of a single adapted organism—one without predators and all of its needs supplied—really describe the very first moment of the supposed SAb of the LS. At the beginning of life, there had to have existed only one "species" of "pre-biological" life form. The very nature of it's coming into being (by chance) would imply that it had no strategy for coping with the continuously changing external conditions of the planet. Thus, how does one explain the survival of that single life form which could not have had the benefits of large population distributed SBAA (Species-Biosphere Attribute Anticipation)? In other words mutations alone—devoid of a population distribution phenomenon already in place—would more than likely decimate any nascent single species that would have comprised the original components of the LS. Thus, we cannot make a case for SBAA in the SAb case because there would not as yet exist the required statistical population distribution required for the mechanism to function. In fact, under these limited conditions, the opposite argument can be made—no mutations would be tolerable under a SAb scenario for the OoL with the existence of only a small population of a single species—the mechanisms of evolutionary change would tend to destroy rather than prolong the life of a single low population species. Yet, just a single species would have been the totality of the LS had the OoL occurred through SAb. Some might conclude that for these reasons alone SAb becomes untenable.

The only logical conclusion we can arrive at is that the LS must control both the mutation rate as well as the resultant bell curve distribution of member organisms in order for adaptive evolution to be effective. We have demonstrated the latter and will consider the former in the pages ahead. In fact, you could say that the LS uses the external biosphere conditions as a kind of *quality control* mechanism for establishing the outside limits of a number of applicable species attributes—thus shaping the SA distribution curves accordingly. The biosphere conditions change continuously and blindly. But only by controlling the critical aspects of the evolutionary process, (allowable mutations versus error correction rates) can the LS engage effective strategies for survival. All of these would have had to exist from the very beginning—at the OoL. And this is what one would expect from a system that was the result of design intent. Perhaps, therefore, design intent is the only way the system could exist at all!

Back To Reality:

But the planet and its dynamic activity are less than ideal and constitute a never-ending menu of dangers that claim large numbers of species continuously. Under these conditions, success of system survival demands strategies that not only keep pace with the unpredictable and never ending modifications to habitats but in fact must anticipate any and all changes by way of adaptation and/or designing new LS models (species) based on "add-on features" applied to the never changing PdP—that can endure or ignore those changes when they occur. Thus, by producing species whose environmental niche conditions amount to a limited number out of the totality of biosphere conditions, and by producing enough species and thus a great variety of niches, each consisting of a limited but different number of BA's, the LS survives—so long as there are species that escape any current biosphere changes. This can be due either to the remoteness of any given geographic location from the effects of change and/or due to the unique conditions of the niche that can act to insulate its species from different kinds of harmful change.

Thus, it becomes obvious that the operative principle of LS is: the more species, the greater the chances of some (at the very least, one) finding themselves in niches that are protected from unpredictable catastrophe. From a systems vantage point it would seem that survival of the whole through the sacrifice of some of the players (organisms)—but the survival of some others—"no matter what" changes occur—catastrophic short term or extreme in the long term—is a system imperative. As a system, then, the LS seems to be designed in order to survive both quick and drastic changes over the short term (drastic changes to many but never all of the attributes represented by niches) as well as the slow and long term changes that characterize an evolving planet.

The Bottom Line—"Evolution Is Strictly An LS Phenomenon":

So, while SAb enthusiasts see evolution being driven primarily by the selection process, that is, that the external conditions select individuals with adaptations of varying fitness, we—following the above exercise—see evolution as being primarily driven by a process that precedes natural selection and even anticipates it. And that has been our limited aim all along.

Seen from this perspective, evolution now becomes a cornerstone in the development of the Rational Design theory of the OoL. We shall continue to develop the idea that different species simply expand the survivability of the whole system of life and represent modular components that can, by their diversity, overcome any and all environmental changes to the planet as a whole. The LS accomplishes this by creating unique species that carve specific environmental niches that are well insulated from other niches and therefore separate the modular components of life, thereby ensuring the survivability of at least some and very definitely at least one. Life goes on.

Evolution Within Its Appropriate Perspective:

We have so far developed the notion that the LS comprises a basic biological eukaryotic PdP—constant both in biological space and time—which includes the built-in capability of creating add-on physiological variations. The resultant life forms, called species, are then able to interface with their respective external environments according to the collective abilities afforded in this regard by the novel physiological structures appended to the bottom line PdP. Evolution is thus responsible only for these add-on changes, and not for the design itself. This idea is a major departure from current SAb dogma, which defines the evolutionary processes in terms of responsibility, not only for the changes in the form and function of individual species, but implicated in the very origin of biological life. However, recent developments in genome technology may indeed lend greater credence to the PdP concept.

The successful sequencing of the first genome of a multicellular organism was received with great fanfare among molecular biologists[3]. The organism—a nematode comprising barely one thousand cells and measuring barely a millimeter in length would seem to have little in common with higher life forms. Yet, despite all appearances of simplicity, this organism has a primitive nervous system that includes a brain, digests food and reproduces sexually. A better measure of its complexity can be gained from the fact that this tiny creature's genome comprises close to 20-thousand genes (comparable to the human genome). Also by comparison, a yeast cell contains of the order of 7-thousand genes. These numbers speak volumes—both quantitatively and qualitatively. Firstly, all three species are made up of essentially one kind of cell model—the eukaryotic cell. By comparing the genomes of the yeast cell and the nematode, it was discovered that they share approximately 3,000 identical genes. The overlap between the yeast cell and worm genomes suggests there is a core of about 3,000 genes that are crucial to the workings of eukaryotic cells. The core genes are thought to encode proteins that play roles in basic cell activities such as DNA synthesis, skeleton construction, protein transport, and chemical signaling. The molecular biologists are planning to compare the balance of the genes—17,000 in the worm and 4,000 in the yeast in the hope of finding an explanation for how multicellular animals differ from single-cell eukaryotes. Our interest, of course, is the core of 3,000 genes. We should not be surprised to one day discover that same essential genetic core within human cells—essentially identical to worm cells and yeast cells. In our view that genetic core—whatever the exact number of core genes turns out to be represents the genomic PdP of biology and represented by the phenotypic PdP—the essential stripped down eukaryotic cell. The SAb point of view will naturally refer to this 3,000-gene core as a core of genes "conserved by evolution". We, espousing the rational design thesis defer to the essential genetic PdP whose core of genes is "conserved from evolution".

Evolution, according to our contrarian view, is limited to a description of the results as well as the processes of change that have transformed the PdP into the enormous varieties of species that exist presently, as well as those that have come and gone in the past, on our planet. The significant principle associated with the concept of a PdP is the implication of a biological constant or "bottom-line", upon which evolution can apply in layers, all manner of novel physiological form and function, which themselves are temporary manifestations—in virtue of the fact that all species appear to be temporary and experimental in nature. The PdP, on the other hand never changes. Only the variable genetic information in the informational database that gets expressed changes. The Leggo-block analogy works exceedingly well here. The biological Leggo blocks are represented by cells built upon a constant PdP, while all manner of variation of structural form and function can be assembled around the versatility built into the PdP. All of the innumerable variations of shape possible are analogous to the innumerable species that have come and gone. In the end, what you are left with are the basic building blocks—Lego-block-like biological cells.

The key to species survival through adaptation revolves around population size. That alone can virtually guarantee both the approximation of a Bell-shaped SA distribution curve and the continuity of the distribution. In this way, the distribution of SA values, and the movement in the corresponding environmental BA's create, not so much a phenomenon of so-called "natural selection" instigated by the external biosphere, with the LS in the role of hapless victim, but rather—the situation whereby the LS prepares (by producing sufficient and necessary distributions of SA's), waits, and anticipates any and every movement in such BA's as they occur. We describe such a survival strategy of statistical response programming as the *"Adaptive Selection"* mechanism on the part of the LS. Natural selection selects nothing. Survival, as we have argued, is based simply and totally on an organism successfully passing through all of its survival "AND" gates and reproducing offspring. Diffusion reproduction, whereby the shape of the SA distribution curves moves in response to changes to the genetic pool of surviving species members, and population genetics accomplish the rest. We would maintain that there is nothing "natural" about it.

Complex Species: Serendipity or Design?

We have made the argument that evolution represents a built-in strategic adaptive subsystem of the LS subject to internal controls and constraints. The results reflect themselves as a multitude of species, finely adapted to their respective distinct environmental niches. And, each species reflects a set of additions (not changes) to the primary cellular design platform that is common to all. As such, the eukaryotic PdP represents the lowest level of complexity of LS form and function. It is after all, the sufficient and necessary biological composition for the LS to operate. Thus, every species derived from the PdP must represent a level of form and function that is more complex than the PdP from which it is derived. You might say that this is a neat way to explain the phenomenon of the evolution of greater complexity within species. Any add-on change to the PdP qualifies as greater complexity. However, it is known that for the first 2 billion or so years of the existence of the phenomenon we call life, the participant organisms were unicellular forms exclusively. So all the different forms of life we find today must have descended from them. But, there is only so much complexity that can be squeezed out of a unicellular form. The real question is how to explain the evolution explosion that occurred during the Cambrian era. It is characterized not only by the quantity of new life forms, but also by the complex quality of many of them. How can the issue of increased complexity be understood and appreciated? According to SAb, "There is no foresight—only hindsight" in the game of organism survival and species evolution. They fortify their point by emphasizing that there is no possible way to predict the direction of evolution and moreover, given the opportunity of a replay of evolutionary history under identical starting conditions, that the results of evolution would probably differ—such being the extent of evolution unpredictability bordering on "chaos". But that, in a sense, is too easy an assessment and fails to adequately address the issue, as we shall eventually see. The answer lies within the design scenario postulated in the RDH.

The Evolution Agenda According to the RDH:

If the LS was indeed a designed system, as our Rational Design Hypothesis asserts, then it can be assumed that the initial seeding of the planet would have been accomplished with the kinds of organisms that could not only thrive on the planet, but could alter the earth in such ways as to eventually permit the system to take hold and flourish. These initial organisms would have had as their first task the initial survival of the system. As such, the mix of organisms (eukaryotes) deposited on the planet for that purpose would have been composed of a large spectrum of evolutionary possibilities, the prime purpose being to permit some of these to accommodate to the particular harsh conditions of the initial planet biosphere at that instant (OoL) in its history. The rest that, over time, could not adapt—because their particular combination of species attributes lay outside of the spectrum of planetary biosphere attributes—would have served, together with the bacteria staple (the only reason bacteria would have been included), as the initial food and resource sources until steady state conditions prevailed for food chain activities to establish themselves. This primordial period of acclimatization of the LS to the planet would have endured so long as the planet itself was undergoing rapid geological evolution. It could be expected that this might last as long as 2 billion years before some of the additional levels of built-in LS complexity potential could come into play e.g., aerobic metabolism when oxygen levels permitted and sexual reproduction to correct an unacceptable level of genomic errors. By the time the primordial bedding-in phase was completed, the LS would have comprised a sufficient quantity and variety of organisms spread across many environmental niches—neatly and firmly in control of its destiny of survival to achieve its design intent.

The number of E. coli bacteria in the gut of each human exceeds the number of humans that ever lived on this planet. The late Stephen J Gould—eminent molecular biologist—raises this point in order to diminish in our minds the importance of relatively few organisms (within the aggregate of complex species including humans) in the LS scheme of things when compared to the ubiquitousness of bacteria both in space (planetary real estate) and time (as long as they have been around). I would only make the point that the basic unit of multicellular life is the eukaryotic cell, and a single human being includes the cooperative contributions of 60 thousand billion such cells, each one of which is vastly superior to the E. coli bacterium in size and composition (E coli is a prokaryote, our cells are eukaryotes). The point could be made that 60 thousand billion cells working in close proximity and harmony might constitute a more efficient (as well as complex) utilization of resources than the same quantity of teeming unicellular organisms—each fending for itself and in danger of choking off those resources when crowding takes place in the environment. It may be a trivial point to suggest that a fairer comparison between the e-coli and human species might be in the realm of genetic information production. Each e-coli bacterium comprises a single copy of its genome (approximately a million base pairs), which gets copied just once when it clones a daughter replica. A single human being comprises 60 trillion cells, each of which contains 2 copies of its genome (one from each parent), each of which in turn comprises 3 billion base pairs. Add countless more as cells replace themselves and male sperm cells are continuously being manufactured (and spent). Taking into account the human population on the planet at 5 billion (5×10^9), we get 1.8×10^{33} base-pair bits of information. And, that's just one species of mammal. Add on to this figure the genetic information of all of the other multicellular species and perhaps his argument can be viewed in a somewhat different light. My intention here is not to compare the importance of one species over another because there exists no valid LS criteria to do so. As stated, prokaryotic bacteria have their role to play, both as recyclers of biological material and constitute the base of the food chain pyramid. Unquestionably, when it comes to numbers, the bacteria win out handsomely. But, when you consider complexity, the case can be made for multicellular species. Nevertheless, each species—past, present and future—comprises an important contribution to the fabric of the LS, and would not exist if it did not fit in exquisitely within the overall structure of the LS. Each species is a winner in the survival game simply in virtue of its having played some role, no matter how short or long its history.

Finally, and in fairness to Gould, (someone I greatly admire) I appreciate his admonition that we humans seem to take ourselves a little too seriously, considering ourselves innately superior in the scheme of life. If that is his main message, I would heartily concur. This acknowledges our argument that complexity is neither an incidental attribute of life, nor its goal. As stated earlier: _The potential for complexity is a primary property built into the evolutionary capability of the LS that affords the maximum adaptive capacity within biological space to insure the survivability of the system._ It might even be described as an _"emergent"_ property of the LS—a term Gould himself has helped to popularize.

We shall expand our appreciation and understanding of the building blocks of the LS, as we contemplate the biological components whose basic form and function comprise the PdP at the Micro level of biological Life. Our task in the following chapters is to define in detail the kinds of phenomena the PdP represents together with the kinds of complex subsystems that allow the LS to function according to a design intent—both as an operating system of survival—all the while serving the well defined purpose or mission statement that the LS design is meant to address. Our first challenge in this regard is to examine the major lifeform classifications of the LS in order to see if we can home in on the physiological nature of the PdP, i.e.: its phenotypic properties. It would be nice if we could do the same from the direction of the corresponding informational genotype, but that would be too much too ask. The technology simply does not exist at the present time. However, we can expect that some time in the future, molecular biologists may indeed be capable of elucidating the genetic components in common that get expressed as the PdP.

---

[1]What Is Life: Erwin Schrodinger p18
[2]The Neutral Theory of Evolution: Motoo Kimura [7a] Scientific American, Nov 1979, p. 124
[3]Science News: Vol 154; Dec 12 98; p 372

10. The Micro Level of Bio-Life

"Biology can neither be reduced to physics nor do without it"

Francois Jacob (1920–), Biologist[1]

The Biological Cell—The Living Building Block of Life:

All living organisms are composed of cells. The biological cell is the basic unit of life and the lowest common denominator of all living things. The single cell represents the minimum requirements of a biological organism (with the exception of viruses, which are a special case). Cell size varies from prokaryotic bacteria, which measure as small as one hundred thousandth of an inch in diameter to the eukaryotic ostrich egg, (which is indeed a single cell) measuring five inches across. The cell is the basic logistical unit of life wherein all the biological functions called "living" take place, under the direction of the genetic information residing in its DNA informational molecule(s). Biologists know a lot about how these complex functions take place. But how a cell "knows" how to perform these amazingly coordinated functions is still a huge mystery.

Few entities within our experience can claim to show so much diversity of form, on the one hand, and similarity of function, on the other as the biological cell. Thus, while no single cell can be said to be typical of all cells, their similarities outweigh their variance by a long margin. The differences are readily apparent when we compare and note the variation in physical attributes of the multitude of unicellular organisms, from acantharia (one celled animal) to the diatoms; from single celled algae (plants), to the many forms of bacteria, and protozoa as examples. Add all of the specialized cells that have evolved to give cooperative life to multicellular plants and animals, and the list seems endless. One aspect of cells that places each within its proper perspective is the fact that every cell owes its existence to a preexisting cell. Rudolf Virchow articulated this generalization in 1858 while researching the origin of cells. He might not have realized it at the time but he was essentially seeking answers to some of the same questions we are asking. What is the OoL if not the origin of the first cells, back billions of years ago, that gave rise to all of the others forward in time? As well, he probably had no idea that he was embarking on an intellectual journey that would have moral and ethical consequences more than a century later. The moral issue concerns the determination of when life begins. The answer we as a society eventually settle upon will carry considerable social and ethical significance. Of course, had human civilization been paying attention to Virchow's message, based on incontestable logic, we would comprehend the simple truth: following the OoL, there has never been a lapse in the continuity of the process. All living things are a part of that nonstop LS enterprise. Therefore, the question of when does life begin becomes, in effect, illogical from a fundamental biological viewpoint. And, philosophically, it probably has no more relevance that asking when does the day begin. We may arbitrarily determine that the day begins at 12 o'clock midnight, but we know that the earth continues to spin on its axis such that there is no real beginning, nor end of a day, but rather the continuity of time. And, so it is with the continuity of life. Morals and ethical constructs are, of course, another matter that civilizations must contend with. SAb (abiogenesis) insists that at the very beginning there must have been just a single cell. The RDH insists that the cells that exist today are the descendants not of just a single cell, but are the survivors of an initial population of cells.

All of Life's functions are essentially the accumulation of cellular activities. Despite the often radically diverse differences apparent in the forms of unicellular species, the principles of cellular function—based on a core of unalterable genes—are virtually identical among all species at the molecular level. And, those principles, of course, are part and parcel of the PdP concept we have introduced. The cells of complex multicellular organisms are further individually specialized, within the framework of evolution, in order to produce the many kinds of tissues, organs and structural elements (e.g., blood, muscle, liver, lung, skin, nerve, kidney, etc) that must function together as a single coordinated living entity. As a consequence of the specialized and limited roles individual cells play within a complex multicellular organism, the vast majority (estimated as high as 99%) of the information within their respective genetic libraries may never be expressed. So, while the many kinds of cells exist and give expression to the respective roles they play within the organisms they comprise, we have defined those differences as add-on configurations to the basic PdP that are the heart of the biological life phenomenon. Thus, any description of cellular form and function inevitably must comprise a description of the form and function of the cellular PdP, which lies at the root of all of biology. How do we make a determination of what constitutes part of the PdP and what can be considered to be add-ons, acquired under the influence of evolution? As suggested previously, one way is to examine the genomes of a group of diverse representative cells, side by side and determine what is common among all of them. If you then subtract the differences, what you have left over should represent the PdP. A figure of 2 to 3 thousand genes has been suggested as representing the core informational database that gets expressed as the PdP of cellular biology.

In the recent past, it was common procedure to group life-forms according to their shared morphological traits. That's how and why prokaryotes and eukaryotes became the dominant classifications—separating bacteria (the prokaryotes) from everything else (eukaryotes). The modern approach, pioneered by Carl Woese, tends to group organisms according to their biochemical and genetic similarities, and attempts to take into account when their respective genetic lines may have diverged from a common ancestor. But, regardless of exactly which life-form preceded which, one thing is clear from a logical perspective: all rely on a common scheme of form and function that is the PdP basis of the biological phenomenon. Abiogenetic SAb insists that there was a single origin phenomenon that would have been represented by a single cellular format, from which all other formats—archaebacterial and eubacterial have sprung. But they go even further and suggest that even that first biological cellular entity itself was derived from an earlier, non-biological self-replicating entity—a protochemical precursor to biology. And, if need be, they will defer to an even simpler model of self-replication in order to bridge any additional gap—physical or logical, real or imagined—that could appear. Again, anyone playing the OoL mystery game must confront the interface problem which separates any easy transition between the sought after chemical analogue that represents an initial self-organized, self-replicating chemical entity—one that represents a departure from chemistry as usual—and the eventual biological entity that goes on to parent all of the biological life that comprises life on the planet earth. The problem is, that while biologists are able to point to evidence suggesting more ancient biological phenomena, such as archaebacteria, nowhere do we find evidence that would tie the most primitive cellular phenomena to a chemical source. Nowhere do we detect an intermediate characteristic of physics and chemistry that could serve as a much needed logical link between inanimate chemistry and biology—that missing would-be chemical state of self organization that could be described as a bridge between the opposite poles that represent life and non-life. As far as we know, chemistry and the laws of nature seem to fall radically short of serving as any kind of logistical bridge. On the biological side, the very simplest life form we can imagine, is the simplest cell enclosed within an environmentally protective membrane, containing the simplest genetic library from which genetic instructions direct the complex protein factories to produce the quality and quantities of biological material required. Of course all of this activity requires copious amounts of energy conveniently supplied by the cell's integrated power plant. What we are describing here is your most primitive biological cellular entity, whose sufficient and necessary composition represents two simultaneous concepts.

a) The biological side of the interface that separates natural random chemistry from biology, and

b) The Primary Design Platform (PdP) of biology below which biology cannot be reduced.

The Cellular Primary Design Platform (PdP) of Biology:

Proteins represent the universal structural elements of life from which all the operational mechanisms of the LS are constructed. It is the proteins and the almost limitless possible kinds that can be constructed and experimented with that in fact account for the results of evolutionary change within the LS. Proteins come in many different sizes and shapes. Some have been conserved for billions of years and have achieved a kind of permanence, being found in virtually every organism and doing virtually the same job. All aerobic organisms, for example, use enzymes called cytochrome oxidases in the manufacture of high-energy storage ATP molecules. They are considered to be primeval proteins that are present in all aerobic bacteria, fungi, protozoans, invertebrates, vertebrates and plants. And because the nucleotide base sequence of the gene that codes for this gene has been slowly changing for hundreds of millions of years in each of the respective genomes, it can be compared in two different species and used as a kind of stop watch to estimate the time elapsed since they evolved from a common ancestor.[1]Indeed, it is just this kind of molecular biological investigation of bacterial genetic material that led Carl Woese to the conclusion that there existed a distinct group of bacteria, labeled *Archaebacteria* that deserved a unique life-form classification. Woese's work involved the study of the RNA in the ribosome protein assembly sites of bacteria (referred to as rRNA). His discovery of three distinct rRNA patterns within bacteria warranted the reorganization of the family tree of biological life forms into three branches instead of two, leading to further speculation about the existence of an ancestor common to all. We shall examine their differences as well as their similarities in order to try to pin down the consequences as they relate to the PdP, and as well, the consequences as they relate to the OoL.

The Family Tree of Biological Life—The Old Paradigm:

Until Carl Woese came along, the old biological family tree paradigm comprised two major classifications of living things within the LS, from which it was considered all present life forms are descended:

Prokaryotes: organisms lacking a cell nucleus, comprising all bacterial species, and

Eukaryotes: organisms and cells possessing a self-enclosed nucleus, comprising all other (and more complex) life forms.

The existence or lack of a cell nucleus represented the most significant distinction between all of the diversity found in living things. This indeed could be considered to be a most extraordinary state of affairs when you think about it. The implication for the existence of a PdP becomes simplified beyond expectation with the realization that the prokaryote entity could qualify by default. It is by far the simpler of the two. But having made the point, you can't define the differences between the two by simply putting the prokaryote and eukaryote formats side by side and subtracting the differences. First and foremost, eukaryotes are of the order of one thousand times larger than the prokaryotes that make up bacteria and have a lot more biological machinery to boot. You can't just strip down a eukaryote and end up with something resembling a prokaryote. Neither can you simply extrapolate the much more complex eukaryote backward and represent the differences as the effects of evolution add-ons. The stretch is just too great to be readily credible. A biological quantum leap separates the two. Before we can render a simple statement about the origin of the eukaryotic cell, we shall have to examine very closely the implications within the new family tree paradigm introduced by Carl Woese.

The Family Tree of the LS—A New Paradigm:

In the old paradigm described above, archaebacteria were lumped in with the prokaryotes as they also lacked a nucleus. But they were considered as peculiar curiosities in comparison, not only with other bacteria, but with each other as well. The new LS family tree model distinguishes archaebacteria as a second separate prokaryotic life-form classification—each in turn radically different again from the eukaryotes:

1] Archaebacteria: Archaebacteria life forms are aquatic or terrestrial, aerobic or anaerobic, and as a rule, are grouped into seven major groupings in accordance with their strange lifestyles. These include:

Methanogens (subdivided into three groups): bacterial organisms that give off methane gas. These are found in such diverse locations as hot vents on the sea floor; oxygen free mud at the bottom of swamps; in sewage disposal plants.

Thermopiles (subdivided into three groups): bacterial organisms able to withstand high heat. These are found in volcanic hot sulfur springs at temperatures in excess of 113 to 122 deg F.

Extreme Halophiles (Halobacterium): bacterial organisms that thrive in salt-saturated water. These are found in salt lakes and the Dead Sea.

It is not only their curious living habits that distinguish archaebacteria from the rest. Morphological differences from the eubacteria and eukaryotes include: the existence of ether lipids instead of ester lipids in the cell walls; the number and structure of their ribosomal proteins; the shape of the ribosomal "S" unit; and the utilization of different metabolic pathways, enzymes, and enzyme cofactors.

2] Eubacteria:—any of a group of so-called "true bacteria" that are not included within archaebacteria. These organisms include the majority of bacteria as well as the photosynthetic blue-green algae (cyanobacteria).

3] Eukaryotes:—any cell or organism that contains a clearly defined nucleus enclosed in a nuclear membrane within which are located well-defined chromosomal hereditary material. Included are a host of complex machinery, equipment of all kinds and support scaffolding totally absent in the other two life-form classifications. The eukaryotic branch of life is certainly dear to our hearts, inasmuch as this branch of life includes us humans. Before the excitement sets in, rest assured that we have a lot of company within our life classification—including all our fellow plants, fungi (any of about 50,000 species of organisms including yeasts, rusts, smuts, molds, mushrooms, and mildews), ciliates (single-celled organisms of which there are some 8,000 species that, at some stage in their life cycle, possess cilia, short hair-like organelles used for locomotion and food gathering), flagellates (protozoans, that possess, at some time in the life cycle, one to many flagella for locomotion and sensation, including parasitic forms that live in the intestines or bloodstream of their host—many other flagellates live as plankton in both salt and fresh water), microsporidia (any parasitic protozoan of the phylum Microsporidia, found mainly in cells of the gut epithelium of insects and the skin and muscles of fish), as well as our animal brethren.

So, while eukaryotes represent only one of three distinct classifications of life as we know it, it is responsible for pretty well all of the life forms we would describe as complex. In truth, everything else is simply bacteria. Given this structural classification of LS life forms, what can we conclude with respect to the issue of a PdP? Do we simply choose the least complex and call that the PdP, as with the old paradigm? Furthermore, can we simply assume that eukaryotes evolved from either of the other life branches? Could a stripped down archaebacterium represent our model of a PdP? Can we consider an original archaebacterium as the founder species of biological life from which later evolved eubacteria and later again eukaryotes? This latter position is becoming popular among SAb supporters for some good and valid reasons. If as SAb postulates, the first biological organism must have been the most primitive and simplest self-replicating cell, then a founder archaebacteria species could certainly fill the bill. On the one hand, their current representative species on the planet are considered to be the least evolved organisms, in virtue of the exclusivity and unchanging environmental niches they have "carved" for themselves. As well, while their respective present lifestyles reflect the whole palette of extremes in harsh conditions to be found on the planet today, those same conditions could logically be considered to be not un-similar to those thought to have prevailed at the time life is considered to have originated, close to four billion years ago. Thus, the argument goes—life on the planet might have started off as archaebacteria—eventually splitting off into eubacteria, and eventually again giving rise to eukaryotes.

With respect to eukaryote complexity, it is becoming popular to consider that much of that complexity arrived, not by slow incremental evolutionary steps, but by its founder ancestor swallowing up some smaller bacteria that cooperated in an exercise in symbiosis that caught on (previously discussed in Ch 8). Such a scenario would seriously consider an early eukaryote absorbing a small bacterium that could perform photosynthesis, and thus possibly giving rise to the chloroplast in photosynthesizing eukaryotic plant cells. A similar scenario is projected for the origin of the mitochondria in both plants and animals that are implicated in a different cellular energy conversion mechanism, converting energy into adenosine triphosphate (ATP), the energy currency of the cell. Mitochondria and chloroplasts share certain structural resemblance, synthesizing some proteins and dividing according to their own genetic instructions. Both have a somewhat independent existence within the cell. Thus, both mitochondria and chloroplasts serve as the powerhouses of the cell. However, despite such analogies there are convincing arguments against the symbiosis scenario and consequently against any attempt to link the eukaryotic cell as having evolved from its primitive prokaryotic cousin. One such argument concerns the fact that genetic information needed for the reproduction of the photosynthetic apparatus is contained partly in the chloroplast chromosome and partly in chromosomes of the cell nucleus. The carboxylation enzyme *ribulose 1,5-bisphosphate carboxylase* is a large protein molecule comprising a complex of eight large polypeptide subunits and eight small polypeptide subunits. The gene for the large subunits is located in the chloroplast chromosome, while the gene for the small subunits is in the nucleus. An extremely complicated procedure is required to combine the two separate messenger RNAs that result from the transcription and translation of the genetic information from both sources to ultimately yield the synthesis of the completed protein enzyme. If indeed the chloroplast was the result of a symbiotic transaction, it is hard to imagine the logical circumstances that would result in the separation of its genetic instructions followed by the formulation of complex procedures that would serve to nullify the effects of such separation during chloroplast synthesis. Complicating matters further in some cases is the fact that the expression of nuclear genes that code for proteins needed in chloroplast synthesis appears to be under control of events in the chloroplasts themselves; e.g., the production of some nuclear-encoded chloroplast enzymes may occur only when light is absorbed by chloroplasts.

These additional complications requiring the extraordinary signaling between separate genetic data bases argues against a simplistic symbiotic negotiation as a basis for the existence of such sophisticated eukaryotic sub-systems.

The Contrarian View:

We begin our dissenting view of the relationships between the three classifications of life with a discussion of where we agree. Let's begin with the obvious. The premise that eubacteria are derived from archaebacteria does not require a terribly difficult bit of logic. After all, both archae and eubacteria are first and foremost bacteria. They both comprise prokaryotic cells, the most primitive biological format possessing the most basic cellular machinery, and have similar chemical form and function of their DNA genetic medium, in which is encoded their genetic libraries. Their metabolism and reproductive mechanisms show more similarities than differences. There are even species of eubacteria that are heat lovers (Therotoga), though less so than the extreme thermopiles of archaebacteria. Woese suggests that all bacteria were originally thermopiles, at a time when the planet biosphere was much hotter.[2] And in general, it would seem to be a reasonable hypothesis to suggest that a more ancient prokaryotic bacterium—archaebacteria could have given evolutionary rise to a more recent prokaryotic bacterium—eubacteria. Our problem (and its a big problem) is in any attempt to make the same kind of causal connection between archaebacteria, (or any other kind of bacterium, for that matter), and eukaryotes.

The differences between archaebacteria and eukaryotes appear to be extreme on a number of levels. Can an evolutionary link be forged between a bacterium (any one you choose) and the cellular format that gave rise to all of the complex life forms on the planet? Putting any chauvinistic notions aside, the answer to this question is resoundingly in the negative. We will soon examine why. But before we do, we should begin to think about the consequences of that position; the moment we raise into question the origin of eukaryotic cells (i.e.: deny that it evolved from primitive bacteria), we are placed in a new position vis-à-vis the concept of a PdP. If, for example, we concede that eubacteria derived from archaebacteria, then logic dictates that eubacteria derived from the appropriate [Go + (M's + m's)] according to the formula derived in chapter 8. Go by definition becomes the conceptual PdP of life, as derived from archaebacteria. Are we now going to suggest that eukaryotes did not derive from the same source? What then happens to our concept of "Go", or the "PdP" for that matter? Our answer is that while we agree that our reticence to accept archaebacteria as the founder species of eukaryotes complicates matters somewhat, such complications are more than offset by readjusting our concept of PdP just a bit. What if we postulate two separate founder species of cellular life—each of which served its cooperative role towards achieving the design intent of the LS? Could that scenario square with the facts on the ground? Could we then resolve the question of the PdP satisfactorily? Do the facts coincide with the RDH? The answer is "yes" on all counts.

Reexamination of the PdP Concept:

Before we examine the prokaryote cells of archaebacteria and eubacteria and compare them with the eukaryotic cell, we should at this point redefine—or rather extend—somewhat our concept of PdP. Any design platform, by definition, reflects the design intent as it appears within form and function. Our concept of PdP as it applies to biological life begins with the establishment of a set of sufficient and necessary operating principles ubiquitous throughout the LS—one that defines the constant biological PdP accordingly. Our definition includes all of the cellular activities common to all cells, whether bacterial or eukaryotic—including the translation of genetic information into physical proteins, and the means of implementation of all of the genetic instructions that all living processes depend upon. Activities such as metabolism, reproduction, feedback control, communication, the form and function of the genetic code, the quantity and types of amino acid building blocks, the chirality of proteins and nucleic acids—are all ubiquitous properties common to all living cells—prokaryotes and eukaryotes alike. If it lives, it is operating according to a basic PdP, which could be described as the simplest generic self-replicating biological cell. This reduces to the simplest prokaryote with the smallest genome capable of life. We shall label this PdPp (prokaryotic primary design platform that enables the simplest life-forms—bacteria—to function as living organisms). So, what of eukaryotes? Where does the eukaryote cell fit in?

Obviously, if eukaryote could not have derived from bacteria, as we believe logic suggests, then it had to have been engineered as a more sophisticated living entity. It could still operate, and indeed it does, according to the dictates of the basic biological PdPp described above, except that its role within the LS design intent is a more sophisticated one than that of bacteria. As such, we could consider the existence of a discreet eukaryotic PdPe—one that is essentially ubiquitous to all eukaryotic cells; one that reduces to the sufficient and necessary level of capabilities that would allow it to function as a generic eukaryote. Of necessity, it would still operate within the fundamental parameters that characterize the PdPp (which operates at the more general and basic levels of biology). But it would also reflect the additional parameters of form and function particular to eukaryotes—the kind of considerably more sophisticated primary design platform that would enable the LS to utilize the full potential of the LS to establish through the internally directed processes of evolution the full spectrum of life-forms that have come and gone throughout its history. What each of these bottom-line PdPs (prokaryote and eukaryote) have in common is their constancy—the fact that they themselves are not subject to evolutionary change over time. That is what the "primary design" designation is meant to imply. Also, the fact that we do not find intermediate forms between prokaryote and eukaryote suggests they indeed represent different PdPs and therefore separate origins as well.

Two PdPs Are Better Than One:

Obviously, if you are going to have two PdPs, their justification should outweigh any complications such a suggestion might cause. Consider the following:

1] The PdPp (bacterial primary design platform) representative of only the very basic functioning of the living process appears to have very limited evolutionary capabilities as evidenced by the fact that while it is considered the biological basis for two out of the three branches of the revised family tree of life, nonetheless its evolutionary achievements stop at the level of complexity of bacteria. Thus, while there may be innumerable species and sub-species of bacteria types built upon the PdPp, there is a barrier that seems to limit their evolutionary line to unicellular, and generally asexual bacteria. In that sense, the evolutionary potential of the PdPp is "closed-ended".

2] The eukaryotic branch on the family tree of life seems to have unlimited potential for evolutionary experimentation. Any comparison between eukaryotes and everything else becomes almost embarrassing by comparison. It is the only branch that has the evolutionary capability of branching out in every direction, and the only one capable of producing species of increasing complexity. By contrast, the evolutionary potential of the PdPe is "open-ended". Most importantly, prokaryotes and eukaryotes are sufficiently different in so many ways to preclude the derivation of the one from the other through the intermediary of evolution.

With the above as backdrop, we can now propose a possible purpose for the existence of each PdP as delineated above:

a) The PdPp—as stated serves as a bottom line technological framework for the biological processes of life. It also serves as the biological limit within the interface between biology and chemistry. While it is the sufficient and necessary logical basis for all life processes, the rudimentary level of biological complexity of the PdPp limits the role it can play in the creation of novel species through evolution to prokaryotic bacteria exclusively. In addition—and most importantly—we will demonstrate that it is the eukaryotic PdP that encompasses the actual design intent of the LS. Prokaryotes will in due course be shown to lack the necessary operative features to be able to serve more than a limited and subservient role within the LS. Thus, from a design point of view, prokaryotes can be viewed as the means to an end—varieties of autotrophic bacteria capable of converting many different kinds of energy sources into stored biological energy. Simultaneously, they have important roles as 1] scavengers (garbage detail), and 2] recyclers of biological refuse. Plus, they are capable of using almost any organic compound as well as some inorganic salts as a food source. Most importantly, as a direct result of these activities, bacteria comprise the very bottom of the food chain pyramid and serve as a universal direct source of nourishment for many species.

b) The PdPe—represents an extremely more complex design platform. The results speak for themselves. If we were to make a choice as to which branch of the family tree of life had the more significant operative role to play, within a design hypothesis, it would certainly be the eukaryotes. As we explore the differences between the prokaryotic and eukaryotic design platforms, we shall come to appreciate, not only their extraordinary differences, but as well the fact that the one (prokaryotes) is ideally suited to play its assigned role—as described above—in the service of the other (eukaryotes) within the context of a RDH design intent.

A hint at this stage of our deliberations would not seem inappropriate. In fact, we supporters of the RDH would suggest (as it will become clearer later on) that bacteria (both eu—and archae-) were introduced to the planet, to serve as the original food source for the original eukaryotes implanted on the planet at the OoL. The availability of sunlight some 4 billion years ago might have been considerably limited compared to today, so that it might have been imperative that the bottom players in the food chain be versatile autotrophs, capable of synthesizing biological resources from a variety of external non-biological sources. Thus, the role of the prokaryotes was meant to serve as the initial food source for the unicellular eukaryotes that were implanted on the planet at the same time. To serve in that capacity, by definition, prokaryotes must be composed of the same building blocks (amino acids) as the more complex eukaryotes. Food chain activity can only function when both "eater" and "eatee" share well-matched components so that the former can recycle the resources of the latter. Thus, from the RDH vantage point, bacteria and eukaryotes were conceived as independently derived entities—based on independent PdPs.

Prokaryotes and Eukaryotes—Different As Night and Day:

There are real problems with any scenario that tries to model the eukaryote cell as the evolved product of archaebacteria. In fact it will become apparent that the only reason one would even attempt to do so would be to validate the SAb option. Like so many of the other issues we have discussed so far, supporters of SAb in effect have no real choice in the matter—they are forced to ignore any difficulties that arise that are a direct consequence of the SAb position—no matter how stretched and contrived the logic involved. The following discussion centers on the obstacles to sourcing eukaryotes from archaebacteria—or, for that matter—from any other kind of bacteria.

Despite efforts to explain away the evolution of eukaryotes from simple bacteria as an exercise in symbiosis, it plainly doesn't make any sense that the one, so complex could derive from the other—so simple. The planet is a large enough place, such that if the one could derive from the other, then we should definitely see evidence of all kinds of intermediate forms, or diverse examples of the kind of symbiosis suggested, as an important mechanism of cellular evolution from the less complex to the other. Additionally, symbiosis cannot account for the many other complex organelles and structures found in eukaryotes—structures such as the nucleus enclosing the DNA library, including its compliment of introns (unique to eukaryotes), the endoplastic reticulum and many other cellular membranes, and a host of other equipment, mechanisms and scaffolding uniquely ubiquitous to all eukaryotes. In addition, let's not forget all of the differences in function from metabolism, to sexual reproduction, to speciation. Where are the intermediate stages that should have found refuge somewhere—anywhere—within the vast biosphere of the planet? These are among the reasons such a clean transition from bacteria to eukaryote is hard to imagine, let alone accept. It just doesn't wash!

As stated, the RDH postulates the premise that each—the archaebacteria and eukaryotes represent two independently designed LS components—each introduced to the planet biosphere as part of a composite system in order to serve totally different assigned LS purposes. The eukaryotes' function is to survive at any cost—in order to carry out the LS design intent. The bacteria's function was to serve as the original food chain for the "operative" eukaryote life forms. The RDH would tend to lump all bacteria together as serving the same basic function. The novel differences to be found among bacteria species currently extant on the planet we would ascribe to bacterial species attributes (SA's) that are in synch within the spectrum of BA's that currently define the planet biosphere. Thus, any bacterial species introduced on the planet at the OoL whose descendants could not adapt to biosphere changes would have disappeared as the casualties of extinction processes. Those original bacterial species whose descendants continue to survive and thrive within diverse environments can be expected to represent a motley assortment of disparate prokaryotic forms. It is up to biologists such as Carl Woese to try and make "head and/or tail" in the attempt to categorize individual species in some organized way. Regardless of the particular design features that separate bacterial species, all bacteria occupy similar roles within the overall system of bio-life on the planet—the very bottom of the food chain. We would suggest that that original role has not changed in any significant way. Today, while still serving in that capacity, bacteria serve, as well, the all-important role of breaking down no-longer-living biological materials into their basic amino acid building blocks in a planet wide recycling program. Not only are valuable biological resources reclaimed, but also bacterial activity serves in an ecological restoration capacity for the biosphere. Without this kind of biological garbage processing, the whole LS could conceivably grind to a halt eventually in a kind of exponential runaway contamination effect that might well choke the system itself. Bacteria collectively operate as an effective biological cleanup crew processing the accumulation of biological debris into bio-reusable resource materials. At the same time, the biosphere is continually refurbished, like some baseball park after a game, made ready to welcome new participants into the game of life.

This is not so farfetched a scenario when you think about it. But, before we get too carried away with the idea, let us examine the typical eukaryotic cell in order to try and visualize how different it is from a typical prokaryotic bacterium. Then, we will be in a better position to judge. Just keep in mind some salient facts: all LS life forms—apart from bacteria—are based upon the form and function of the eukaryote design format. It thus also appears to be the sufficient and necessary cellular configuration for the existence of complex biological life. Archae and eubacteria, on the other hand, seem to be only the sufficient and necessary cellular configuration for bacteria, and appear to lack the capability of evolving into little else. We are confident that if that statement were false, then many examples of "something else" would be evident. The implication in all of this is that there appears to exist an impenetrable physical and logical interface that separates prokaryotic bacteria and eukaryotes—one every bit as important (if not as distant) as the interface that separates chemistry from biology. In the final analysis, it is the RDH alone that can not only justify these seemingly impenetrable interfaces, but explain them as well. SAb, unable to do either, simply refuses to acknowledge their existence. Let William of Occam (and ultimately you, the reader) be the judge.

The Generic Cell—A Study In Genuine Complexity:

Our aim in the pages ahead is to convey the fact that at the micro(scopic) level, biological activity is a far cry from inanimate chemistry. While much of biology is indeed chemical in nature, it can be argued that biology, far from reducing to chemistry, in fact actually "utilizes" the medium of chemistry, as part of its design, to achieve its goals. The uniqueness of LS form and function as differentiated from natural phenomena really becomes apparent with the realization that all of the functions of bio-life derive from, and all of its activities can only take place within, a very specialized and protective environmental enclosure—that of the cell. This reality in particular—the cell serving as an absolute physical interface separating life form and function from the randomness of the natural world outside—argues convincingly that what goes on inside the cell is not just special, but anything but natural. The added fact that we have yet to find any other examples of anything remotely resembling this kind of phenomenon and that most of what happens within the confines of the cell never occur, nor can occur, anywhere else but within the confines of the cell simply reinforces both the perception and reality. The implications are that any attempt to extrapolate biology backward in space or time to natural chemistry is bound to come up against logistical challenges of the highest order. Indeed, these are the challenges faced by any SAb OoL option. Our position all along has been that it absolutely cannot be done. Let's take a look at some more of the reasons why not.

From the menu of activities to be found going on in the sophisticated biological structures within all living cells it is easy to imagine and accept that the bonding forces characteristic of universal chemistry—that hold together individual atoms in the macromolecules of life—assume extraordinary complex roles. This is due in large measure to the fact that biological molecules are in general so much larger than ordinary chemical molecules and can interact with many other such entities. A relatively simple protein may comprise many hundreds of amino acid building blocks whose atoms help to shape it's three dimensional structure—each atom occupying a specific place and assuming its unique bonding influence within the molecular architecture. As a result of the myriad combinations of amino acid components within protein structures, bonding forces "compete," almost, in trying to influence and restrain adjacent atoms. This imparts a unique dynamic to the architecture of proteins that elevates their capacity of function many levels of magnitude above the characteristic activity of ordinary random chemistry. And while the composition of all biological life-forms (bacteria as well as eukaryotes) consists primarily of protein and other material produced within biological cells, the eukaryotic cell contain so much more biological machinery and represent the highest biological level of cellular form and function.

> *"A host of microscopic machines keep things moving: pumps, motors, channels,*
> *highways. So much so that you have the feeling that we never invented anything,*
> *life did it before. We are just discovering!"*[3],

is how one noted scientist put it. The cell can be regarded as the manufacturing facility for all biological materials called for in the functioning of the activities of life. The cell also houses within its DNA library all of the detailed instruction manuals that direct its internal housekeeping activities including instructions for damage repair, and the complete set of instructions for the cell's own duplication as well as that of the organism (be it "multi-" or "uni" cellular) of which it may form a part. The total DNA library of information forms, in effect, the "genetic blueprints" of the cell and hence the blueprints of life.

Fig 10A: Schematic Diagram of the Generic Eukaryotic Cell

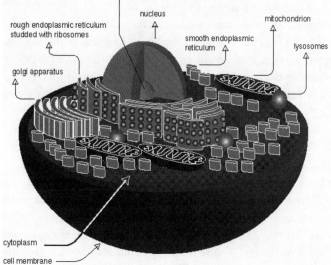

As stated, the bottom-line basic living entity is the simplest prokaryotic bacterial format. It is a fully operational manufacturing facility and as such can be described as a set of discreet functional components. (At this level, we will only be interested in cell form and function). From the above schematic diagram of the eukaryotic cell, we can appreciate the analogy of the cell as a manufacturing plant (perhaps industrial complex is more accurate). In practice, it works well because indeed the layout of the individual and various cell machinery within the protective cellular environment is distinct and systematic. But actually appreciating the reality of the metaphor seems to be a problem for most of us. The reason is not difficult to surmise.

Our life-long experience with biological material of all kinds has generally left us with an unhelpful ingrained impression. Let's face it, in contrast to hardware—which has a solid mechanical feel about it—the wetware of biology is squishy to the touch, and more often than not, has an unpleasant smell. And I'm referring here to living tissue. Nothing about it betrays a sense of the kind of mechanical efficiency we have come to respect as exemplified by the mechanical wonders engineered by humans. When a mechanical machine breaks down, we can put it in a corner somewhere and come back any time later to repair it. It still looks and feels like the machine it was designed to be. When biological machines break, repair must be immediate or the whole thing becomes subject to attack by other living things (microbes and the like) and begins to disintegrate almost before our very eyes. The result is an odoriferous, pulpy mass that is best removed quickly before it causes damage (disease) to healthy organisms. The very sight of damaged life of any kind leaves many of us squeamish. Indeed, the physical aspects and appearance of most biological material belies any idea of an orderly, organized, exquisitely controlled and functional facility. Throw bacteria into the discussion and the general impression is one of danger. They are responsible for spoiling our food and making us ill—and best dealt with utilizing measures to effect their immediate eradication. In sum, our general attitude towards bacteria is: "A good bacterium is a dead bacterium!" But, make no mistake about it. Any genuine appreciation of the functioning of the biological processes at the microscopic bacterial level at which the cellular machinery operates, leaves little doubt about the naiveté that characterizes the intuitive feel most of us possess for the subject. Most of us have never examined the living cell under the microscope. And even if we did, there is nothing apparent that could really excite the imagination. From time to time we have seen pictures in the media showing electron microscopic views of cells magnified tens of thousands of times. Exciting is hardly the word to describe the experience. By contrast, the publication of a miniaturized computer chip magnified to show all those neat parallel lines evokes a sense of wonder at the ingenious technologies of which they are superb examples. We are further impressed when informed the huge sums the chip manufacturer has spent in the development and manufacture of these postage stamp-sized marvels that control computer operations.

By contrast, what does a cell cost? We have been told variously that the market value of the raw materials that go towards the makeup of an adult human being amounts to no more than a few dollars—perhaps $100.00. Now, we know that the adult human body at any given moment comprises of the order of 60 trillion (60,000,000,000,000) cells. At that rate the average cost would run around about six billion cells per penny, more or less. But remember—that is only what the raw materials are worth. If we had to factor in production costs by some hypothetical outside contractor, at the price per unit commensurate with today's computer chip costs, we might find the price of a human sized organism quite staggering—and that of an elephant all the more so. And then there are design costs to consider. But, living things that form part of the LS don't have start-up costs in the traditional sense, nor production costs, for that matter. They remarkably, and casually, reproduce themselves without great difficulty and just for the energy outlay of gathering the necessary raw materials (food) alone. Then again, every minute, a thousandth of a penny's worth of cells are replaced in the continuing rhythm of repair and maintenance that comprises the living human organism. No wonder it is difficult to really get excited about a phenomenon that is so cheap, so small, and so common. So much for perceptions.

The fact remains, that even the simplest prokaryote bacterial cell is a feat of miniaturization, precision, and accomplishment that has no equal in human experience, and whose origin continues to defy explanation, despite some fanciful scientific speculation. As biologists of all kinds elucidate and gain access to knowledge of the multiple levels of LS operation and control, the true extent of the microscopic marvel that is the living cell becomes increasingly apparent. And when we describe the biological cell as a factory or production facility, we are in fact being restrained by our own limited experience. Nothing the human intelligence can conceive of—including the fanciful exercises at artificial life simulations—comes even remotely close. And far from being magical or mystical, the operative procedures of life at all levels are being shown to lie well within the logical application of the universal laws of our universe. In truth, nothing at work in the living processes as exemplified by the biological cell lies outside the bounds of ordinary physics and chemistry. Even the cells that comprise the wetwear of the human brain obey these basic tenets of nature, and yet their resultant collective output that we call the mind continues to boggle that same mind and defies our comprehension. It is our intention in these pages to reawaken you to the complexities and the mysteries that accompany any genuine description of this phenomenon that we call the living cell. But rather than dwell on the difficulties faced in uncovering the different parts of the LS puzzle at the microscopic level, our approach and intention is to portray the LS in a context that makes it's form and function easier to appreciate in terms of its two PdPs we have defined above. At the same time we intend to raise new possibilities as to its origin by elaborating on the idea of LS purpose and design intent. Again, we can only hope to accomplish this because of our recognition of the way the basic unit of life functions—as a fully integrated industrial complex complete with hierarchic controls and management. Happily, this is a field that the engineering mentality can relate to and appreciate. Through it all, our purpose is to glean some sense of the overwhelming complexity that sets apart the PdP of life from ordinary chemistry.

Prokaryotes and Eukaryotes—A Comparison:

Structural biology is a relatively recent innovative field of biological research that serves to delineate further the continuing specialization occurring in all bio-scientific research. It concerns itself with, the mechanics of the molecular machines that mediate the basic complex biological processes of the LS. It attempts to elucidate the structures and functions of the molecules of life. These macromolecular complexes are characteristic of all cells; the agendas of all living cells are similar. But, how they go about achieving those goals vary considerably. In addition eukaryotes have an additional agenda item associated with their extraordinary open-ended abilities to evolve the whole canvas of complex life forms—including our human selves.

Our concern with structural biology is limited to how it is implicated in the generic workings of the life processes within both kinds of PdP at the molecular level. It parallels the study of transistor and computer chip materials and circuits and how they react under different conditions to the applied electric fields at the molecular level. In both instances, what happens at the level of molecules and their constituent atoms determines the emergent results at the micro and macro levels. As we have often stated, the atomic and molecular phenomena present in the biology of life adhere precisely to the same universal laws that dictate the chemistry of non-living phenomena. The only difference between the two concerns the limited canvas of chemical elements used within the LS and the explicit and precise directions that control every aspect of LS chemistry, as compared to the total randomness that characterizes inanimate chemistry. Also the non-random living processes have the distinction of being capable of creating future generations of more complex assemblages of living molecules. Our aim here is to provide a sense of the complexity of the sub-systems operating at the molecular level that propel the system of life and elucidate some of the differences that exist between the operating PdPs of the prokaryotic and eukaryotic branches of life. While we may marvel at the level of extreme miniaturization at which the machinery of life operates, we should not lose sight of the fact that these complex subsystems are no less machines than the printing press, the water pump, the electric generator or the catalytic converter that human engineers design to solve their problems. Biological machines, in contrast, are extremely small and don't have the same kind of mechanical moving parts. These little machines produce results that are not to be found outside of living systems and therefore have particular significance from a systems engineering point of view.

Cell Functional Components:

A) THE ESSENTIAL CHEMICAL COMPONENTS OF BIOLOGY:

The acronym CHONPS is composed of the six single letter symbols for the six lighter elements that comprise the atomic constituents of the decisive polymers of life. Carbon, hydrogen, oxygen, nitrogen, phosphorus and sulfur are the essential components of all of the nucleic acids, most proteins, all of the sugars, and the structural substances such as collagen, cellulose, chitin, and lipids of cell membranes. They also make up the structures of metabolism such as the energy donor ATP, as well as all of the pieces of the Krebs cycle—the chemical engine that produces it. In addition, chlorine, sodium, potassium, calcium, and magnesium play indispensable roles within the fabric of living biology. The roster of elements found in biology round out with iron, manganese, cobalt, copper and zinc—any of which are involved in trace amounts as single atoms held in an organic complex such as chlorophyll or heme, or built into specific enzymes such as catalase or reside within ionic fluids in or around cells. In all, only 25 out of the total of 83 long-lived elements are known to be required in the operational form and function of biological life. Fourteen are essential at levels of one part in ten thousand (by weight) or less.

The above information provides a clue as to how modern industrial environments have become implicated in pathologies that negatively affect health processes. If traces of zinc are essential to tissue growth, for example, then traces of cadmium—an element alien to biology—can replace and mimic zinc, generating embryonic defects not unlike those that follow zinc deficiency. The fact that only 25 out of 83 natural elements (30%) found in the earth's biosphere are used by the LS could also be considered as a telling and significant clue with respect to the OoL. One can question whether an LS derived naturally within the biosphere of the planet would have neglected fully 70% of the elemental resources available to it. One can also question whether an LS derived naturally would tend to or even be able to prevent the casual substitution of deleterious trace elements, such as cadmium, in place of those essential for the operation of complex biological structures. These are the kinds of questions our SE inquiry must address and explore. These are the kinds of unsettling issues SAb has so far neglected to deal with.

B) THE CELLULAR PLASMA MEMBRANE:

The external cell envelope, only one half-millionth of an inch thick, encloses the stuff of life and serves as the interface between the living cell and the external environment. This separation of the inside living system space of life from its outside environment is known as *"compartmentation"*. In this respect you could say that the cellular external membrane—sometimes referred to as the *"plasma membrane"*— is what both separates and joins the living processes from and to the external environment. (In addition to the plasma membrane, plants exhibit an external cell wall made of cellulose.) The plasma membrane assumes different but equally important roles in both prokaryotes and eukaryotes. In prokaryotes, it is probably the most complex structure of the cell, responsible for energy generation, protein secretion, chromosome segregation and the active transport of nutrients. This multi-purpose structure also regulates the flow of nutrients, and maintains the necessary cellular milieu, while preventing the loss of the cell contents, referred to as the cytoplasm. Not only must the plasma membrane protect the delicate living system from the exterior environment but must as well communicate with that environment in order to "know" what the conditions of the neighborhood are. Within bacteria, this ability is limited and the response can vary depending upon whether the cell has means of locomotion (flagella or pili structures)—in order to move towards food and benign environments and away from toxic and incompatible environments. In eukaryotic cells, the business of knowing what goes on within proximity of the cell is serious business indeed, and in multicellular organisms can involve the cooperative reactions of multitudes of sensitive cells.

Tens of thousands of receptors stud the eukaryotic cellular membrane like so many radio antennas tuned and sensitive to signals of interest to the welfare of the cell[4]. The messages and receptors, in the form of proteins come together and form the first step in a chain of such reactions that extend protein-to-protein, ultimately resulting in triggering actions and responses that emanate from the genetic library in the nucleus of the cell. This communication network, from membrane to the DNA library, is the quintessential stimulus-response phenomenon that characterizes any centrally controlled system that can take appropriate measures demanded by and in response to changing external conditions. (In systems engineering, it is referred to as "feedback control".) As well, the membrane must serve as the gateway for the acquisition of nutrient resources and raw materials and the exit pathway for the waste products and heat resulting from the metabolic processes going on inside. The above list of functions dispels any simplistic notion of the external cellular membrane as merely some kind of sac holding the guts of life together although it does that job impressively well. The plasma membrane defines the internal spatial limits of the cell's activities and serves as the front line of defense against changing external conditions. Through the channels and pathways that permeate its surface, the cell can send and receive electrochemical messages, as well as permit the entry of all sorts of chemicals, salts and liquids. At the same time it must keep harmful things like poisons and viruses out. It must be sufficiently resilient to withstand abuse, sufficiently flexible to withstand division without losing its contents and sufficiently permeable to the selective diffusion of materials in and out of the cell. All of which leads one to inquire: What kind of space-age material is this membrane made of? The answer is *"lipids"*.

To be more precise, the membranes of all eukaryotic cell structures are composed of four kinds of *phospholipids*, which bear a special relationship with water molecules. This is important when you consider that cell membranes essentially form divisions in cell space, both sides of which are essentially aqueous. Phospholipid molecules have a special shape and chemistry characterized by a phosphate head region that is *hydrophilic* (water loving) and a hydrocarbon tail that is *hydrophobic* (water hating). Thus, a membrane typically is composed of a bilayer composed of two sheets of phospholipid molecules, each composed with all its hydrophilic phosphate groups oriented in the same direction. The two sheets line up such that the hydrocarbon tails of one are in contact with the hydrocarbon tails of the other, forming the interior of the membrane while the phosphate heads are in contact with the water molecules on each side of the bilayer. How truly effective a membrane seal is created by these phospholipid molecules can be appreciated when you consider what happens when you puncture a cell with a micro-needle—

nothing. The molecules of the bilayer move toward one another sealing the hole and preventing the cell from bursting or collapsing. Although both sides of the bilayer have been shown to be physically symmetrical it has been found that the chemical properties of each are fundamentally different and depend on whether they are facing the exterior aqueous environment or the cytoplasm (inner) side. It is considered that this same bilayer membrane design has been in existence since the very beginning of life on the planet. (If that is so, one might well wonder how it came into existence). As such, it can be considered to be an integral part of both PdPs.

c) Shipping, and Receiving Through the Cell Membrane:

Cellular activity consumes large amounts of raw materials and energy, which must flow into the cell, and the products of _respiration_ (oxygenation) and waste materials must flow out. Both are accomplished by means of complex mechanisms of membrane fusion called _"pinocytosis"_—that permits the uptake of nutrients from the solution surrounding the cell, and _"exocytosis"_—which does the opposite.

External cell membranes contain a variety of "pumps" and "gates" that selectively allow the passage of food molecules, inorganic ions and intercellular metabolites from one side of the membrane to the other. Using systems of ion channel pumps, electrochemical and osmotic pressures create the flows necessary to welcome desired materials into the cell and expel waste to the outside. Protein complexes are able to pump molecules against concentration gradients in order to maintain the critical living environment and internal conditions that both permit and promote the operation of the life processes within. One such mechanism, the sodium-potassium pump uses about one-third of the total cellular fuel (ATP) just to maintain the sensitive intercellular low sodium and high potassium level ambiance. Other protein structures act as tiny gateways through which pass oxygen and nutrients in one direction and carbon dioxide and waste products in the other. In vertebrate cells, calcium sensitive _"gap junctions"_ permit the unimpeded transfer of many small molecules such as sugars, amino acids and nucleotides from one cell to another. These gap-junctions can close down in response to an abnormal rise in calcium levels.

Cell membranes serve as a combination of structural walls, alarm systems, shipping entrances and exits, conduits, plumbing and cell communication system that interfaces with the outside world—all rolled into one. They serve as both barrier and interface that separates and bridges, respectively, the business of life from the external dangers that life must avoid and the resources that life requires. Everything must be kept in precise balance. They are at once multi-functional, efficient and astonishingly complex.

d) Additional Physical Structures of the Eukaryotic Cell:

Physically, the cell comprises three basic components, which provide the protective internal environment for life: the first, discussed above is the plasma membrane, which typically comprises 100% of the cellular membrane surface area of prokaryotes compared to only 10% in eukaryotes. Within the interior of the eukaryote cell can be found two additional internal membrane systems labeled the _endoplasmic reticulum (ER)_ and the _golgi apparatus (GA)_ that divide up cell space into specialized operational compartments. The ER plays a significant role as ribosome attachment sites for protein synthesis as well as sites for lipid production. *Golgi complexes* comprise thin, flat saucer-shaped storage containers for cell products. They take in polypeptide chains produced by the ribosomes and connect carbohydrates forming *glycoproteins*. The GA is involved in the packaging of proteins as well as the production of protein derivatives—products that are exported outside the cell. In plants, the GA serves as well to provide the material from which the cell walls are constructed.

Lysosomes act as storage bins for the hydrolytic enzymes used in the digestion of nutrients. Digestion involves the break down of long protein chains into smaller building block components (amino acids) that can be recycled by the cell for the production of the proteins it needs. Most cellular membranes contain a variety of protein molecules inserted into the lipid bilayer, some of which pass right through and protrude from each side. These are non-symmetrical with specific regions that face exclusively inward or outward.[5] Individual phospholipid and protein molecules do not maintain fixed orientations but are in constant motion and movement within the two-dimensional fabric of a given membrane. As such the cellular membrane has been described as a two-dimensional liquid (referred to as the "fluid mosaic model"), with all of its constituent components in continuous diffusion motion. A "self-sealing rubber tire" is one description of the cell membrane able to repair tears and holes by means of the diffusion of adjacent hydrocarbon molecules.

E) THE CELL NUCLEUS:

The cell nucleus is the specialized membrane enclosure that protects the critical integrity of the genetic instruction library from contamination or alteration as a result of the frenetic activities within the cell proper. It exists in eukaryotic cells and is non-existent in prokaryotic cells that characterize bacteria. But then, bacteria are a thousand times smaller than the eukaryotic cells that comprise plant and animal organisms. Because both their role and evolutionary potential within the LS is considerably limited, bacteria need contain remarkably less DNA and obviously function relatively simply, yet well enough, without the added protection afforded by a separate enclosure membrane for their genes. The nuclear membrane envelope evident in eukaryotes has been shown to comprise a special outpocketing of the *endoplasmic reticulum*. It contains large numbers of uniform pores through which must pass all the transcribed RNA that encodes the genetic information the cell manufacturing facilities use as the working instructions in their protein manufacturing activities. Within the nucleus reside the intricate and tightly packed chromosomes and hereditary apparatus comprising the total genetic library of the cell—all the instructions the cell will ever require for its life function, repair and reproduction encoded within the DNA molecular medium. Interestingly, it has been demonstrated that a surprisingly large percentage of the information in eukaryotic DNA never leaves the nucleus. A little later on in our exercise, this fascinating fact will be thoroughly investigated—but not merely as one additional difference between the eukaryote PdP and prokaryote PdP. It will ultimately prove to be one of the most important physical clues pointing the way to the resolution of some of the most controversial issues plaguing our discourse.

Nucleoli are the manufacturing sites for RNA molecules and contain concentrations of RNA used to create the messengers that convey genetic instructions to the ribosome production facilities of the cell. *Chromatin*, a network of DNA rich material, contains among other things the specialized proteins (*histones*) which play a critical role in the packaging of all that DNA so as to fit comfortably within the chromosomes without becoming entangled. The nucleus is also the site where the DNA copying processes occur—to prepare working copies of individual genes and the total replication of the genetic library when the cell divides to become two cells. Because the genetic information is encoded within the molecule of DNA itself, it can be argued that DNA represents the ultimate compact information storage and retrieval system—the envy of every computer chip designer. Perhaps the day will come when technicians will be able to package extraneous information within a chemical medium like DNA. Perhaps someone already has!

F) THE CYTOPLASM:

While bacteria may differ substantially in their surface characteristics, their interior contents display similarities, homogeneity and relatively few structural features; not quite so simple in the eukaryotic cell where the cytoplasmic ground substance comprises the balance of the internal aqueous cell environment, containing the various organelles and microbodies vital to cellular operation. This comprises two distinct phases: 1) a complex protein—rich polymer support structure referred to as the "*microtrabecular lattice*", and 2) a fluid water-rich, gel-like phase that fills the interstices or spaces in the lattice.[6]

Being directed within a typical eukaryotic cell are a whole menu of complexes: the *ribosomes, lysosomes, mitochondria, centrioles, Golgi complexes, endoplasmic reticula, cytoplasms, nucleoli* and *responsive "G proteins"*. If we consider each of the above as a different and independent system, then each must carry out a specific function, producing or storing a specific product. Additionally, there are the cell's "*proteus zones*" which have been described as the cell's internal garbage incinerators where unneeded proteins are destroyed and recycled. What's more, the nucleus, wherein resides the instructional database, must also act as a sophisticated communications center in order that these different production facilities be able to communicate with each other, as well as respond to all kinds of external signals, as in any cooperative venture. It must be able to receive progress reports about what each subsystem is doing from the far flung reaches within the boundaries of the cellular domain in order to coordinate the orderly flow of goods, energy and services to and from the various parts of the cell. Everything must be kept in precise balance to counteract the tendency of natural physical and chemical forces toward randomness and chaos according to the dictates of 2nd law thermodynamics entropy. It has been demonstrated that proteins can pass along molecular signals through the "proximity effect" of dimerizing whereby they latch on to each other or to other molecules in relay fashion. In this way, the nucleus generates and transmits messages to the rest of the cell informing the different manufacturing units to turn on, produce more, or less of their specialty products or cease operation altogether. These messages are able to stimulate particular actions on the part of distinct facilities as well as selectively inhibit activity in others. As well, the cell must be able to act upon the streams of information continually arriving from the outside world (outside the cell plasma membrane). *Signal transduction*—as the process is called—permits signals that emanate from outside the cell to activate selected genes to produce specific and appropriately balanced responses.

g) THE CYTOSKELETON:

In general, the stuff cells are made of has been termed *protoplasm*. Long thought to be a homogeneous protein rich solution, the term evokes images of some kind of soft and gooey mass within the cell enclosure without having any definite structure. The fluids in cells had been known to have sufficiently high viscosity to impede all motion while their molecules constantly jolt and jostle the minute cellular bodies as a result of thermal agitation (Brownian movement). Because of the small size (ratio of volume to surface area) and generally homogeneous nature of the interior, this is not problematic in prokaryotic (bacterial) cells. Eukaryotic cells are a somewhat different matter. They are typically a thousand times larger than bacteria and contain a quantity of internal specialized machinery. Thus, the inclusion of a physical framework to preserve the cell's internal spatial integrity becomes a physical necessity. The accurate picture of eukaryotic cellular structure that has emerged in recent years is that of an elaborately scaffolded interior providing a well laid out support framework of spaces and passageways that house the cell's many organized facilities and activity sites. But, this is a support framework with a difference, comprising fully one quarter to one half of the protein in a cell. The eukaryotic *cytoskeleton*, as this active framework is called, maintains the cell's desired shape and provides anchoring for a variety of cell bodies called *organelles*. It is dynamic in the sense that its fundamental components are often assembled, disassembled and moved from one end of the cell to the other.[7] *Centrosomes* and other so-called cytoplasmic elements act as organizing centers and initiating sites for some of these activities that influence cell shape. Throughout the cell, structural elements such as *microfilaments* (made of the protein actin which can bear tension and of myosin which can initiate contraction), *microtubules* (made of a protein called tubulin which provides rigid support), and *intermediate filaments* (which are elastic, flexible and strong)—serve such purposes. Microtubules also serve as intercellular highways along which all kinds of organelles and vesicles are shuttled about by mechano-chemical proteins operating as organic engines. Although all eukaryotes possess cytoskeletons, it is recognized that the shape and component structure vary by kind of cell. Thus, the amino acid sequence of tubulin in sperm cells is similar but unidentical to that in nerve cells. The same is true of the different isoforms of actin. But, the actin found in human muscle more closely resembles that in fish muscle than does the actin in human neuron. This strongly suggests that each family of protein is derived from a single genetic ancestor and modified through evolution over time. The cytoskeleton—implicated, as it is, in the most fundamental activities of eukaryotes, including reproduction, interaction and movement—also acts as a kind of grid system that works in conjunction with a genetic addressing stratagem to direct molecular traffic around the cell. It is thought that messenger RNA contains a biological version of a "zip-code-like" identification scheme that the cellular version can scan to identify and direct RNA to the appropriate cytoskeleton address. Indeed, the end of the messenger RNA for one such protein, vimentin, has been considered as possibly serving in that capacity as it does not contribute code for protein expression, yet has remained a cellular constant for some 200 million years. Cytoskeletons, as well as their associated protein components, are absent in bacteria.

H) LOCOMOTION:

Both prokaryotes and eukaryotes may be equipped with "motorized" *flagella*, that provide for physical locomotion of the single-celled organism, or with *cilia*, that provide for the transport of material along the cell membrane surface similar to the actions of a conveyor belt. Microbiologist, Lynn Margulis has suggested that the first such flagellum might have resulted from the engulfing of a spirochete (long twisted bacterium) by an early prokaryote, through a process referred to as "*endosymbiosis*".[8] (You will recall that this same mechanism is believed by some scientists to be responsible for the acquisition by an ancestral eukaryotic cell of other external components as well—including mitochondria and plant chloroplasts. You will also recall our skepticism.)

Feedback Control—A Defining Ingredient For PdP Viability:

If we tried to give credence to Henri Bergson's "elan vital" (living force of life), we would probably have to settle for the extensive system of feedback and control mechanisms that permeate the PdP of biology. Indeed, it can be said that the difference between inanimate chemistry and animate biology is that the latter comprises integrated complexes of controlled chemistry, and more precisely "feedback" controlled chemistry. Considering its ubiquitous application throughout human designed systems, we would do well to examine carefully the unique capabilities of "feedback" principles and how they might contribute to phenotype integrity in particular and LS operation in general. This is another instance where human "feedback control" design efforts pale in scope as compared to that found within the operational biological cell. We have become used to discovering in nature, and particularly biology, examples of design principles that engineers then borrow and utilize. Human concepts such as insulation (animal fur), and flight (wings of birds, bats) derive from biological sourced analogs. In our present systems engineering exercise, we are put in the position of reversing the traditional flow of ideas. By using our experience with human engineered control systems we will try and identify in a general way the operation of similar control systems fundamental to the operation of biology—not only those that comprise an integral part of the primary design platform of the LS, but implicated within the concept of embryogenetic viability success and viable organism integrity as well.

It is probably true that no real understanding of biological life is complete until the control mechanisms that maintain life-system operation are understood. However, the basic principles of all control systems share common elements, regardless of their application. Control systems come in an assortment of general variations—all of which may, in one way or another, be implicated in the governing of biological phenomena. The advancement of the theory and practice of automatic controls has paralleled that of systems engineering—both greatly accelerated by the high performance requirements of sophisticated military equipment. There are two distinct kinds of automatic-control systems used by human engineers in system design: "open-loop" and "closed-loop". It is understood that the systems that control and direct all of the many subsystems that allow the LS to function have been around a lot longer and are noticeably more complex than anything we may have dreamed up. Human designed control systems rely on some general principles:

Open Loop Automatic Control: In an open-loop system, an input signal (or command) is applied and a power output is obtained, e.g., a temperature control for an electric furnace. The input is the manual setting of a dial calibrated in degrees. The output comprises the power given up by a heating coil and the controlled quantity (or load) is the temperature of the furnace. The key to open-loop control systems is the one-way flow of information. The input signal alone dictates the output action.

Closed-Loop Automatic Control: The closed-loop automatic control system has essentially the same basic components as open-loop plus some additional features. The actual output is measured and a signal corresponding to this measurement is compared with the input (desired output). The difference signal is processed and used to modify the input signal. When the two signals compared are the true input and output signals, that difference signal is called the "error". Thus, in a closed loop system, the command signal can be designated as the "actuating signal" comprising the combined influence of the desired result (input temperature dial setting) and the real-time result (actual furnace temperature). Control systems are classified according to the manner in which the actuating signal is used to control the power output:

"on-off" Controller: This type of controller uses the "error" difference between input and output to turn a process on or off. Typical examples are room thermostats and electric refrigerators—where the heaters or compressor, respectively, are either on or off.

"step" Controller: Adding one or more timing mechanisms to the basic on-off controller permits the application of power in steps to achieve the desired output. The output is measured and continuously compared with the desired condition. The error can then be used to adjust power input only at preset time intervals. As a refinement of the technique, the duration of applied power can be made a function of the error magnitude. The power can thus be applied in pulses and the temperature rises in steps (rather than continuously).

"continuous" Controller: Commonly referred to as "feedback control systems", the error is used to control the magnitude and direction of the power applied. Continuous controllers can be sub-classified as regulators and servomechanisms. The term servomechanism defines the basic unit of control used in human designed mechanical systems. One of the principle pioneers in the field of feedback control was H.L. Hazan who originally defined the term "servomechanism" as "a power-amplifying device in which the amplifier element that drives the output is actuated by the difference between the input to the servo and its output"[9]. They are used in almost every field wherever accuracy of control is essential. From inertial guidance systems to reaction controls in nuclear reactors, the development of sophisticated feedback control systems have made possible the technological advances that have come to define the age we live in. In the process, we have also come to appreciate to some extent the sophistication of the many control systems required to manage all of the varied processes of biological life.

Feedback, as the name implies, is the principle and method of controlling the output of a system by continually comparing the actual output to the desired result and making necessary changes accordingly. By defining the difference between what we get at the output and the actual desired result as the *error* then the obvious aim of such a control system is to reduce the error to zero, i.e.: make the actual output exactly equal to the intended result. There are many kinds of feedback control systems, ranging from a computerized thermostat that keeps the temperature of your room cozy regardless of the temperature outside, to having an intelligent human with or without a thermometer in his or her hand, who turns the heat on whenever it feels cold and turns it off whenever it gets too warm. In this case the human is the controller, sensing the temperature level and comparing it to some personal comfort level. The difference between comfort and "too cold" or "too hot" is the effective error signal and the person's brain decides the appropriate action (turn heat on or off) accordingly to reduce that difference to "zero discomfort". Regardless of how sophisticated the application, it becomes obvious that feedback is part and parcel of any intelligent system (where one set of information can be compared to another) and is implicated in all systems where the outputs are non-random and must be continuously monitored in order to achieve preconceived desired results.

Control Systems In Biology:

In biology, we can envisage the application of open-looped control systems within the context of input signals derived from the genetic instruction library. Some of these applications would involve the timed initiation of biological activity within a programmed sequence of events. Open-loop biological control would then comprise two kinds of logic: 1] the start of an activity (like throwing on a switch); and 2] converting input signal settings emanating from the genetic library into the desired outputs. Some examples of open-loop control mechanisms would be the start of the organism replication process, and the triggering of each of the essential processes that must go to completion within the sequential program involved. In many cases, the start of a subsequent process depends upon the successful completion of all of the previous processes.

Human experience with designed systems teaches us that the more complex a system is, the more sophisticated and complicated are the automatic control systems required to manage it. It thus follows that the controls that manage the most complex system of all—the LS—must of necessity be all the more complicated and extensive. It can be argued that the principle activity of the cell is the synthesis of complex biochemical products, such as lipids, glycogen and proteins. Each biosynthetic pathway utilizes a chain of enzymes, which builds complex precursor molecules from simpler ones such as amino acids, purines and pyrimidines—themselves products of biosynthesis. While every biosynthetic system has unique characteristics, all utilize some general mechanisms, including feedback controls, which serve to limit the extent of production to finite quantities dictated by the needs of the cell. Effectively, negative feedback uses the presence of the product being manufactured itself to suppress its continued synthesis. This process is referred to as *end-product inhibition*. Thus, the biosynthesis of a given amino acid is regulated by the amount being produced, as the end product of a reaction sequence. This form of feedback control is ubiquitous throughout biosynthetic systems and is considered to be a major regulatory mechanism. Variations in the sophistication of the use of logical operators to effect end-product inhibition includes control by enzyme multiplicity that can selectively inhibit production in a group of products that are formed from the same precursor building blocks. Other feedback mechanisms reduce production in progressive steps, allowing a measured tapering off of production rather than a complete shutdown. The elucidation of the widespread (particularly in micro-organisms) regulatory system based on the "operon" principle of interaction between inducer, and repressor proteins on promoter and structural genes won Jacques Monod and Francois Jacob a Nobel prize in 1965. They showed how a cell could control its protein synthesis by manufacturing the enzymes that control the biosynthetic pathways only on an as-needed basis. Regulatory systems assume considerably more sophistication in multicelled organisms where hormones are used to communicate similar messages to a great number of cells at the same time. The same principles apply to insect colonies where pheromones act as chemical messengers that convey information from one member of a colony to another as biological analogs of hormones, which convey information to different segments of an integral multicelled organism. Also, mechanisms are in place to shut off great portions of the genome in cells specialized to act in a limited capacity (e.g.: skin cells need not synthesize hormones). Thus, it is easy to imagine the consequences for phenotype operational integrity at the micro level of the LS, if any of the essential processes within any of the biological feedback loops, such as those described above, fail to function.

If a chain is only as good as the commulative contributions of each of its interconnecting links, it can be stated with as much assurance that organism operational integrity, as well, is only as good as the interaction of all of its many subsystems intimately connected through wide-ranging open and closed-loop feedback mechanisms, all acting in concert to pull it off. Open any of the essential control loops and the whole process of organism life could conceivably come to an abrupt halt. But feedback does not end at the micro and macro levels of the LS. They are also seen to function as well within the context of the processes of Darwinian evolution.

Feedback Implications For Evolution:

In the Scientific Journal "Complexity" there appeared an article entitled: Feedback and Chaos in Darwinian Evolution.[10] The article contends that to the conventional list of elements that make up Darwinian evolution:

1] reproduction with heritable variation, and
2] natural selection,

must be added a third essential component called "feedback". How essential? The authors—Douglas S Robertson and Michael C Grant consider feedback to be:

> "...the dominant, controlling factor in nearly all cases". They go on:
> "...Darwinian natural selection is a mathematically unstable and chaotic process. As a result of the chaotic instabilities introduced by feedback, natural selection will commonly cause fitness to decrease in sharp contrast to the conventional view that selection only increases fitness. Finally, feedback theory provides a powerful, unifying conceptual framework that coherently explains a wide variety of seemingly disparate biological phenomena, including topics as varied as Cope's rule, punctuated equilibrium, density

dependent selection, coevolution and sexual selection."

Feedback control thus becomes a kind of common link tying together the principles derived from design theory utilized within human engineered enterprises to diverse biological phenomena including biological evolution. From the RDH viewpoint, feedback is one more example of the inclusion of a sophisticated design feature, one that is not only understandable to human system designers but one that is the fundamental logical element involved in all automatically control systems, including biology. The fact that all of this works so well (and at all) speaks to the issue of "excellence" of applied form and function as we perceive it. Indeed, as amateur engineers (the role each of you assumed when you began this inquiry) the fathoming of just some of the complex functioning of, what is after all, just your average (and dirt cheap) eukaryotic cell has to be a humbling experience. No less so for experienced engineers (and biologists) for whom just grasping and appreciating the feat of miniaturization that is the living cell represents a formidable challenge. Then, of course, couple all this wonder with the economies and efficiencies involved and one is left literally breathless—what human engineers can only envy.

Making It Tick:

In effect, the physical plant we have described above reminds us of a dynamic macroscopic production facility furnished with computers, machinery and materials. A human designed plant requires managers that must apply the necessary intelligent direction before it can function according to design intent. Interestingly, both the living cell and human operated plant exude dynamicism that screams of life. This living quality—common to both examples (the living processes direct the cell, and living human beings composed of living cells direct production facilities)—involves intelligence directed controlled function—a quality exclusive to LS systems—without which form can have no function. Unlike human created physical plants, whose piecemeal construction must precede the implementation of the processes they serve, the creation as well as upkeep of biological cellular structures is part and parcel of, and integral to, those very living processes. Living systems represent the integration of, and interaction between, the creation of form, function and end results.

We are now in a position to describe and discuss the 'intelligent' heart of the LS. The intelligence aspect provides detailed and individual instructions for running and controlling all of the individual LS component organisms. All cellular processes occur in what is essentially a chemical medium subject to an extraordinary level of controlled supervision. It is this ubiquitous controlling aspect that attends all life's interactive processes (together with the food chain) that accounts for and, indeed, virtually defines the LS as a single coherent system. The ability of the LS to control its activities—together with the sophistication of that control (in both quality and extent)—stands life in stark contrast to non-life activity. This qualitative difference between life and non-life defines as well, in our view, the logical interface that separates natural chemistry from biology. This statement is no exaggeration and cannot be overstated nor repeated often enough. Again, and precisely:

Biology is not chemistry and cannot be reduced to chemistry—it is, in fact, "directed and controlled chemistry".

This reality is reflected within both PdPs of the LS. Absent both the direction and control, all you have left is ordinary random chemistry—subject only to the controlling influence of the ubiquitous laws of nature. Life, on the other hand behaves as if it is controlled and directed by an additional layer of intelligence that seemingly mediates between those same laws of nature and life form and function—effectively fine-tuning the laws of nature to its advantage. If this exercise leaves the reader with any lasting impression, it is both the veracity and implications attached to the above statement.

The Information System:

The Genetic Library:

The instructional library of all cells contains all of the information that it's organism will ever require to accomplish its LS mission of life. At the local level, it directs the cell's actions and operations. The genetic information library is contained in the *chromosomes* of an organism. The actual information is written in the genetic "language" composed of "letters" referred to as basepairs. Thus, the number of basepairs that comprise the genes within the genetic library of an organism can be considered to be a reflection of the size of its library of genetic instructions and consequently is also somewhat of a gauge of its complexity. The more instructions, the greater, it would seem, the scope of form and function it is capable of. In most bacteria cells, the DNA medium that encodes genetic information libraries comprises a single circular chromosome, plus a variety of smaller circular DNA molecules called plasmids distributed in the cytoplasm. The volume of information in prokaryotes can range anywhere from 840,000 basepairs (genetic alphabet letters) in the M. pneumoniae bacterium, for example, to a high of around 6,400,000 in the cyanobacterium 'Anabaena'. In contrast, the entire sequence of the genome of the X 174 bacteriophage virus—the first genome of an entity (viruses are not quite considered to be organisms) to be sequenced, amounts to just 5386-base pairs. [13]

In eukaryotes, by comparison, the DNA information content is staggering (e.g., The human genome, comprises some 3 billion base pairs). DNA is packaged as bundles of molecular strands called chromosomes, whose molecular elements are encoded in the genetic language (genetic code) that can be understood by the production machinery of the cell as individual genetic instructions called genes. A *structural gene* is more akin to a recipe that describes the composition and placement of amino acids from which proteins are constructed. These proteins come in thousands of varieties and exhibit very contrasting and varied physical and chemical characteristics that the single umbrella term "protein" fails to convey.

A *gene* is defined as a single genetic message or unit of *heredity*. It is an instruction that is chemically encoded along with all the other genetic instructions in the DNA molecular medium located in the cell nucleus. Obviously the more genes contained in the genome of a species, the greater can be expected its complexity to be. Before the advent of decoding genomes, biologists could only guess at the number of genes. The highest estimate for invertebrates was put at 25,000 while vertebrates were thought to range upwards from 50,000 to 100,000. The human genome project has revealed that the human genome comprises far fewer genes than originally thought—of the order of 30,000 genes. The lowest number of genes among eukaryotes occurs not surprisingly within yeast cells at about 7,000. Bacteria contain on the average 2,500 genes.

Three classes of genes have been recognized:

1] *Structural* Genes, (as described above);

2] *Protein Synthesis* Genes—that specify the molecules involved in protein synthesis;

3] *Regulatory* Genes—non-coding recognition sites for enzymes and other proteins that control protein synthesis.

A structural gene is read, transcribed (copied) and edited into another biochemical form—called messenger RNA (mRNA) that can be used by the machinery of the cell to carry out some task. It usually forms the recipe for a <u>structural protein</u> or <u>catalytic enzyme</u> (also a protein) that functions to facilitate chemical reactions at the moderate temperature of liquid water (typical non-biological chemical reactions occur at temperatures that would destroy the living cell.) The instructions and the mechanism for interpretation are complex. Included must be the ability of the cell to call upon only those instructions necessary for the particular process or material required of it. There must be a way for the cell to discriminate which information it will access in order to provide the required instructions to meet immediate demands. Of course, many instructions will be carried out in parallel considering how complex the cell's life activities are and the necessity of responding to many simultaneous needs as they arise. Cells must also be able to communicate with adjacent cells—in multicellular organisms—in order to control and coordinate their differentiated, yet cooperative, activities. Such communication can take the form of electrochemical signals as well as chemical messages (such as hormones). So-called "G Proteins" have been identified that can relay signals from "specific receptors" that stud the plasma membrane to "effectors", enzymes within the cell that, in turn, trigger a cascade of enzymatic reactions resulting in a desired end product which the cell may exude[14].

READING AND EDITING:

Once a genetic instruction has been located within a portion of the lengthy DNA molecule that makes up a single chromosome, only that segment of encoded information is copied unto another slightly different kind of informational molecule referred to as RNA (Ribonucleic acid). Think of a single chromosome as a just a single volume of a many volume set of manufacturing instructions and blueprints that describe and control the production procedures for the many products fabricated within a manufacturing plant. The continuous sequences of printed information located on page after page would represent the continuous information encoded in the DNA molecule. If a particular instruction or drawing is required, a working copy is transcribed ("photocopied", if you will) from the master set rather than working directly from the precious originals, which could become damaged or misplaced. Similarly, a working copy is made within the nucleus of the cell of that portion of the genetic DNA database that contains the desired information. Only the copy leaves the library and is used in production—never the original.

But the instructions encoded in the DNA of all eukaryotic cells have a curious feature. They are often interspersed with large regions written in a non-genetic-functioning language. In fact, molecular biologists refer to these non-genetic coding regions of DNA as "junk DNA". The actual technical term is:—introns (intervening sequences). Intron language cannot be used, read nor utilized by the production machinery of the cell. But they are there and during reproduction, get copied right along with the genetic-information-coded regions of DNA referred to as exons (expressed sequences). Precursor RNA is the copy of the gene made from the master DNA, containing both introns and exons as they appear in the original. Thus, before a working copy of a "mosaic" gene (one which contains both introns and exons) can be passed through the nucleus into the production departments of the cell, these introns must first be edited out of the "pre-cursor RNA" copy. Editing is required in order to leave intact only continuous genetic information. The very nature of how genetic information codes for proteins implies that this editing procedure is critical, leaving virtually no margin for error. Thus, it is only the edited version of the gene, containing exons exclusively, that gets transported outside of the cell nucleus. (We will come to appreciate the remarkable significance of this fact a little later on in the chapter entitled 'The Information Level of Bio-Life': Chapter 12) The introns—and any information they may contain—never make it past the walls of the nucleus. It is the biological equivalent of solitary confinement as generation after generation of introns get copied and passed on to future generations seemingly never to leave their perpetual prisons the nucleus represents. Scientists are frankly puzzled by this curious state of affairs. We shall have occasion to cast some light on the important significance of introns, as they impact remarkably on the SE exercise we are engaged in. Curiously enough, introns are totally absent in prokaryotic cells—those that constitute bacteria. As such, the data processing intron editing-out mechanisms are absent as well.

GENETIC EXPRESSION:

The final edited version of the working copy of a gene is chemically written in a slightly different nucleic acid designated as *messenger RNA (mRNA)*. As stated above, it is only the mRNA working copy of the encoded gene that is physically passed through the membrane wall of the nucleus and transported to the complex 'machine tools' of the cell where it is read and the instruction followed to a tee. The miniaturized cellular "tape-reading" machines that interpret and carry out the genetic instructions are called <u>ribosomes</u>. *Ribosomes are the production tools that translate mRNA instructions into proteins.*

Ribosomes—those complex manufacturing units which know how to read and translate (express) the edited, ticker-tape like mRNA recipe—are located on the surface of *endoplasmic reticuli,* within the production areas of the cell. Each mRNA codes for one of hundreds of thousands of possible proteins required and called for by the cell's machinery. The cell has many ribosomes that can simultaneously produce all kinds of proteins from the <u>amino acid</u> raw materials kept in stock (in the form of transfer RNA (tRNA)) within the cell. The ribosome is composed of two subunits: the small subunit is where the decoding of mRNA occurs and the large subunit is where the actual chemistry occurs. When enough of a particular protein product has been produced, production is halted and the ribosome is retooled with new mRNA production instructions. In this way, different instructions can be given to the same production facilities of the cell to manufacture whatever protein parts are required in order to repair and replace worn out structures, for example—or to produce special products in response to dangerous external conditions detected by the cell's many defense mechanisms.

The ribosomes literally "read" the instructions encoded in the mRNA. It reads a part of the message telling it, for example, which amino acid to add to the chain of amino acids it is assembling. The ribosome then moves along the mRNA tape to read the next part of the message in order to determine which amino acid to add next. In this way, it assembles one amino acid link after another into a polypeptide chain, somewhat like beads on a string. Once the instructional message runs it's course and the order to terminate the amino acid chain is read, the ribosome releases the constructed polypeptide into the aqueous environment of the cell, (the *cytoplasm*), whereupon it folds into a three dimensional configuration that defines the resultant protein architecture. Thus, from only a total of twenty amino acids, but a nearly infinite number of combinations, any of the 100 thousand different proteins used within and by the LS can be assembled with the same machinery. It's not unlike a universal machine tool that can be refitted with different dies, drills and shaping bits, depending upon the desired end product. These protein products are then used to construct and operate the whole gamut of cellular mechanisms that constitute the living condition. It remains one of the great obstacles of abiogenesis to come up with a rational explanation for how such a system of information processing leading to the production of specific and precise proteins could have evolved. We shall elaborate on this topic further on.

The Power Plant:

Primary Fuel Production:

One of the most distinguishing features that separates live cells from dead ones is their ability to maintain the existence of an electrochemical potential across their plasma membranes. Depending upon the type of cell, a voltage potential of between 20 to 200 millivolts is established. Numerous toxins kill their target cells by effectively shorting-out the electrical circuit involved by punching holes in the cell membrane allowing charged particles called ions to rush across the barrier causing the voltage potential to collapse. A continuous energy input is required to drive the many operations of the cell. That energy must come from the external environment outside the cell and with few exceptions, it originates from the sun. The primary engine of life—the machine that, with few exceptions, powers virtually the total LS, is "photosynthesis". This engine—contained only in the chloroplasts of green plants and certain algae—converts sunlight, the primary energy source, into six-carbon sucrose molecules—derived only from carbon dioxide and water. Non-photosynthesizing organisms further up the food chain must get their primary fuel second hand by consuming either plants or other organisms that eat plants. In animal cells, the energy is stored as the polymer glycogen, which can be converted back into the fuel, called glucose, as required. Thus, food resources (containing both protein and energy) yield both the amino acid building blocks from which proteins are manufactured as well as the glucose (sugar) sources of fuel that can be converted into energy molecules when broken down and recycled in the digestion process.

In this way, the energy derived from the sun wends it's way up from the very bottom of the food chain in the compact form glucose, ready to be converted into a usable form within the "furnaces" of successive cells as required.

RESPIRATION: THE CONVERSION OF FUEL INTO ENERGY:

In the modern cell the mitochondria serve as the main sites for metabolism—the production of free energy that powers cell activities. Comprising elaborate folds of membrane, these one-thousandth of an inch structures oxygenate the glucose food elements, producing in the process nucleotide molecules of adenosine triphosphate (ATP). These act as quanta, or packets of energy, that can be used anywhere within the cell as required. Packets of ATP are converted into adenosine diphosphate (ADP) once they release their chemically stored energy. To conserve efficiency, ADP molecules are then re-energized back into ATP, in an effective energy recycling process (analogous to the recharging of nickel-cadmium batteries). The electrical energy of ATP resides within the quantum mechanical electronic bonds between its phosphorus and oxygen atoms as potential energy that is released (oxidative phosphorylation) where needed in the various parts of the cell.

In this way, through a complex set of conversion procedures called respiration, the cell is continually supplied the considerable energy needed to power all the activities we call life. The early set of conversion pathways grouped under the heading glycosis are common to both anaerobic (without oxygen) as well as aerobic (with oxygen) respiration. If the respiration remains anaerobic, then glycosis terminates in reactions that produce either alcohol or lactic acid. If on the other hand, aerobic respiration is to succeed glycosis, then the final metabolite of glycosis is fed through an intermediate into what is called the citric acid cycle or Krebs cycle (named for the discoverer).

Design Implications for Evolution:

The Krebs cycle can provide added insight as to why the flooding of oxygen into the atmosphere by photosynthesizing cyanobacteria turned out, in the end, to have a remarkable effect upon the future results of evolution. While the anaerobic organisms that existed at the time would certainly beg to differ (for them oxygen was a poison), it turns out that the burning of glucose in the presence of oxygen, as a provider of energy for cellular life, is eighteen times more efficient than the oxygen-free fermentation process of anaerobic respiration. In practical terms, the new and improved aerobic metabolism would require one-eighteenth the amount of glucose food energy for the conversion process. Thus, 17 additional cells using aerobic oxidation could thrive on the same amount of energy that a single cell had required using anaerobic glycolysis. An eighteen-fold increase in energy efficiency should be expected to create many new logistically complex alternatives and innovation possibilities, as well. Accordingly, the case can probably be made that this new and improved metabolic efficiency opened up a whole new menu of evolution opportunities for biological complexity, that ultimately led from single celled eukaryotes to multi-celled organisms and eventually the host of complex creatures that presently inhabit the planet. But through it all, bacteria have probably remained essentially just as they always have been and benefiting little from the transition toward an oxygen-rich planetary biosphere. In human experience this transition could be compared to the replacement of the electron tube by the transistor. (The electron tube required an impressive amount of energy simply to heat its filament in order to create the thermionic emission effect characteristic of its principle of operation. The transistor, operating as it does on solid-state principles, requires a minute fraction of the electrical energy of the electron tube it replaced, with all kinds of additional advantages accruing. These include small size, physical robustness and minimal heat removal problems. These qualities opened up the prospect of the evolution of whole new technologies including the integration of circuits yielding greatly improved production costs.) Any marked improvement in the efficiency of energy use, whether in electronics or biology, can be expected to have a revolutionary effect on operational efficiencies in general, leading to the adoption of new and better ways of doing things. In electronics it was the transistor revolution; in biology it was the oxygen revolution.

Now, we have come to believe that if living things can find, by happenstance, an improved or more efficient way to accomplish Life processes, then Darwinian natural selection may allow organisms so equipped to pass on such traits and attributes to future generations. So while the introduction of oxygen several billion years ago turned out to be disastrous for most of the species alive at the time, you might surmise from the above that the LS exploited the opportunity that oxygen presented to create organisms that could take advantage of the potential to improve metabolism efficiency by a factor of eighteen. But remember, none of this could occur until such time as oxygen changed the character of the planetary atmosphere. But how did this change in planetary atmosphere come about? Was it not brought about by the LS itself? In effect, the LS took advantage of a new condition that it itself brought about, and that is our point. SAb would simply say it was a stroke of luck. RDH would contend that the oxygenation of the planetary biosphere could have been prearranged as part of an LS program of terraforming and biosphere modification. Consider the following:

The introduction to the planet of the LS—comprising of a large variety of unicellular species, (both prokaryotes and eukaryotes) including photosynthesizers—began an "acclimatization" phase wherein individual species attempted to establish environmental niches within which they could thrive and reproduce. Eventually, the production of free oxygen would have permitted the LS to enter an "entrenchment" phase that would enable the expansion of the pallet of potential species while opening up the many new environmental niches they could occupy. This entrenchment phase fits precisely the Gaia concept, except that Gaists see it in a somewhat different light. Gaia implies that the biosphere and living things are a continuum and have always existed that way. Accordingly, Gaia sees the OoL as a natural phenomenon and that the transition from the lifeless planet to one with life was seamless and transparent. It therefore sees the evolution of life as part and parcel of the natural evolution of the planet itself. In direct contrast, the RDH sees nothing natural in the coming together of the two—Life and the biosphere—because the chemistry of the biosphere does not and cannot abiogenerate life!

Reproduction and Morphogenesis:

The human body contains some 60 thousand billion cells. Every minute of every hour, 300 million of those cells die. If those cells were not replaced by *mitosis* (cloning), every cell in the body would be dead within 139 days (you can work out the math yourself). The real piece-de-resistance of the LS's many tricks and wonders has got to be the process of cellular self-replication. This occurs on two levels: The cellular level and the organism level. (In single celled organisms the cellular level is the organism level.) With few exceptions in multicelled organisms, organism reproduction involves the sexual fertilization of a solitary cell egg which then proceeds to divide and differentiate into the cells that culminate into the many varied cellular structures called for under the control of genetic instructions. Through this process referred to as *morphogenesis* (the development of tissues), and *organogenesis* (the origin and development of bodily organs) eventually a fully formed, if often immature, organism emerges to take its place within the environmental niche of its species.

But, all reproduction of organisms begins with a single cell capable of self-replication by division. Upon command—when the cell divides and replicates—it not only reproduces the machinery of the cell, but also the full set of genetic instructions that serve as both 'owner's manual' and 'repair manual' that code for all of the living activities it can be expected to perform while it is alive. In addition, these identical genetic instructions, present in each and every daughter cell are turned on and off selectively— resulting in the many different kinds of cell physiology that make up a multicelled organism comprising umpteen billions of individual cells. As miraculous as the process seems to be, there is really nothing magical about it. It is all very methodical, controlled, and indeed quite special. Morphogenesis is both a phenomenon involving quality and quantity—genetic differentiation as well as a geometric progression to the 2nd power. Consider for a moment what it is that gets passed on from one generation to the next.

On the one hand, parent and daughter cells must be sufficiently identical in order that all of the processes of embryogenesis that gave rise to the older generation are able to recur in the new generation. But, during the processes of division within embryogenesis, cell differentiation must occur selectively. In fact, what is passed on from parent to daughter cells during replication is "information" encoded within their DNA. Every new cell receives a complete copy of the information that defines the genome characteristic of its species. But, once the reproduction is complete, the new cell is free to access and carry out only the instructions relevant to its ultimate role as a cellular building block of a more complex organism. Thus, much of the information within the genetic data bank of a cell never gets read. And when that cell itself clones another, it will pass on as well the place in the genetic manual that will define its particular role within the organism it is meant to serve. It is no surprise that human babies born prematurely are smaller and lighter than those born at full term. They simply have fewer cells, even though they must comprise a sufficient quantity of all of the right cells in all the right places that define its phenotypic form and function. And of course, the processes of development are still incomplete at birth but continue well after a newborn joins other members of its species in its specific environmental niche. Thus, complex organism birth is simply one stage out of many on the road toward organism development, maturation, and fulfillment. So well known are the many stages and processes involved that biologists are today capable of intervening in order to genetically engineer and modify the results. But, the significance of organism reproduction for the LS involves more than merely the act of replication. It symbolizes the system dynamic that allows the LS to transcend the dimension of time through the propagation of succeeding generations and perpetuate itself on the planet. This aspect of the LS will turn out to have important systems engineering significance as we proceed with our exercise.

Death—An Essential Part of Life:

The food chain exemplifies the fact that life and death are intimate partners at the organism level. Organisms and their cells die and their contents recycled when they become prey to other organisms or can no longer endure the conditions of their environment. In these cases, it is the external forces that determine organism survival. However, cells in multicellular organisms, can be selectively instructed (programmed) to self-destruct when their job is complete or their continued presence become a hindrance to the organism—a liability rather than an asset. During *embryogenesis* (the process by which organisms are fashioned following the fertilization of the egg), for example, many cells are produced that serve essential but limited purposes and must be eliminated before embryo development can proceed to a subsequent stage. This phenomenon is obvious as well during the *metamorphosis* stages many insects undergo whereby wholesale death of cells occur in order to allow the progression to the next stage in organism development. Probably the most common form of cell death occurs in *tissue turnover* whereby specialized cells are replaced continuously and at different rates respectively. This phenomenon of programmed cell death is referred to as *apoptosis*. The mechanisms that attend this process are becoming increasingly understood with the discovery of molecules which trigger cell death by binding to specialized receptors located on the eukaryotic cell surface[15]. Then apoptosis proceeds rapidly with cytoplasm compaction and DNA fragmentation, leaving a treasure lode of complex raw materials for healthy cells to scavenge and recycle. Programmed cell death is not restricted to specific sub-populations of their own cells. Curiously, it can occur as a survival strategy in the microbial world. It has been shown that many bacteria respond to repeated stress with offensive and defensive measures that involve self-sacrifice. Seemingly, the sacrificed portions of these bacterial populations are cannibalized by surviving members.

Thus, it would seem that life and death are not necessarily antithesis to each other in the overall scheme of the LS. In all cases—programmed or otherwise—death implies a cessation of living activity in some direction while the LS directs life forces in some other. Think of it as the selective funneling of biological raw material by halting it's production through the death of one cell or organism and directing those same raw materials forward—both in space and time (through organism reproduction) via the life of another deemed equally important. The goal in all of this—as always—is the thriving and survival of the system itself; the ultimate perpetuation of the LS.

SE Summary at the Micro-Cellular Level:

The bottom line on the significance of LS form and function is this: Life is not your basic chemistry taking place—no matter who tells you otherwise. The exquisiteness and sophistication of LS composition and activity as exemplified by all of its controlled cellular mechanisms operating within the protective environment of the plasma cell membrane in accordance with both respective PdPs begs the obviousness of the difference between the biological life state and the non-life state (random everything else). The conditions of each are so different that for all intent and purposes they might be considered to be operating in totally different universes—we would argue that they do: one inside the cell and the other outside. The only valid non-life comparison we can make with the phenomenon of biological life is an idea that does not exist in the real world but is the product of the imagination of one of the great thinkers of our century: the living cell can only be compared to the hypothetical universal replicator machine envisaged by von Neumann. Inasmuch as he presented his theoretical notion before the functioning of life processes at the fundamental molecular level was understood, it can truly be said that the eventual revelation of the basic principles of biology indeed represented a stunning example of Life imitating art. How else to describe the subsequent discovery that scientific revelations into the workings of the living cell and its DNA instructional tape actually coincide conceptually with von Neumann's imaginative mechanical replicator concept?

While each cell operates as an individual and independent entity able to communicate with it's external environment from which it obtains the material and energy resources required for survival, each and every cell owes its existence to one that preceded it in the continuing chain of life. At the bottom of it all, each individual living cell represents the sufficient and necessary set of physical conditions for LS biological life to exist—under the strict control of the genetic information encoded within its DNA library. An organism, in effect, becomes the emergent qualities of its individual cells that engage in a complex cooperative and exquisitely organized framework within which the living processes takes place. We have defined two distinct kinds of organisms: bacteria and eukaryotes—each having its distinct functional abilities and its own PdP. Each reflects a level of biological activity commensurate not only with its respective form and function, but also its use and purpose in the overall LS scheme as well. Every cell represents an incremental unit of a species population at any given moment in time, and also a generational time increment in LS history. Thus, cellular reproduction is the link that joins both LS axes elements of time and space.

A Personal Commentary:

We humans may not know how to create life from raw chemicals, but we are certainly getting a handle on many aspects of what life does and how it does it. Every new explanation brings further the realization that the living processes of biology are understandable in ways no different from the other technological processes engineers engage in. The mysteries of life continue to yield to the logical principles that underlie the scientific approach to these problems. As our knowledge grows, we are becoming that much more privy to the exquisiteness of detail that leads to the grandeur of result—manifesting itself as the biological LS on our planet. And judging by the present rate of assimilation of scientific information, chances are we will gain knowledge of the core essence that defines the biological phenomenon—at some time in the future (assuming we have a future). For now, researchers will have to content themselves with the kind of transgenic tinkering that defies and redefines the veggie-animal boundary. They have learned, for example, how to place within the tomato genetic library a gene from fish that allows it to withstand icy waters[16]. In so doing, genetic engineers have produced a tomato that is resistant to frost. There is no reason to underestimate the probability that biological engineers of the future will be able to—not only comprehend the full nature of biological life down to its most intimate details—but will be, as well, in the position of being able to tinker and innovate at the very core of the phenomenon of life; ultimately able to create other versions (different PdPs) that might function as well. But that is all a long way in the future.[17] The door to understanding the intimate mysteries of life has just been jarred open. Creating a new life form from scratch is a challenge of a different order. I believe that before we do, we will first have acknowledged and later found a way to cross the logical barrier separating the natural laws of physics and chemistry from the LS technology that leads to the PdPs that make it run.

If the LS is a designed system, then proof of design must indeed exist somewhere within the LS. Furthermore, we are confident that we can locate where such incontrovertible evidence is to be found. There remains some important unfinished business ahead before it all reveals itself.

---

[1]From So Simple A Beginning: P Whitfield, p 174
[2]Blueprints: p 313
[3]SA: March 96, p42
[4]Discover Magazine: Feb 96, p 50
[5]Molecular Biology of the Gene: Watson et al p57
[6]SA: The Ground Substance of the Living Cell; Porter & Tucker, p57 [24A]
[7]Small Wonder: The Sciences; May/June 93: Alice B Fulton [1]
[8]Scientific American: Microbodies in the Living Cell—Christian de Duve, p74. [9c]
[9]Analysis & Design of Feedback Control Systems: McGraw Hill; 2nd Edition p1
[10]Complexity: Sept/Oct 96; p10-14
[11]Small Wonder: The Sciences; May/June 93: Alice B Fulton [1]
[12]Scientific American: Microbodies in the Living Cell—Christian de Duve, p74. [9c]
[13]Enc. Brit.: Electronic Edition
[14]SA: July 92 "G Proteins"—Linder and Gilman [Special Issue "Medicine" p 70
[15]Fascinating Death Factor: Nature; 27Jan94 [271]
[16]Omni: Jan93, p8
[17]Omni: Jan93, p8

11. The Energy Level of Bio-Life

"In this house, we OBEY the laws of thermodynamics!"
—Homer Simpson, Cartoon Character

Energy Conversion—A Two Step Process:

The term *"vitalism"* was coined to represent the special driving energies, forces, and influences that could account for that very special phenomenon we call life. It is a throwback to a time when living creatures were thought to lie outside of a subject category suitable for study and understanding. It preceded the realization that living matter is, at the molecular level, only a different manifestation of the same essential particles and natural laws as those governing nonliving matter. As such, it is now considered that there can be no "vital principle" that pertains to the one and not to the other. We, on the other hand, are making the case that there are fundamental and, for the moment, irreconcilable differences between the living and nonliving states. In fact, from the RDH viewpoint, the actual events that lead to the OoL could be considered "vitalistic" in the sense that bio-life is considered not to have been derived from natural causes. This simply acknowledges the RDH premise that the OoL is a contrived phenomenon that required deliberate and intelligent design for its origin and a "jump start" to get it going. It is understood that the RDH (as do all the other scientific OoL hypotheses) considers that once bio-life was in place and operational on this planet, no additional influences, other than the universal laws of physics and chemistry, were required for its continued survival. However, the RDH insists that at the molecular level biology can be reduced to "intelligently controlled" physics and chemistry, and other interactive life processes—to "intelligently controlled" events. The intelligence we refer to is internal to the system and is represented by the built-in control mechanisms that are unique to life. Our challenge throughout this work is to demonstrate this to be so.

Life, like all dynamic phenomena, does require vital energy in order to function. But, there is nothing "vitalistic" about where this energy comes from. Without exception, the energy that drives all of life's activities are the products of energy conversion processes that extract energy from the outside, and import it into, the LS. At present, the most important energy source driving the LS is the sun. I use the term "at present" in order to make the point that this may not have always been so. Scientists cannot know with any certainty the effective amount of sunlight that photosynthesizers could use efficiently when life originated on the planet billions of years ago. They do know that the amount of sunlight reaching the planet surface depends on many factors including actual photon output from the sun (a variable) as well as the filtering effects of atmospheric gases. It is also known that the sun's ultraviolet rays represent a threat to biological organism survival. Thus, since the ozone layer probably could not exist until the atmosphere contained sufficient oxygen (over a billion years later), organisms able to convert the sun's energy might have had to do so from the protective shield afforded then by seawater—where the light filtering effects would again have diminished the intensity of sunlight. Descendents of several species of the archaea family of microorganisms—that can still derive energy from sources other than the sun—survive in obscure habitats. Microbes called *methanogens* are able to use hydrogen as an energy source to convert carbon into organic compounds, including methane as a byproduct (the carbon derives from carbon dioxide dissolved in water). We do know that eventually, when conditions were right, photosynthesis became the energy conversion process of choice driving the food chain that fuels the LS. All of the alternate energy converters became relatively obscure and their descendents have managed to survive as inconsequential LS relics—like steam engines in the atomic age.

The conversion of the sun's energy into a form that can be used by living things, of necessity involves a two-step process.

1] The direct conversion of sunlight into energy storage units within a photosynthesizing cell, and

2] The conversion of stored energy into useful work as needed by the energy converting cell. Energy distribution is then carried out to the rest of the LS organisms via food chain dynamics (an organism unable to convert the sun's energy eats one that can).

This two-step conversion process is similar to the charging of a battery using a photovoltaic cell. The battery is charged and energy stored whenever the sun shines (which excludes night time and cloudy days). However, the energy stored in the battery now becomes available any time there is a demand and not only when the sun is shining. There is always a demand, as life processes require energy all the time. The direct conversion of sunlight by the "photovoltaic" chloroplasts of plants into the stored energy sugar molecules is the process of *photosynthesis*. The conversion of stored energy molecules into molecules that can provide instant energy to do useful work within the same plant is called *respiration*. These mechanisms were discussed in the last chapter.

From the SE point of view, the mechanics of energy conversion engaged in by the LS is a marvel of technological efficiency. It all begins with photosynthesis. Plants harness the sun's energy in the form of photon units within a series of complexes resulting in 6 molecules of carbon dioxide and 6 of water producing a single molecule of glucose plus 6 of oxygen. When organisms, including the plants themselves, utilize this stored energy, the action is reversed. The oxidation of a single molecule of glucose involves its interaction with 6 molecules of oxygen to produce 6 molecules each of carbon dioxide and water liberating many calories of free energy in the process. As previously discussed, biological energy conversion involves the intermediate stages whereby ATP is reduced to ADP and itself is recycled back into ATP in cycles variously referred to as the Krebs and Citric cycles. The LS uses energy conversion to fuel two distinct kinds of activity:

> 1] *The steady state production, repair and housekeeping mechanisms that characterize the cell's ongoing activities and,*
>
> 2] *The reproduction process—whereby an organism recreates itself entirely in a slightly altered version, upon which evolution depends.*

Photosynthesis—The Engine of Life:

In discussing photosynthesis, we will not be trying to compete with the information readily available in high-school texts. Out treatment of the subject here will remain within the special context of the SE analysis we are engaged in with the goal of understanding the very special differences between life and non-life. These differences become especially delineated within the realm of how each deals with energy and the outcome. Earlier in chapters 3 and 10, we briefly touched upon the classical chemical reactions—that convert the energy of the sun into chemical free energy. Plants and other specially equipped organisms utilize sun-energy to produce carbohydrates from the carbon dioxide and water found in the biosphere. This serves to fuel the synthesis, growth and replication activities of the photosynthesizing organisms. These organisms, in turn, form the bottom of the food chain and fuel all the other species that make up the LS. As stated, today bio-life on earth derives virtually all of its energy from this process. We can delineate between two distinct ways that this is accomplished, each a unique characteristic of its PdP:

1] *Eukaryotes* : cells of green plants and algae (cyanobacteria). These are capable of a) fixing carbon dioxide to form carbohydrates, such as glucose, as well as b) producing free oxygen from water. These two processes require two separate photo-systems, (called *PS1* and *PS2* respectively).

2] *Prokaryotes*—bacteria engaged in photosynthesis that does not produce oxygen. As a result, they possess only one of the two photo-systems.

These energy-processing variations relate directly to fundamental differences in their respective PdPs.

Over the past 30 years, much has been learned about the structure and functioning of the reaction centers implicated in the electron and proton transfer phenomena at the heart of the photosynthetic processes. Our interest is to view the connection between structure and function that finally results in the familiar and deceptively simple chemical equation that defines the consequences of photosynthesis in plants:

$$CO_2 + H_2O + photons \longrightarrow (CH_2O) + O_2^{\char`^}$$

A cursory look at the above equation will immediately disclose the fact that the left side of the equation comprises small inorganic molecules that are converted on the right side to the much larger organic molecule and free oxygen. The organic carbohydrate molecule (CH_2O) is a *high-energy* molecule, in contrast with the low energy molecules of carbon dioxide (CO_2) and water (H_2O). The addition of hydrogen (H) to the carbon-oxygen combination requires the formation of new bonds that require a contribution of energy. That energy comes from the sun. This is the basic energy equation that links the nonliving inorganic world and bio-life. This conversion represents a synthesis or *anabolic reaction*.

All the complex processes that comprise the photosynthetic energy transfer phenomena take place in a self-contained double-membrane envelope referred to as the *chloroplast*. The physical structures contained therein and involved in photosynthesis are found in the specialized group of membranes referred to as *thylakoids*. These contain antenna-like *light-harvesting* structures that trap individual photons of sunlight and direct them to the *reaction centers* where energy conversion occurs.

The photosynthetic process can be separated into a sequence of complicated events as follows:

a) The Trapping of light and transfer of excitation energy;

The first of these is alluded to in high-school texts and comprises *light-harvesting complexes (LHC)* we know as *chlorophyll*. These light-sensitive protein structures are contained within the highly organized thylakoid membranes, designed to increase cross section for the efficient capture of light. Once stimulated by the photon energy of the sun, the excitation is transferred from molecule to molecule like some kind of "hot potato" until it is trapped by the *reaction center (RC)*. To increase the efficiency of light collection, each of these 'antenna-like' light harvesting complexes contains several groups of pigment centers with slightly different wavelengths for maximum light (and therefore photon energy) absorption across a broad spectrum of light frequencies.

b) Electron transfer in the RC (reaction center):

A single molecule within the RC chlorophyll eventually traps the excitation produced within the LHC. This causes an electron to be ejected from a primary donor molecule in a sequence of well-timed events that takes it down an electron transport system to the opposite side of the RC.

"The remarkable thing about this process", according to G. Feher, Dept of Physics, University of California, La Jolla, "is that for each photon absorbed (from the sun), one charge separated state is formed" i.e., the wasteful de-excitation processes and charge-recombination reactions are negligible with respect to the forward electron transfers.[1] In other words: We have one extraordinarily efficient photocell here. One photon particle of light energy leads to one electron transfer. Human designed energy-conversion device efficiencies cannot compare to what casually occurs in photosynthesis in a "dirt-cheap" cell of a green leaf. The next stages in energy conversion, called respiration, are considerably less efficient.

c) Biological Energy Molecules:

Of course, the ultimate aim of all of this is to make external energy available to the life processes in a form that can be used as a direct energy source—one that must be available all of the time. Again, the sun only shines during daylight but life processes continually require copious amounts of fueled energy. As previously described, once you strip away the details, you eventually end up with the production of packets of ATP energy molecules. These can dispense their stored energy—to fuel any and all of the various biological activities that occur in the cell. At the same time nutrient organic raw materials (carbohydrates) are supplied that represent the basic Lego-like building blocks for biological structures such as the nucleic acids, and the amino acids from which proteins are manufactured. Thus, photosynthesis is more than simple energy conversion—also liberating raw materials important to the processes at the PdP levels of biological form and function. Each ATP fuel molecule can be considered as a "quantum" of stored energy—much as does a cartridge of compressed carbon dioxide or an individual coiled spring. The only difference is that ATP stores its energy chemically. Once its energy is tapped, it is no longer ATP but converted to ADP. This chemical state is similar to the uncoiled spring after its energy has been sprung, or to the empty CO_2 cartridge after it has been spent. Now, if processes requiring energy are ongoing and additional energy units are needed, there are two ways, in theory, to replenish energy resources: You can do it the inefficient and wasteful way e.g., throw out the spent CO_2 cartridges and purchasing expensive cases of new and fully charged ones; or the efficient and thrifty way—find a way to recycle and recharge the old ones. The LS, for its part, has elaborate built-in procedures and machinery for cycling spent ADP molecules back into energy rich ATP, saving enormous amounts of energy and resources in the process.

It was only as recent as 1978 that British biochemist Peter Mitchell received the Nobel Prize for his discovery of the fact that: the production of ATP was linked to the electron transport system in photosynthesizing plants. The proof came in a famous experiment by André Jagendorf of Cornell University that showed the significance of pH acid levels, hydrogen ion flows, and concentration gradients that occur in the recycling of ATP from ADP. It seems that the "recycling" concept is more than just a slogan commonly associated with human attempts at saving precious planetary resources. It has been around much longer than we think—integral to the energy storage and supply subsystem within the PdPs of biology.

D) It Is "Really" Complicated:

An understanding of photosynthesis on a quantitative molecular level entails a knowledge of the three dimensional structure of the RC molecular machinery. To this end, molecular biologists have used X-ray diffraction techniques to unravel the remarkable series of light-driven electron and proton transfer events that occur in the membrane-bound RC. In addition, researchers have studied the effects of applied magnetic and electric fields as well as externally applied pressure in order to shed additional light (no pun intended) on the relationship between structure and function.

The point is—that just as the cell membrane encloses the contrived environment that brings together and protects the whole gamut of complexes and machinery that interact to produce the biological reactions of Life—so too does the double membrane enclosed chloroplast, located within the cell itself, provide the necessary production plant, facilities, and environment that serve as the engine that drives Life. Of course, besides entertaining you with explanations of just some of the sophisticated mechanisms involved, our main purpose here is to raise your consciousness of the emerging reality. It takes a lot of explaining to argue how it is that, even in its simpler original form, all that is covered under the energy conversion umbrella "photosynthesis" could have developed independently, and prior to, the actual origin of life. This is what is implied within any SAb OoL scenario. This is not analogous to the mystery of the evolution of other irreducibly complex evolved biological structures that have developed over time within species (such as the classical case of the eye or other such complex organs). Remember that any kind of primitive "founder" life-form envisaged by a SAb origin would have required such an energy conversion mechanism from the word "go". We are here talking about an essential component that is ubiquitous throughout the LS, responsible for the energy that drives every aspect of life, and without which the whole process doesn't even get off the ground. And, in order for it to work, it requires all kinds of specialized proteins and structures all working under coordinated supervision, many of which would be difficult to account for under a SAb scenario for the OoL. For it to have evolved conveniently at the beginning of life, and from nothing, strains logic. Think about it!

E) THE BOTTOM LINE ON PHOTOSYNTHESIS:

What we have tried to demonstrate and what becomes imminently clear is the fact that photosynthesis is not just complex chemistry but involves extremely complicated nano-technological machinery as well. The laws of chemistry determine the binding forces and reaction conditions of the molecules involved in the source materials—carbon dioxide and water. However, it is the complex photosynthetic machinery—exclusive to the LS (i.e., found nowhere else in nature)—that mediates and manipulates the photon energy arriving from the sun and brings it to bear upon these source commodities in a remarkably controlled sequence of events. The result is the conversion of energy on the one hand, as well as the production of essential end products on the other. What becomes obvious is that the chemistry alone does not, and cannot account for the complex structures involved, or for the processes responsible for the results. Again, for SAb to be credible it must conjure up a reasonable scenario to show how the engine of life, no matter how simple it can be envisaged, could have been there at the SAb point of origin—the OoL.

We have discussed extensively (in fundamental SE terms) how the photosynthetic engine that drives the LS converts sunlight into the forms of energy that fuels the biological processes of both the steady state and reproductive activities of the organism and the cell. We will now examine energy considerations at a totally different logical level—in terms of the universal Laws of Thermodynamics. These offer important SE clues that will impact in significant and exciting ways upon the RDH for the OoL.

The Laws of Thermodynamics—More Than Just Energy Bookkeeping:

Thermodynamics deals with the relationship between heat, work and energy in our universe. Physicist Rudolf Clausius formalized that relationship more than a century ago when he set down the "Laws of Thermodynamics" in just two sentences:

1> *The energy of the universe is constant.*
2> *The entropy of the universe increases to a maximum.*

These two so-called "laws of nature" are implicated in the production and spending of energy in the

LS (as well as in every other phenomenon in the universe). We refer to them as "so-called" laws of nature because of the metaphoric description involved. The likening of scientific discoveries to "laws of nature" is in fact an anachronism to a time when the "Almighty" was thought to have established the laws of nature and to have decreed that nature must obey them. While what you call them does not change for one moment their reality or precision, it is generally regarded as unfortunate for the Philosophy of Science that the word "law" was ever initiated.[2]

But, the metaphor may be forgiven with respect to the 1st and 2nd laws of thermodynamics in virtue of their importance as the bedrock principles upon which all else in the universe seems to rely. From the Big Bang to the operation of Life itself, these laws of thermodynamics are implicated to their very core. Let us see how the engineering mind can clarify some of the implications and consequences for an understanding of biolife that derive from the 1st and 2nd laws.

The First Law of Thermodynamics

The first law of thermodynamics is often called the law of "conservation of *energy*" (actually, *mass-energy*). It says, in effect, that when a system undergoes a process, the sum of all the energy transferred across the system boundary—either as heat or as work—is equal to the "net change in the energy of the system". The total energy of a system equals the sum of a) the internal energy—which depends only on the thermodynamic state, b) the kinetic energy—which depends on the system's motion, and c) the potential energy, which depends on the system's position with respect to the chosen coordinate frame.

The law, as stated above, implies that "energy is neither created nor destroyed"—that it can only be converted from one form to another, and that the sum total of energy within any given system is conserved. This law is considered to be the most powerful generalization about the universe that science has ever been able to express. In over one hundred and twenty five years of careful testing from the atomic level to the astronomic level, no scientist has ever been able to show a violation of energy conservation[3]. But in fact, the law is understood today in terms of the conservation of "mass-energy" inasmuch as Albert Einstein defined the conversion of the one to the other in the classic: $E = mc^2$. And, of course, stars operate accordingly liberating copious amounts of energy during their "matter" to "matter-plus-energy" fusion (thermonuclear) transformation processes.

The question is occasionally raised as to whether the 1st Law of Thermodynamics was possibly violated when the universe as we know it came into existence. The implication is that our universe and all that is in it was created only at the very instant of the Big Bang, prior to which there was nothing. The Energy Conservation Law as noted above, is one of those scientific statements that underlie the very foundations of every physical phenomenon. It is the very bedrock supporting the whole structure of science. Implying the possibility that this law of nature may have been violated—even under the trivial case circumstances of the origin of the universe—is serious stuff indeed. But, then again, the origin of the universe event and its predecessor, whatever that means, is not your "business as usual universe" either. Simply put: "Was the Law of Conservation of Energy violated at the time of the "Big Bang" when our universe supposedly came into being?" It is a bit like the corollary of "Now you see it—now you don't". Where did all that mass-energy come from? Is our universe to be considered the "ultimate free lunch", as cosmologist Alan Guth once suggested or, was it there all the while before the Big Bang? While this topic is admittedly a digression from the OoL question, one might ponder what the engineering mind could contribute to this curious question? We have thought about it and have come up with an admittedly simplistic solution that is in fact staring us in the face. It relies simply on Einstein's energy-matter conversion formula: $E = mc^2$. Let us examine the Law of Conservation of Energy as it impacts on the Big Bang.

The First Law and the Big Bang:

Let us simplify the problem as follows:

1] All the matter of the universe derives from energy according to the conversion formula: $E = mc^2$ (energy equals the product of mass and the velocity of light squared).

2] At the time of the Big Bang origin of the universe, there was only energy E, and nothing else (no matter). Our concept of "Energy" (the E on the left-hand side of the formula) requires provision for neither "space" nor "time". Our concept of "mass" or matter requires both. (This is implied from an examination of the right hand side of the energy-to-matter conversion formula: the mc^2 has the dimensions: g-m^2/sec^2 "grams-meters-squared per second-squared".) Thus, we can envisage the universe, at the instant of the Big Bang, as an "infinitely small dot" containing its total (and constant) Energy "E".

3] At the actual moment of the start of the Big Bang, when some of that energy began to convert into matter according to $E=mc^2$, matter (m) acquired (and requires by definition) the additional properties of 3-dimensional space (the "meters-squared" aspect of the equation) and a time framework (per "seconds-squared" aspect of the equation) which seems to accompany space. In fact, you might even surmise that the Big Bang began when time actually came into existence (together with space)—as a direct consequence of the beginning of the energy-to-matter conversion process—according to the Einstein formula.

4] Now we have arrived at the logical position where we can accordingly redefine the origin of our universe (the Big Bang) as: "that point—just before "space-time" came into existence—when some of the energy within our energy-only "dot universe", for some unknown reason, began to convert some of that energy into matter, creating at the same time the "energy-matter-space-time" framework we perceive as our universe".

5] As energy was converted from its point source, space was produced as a radiating spherical wave-front (the most efficient geometrical configuration)—expanding outward from the point of origin and according to the space requirements of the matter being converted from the original source energy. So far, the Law of Conservation of Energy has been maintained. The sum of Energy + Matter equivalent at any given moment in time forward from the Big Bang remains constant, as the law dictates.

6] We can perhaps define time in a similar manner: a function of the wave-front radiating outward and the essence of the incremental change in the expansion of our universe occurring as more energy is converted into matter. We, of course, define time as the perceived chronological sequence of events.

With respect to the origin of time in our universe, "incremental change" refers to the rate of conversion of energy into matter, and the creation and expansion of space-time as a consequence.

7] It then follows that if we define our universe as that particular totality of energy that at the time of the Big Bang began to convert into matter (this is a "zero-sum" phenomenon), and the beginning of space-time as an effect of the start of that conversion, then we should be able to simply define the "pre-Big Bang universe" as the "timeless pure-energy state", comprising neither 3-D space nor time.

8] Thus, if we extrapolate the universe we know, backwards in time to the beginning of time itself, "time", as stated, becomes merely a consequence of the energy-to-matter conversion process and not the other way around. And of course, once we reach the "beginning of time" at the moment of the Big Bang, it is meaningless to ponder the existence of the universe further back to a time where time need not exist, all because matter did not exist—only pure energy. Thus, we have a situation where the Big Bang need not define the beginning of the universe which—under the circumstances described above—seems meaningless, but rather defines only the beginning of the phase-shift from "timeless pure energy" to "energy + matter + time", as a consequence of the conversion process itself. Thus, any confusion we may harbor concerning the origin of the universe only arises, I maintain, because we have no way of contemplating, in our minds, the idea of our universe without time. We will just have to be satisfied with the statement that at the interface of the pre-universe and the Big Bang, we can contemplate an energy-only state when matter and time did not and need not exist. The very concept of the universe we know, before the advent of time, therefore becomes meaningless.

Conclusion:

There is nothing inconsistent with a "point universe" (the small dot universe containing all of the energy it would ever possess, some of which it would convert into matter) and the Law of Conservation of Energy. The case can be made that the universe was never created, as is sometimes expressed, but actually predates time as pure energy. It is, thus, not a function of time—but is effectively timeless! No free lunch here. Nowhere do we have to explain the coming into being of energy-matter. Its existence can be considered to be a physical constant. The significance of the big bang for our kind of life-form is that it signals the beginning of the "knowable universe"—whereby matter was created from energy making possible the existence of our kind of intelligent beings that rely on both space and time as reference points for reality. In his book, *Cosmic Blueprint*, Paul Davies puts it this way: "The existence of the universe is not explained by the big bang: the primeval explosion merely started things off".[4] I agree but would wish to clarify the meaning of "things" to refer to the "space-time" phase of the universe, which is the only phase we can understand. Thus, the Big Bang may simply signify a transitional interface between different forms the universe can adopt. At no time (pun unintended), before (whatever that means) or after the Big Bang do we have to deal with the issue of energy audit because under no circumstances must we envisage a state where the totality of "energy+matter" changes (was zero, for example).

Therefore, if Einstein's conversion formula can be considered applicable under Big Bang conditions, then according to the logical circumstances described above, it follows that the 1st Law of Conservation of Energy has never been violated. As a final note on this topic, the conversion from the "initial-energy-only" state to one where energy and matter coexists produced our 4-dimensional space-time continuum framework that eventually gave rise to intelligent beings that perceive the universe as we do. This touches upon the major question that we must eventually deal with : "How can we validate the origin of intelligence within this same universe—that responsible as the source intelligence from which all other intelligence could arise?" Some would describe such inquiries as necessarily philosophical, religious or both—but definitely not subject to rational analysis. Later on we shall demonstrate this conclusion to be patently false—that intelligence is a fundamental component of the functioning universe (just as are matter, energy, space and time) and logically subject to rational inquiry. On a personal note, it never ceases to amaze me, that: "Here we are, products of the universe phenomenon, trying to objectively piece together the original cause of it all."

1st Law Implications For The LS:

The first law of thermodynamics is nature's way of bookkeeping, if you will and implies that the energy available to the LS to fund it's cellular activities is no more than (and in fact less than) the energy produced by the LS and generally originating through the photosynthesis of sunlight. Thus the caloric energy converted from a carbohydrate (glucose) into useful energy available to the cell as ATP molecules must be matched by the energy that produced the carbohydrate in the first place (plus a little bit more to account for the fact that no energy conversion process operates at 100% efficiency. This universe takes a dim view of "perpetual motion machines"—regardless of origin). But since the unrecoverable heat energy still remains in the closed system of the universe, the total energy of the universe remains constant—according to the first law.

The Second Law of Thermodynamics:

In the first law of thermodynamics, energy transfers across system boundaries are classified as either work or heat transfers, and the energy of the system itself may change in any process that progresses from one state to another. There is nothing in this analysis to prevent everything from reversing, flowing or changing in the opposite direction, because the energy terms would all balance in the same manner. The first law only concerns the conservation of energy—not the direction in which processes may proceed. The direction of processes is the subject of the second law of thermodynamics, which ultimately states that: "every process that a thermodynamic system may undergo can go in one direction only and that the opposite process, in which both the system and its surroundings would be returned to their original states, is impossible". This applies to systems small and large, simple and complex. There is no larger system than the universe itself, whose unfolding following its Big-Bang origin could arguably be a consequence of and in accordance with the dictates of the 2nd Law of Thermodynamics. Extrapolating forward in time, we shall see that the 2nd law has implications for the ultimate fate of the universe as well. If that indeed were the case, then as a consequence, the 2nd law could logically be considered to be the true Theory of Everything (TOE)—that can explain the evolution of the universe from the point in time of the Big Bang onward, as described above. Unquestionably, it would seem to be good strategic planning on the part of any participant in any debate to be able to argue that the 2nd law agreed with their side. All the more so when it comes to the OoL debate. So formidable an influence is the 2nd law upon our universe that it should come as no surprise if it turns out to represent a most formidable challenge to any OoL option as well. In this respect, our RDH can gain much comfort. The RDH effectively avoids the challenge completely. The same cannot be said of SAb. For SAb, the 2nd law of thermodynamics represents its greatest challenge—every bit as much as the challenge of trying to explain SAb operational mechanisms (how they could have come about). So potentially threatening are the consequences of the 2nd law for the SAb OoL option that they have contrived a vehement defense against it, effectively banishing out of existence any acceptable reference to it. Science has effectively declared the 2nd law as irrelevant to OoL discussions. Just so there be no misunderstanding on the issue, the 2nd law would be considered "inadmissible evidence" in any scientific court of law. Our position on the 2nd law is contrarian (what else is new?). We shall demonstrate that the 2nd law not only supports the RDH (rational design hypothesis) as the only possible OoL option, but also that the logic of the opposing intellectual camp (all of those SAb supporters that have satisfied themselves that the 2nd law is irrelevant to the debate) is flawed. Let's see why this (SAb state of near panic) is so.

We will now examine the thermodynamic principles that are implicated in the controlled application of energy in the LS in order to try to understand the differences in the results between random chemical reactions and the chemistry of life. First, let us review some essential concepts of thermodynamics. We shall only access those that are sufficient to illuminate our subject without getting bogged down unnecessarily. Much of the detail we shall ignore has to do with the nature of the basic chemical and physical processes. Since these are common to both non-life and life processes alike, we shall concentrate our efforts towards the principles at the PdP system macro level that separate the two. In the end, we want to show that living systems are fundamentally different from non-living systems precisely because they behave in such a way as to defy the assumed automatic link between energy and information that a traditional interpretation of the 2nd law implies. In the process, and based on our findings, we will present a new definition of Life—one specifically derived from the distinctiveness between Life and everything else in the universe—in terms of, and imposed by, the 2nd law of thermodynamics.

Important 2nd Law Thermodynamic Concepts[5]

1] Equilibrium State: A system in an equilibrium state is one that undergoes no further detectable change. To take a system away from equilibrium, work must be done on the system by the surroundings.

2] Reversible Path: A system that undergoes a change of state by a reversible path is always in an equilibrium state. Every state of the system—the initial state, the final state and every state in between—is an equilibrium state.

3] Reversible Process: A change of state by a reversible path is called a reversible process.

4] *Irreversible process:* A change of state in which there are one or more intermediate states that are not equilibrium states.

5] *Spontaneous Change:* If a system is not in an equilibrium state, a spontaneous change is not merely possible; it is inevitable and irreversible. The system will undergo the change in state that is necessary to reach equilibrium. A system in an equilibrium state does not undergo any further spontaneous change in state if it is left undisturbed.

6] *Entropy:* Entropy is a state function. A change in state is accompanied by a change in entropy. When an irreversible spontaneous change occurs, the entropy of the universe (a system and its surroundings) increases. When a reversible process occurs, the entropy of the universe remains constant. At no time does the entropy of the universe decrease.

7] *The Law of Entropy (2nd Law of Thermodynamics):*

a) The entropy of the universe is constantly increasing. "You can never get back as work all the heat energy that goes into a process (i.e., there is no free lunch)".

b) The entropy of a system in a given state is a measure of the number of different microscopic states that correspond to a given macroscopic state; the greater the number of microscopic states, the greater the entropy and the degree of disorder.

The above thermodynamic concepts should be sufficient to convey the differences between life and non-life activity.

The 2nd Law and Life:

In inanimate (nonliving) systems, the equilibrium state represents non-activity at the system macro level. That is to say that while there is activity at the atomic and molecular system levels with respect to the motions and vibrations of individual particles (any of which can have more or less energy at any given moment in time), these are subject to statistical rules which average out individual microscopic contributions. The net result at the macroscopic level leaves no possibility of any further kind of detectable change (action or motion) in the system. Obviously, this description is the antithesis of the LS, which is characterized by perpetual frenetic activity at all of its levels. If anything, the equilibrium state is closer to defining our understanding of death, (the cessation of life) where all organized action at the organism level ceases. The immediate conclusion, then, is that: a living system is one that is not in an equilibrium state. According to the rules of thermodynamics above, any such system (one not in equilibrium) must necessarily (according to 2nd law dictates) undergo spontaneous change in the direction to bring it to the equilibrium state. Now, living things comprise not just a single system, but also a conglomeration of multitudes of subsystems, each subject to the same above rules. The form and function of the living organism, in fact, comprises the emergent consequences of the interaction of all of these subsystems. Thus, each subsystem within a living organism can be considered not to be in equilibrium and will be subject to forces that will try to bring about spontaneous change in the direction of equilibrium. If that were the case, then it follows that we can credit the resultant spontaneous changes as being the cause and source of all activity within living systems. The logic proceeds as follows: Living systems have the capacity to maintain all of their subsystems in a state of disequilibrium. This ability is a direct consequence of the form and function of the biological PdP and can be considered to be its most defining attribute. The rules of thermodynamics come into play in order to restore, spontaneously, all non-equilibrium states to equilibrium and at the same time move to increase their degree of disorder. This applies to all systems—whether living or not. However, living systems can control qualitatively and quantitatively all of the processes within all of the subsystems involved. Thus, while at the micro level of atoms and molecules the 2nd law imperative of (microscopic) systems tending toward the equilibrium state is everywhere evident, at the PdP level perpetual dis-equilibrium is apparent. One might even conclude that the prime functional responsibility of the biological PdP is to maintain its biological states in disequilibrium—precisely controlling and organizing all cellular activities at the macro level and giving rise to the dynamicism of life (its élan vital, if you will). To accomplish this technological feat, the PdP must take in energy and apply it through its many interactive subsystems to maintain the stated overall dis-equilibrium state. It acts like a pump that maintains an artificial waterfall—continually pumping water from the ground equilibrium level back up to the top of the falls. As long as energy is supplied and the system is maintained, the water keeps running. In biological processes, all kinds of organized activity are produced in each individual subsystem. Thus, life displays two distinct but equally important functional characteristics:

1] The capacity to convert outside energy into LS usable energy, and the use of that energy to sustain all of the dynamic biological activity—collectively referred to as metabolism. The RDH characterizes this same activity—from the point of view of 2nd law thermodynamics—as the initiation and maintenance of dis-equilibrium states at the micro level, and

2] The separate capacity to coordinate all of the resultant individual activities into a cooperative system at the macro (organism) level which accounts for its overall organization and complexity—including maintaining and directing a steady stream of energy into the system. The RDH considers this important characteristic of bio-life as operating against the negative energy and organizational gradients imposed by the 2nd law—gradients which spontaneously direct all systems towards ultimate equilibrium and increased disorder.

The first characteristic above is the only aspect of biology that has been subject to scientific investigation. Scientifically controlled energy audit leaf studies have revealed that the chemical reactions that take place within biological systems adhere stringently to predictions calculated according to the 2nd law. From the RDH point of view, we have no problem accepting all such results. Unfortunately, because the second characteristic—that of control and organization—is more difficult to quantify or qualify, researchers have tended to dispense with such characteristics as simply subservient consequences of the former. Thus, the generally accepted view is that any uniqueness that can be ascribed to bio-life—while interesting—fully adheres to the energy provisions of the 2nd law, and is therefore deemed to be in full compliance with the 2nd law, both in fact and spirit. Accordingly, the phenomenon of bio-life can thus be viewed as a natural phenomenon of our universe (after all, it complies with the laws of the universe)—one that is virtually unavoidable given similar planetary conditions and history. Admittedly, this kind of logic has some appeal—if only the basic premise were accurate. The problem that refuses to disappear concerns those pesky organizational and complexity details. But, as we are discovering—when it comes to the mysteries associated with the OoL—the really interesting story is to be found within those pesky details.

As it turns out, an understanding of the LS phenomenon ends up being a classic case of "the whole being greater than the sum of its parts". At the microscopic level, each individual reaction indeed functions according to the classic interpretation of the 2nd law, no different from non-life systems. The trick—unique to life—is the bringing and keeping of all of those parts together under a master control, replete with feedback control systems. It is only the collective results viewed at the macro organism level that produce the distinctive increase in order that the 2nd law says should not, but, (and many unbelievably still refuse to acknowledge) does occur. Again, left to their own uncoordinated devices, there is no question that each microscopic subsystem of the LS (e.g., biochemical reactions) spontaneously tends toward and achieves its equilibrium state in the direction of maximum possible disorder. But, within the context of the biological PdP as a quantified state of organization, the overall result—representing the collective contributions of innumerable microscopic subsystems, each tending toward equilibrium and greater disorder—somehow results in the achievement of an astonishing state of increasing order. How this is achieved—seemingly contrary to all other kinds of phenomena—speaks directly to both the measure of complexity that comprises the PdP of life, as well as the probability that the biological LS is not like other natural phenomena, and most arguably, not natural to begin with. Putting the question in terms of entropy—as a measure of the number of microscopic states (see definition "7" above)—how is it that living systems, which owe their talent for activity to their spontaneous changes toward equilibrium and the resultant increased entropy at the micro level, can function without at the same time increasing the number of microscopic disordered states as demanded by the 2nd Law? The answer has to do with the relationship between naturally occurring randomness—that conferred by the 2nd law upon all systems over time—and its antithesis "intelligence"—a characteristic uniquely apparent within the LS. Perhaps an example will help clarify our point.

The Case of the Five Coins (No Fountain):

Let us take as an example a set of 5 identical coins, in a closed box each having two possible configuration states: heads or tails. We can define a microscopic state as the configuration of each single coin—head or tail. The aggregate configuration of all of the coins in the box can be described as the macroscopic state. The system comprising all of the coins can exhibit two macroscopic states: a) an orderly set (arbitrarily chosen) showing all heads, for example, or b) a disorderly set having a random mixture of heads and tails. Only one macroscopic state can provide an orderly all-heads set. On the other hand, numerous macroscopic states can produce a mixture: 4 of one and 1 of the other; 3 and 2; 2 and 3;—a total of 31 such disorderly states out of a total of 32 states (2-to the-5th power). Now, if we shake the box, the odds are 31 to one that the coins will come up disorderly, regardless of the initial setting. As we increase the number of coins (and therefore their microscopic states), we increase as well the number of possible macroscopic states. Notice that the odds of an orderly set decreases rapidly—while the number of orderly sets remains constant at one. As stated, our choice of "all heads" as a so-called orderly set is arbitrary. We could have selected any other specific combination of coins (all tails, for example) as our designated matched-set choice. But, once a matched-set configuration is selected, the odds of it coming up on a subsequent shake of the box are the same. Shake a hundred coins and your odds of coming up with a designated orderly set is one chance out of 2-to-the-hundredth power possibilities. As we change the microscopic state of individual coins randomly—as occurs when we shake the box—the probability of moving the system to the ordered, non-equilibrium state is subject only to the laws of mathematical probability that apply to random events. And, as we have seen, any increase in the number of microscopic states (by increasing the number of coins) decreases the probability further and also increases the system entropy.

Probability mathematics can reveal a lot about entropy by providing an indicator of how random events can yield organized and ordered states and thus the degree of orderliness of a system; the degree of orderliness of a system is also referred to as its "information" component. In a disordered state, we have little information concerning the microscopic states of the coins. In this respect, all disorderly states can be considered to have the identical low information content. Only the orderly state represented by all heads coins can be said to have a high information content in virtue of the fact that the state (heads or tails) of each micro event is known for sure. Science has had difficulty, dealing with this aspect of entropy—as opposed to the purely energy aspect which can be calculated. And difficulty transforms into downright confusion when such discussions center on the LS phenomenon, as compared to non-living systems. There is little doubt that the LS obeys all of the energy aspects of 2nd law entropy at the micro level of physics and chemistry, yet seems to abandon the 2nd law with respect to its information aspect by exhibiting greater orderliness and complexity in both space and time. Let's continue to explore our coin example above, for the light it can shed on this glorious dilemma.

Intelligence—A Random-Error Reduction Scheme:

Now comes the clincher question with respect to sets of coins. How is it possible to arrange a set of 100 coins as an ordered set—e.g., all heads—against seemingly insurmountable odds of it happening by itself? We know that randomly, matched sets of coins do not spontaneously occur. But, a human hand—guided by the sense of vision—can arrange 100 coins (or any number, for that matter), in no time at all, into any kind of combination—including a matched set. How is this explained in classical entropy terms? Well, some might claim that the picking up and turning over of the necessary number of coins, involves an injection of energy into the system from the outside in the form of "work", which is said to make up the difference and thus account for the decrease in system entropy called for by the 2nd Law. I would disagree. We have already seen that the energy required to shake a box of coins produces nothing more than a random configuration and consequently the results must be subject to the laws of probability—regardless of how much work is done. This is, in fact, the situation every time the coins are shaken to produce a new set of microscopic states. Between shakes, the system of boxed coins can be considered to be in thermodynamic equilibrium. The energy injected into the system from the outside effectively removes the system from the equilibrium state, regardless of whether the results produce an orderly or disorderly state. Assuming for the moment that the added energy is the same in both cases, then the only difference between them is that the "information" content in the orderly state is considerably greater than that associated with a randomly disorderly state. Is there an obvious linkage between the intelligence applied to the input energy to create the ordered state and the increased information content associated with that state? There definitely is, and that is the point of this exercise.

Thus, it is not work alone that comes into play in producing a matched set of coins, but rather the removal of the randomness factor associated with the shaking of the box and replacing it with the application of "intelligent and controlled" work, that makes all the difference. Without intelligent intervention, the energy audit in the process is meaningless. It is the application of "controlled work" to discreet and individual microscopic states (e.g., individual coins) that actually defies the randomness that the 2nd Law decrees should increase, under non-intelligent conditions. What does "controlled work" actually imply? At the cognitive level, it involves the ability to match the actual physical state (a set of randomly arranged coins) to a preset mental state (a matched set configuration) and then being able to make the necessary changes to precisely align the two. The work energy involved—while a necessary system input factor—is quite incidental to the relationship between the idealized state (ordered configuration) and the reality of the physical state (present disordered configuration). The intelligence in the process involves complex feedback control mechanisms that enable the intelligent intervener to recognize the error difference between both, and an understanding of how to reduce that error to zero—resulting in the physical state matching exactly the preconceived orderly state. Inherent in the process—and what emerges as a significant operative principle—is the fact that the controlling intelligence characterized by the idealized mental state of the observer must precede the actual, and in this case incidental, application of energy (the moving of coins). It is only then that the process of removing the randomness associated with all other disordered states can proceed.

What becomes apparent in the process is the obvious separation of the input intelligent element from the actual application of the work energy to effect the necessary changes. Because the information aspect of the exercise is essentially independent of the raw energy required to turn over the coins, the information itself precedes and is in fact independent of the energy part of the equation. Remove the intelligence from the train of events and the energy introduced can only produce random results—those predictable and calculable according to mathematical probability. The inescapable results are the following: the introduction of intelligence—being the only factor that can predictably defy the laws of probability—also becomes the only factor that can predictably defy the information component of the entropy provisions of the 2nd law. Thus, intelligently applied energy introduced to any system is able to overcome randomness and to control the outcome of events—the whole, contrary to the provisions of the 2nd law of thermodynamics, as they apply to the universe in general. Let's return once more to our coin example. A matched set (all heads, let's say) can be achieved in only one way:

1] Under random conditions: tremendous odd against, increasing exponentially with an increase in the number of coins—1 chances out of n $(1/n)$ possible combinations (according to the laws of probability), or

2] Under intelligent control (reducing the feedback error to zero): certainty regardless of the number of coins—n chances out of n (n/n)—a dead-on matched set every time i.e., no random chance involved at all.

Only two kinds of actions are possible: controlled (intelligent) and uncontrolled (random chance). In the case of an external system involving coins, the intelligent control must come from the application of the human hand controlled by the human mind. In the case of the internal subsystems of the living cell, the source intelligence derives from the genetic library of the cell. In both cases, the common element is the intelligent control, which precedes the discrete application of energy. Intelligence alone is the necessary ingredient, which can direct appropriate energy in ways that increase the orderliness of the respective system, contrary to the 2nd law gradient against orderliness the natural universe adheres to; be it a system comprising a set of coins, or any and all of the hierarchy of systems that comprise the LS. We are now ready to put aside coins and look at why living systems behave as they do.

Entropy—Two Concepts For The Price Of One:

The second law is considered to apply to every type of process—physical, natural, biological, as well as industrial or technological, and examples of its validity can be observed in every day life. In order to use the second law in a quantitative sense, it is necessary to introduce an appropriate working variable, which is called entropy (concepts 6 and 7 above).[6] But, as demonstrated above, entropy also has a qualitative aspect about it, which reflects the fact that the 2nd law has two distinct characteristics—it is, in fact, a two-part law:

The entropy of a system increases as:

i) Energy spent to do work is always greater than the amount of work accomplished i.e.: unrecoverable energy is lost in any dynamic process and;

ii) Systems tend to move from order to less order.

The term *"entropy"* refers to the amount of unrecoverable energy in the first part, and the degree of increased disorder, in the second. The entropy of any system is said to increase in proportion to both the amount of unrecoverable energy losses and the degree of increased disorder—the latter being a characteristic which current scientific wisdom considers to be the consequence of the former. In practical terms, entropy is a rather spontaneous kind of phenomenon in which everything deteriorates, collapses, breaks down, and wears out all by itself.[7] It accounts for why children's rooms become messy unless directed energy is spent tidying up, as well as why you cannot build a perpetual motion machine (analogous to Alan Guth's "free lunch"). The question of entropy is also implicated in the field of information theory, which is based on the principles put forth by Claude Shannon. These have traditionally dealt with noise, error rates and efficiencies involved in the transmission, over distances, of human derived information. We shall have occasion to explore how some of these same principles may apply to the information system that lies at the heart of biological form and function.

On the surface, at least, the *2nd law* applies equally well as does the *first law* to the natural world.

But, as we have pointed out, there exists that singular phenomenon, the LS, where the second law has evoked considerable confusion and debate over the years. If, according to the 2nd Law, all systems must tend spontaneously toward an increase in entropy—meaning greater disorganization—then how do you explain the fact that the LS seems to be engaged in creating the opposite—greater and more complex organization? Some scientists would maintain vigorously that there is no confusion and that the 2nd law applies equally to the non-living world and the LS—that there are no exceptions. Others frankly admit to an ambiguity that seems to implicate the 2nd law in the very delineation of life from non-life. We will go further and state that in our view, the 2nd law lies at the heart of what separates the *living biological state* on our planet from the natural *non-living state* and more generally, that which separates the very concept of life from non-life. As a result, ultimately, the whole question of entropy must be very much implicated in the OoL question because of the very different ways the 2nd Law appears to apply in life and non-life situations. We shall undertake the challenge—heretofore unsuccessful—of conclusively demonstrating this to be so. In the process, this very real difference will be seen to highlight considerable challenges for SAb with respect to the effect and consequences of the 2nd Law at the very interface separating life from non-life at the OoL. Since SAb insists that any such interface is transparent and seamless (within its insistence that biology derives naturally from inanimate chemistry), it must accept the challenge of explaining any 2nd Law inconsistencies that may be shown to exist at the dramatic transition between these two distinct states. In the course of our proceedings, the RDH will use the 2nd Law to totally invalidate the SAb OoL option, as well as use it as a cornerstone to bolster its case for design.

The LS is exemplary as a phenomenon as it seems to defy the 2nd law in its unique characteristic of gaining in complexity over time. The interface issue raises the all-important question as to when this reversal of the natural state of affairs actually began. In an abiogenetic (SAb) OoL scenario, it would have had to have begun at, and indeed be responsible for, the very beginning of the life process—at the same time as the chemical precursors of life would have acquired a talent for self-replication. Again, this poses an additional hurdle for SAb with respect to the transparent and seamless nature of the questionable interface between life and non-life that abiogenesis implies, because that same interface must now accommodate as well the transition of the matter involved from the natural state, that behaves in the normal way with respect to 2nd Law entropy, and self-replicating living matter which behaves differently in that regard. The origin of the "negative entropy" question will figure prominently in this debate. We shall be deliberating on this delicate issue, which seems to have split scientific thinking. But, before we do, we wish to set the stage by presenting some of the thinking on the question by some of science's most respected personalities.

In his book *Nature of the Physical World*, Sir Arthur Eddington admonished anyone trying to proclaim a theory that went against the 2nd law—implying that the inevitable result for it would be nothing but "collapse in deepest humiliation.[8] Frank A Greco of the Harvard Medical School, in answer to the question of whether the 2nd law could be circumvented simply replied: "Not yet".[9] A. B. Pippard of Cambridge University, commenting on the suggestion that the 2nd law was only "statistically" true, replied that there was no evidence ever presented that the 2nd law breaks down under any circumstances.[10] Richard Morris suggested that the 2nd law is the most general of all scientific laws and applies to everything.[11] Arnold Sommerfel asserts that the quantity of entropy generated locally cannot be negative regardless of whether the system is isolated or not.[12]

Not surprisingly, there are contrary points of view as well:

V.F. Veisskoff, head of the Dept of Physics, M.I.T., described the history of the world, from the 'big bang' to the present universe—as a series of gradual steps: from the simple to the complicated; from the unordered to the organized; from the elemental particles of matter to the sophisticated living organisms. There is, in his view, an obvious tendency of nature from disorder to order and organization.[13] Charles J. Smith raises the question of how and why the apparent lowering of entropy within the ordering process has arisen, implying that a number of scientists have and continue to wrestle with the issue. He refers to Ludwig von Bertalanffy's suggestion that the relationship between irreversible thermodynamics and information theory was one of the most fundamental unsolved problems in biology.[14] Bertalanffy's "general systems theory" attempts to provide a common methodological approach for all of the sciences, based upon the idea that systems of any kind—physical, biological, psychological, and social—operate in accordance with the same fundamental principles[15].

G.G. Simpson and W.S. Beck make the important point that the simple expenditure of energy is not sufficient to develop and maintain order and complexity (which is how most supporters of SAb qualify increasing biological complexity). Referring specifically to biological life, they differentiate between work that creates nothing and particular work that follows specifications (genetic instructions) that provide the information on how to proceed.[16]

Harold Blum of Princeton University—while arguing that there is no evidence of defeat of thermodynamic principles—does acknowledge the degree of complexity found in life that appears to be absent in the non-living world.[17] (We would replace the phrase "appears to be" in the above statement with the single word "is"!)

Probably the most succinct description of the relationship between the 2nd law and biology is that of Nobel Laureate Ilya Prigogin who lamented the fact that the second law *cannot* explain the formation of biological structures. He concludes therefore that the probability of spontaneous genesis of life is highly improbable, as is the assembly of highly ordered structures engaging in the coordinated functions that characterize living organisms from a macroscopic number of molecules. This, despite the billions of years during which prebiotic evolution is thought to have occurred.[18]

Then, there is Stephen Jay Gould's special contribution to illuminating the subject of life's tendency toward complexity. While not referring specifically to the 2nd Law, Gould argues that natural selection in free-living forms imparts no bias toward complexity in either direction.[19] The common assumption that trends to increasing complexity through time must confer a "primary and predictable direction to the history of life", as he puts it, is nothing more than a misunderstanding of evolution in his view. He sites the phenomenon of "parasitism" as offering a countervailing bias affording a clear edge toward simplification, and further offers that a study of just how widespread a phenomenon it is might indeed indicate that the number of cases favoring simplification are as common as those favoring increasing complexity. While this is not the place to engage in a free wheeling discussion of parasitism as an example of a life-tendency to simplification, suffice it to say that Gould offers a rich source from which to ponder the issue. The question that immediately arises is whether, and how, Gould's contrarian contention is relevant to our proceedings herein. It is—in at least a couple of ways. First, the RDH would agree with and, indeed, has previously concluded in Chapter 6 that (increasing) "complexity", in and of itself, is not the primary objective of the LS—that "survival through time" is. Secondly, Gould's argument simply draws attention to the distinction between "*macro-complexity*" and "*micro-complexity*". Gould's description rightly describes trends in macro-complexity whereby organisms are free to evolve and adapt in any direction open to them that affords them survival—whether that be towards "more" or "less" complex form and/or function. His conclusion with respect to the ubiquity of the phenomenon is another matter altogether—one which we might want to question. Concurring with Gould are Eors Szathmary (Collegium Budapest) and John Maynard Smith (Univ. of Sussex School of Biological Studies) who in a joint article entitled "The Major Evolutionary Transitions" tend to agree that there is no theoretical reason to expect—nor empirical evidence to suggest—that evolutionary lineages increase in complexity with time.[20] Indeed, they make the point that there is no generally accepted measure of biological complexity. However, they do offer that both the richness and variety of morphology and behavior together with the number of protein coding genes present two candidate possibilities. They go on to describe what evolutionary biologists already understand: how eukaryotic cells are more complex than prokaryotes, animals and plants more than protists, and discuss the implication of how genetic information is stored and transmitted—to account for increasing biological complexity. But, despite the denial of an evolutionary tendency of lineages towards increased complexity with time, the article in question ends up seeming to represent a somewhat concise review and affirmation of the progression of developmental complexity over time—in quite a reversal from their basic premise.

However, with respect to micro-complexity—the tendency of the biological system of life to create more and more complex molecules over time, (as opposed to the macro-complexity issue discussed above), there can be no doubt. Here we refer to the harvesting of the simpler inanimate chemical resources from the external biosphere for inclusion within the LS—in the creation of "more and more complex biological molecules". Increased complexity occurs both in terms of increased quantity as well as the increase in the quality of biological molecular production that end up in living organisms. And all of these organic molecules, wherever they reside, are the products of the execution of instructions contained within information genomes—molecular chromosomes that themselves constitute trends toward greater order and complexity—uncharacteristic of anything to be found in non-life. Szathmary and Smith cover this ground as well, as exemplified by their table listing genome sizes and percent of coding DNA for a progression of species of increasing complexity. But at the bedrock level of our discussion, there is little question that over time, more and more of the raw chemical materials of the planetary habitat are converted into the complex amino acid building blocks and proteins that constitute the physical makeup of all organisms. Once created, amino acids, are generally recycled over and over—in space, through food chain activities—and time, through the reproduction of future generations, as they become part of the growing and permanent (if variable) reserve of complex biological constructs that form the LS bio-mass of the planet. The same can be said for the recycling of purines—when old mammalian cells are replaced by new ones. Fully ninety percent of purines are salvaged by means of the enzyme "HPRT", to serve again as the building blocks for DNA and RNA[21]. Thus, while we can debate the proclivity of biological evolution toward or away from macro-complexity of form and function within specific evolving species, there can be no argument that can hold sway against the ubiquitous and phenomenal increase in micro-complexity across the whole phenomenon of life—as mentioned, in both space and time,—nor any with respect to the obvious increase in macro-complexity at the highest rungs of the evolutionary ladder (e.g., humans).

With the foregoing as stage setting, we shall now try to make some sense out of the confusion that attends the very important, if seemingly tenuous, relationship between biological life and the 2nd law. It is at once captivating and enigmatic because of the very special character of life—whose biochemistry unquestionably functions at the atomic level according to all of the physical laws, and yet whose growing presence on our planet seems to defy the most fundamental of those laws. How do we resolve this issue? It is essential that the SE analysis in which we are engaged address this compelling question, as it goes to the very heart of the OoL controversy. Think of it this way:

Question: "Does or does not the LS defy the 2nd Law of thermodynamics?"

This most fundamental query with important OoL implications requires some very serious thought, indeed. Implicit within the question is the tacit sanctity of the universality of the 2nd law (also known as the Law of Entropy) as opposed to the enigmatic character of biological life that seems, at certain levels of activity, to be oblivious to it. If we simply postulate that life must, by definition, conform to the 2nd law (as the law is presently constituted), then we are forced to also acknowledge the conclusion that there is nothing extraordinary or unique about the LS—that it is simply another case of physics and chemistry, and not necessarily a special case at that. This interpretation serves the vested interests of SAb. But, if we consider the possibility that life may not be a natural phenomenon—that it could have originated by design—we then place ourselves in a position to ponder whether the LS had to be engineered and "jump started" into operation—precisely and in such a way as to overcome any and all 2nd law limitations that would, in fact, obviate a SAb origin. And if that be the case, then the question is also raised as to how and under what exceptional circumstances the 2nd law can be circumvented, if not violated completely. At the same time, such exceptional conditions—if they can be demonstrated to exist—might also serve to justify the conclusion that any possible spontaneous abiogenesis in the absence of such special conditions, just could not take place. This raises the interesting question as to whether the LS phenomenon might possibly represent, in some obscure way, the implementation of a set of extraordinary startup and operational conditions that can effectively sidestep certain provision(s) of the second law. The only other example I can think of where such a discussion of skirting the 2nd law takes place periodically concerns the ignomious issue of the "perpetual motion machine" (this recognized to be an impossibility). We know that such hypothetical machines represent an impossible defiance of the energy restrictions imposed by the 2nd law (even under design conditions). This acknowledgment simply recognizes the seriousness of the challenges we face with this kind of inquiry as applied to the LS. The track record in this arena is poor indeed. And yet, the existence of the LS faces us with the uncomfortable prospect that, if indeed it does not represent an outright defiance of the energy provisions of the 2nd law, then—at the very least—it behaves in ways that can only be described as exceptionally uncharacteristic of matter in general and in its tendency towards greater complexity over space and time in particular.

We shall now tackle this problematic relationship which both joins and separates life and non-life, forthwith in a novel way and within the context of the above discussions—that will serve at once to highlight at a fundamental level the differences between life and anything else we can experience in our universe—within the context of the provisions of the 2nd Law. Best of all, our deliberations will lead us to some fascinating insights into that relationship culminating in a statement of a novel definition of the phenomenon we call life—a first, in terms of the 2nd law.

Thermodynamics and Biological Life:

Whenever energy is converted from one form to another, the resulting *entropy* is said to increase. This increase in entropy implies both a change in the system order (increase in the number of microscopic states) together with an energy bookkeeping aspect that must be accounted for as well. The LS gets (nearly) all of its energy from the sun. When the sun's photon energy impinges upon a plant leaf, for example, it provides the source energy for the building up of biological systems through the processes referred to as *biosynthesis*. The energy conversion process called *photosynthesis* causes the leaf cell to become more orderly and structured in the sense that energy is being bound into a more complex form, namely glucose (a biochemical fuel). So, what happened to the entropy? Does it mean that the plant cell exhibits *negative entropy* because of the increased order? Well, not really. Current wisdom considers that any decrease in entropy by the plant cell is matched by the fact that the sun itself becomes more entropic, as its own energy processes wind down incrementally. Entropy appears to be a zero-sum game. If it decreases here, then it must increase somewhere else. Thus, the operating logic in any entropy audit is to expand the size of any system to include any outside influences, such as external energy sources as represented by the sun. Similarly, when the cell burns the complex glucose food molecule and useful energy is released to do work, the entropy of the cell increases because some energy is lost in the form of wasted heat and the products of glucose oxidation are less orderly than before. Thus, from the traditional bookkeeping point of view, it is considered that if you add up all the order and disorder involved within the cells activities, and take into account the train of progression of energy beginning with the sun and ending in the burning of glucose and the cell's spending of that energy—that the decrease in the cell's entropy can be accounted for by the increase in the entropy of the sun, and ultimately that of the universe. In fact, the entropy of the universe is expected to continually increase *spontaneously* until an ultimate state of equilibrium is reached. This state of affairs has been described as the famous *"Heat Death of the Universe"*—a time when all the available energy will have been used up, with no further energy exchanges possible. And, by considering the question of entropy within the context of the Universe itself, as the ultimate single system, it is considered that any alleged anomalies that might exist within it, such as biological life, are simply an extension of the statistical nature of energy distribution. They are thought to represent merely localized events (without special significance in the overall scheme of things) that in the end are canceled out. Indeed, at the local level of energy dynamics of plants, plant leaf studies seem to confirm adherence to the 2nd Law. Indeed, the process of energy conversion is not 100% efficient. But, what the same studies do not address is the difference in *quality* in biological reactions between what you start with and what you end up with as results. Refer again to the chemical equation that describes photosynthesis above that says it all. The results on the right hand side of the photosynthesis equation are considerably more complex than the carbon dioxide and water molecules on the left. While this reaction may be seen in isolation by some—as perhaps a local thermodynamic anomaly—it actually represents just a single level among many that represent LS activity. From there on in, every additional biological reaction fueled by this so-called anomaly results in progressively greater and higher levels of complexity—like the rungs on some complexity ladder—culminating finally in the production of new living cells and conglomerations of such cells cooperating exquisitely to produce intelligent beings— beings that themselves are capable of designing and building external contrivances (machines) that can do work. As discussed above, this push toward greater complexity in life is unexplained by the 2nd law, and furthermore operates essentially contrary to the way all other natural phenomena operate. Thus, there are aspects to the rules of entropy that seem not to apply to the LS—at the very least they present a paradox that not only cannot be ignored, but begs an explanation.

Entropy—A Confusing Duality:

With respect to the biochemical Life processes, I have no qualms with the first law (Law of Conservation of Energy) in it's insistence that all of the energies involved in any closed system can be accounted for because energy (strictly speaking, the combination: "energy-matter") can neither be created nor destroyed. There is indeed a problem with respect to the 2nd law however, and for a very clear reason. The confusion arises simply because the 2nd law comprises a two-part imperative, tying together two very distinct concepts—"energy losses" and "disorder" within the concept of entropy. The first part involves the bookkeeping of energy, similar in a sense to the first law. The difference being that the 2nd law insists that in any process some of the energy is lost to the universe (which is the ultimate closed system), and unrecoverable to do useful work in any future energy conversion processes. No problem! Our dilemma specifically concerns the component of 2nd law entropy that deals with the measure of disorder. While the effects of entropy energy and information (order) are normally entangled in all natural (non-life) phenomena (whereby an increase or decrease in entropy entails a parallel decrease or increase in both energy and order respectively), it seems, that the LS defies this readily associated duality. In other words, while the increase in entropy in the natural world intimately connects energy loss with increased disorder, this relationship is blatantly lacking in the LS phenomenon in particular. While the 2nd law relationship of energy loss and disorder may always hold in natural non-life systems, it definitely does not in the case of biological life. This can be explained in only one of two ways: either the linkage between energy and disorder is, in fact, not as absolute as our traditional interpretation of the 2nd law implies, or living systems (e.g., the LS) violate a major provision of that law. Either way, we have some important explaining to do. Without question, let us state at the outset that it is much preferable to consider the former possibility over the latter. The obvious reason is that consideration of the violation of a uniquely important major rule of science—even by an exceptional case such as the LS seems to be—is not an arena one enters casually. It is much easier (and in the end more logical) to contemplate the distinct possibility of a modification of the applicability of the rule in order to accommodate special circumstances. Well, at the very least, no one can deny that the LS is, indeed, a unique and very special circumstance. Let us restate the issue as follows:

The 2nd law of entropy involves two distinct concepts, that of energy and that of information. Common wisdom holds that the two are inexorably tied together such that whenever energy losses occur due to entropy there is a corresponding system loss in orderliness or complexity. Conversely, we are also told that the only way you can reverse the natural tendency towards disorder is by investing energy from outside the system. Life turns this logic on it head. The simple expenditure of energy is not sufficient to develop and maintain order, according to G Simpson and W S Beck (above). The point we have been arguing (e.g., in the coin example above) is that energy bookkeeping alone is not the issue because the LS pretty well adheres to the energy provisions of the 2nd law. Our problem has strictly to do with the increased orderliness and complexity that the LS is famous for. How do we explain it? Do we simply point out, as others have, that this is simply a statistically permitted local phenomenon and that greater energy is being spent to account for it while the sun that supplies the energy is paying the entropy price? Can this simple traditional answer—that the LS is just a local system where order can increase temporarily at the expense of greater energy cost, account for the LS tendency to greater complexity, and counter to all other natural phenomena? I don't think so. But, before we can attempt to explain this phenomenon, we would do well by starting with a discussion of the 2nd law relationship between energy and complexity and the nature of LS complexity as well.

2nd Law Relationships:

A) The 2nd Law: I would suggest that while there may indeed be an intimate relationship between energy and orderliness (complexity) that is compelling in all natural and spontaneous phenomena, that in fact:

1) they are separate and different attributes within the 2nd Law, and the relationship between energy and information content (order) are not necessarily consistent nor universal; and,

2) this is particularly so in the case of biological Life.

B) The LS: With respect to LS processes, we cannot simply add the two components of entropy together (it couldn't be done, even if you wanted to) and come up with a meaningful understanding of entropy increase or decrease? Furthermore, any such considerations must also take into account the fact that the organisms that make up the LS are capable of two distinct activity levels, both of which treat energy and information differently:

1) *Chemical activity level*: the conversion of energy into other forms plus work, all in accordance with strict adherence of the 2nd law, and

2) *Cellular (biological) activity level*: responsible for generating two kinds of untypical (un-natural)

complexity:

    a] self-organizing complexity that binds more and more low-information inanimate matter from the biosphere into the highly organized living cellular biomass we call the LS, and

    b] self-replicating complexity, which generates a duplicate but un-identical copy of a complete, and often incrementally more complex, living organism.

Both processes above occur at a geometrically progressive rate over time.

    At the strictly chemical level of biological activity, the chemical reactions involved in energy conversion processes are "oblivious" to the conditions that set them in motion. As such, they are no different from all other natural processes and are subject to the same universal rules, including the traditional energy-information application of the 2nd Law. Yes, we even concede that at the molecular level, the two 2nd Law components of entropy energy and information are connected such that the products of some reactions at the bottom levels of biochemical activity may be less orderly and less complex than the reactants. But, it is the cellular activity macro level that truly separates life from non-life—which will in due course be shown to violate an orthodox interpretation of the 2nd law. What is at issue is that despite the increase in cell entropy that scientific measurements insist is taking place within the cell's energy audit (as glucose is burned to produce free energy, yielding in the process the less orderly exhaust reaction products), both LS cellular activities above somehow do result in the remarkable increase in system-wide organization over time. Also, we must not ignore the contribution of evolution that continually introduces changes to design at the organism level that result in yet additional levels of increased system complexity and orderliness—against the normally expected 2nd law gradient of system disorder. Put another way, the processes of chemical activity within living cells exhibit the expected increased entropy from the strictly energy standpoint but an unexpected decrease in entropy over space and time from the organizational and informational stand point. Where you started with one organism before replication, you now have two, one of which (the offspring) may be of somewhat more complex design than the other (parent). All the while, more non-living disorganized stuff is transformed into the highly organized living stuff of the cell. (The root word in "organism" is *organization*.)

    We acknowledge that within the process of self-replication, the amount of energy spent in the copying processes at any given moment in time represents only those energies required to reproduce the physical parts needed for the daughter cell, and that no additional energy is invested nor required to create the complex information content of the offspring cell. This is analogous to the copying of information stored on a computer diskette. The amount of energy that is required in the copying process is independent of the complexity of the information stored. In fact, the same amount of energy is spent to copy a diskette containing complex programs or junk. Each elemental bit on the diskette is treated like every other bit, regardless of the emergent quality of the information written there. The same goes for replicating the information in the DNA of an organism. Off course, biological self-replication involves more than just copying information (genotype). What is copied is 1) the genetic library, which contains the instructions for building a new organism and 2) the rudimentary physical biological equipment (phenotype) necessary for carrying out the instructions encoded within the genetic library. Our interest, for the moment, concerns only the process of replicating genetic information.

During the copy process both genetic instructions as well as any "junk DNA" are copied together, bit by bit (base pair by base pair). Included is the design information and instructions which when expressed, will yield the basic machinery (element by element) that constitutes an organism's first cell. This, of course, assumes that the parent and daughter cells are identical with no changes that could be considered to provide the offspring with greater complexity than the parent. But, that is not how biological reproduction and genetics works. What is not considered is the element of incremental organism redesign (as opposed to the PdP which remains constant) that occurs generation after generation that evolution is responsible for, resulting ultimately in more, rather than less, organization. So, while the chemical processes at the very bottom level of life activity obey unequivocally the dictates of the 2nd law that demands inefficiencies within any energy audits, there is an obvious lacking of such obedience when it comes to the audit of orderliness and information content. So, a key question is: which part of the LS-2nd Law relationship is at odds with our understanding of reality—the LS or the 2nd Law? I would think that because the LS exists within the confines of a consistent universe, that it must a priori adhere to any rules or laws that pertain to that universe. As such, we are left to consider that perhaps there is a flaw in our understanding of the energy-information relationship implied by the 2nd Law—in particular as it applies to specialized complex systems such as the LS—and not a flaw in the law itself. But, the good news is that the confusion can easily be made to disappear, as though by magic: all you have to do is disengage the energy-information relationship connection that is presently part and parcel of the usual scientific description of the 2nd Law, and we then find we can include the biological activities of life within its application. Once we do that, we are obliged to acknowledge that the 2nd law provision that the heretofore entangled energy and complexity within a synchronized relationship must not, in fact, be absolute; it is variable according to circumstances. Thus, the whole question of whether bio-Life obeys the second law may in the end depend upon how the 2nd law must be interpreted (or reinterpreted, as necessary). At the conclusion of our inquiry, we will be left with one of two possibilities:

a] If we continue to interpret the 2nd law such that energy and information are bound together so that any increase or decrease in the one automatically signals the corresponding change in the other, then we are left with only one conclusion—that Life defies the 2nd law; or

b] The logical alternative allows a somewhat modified interpretation of the 2nd law—one that permits a looser relationship between energy and information (order), allowing their entropy connection to be somewhat variable according to the circumstances depending on whether the system in question is animate (living) or not. Accordingly, each may have an independent direction—again, depending upon circumstances. Within this kind of logical framework, we might be able to state: "life is a phenomenon in which the energy aspect of entropy is preserved (resulting in energy losses) while the information aspect, for whatever reasons, is not (resulting in greater system order)". This interpretation of the 2nd law accommodates the LS. Consequently, Life adheres to the 2nd law.

We are now faced with the enigma: "why should life behave differently from non-life phenomena with respect to the information aspect of entropy?" To date, biological life is the only such example (of an LS) within our experience. That fact alone probably accounts for our confused inability to classify it objectively and in a meaningful way. Perhaps the dis-entanglement of *entropy energy* and *system order* within our understanding of 2nd law imperatives will change all that. In so doing, we may have inadvertently stumbled upon a fundamental definition of that unique phenomenon we call "life" in terms of one of the most fundamental laws of nature—the 2nd law of thermodynamics. Additionally, we shall discover that the clarification of this important issue bears significantly upon the very important "interface question" that has been implicated earlier in our search for the answers to the OoL. A formal consideration of these issues follows.

Biological Life—A Very Special Case:

Energy Considerations: As stated above, the components of cellular life comprise biological machines that depend on energy to fuel their activities. There is no question but that these cellular nano-machines are subject to the same energy rules of the universe that all other machines and their systems, whether mechanical or molecular, must obey. As such, more fuel energy is required to drive their biological processes than is realized in resultant work or biochemical energy. In this respect, living organisms are subject to the same energy losses due to entropy demanded of all systems by the 2nd law of thermodynamics.

Information Considerations: As discussed above, Life unquestionably has unique characteristics—specifically in the way it organizes, converts and binds more and more of the inanimate matter of the planet into the greatly more complex biological molecules from which the systems that comprise the web of life are fashioned. In addition, over time the system components—as well as the LS as a whole—tend towards increased complexity and consequently greater order. Regardless of how one wishes to interpret these results, one cannot refute the uniqueness of the phenomenon. And if it appears to some to be contrary to the increased entropy provisions of the 2nd law—which demands an opposite result over time—then again this comes as no surprise. We have gotten used to the idea, even though we have been at a loss to explain it. The question has always been asked whether this curious property of Life is necessarily sufficient to qualify it as defying the 2nd Law of Thermodynamics? In the light of our discussions, there is no way to get around the definitive answer: The answer is an absolute "yes"—if we persist on interpreting the 2nd law in such a way that demands that entropy complexity and orderliness always increases or decreases in the same direction as entropy energy. What has not been considered, until now, is the distinct possibility that while that may be so in all non-life systems, it certainly does not hold with respect to the LS. The only logical solution is: allow the energy and information components of entropy to be independent entities, because in fact, they are.

Break The Law In Two:

From the above discussion we have acknowledged that the energies required to maintain form and function of the biological machines that comprise the living organisms of life are greater than the equivalent work accomplished, and that these losses can be defined as an increase in entropy—the whole according to the entropy energy provisions of the second law. Now, while you cannot measure entropy directly, we can calculate the entropy change associated with "a change in state of a system at constant temperature". The following mathematical expression is useful for describing the thermodynamics of mechanical systems such as steam engines.

$$\Delta S = q_{rev} / T \qquad\qquad\qquad \textbf{(1) where,}$$

q = **the heat that accompanies the change of state if it takes place by a reversible path;**

ΔS = the change in the entropy of the system—considered to be a system state function in the same way that pressure (P), volume (V), and temperature (T) are.

From the formula, it is apparent that as the temperature decreases in a mechanical system (heat is lost to the surroundings), the change in entropy is positive (increases).

The following expression is more useful for describing the chemical aspects of thermodynamics:

$$\Delta G = \Delta H - T\Delta S \qquad\qquad\qquad (2) \text{ where,}$$

ΔG = the change in the "Gibbs free energy" of the system

ΔH = the change in the "enthalpy", or *heat, of the system;*

T = the temperature of the system (deg Kelvin);

ΔS = the change in the entropy

Written in terms of ΔS:

$$\Delta S = (\Delta H - \Delta G) / T \qquad\qquad\qquad (3)$$

Again, entropy is seen to increase as the system temperature drops.

Our purpose here is not to engage in a formal discussion of applied thermodynamic principles. Rather, our cursory introduction to these topics is meant to shed light on the concept of entropy and its relevance to the phenomenon of life. Although entropy is hard to define precisely, all of these mathematical expressions make obvious the fact that changes in entropy are related to changes in system energy in general and to system temperature in particular. One would expect as much from a concept said to be fundamental to an understanding of the 2nd law of *thermo*dynamics. More interesting—than how these formal mathematical expressions define the relationship between entropy and heat and temperature (all measurable quantities)—is the fact that none of these relationships provide any kind of clue to the qualitative results inherent in any entropy change. Up until now, every definition of ΔS has been deemed to be incomplete if it does not include along with the change in the entropy of the system the phrase "the change in the number of microscopic states, or change in the amount of disorder of the system".

So—what is "entropy"? On the one hand, the formulas establish a relationship between intrinsic variables (within the equations above)—quantities that are easily measured. On the other, it is described, as well, as a measure of disorder—something not easily given to quantitative analysis. In addition, we are told that entropy—along with enthalpy and Gibbs free energy—is an intrinsic property of the chemicals forming the system in question. Nowhere in any of the equations is there any reference to information, orderliness nor complexity. This supports (and possibly has encouraged) the reasoning behind the conventional interpretation of the 2nd law, which considers that for all systems, a change in the entropy of "orderliness" simply reflects a secondary and resultant constant effect that accompanies any changes in the measurable entropy of "energy". This reasoning also follows from experience—it has always been observed in the simple experiments involving gases in closed inanimate systems and, thus, the results have been extrapolated to include any system. In fact, the reasoning has worked rather well to include all systems, manmade and natural. Where does "life" fit within this tidy scheme? Interestingly, at the time when these ideas were being formulated in the 19th century, no-one considered applying the 2nd law to life systems, because life, and particularly human life, was regarded as being outside of the spheres of influence of most natural laws. The question never arose then—as to whether life obeyed or disobeyed the law of entropy—because it was considered to exist outside the law. It was only in this century that the question became relevant as the metabolic processes became better understood and could be subjected to energy audit studies. But, even before these studies, the 2nd law principles were beginning to be extended to include the LS, as the realization sunk in that at the heart of life processes, some of the same principles of physics and chemistry were at work. In time, the increased scientific popularity of an abiogenetic OoL hypothesis and all that it implies eventually focused attention on "entropy and life" issues. From an abiogenesis OoL point of view, it is easy to understand why any entropy differences raised between the LS and natural systems were of necessity, not just glossed over, but also effectively rationalized out of existence. If bio-life is to be considered the results of natural phenomena, it must, defacto, obey an orthodox interpretation of any and all natural laws. Concurrently, the complexity interface at the OoL between life and non-life was rendered seamless and transparent in deference to the popularization of the "chemical soup" hypothesis for the OoL. Thus, the circle of logic appears complete. Today it is considered by the mainstream scientific establishment that there is scant reason for any scientist to seriously question the premise that the LS behaves strictly in accordance with the 2nd law—no differently from any other system. One popular scientific tradition (which does not sit well with many scientists) has been, simply, to deny that distinction altogether—by explaining away any seeming contradiction as some statistical anomaly within the universal scheme of things— that the universe compensates by always ending up more entropic overall, regardless of any anomalous reversals along the way. But this kind of logic actually ends up being a blatant cop-out because we know that the differences described above are not simply the speculative products of anyone's imagination. Those differences are both quantitative and qualitative within the LS. Indeed, probably the primary reason for skepticism on the part of dissenting scientists (those who believe in the <u>unlikelihood</u> that life began by a process of abiogenesis) is due solely to the inevitable acknowledgment that there is indeed a problem when it comes to the issue of the observance by the LS of some provisions of the 2nd Law. So, can everyone be satisfied: the mainstream scientists who insist on orthodox observance of the 2nd law, their skeptical colleagues who recognize fundamental phenomenological differences exhibited by the LS compared to all other systems, and the creationists who share the skepticism of their scientific allies in the pursuit of their agenda? Perhaps!

There is no denial that a change in orderliness may, of necessity, accompany an increase in the entropy of energy: it is just the *direction arrow* of that change—under different conditions—that is at issue. In terms of direction, we have seen that in all systems, with the exception of *life, the arrows of entropy (energy and information)* follow a parallel direction. And, the only system we know of that exhibits a divergent arrow of information entropy over time is the LS phenomenon. Now, an interesting question cannot be ignored: Which is the cause and which is the effect? With respect to entropy information and orderliness, the 2nd law may be useful as defining a system to be *living* if it functions such that, over time, and contrary to the 2nd law as it is presently conceived, its information and orderliness increases. Conversely, it is *not alive* if the direction of system entropy information and orderliness is tied directly to the direction of entropy energy provisions, as the scientific interpretation of the 2nd law presently describes. Thus, the solution to our problem is relatively simple: just change the way the 2nd law is interpreted—split the 2nd law up into its two separate entities:

a) *energy*, and

b) *information*.

It is important to recall that there is nothing in the entropy equation above that would prevent us from doing so because nowhere in the equations is there an indication of information or orderliness. The very fact that a critical component of entropy—its information—is missing from the entropy formula altogether gives us all the license we need to state that these are, in fact, separate if associated entities. Thus, orderliness and information can be legitimately considered to be the secondary effects of the law (nothing new here), and not causes in and of themselves. Furthermore, just because in all non-life (inanimate) situations the two parameters—information and energy—are always bound together and move in the same direction, need not imply that they are formally forever entangled, nor that this is universally the case. And, indeed, when it comes to the LS, we have good and valid reason to believe that any linkage between the two is reversed and unique.

The Problem of Interpretation:

Compared to any naturally occurring systems (unaffected in any way by biological life) the LS seems to behave differently, in that—while entropy does increase with respect to energy, it seems to decrease over time with respect to orderliness. The problem up until now has been how to interpret this difference in some meaningful way. The point is that the LS represents a special case phenomenon unlike any other system we can describe. And, one particular aspect that makes it special is the way it appears to not fit comfortably within the 2nd law provisions—provisions that seem to accommodate so well all other systems within our experience. To account for this "specialness" from a thermodynamic point of view is to acknowledge that living systems are the only systems that can "buck" the tendency of entropic energy losses that produce only disorder. The suggestion I am making is to interpret entropy exclusively in terms of entropy energy—freeing it from its traditional entropy-orderliness-complexity component (that's how Rudolf Clausius originally intended it to be). Then the second law becomes universal. Once this is done, we can deal with the orderliness-complexity component independently. Accordingly,

If a system is natural and inanimate, then it will naturally tend toward disorder over time. If the system is a living system, it will (by definition) tend toward increased order over time. Conversely,

If a system tends toward greater order over time, it must be an animate system; if toward greater disorder, it must be inanimate.

Thus, living processes and systems are different from all other "natural" systems precisely in virtue of the fact that they are able to continuously function against the universal information gradient of entropy while adhering strictly to the energy provisions of entropy. In fact, as evidenced above, this conspicuous distinction serves as a broadest and fundamental kind of definition of life. As such, we are faced with the prospect that for the second law to be universally relevant, we must acknowledge that under certain circumstances (living systems) the link between degradation of useful energy and a corresponding degradation of associated information does not apply. In other words, the second law, as it is presently constituted, is only universal (can include the LS) with respect to entropy energy losses. The resultant number of micro states (degree of system order) can increase or decrease according to whether the system is a LS or not.

The system of biological life is known to proceed from less order to greater order over time. This is a ubiquitous quality that life has exhibited since its inception on our planet close to 4 billion years ago. In fact, the very survival of the system of bio-life on our planet (survival, we have argued, being the only design intent of the LS) is considered to be based on its two-fold ability to:

1] evolve different species—many of which exhibit increased complexity—affording their offspring unique aptitudes and opportunities for overcoming the many obstacles to survival within a continually changing biosphere, and

2] increase in an exponential way the numbers of participant organisms over time.

As stated above, this latter LS ability impacts directly upon the issue of increasing complexity as more and more less-orderly inanimate matter increases in orderliness as it becomes transformed and incorporated within the cellular environments of increasing numbers of living things. At the heart of this unique LS phenomenon is that singularly unique quality that allows it to happen. For the moment, let's call that quality: the *life system intelligence*. What does that mean?

The Helping Hand:

The solution to an understanding of the causes underlying the thermodynamic differences between the LS and the rest of the inanimate world may, in fact, depend on an additional qualifying parameter whose existence or not is implicated in how energy is applied to a system. As argued above, if the energy is randomly applied—as in all natural systems—then the link between energy and information may be absolute in such instances and consistent with how the 2nd law is presently interpreted. Randomness, characteristic of natural systems, would tend to mitigate against any kind of resultant and lasting increase in order, with a decreasing state of orderliness being the only conceivable result. In this respect, the randomness aspect of energy interaction can be likened to a causative agent whose only possible effect must be the reduction of overall system order as well. This could explain the spontaneous tendency of natural systems toward disorder. If, on the other hand, the application of energy is itself the result of the implementation of an intelligent set of instructions, then the causative agent is no longer randomness—it is the controlling intelligence that precedes and directs the application of that energy. Accordingly, the results of having an intelligent controlling agent that precedes and directs the energy interactions in a system can be expected to yield more orderly results. In fact, within the LS, the controlling agent is information, in the form of genetic instructions that precedes and directs the application of energy in all biological reactions in contrived ways and in directions that energy would not normally flow. Intelligent control, replacing randomness, must account for the difference between the more orderly and complex results in the one case and the less orderly, less complex results in the other. This applies equally to a human intelligence guided hand turning over coins to create an ordered set as it does to a DNA derived intelligence guiding and directing biochemical reactions to create and maintain ordered biological processes within organisms. Again, while there may be local increases in the disorder of some of the reactant products that follow directly the entropy associated with all basic chemical energy reactions, the overall increase in order in living systems is the grand result of the intervention of intelligence that controls and direct all processes, in all of its subsystems. Again, you cannot just rationalize this result as a local anomaly permissible within the statistical parameters that apply—with the universe, again, always paying the entropy price. You just cannot treat the increase in order and complexity within the LS phenomenon as if it were simply the product of some temporary statistical aberration because, in fact, the effect is ubiquitous throughout the LS. The LS phenomenon has been consistent and has gone on too long to be trivialized as just an anomaly. And there is a possibility that it could continue in this way for the long-range foreseeable future—if intelligent life can survive long enough to develop technologies that permit it to ultimately seek refuge elsewhere. It is important to remember that biological life, as we know it, has been a part of this planet for close to 4 billion years—an appreciable proportion of the time the universe has been in existence (speculated at anywhere from 10 to 16 billion years). Who knows whether other such instances of biological life exist elsewhere in the universe that may predate our own? Make no mistake about it: this is no temporary anomaly! However, one thing is certain—biological life is subject to the same laws of nature as all other phenomena. If it seems to defy any particular law or rule of the universe or any aspect thereof (e.g., the information aspect of 2nd law entropy), then we can safely assume that it is not the law that is in question, but rather our interpretation of that law.

Life In the Balance—A Question of Equilibrium:

The following exercise will help further clarify the issues involved:

The basic unit of biological life is the cell. The cell is capable of existing in three states; none of which are thermodynamically in equilibrium:

1] The living cell under steady state conditions;

2] The non-living cell (at the moment a live cell has ceased to engage in living activity i.e., cell death).

3] The living cell under self-replication conditions;

A comparison of the three states above delineates different conditions and circumstances that effect how the 2nd law must be applied to biological life. The first and third cases above describe states of cellular matter under the continuous control of its genetic instructions. This intelligent control operates against forces that "want to" spontaneously change all subsystems into thermodynamic equilibrium states. As long as these anti-equilibrium controls can remain in place, the living processes will continue, organizing matter in more ordered states within living systems and subsystems, each living entity contributing to the overall complexity of the interactive LS. The cell that no longer engages in life has, in effect, become deprived of that control. In that lifeless condition, its particular subsystems can only engage in spontaneous and random irreversible thermodynamic processes that will proceed in a preferred direction (decreasing energy and order) until an equilibrium state is reached. This difference not only describes the distinction between living and non-living cells, but also can serve as well to delineate the variance between the LS and non-living systems. The cell at the time of death has, in effect, lost the single important attribute that afforded it life. It can now be considered no different from inanimate matter and subject to the classical application of the 2nd law accordingly; indeed, its future actions bears out that claim. Although just at the moment of death the cell can be considered to be just as complex as it was prior to its demise, the immediate consequence of the break in communication with its genetic library that controls the application of energy for all living cell functions, is that the individual cell components (subsystems) are now freed to react independently to local chemical forces in the same random manner as inanimate matter does. The process of deterioration (spontaneous tendency toward the equilibrium state) that proceeds without delay within the cellular remains is the most poignant application of the provisions of the law of entropy—as all of the complex structures contained in the living cell that served the processes of life are disassembled into their constituent molecular parts. In the process, both energy entropy as well as information entropy increases, as they must. This degradation process is a direct result of the relinquishing of control exercised by the genetic control center of the cell in life. It is no different from the removal of the hand that can quickly create an ordered state within a box full of coins. Withdraw the element of controlling intelligence and what you are inevitably left with is the same randomness that applies to any inanimate system. Thus, we can conclude that it is precisely the effect of this control in the living cell that signifies the difference between the living cell and non-living cell; between life and non-life; between intelligent control and randomness.

The effect of intelligent control can now be extended to signify the difference between living and non-living systems—between life and non-life. It follows that it is the key to the non-observance within life of the otherwise universal tendency toward disorder demanded by the 2nd law. Accordingly, it is that same control element that would seem to account for the breakdown in the energy-information relationship that is a pillar of the 2nd law. And finally, it is this very detachment that permits the creation and maintenance of all kinds of dis-equilibrium states that define the activities of life.

In effect, the final act of any living entity that dies is the ultimate achievement of that which is denied the living: the equilibrium state—a virtual impossibility in life and a virtual certainty in death. (In practice, it should be noted that the remains of non-living cells rarely get the opportunity to reach equilibrium in virtue of their continued value within LS Food Chain interactive processes. Long before the equilibrium state is achieved, complex protein and carbohydrates are recycled—somewhat randomly and opportunistically by organisms trying to stay alive. This serves to emphasize the fact that the LS represents the ultimate interactive system and that LS complexity comprises more than just the sum of its parts.)

In Defiance After All:

Thus, the intricate activities of life represent thermodynamic states that, on the whole, are not in equilibrium—all the result of intelligent controls unique to the LS that can intercede, as it were, in order to break the normal connection between energy and complexity in nature. And when and where equilibrium is established within living systems, it is more than likely that such equilibrium states are tentative—awaiting directions to engage in one kind of required cellular activity or another. Accordingly, the net increase in complexity in living systems ends up being the consequences of the establishment and maintenance of these dis-equilibrium states—both characteristically contrary to the normal activity of inanimate matter. In contrast, the cell in death can no longer do so. Instead, as stated, the only activity it is now capable of are the random reactions, typical of inanimate chemistry, in the direction where all of the available energies still bound up in the cell are liberated—pursuant to the process of restoring the constituent parts to a natural state of equilibrium. But, in order to do so, the connection between energy and information must become reestablished. I use the term "reestablished" rather than "established" as a subtle reminder that the "normal" state for all molecules is the equilibrium state towards which all systems tend. It is also a reminder that when a cell incorporates non-living molecules within its living system, it is in effect taking molecules from their equilibrium state and elevating that matter into the non-equilibrium states that characterize life. Thus, the difference between a non-living cell—which behaves normally (tends toward the equilibrium state) with respect to the 2nd law, and the living cell—which behaves abnormally (tends away from the equilibrium state) with respect to the 2nd law, represents the fundamental difference between Life (the living state) and non-Life and why that law must accordingly be differentially applied respectively to each, and reinterpreted to accommodate these differences. A reinterpretation of the 2nd law in terms of energy and complexity can then be able to account for all of the dynamic activities that living systems do and which non-living systems do not. Ultimately, the 2nd law can serve to define: a) what it means for a system to be "alive", b) why living systems are perpetually active systems, c) why it is that living systems can determine their energy needs and can bring that energy to bear where, and as, needed, d) how it is that the LS has the ability to direct non-random energy to do work—all in terms of non-equilibrium states that give rise to the unique activities of life. All of these things are in sharp contrast to non-living systems, where it is the random interaction between matter and energy that leads in all cases toward the equilibrium state in abeyance of the forces of 2nd law entropy, whereas once achieved, it can undergo no further detectable change.

Then, again, perhaps we can describe the 2nd law in such a way as to acknowledge the fact that it behaves differently according to whether the cell is alive and comprises living matter, or dead, when it comprises inanimate matter. Either way, the difference in the way entropy operates between the two cases can only be explained directly by the differences in activity between a live cell and a dead one and by the differences in attributes that account for that distinction. From the above, we can state categorically that the fundamental difference must be directly linked to some faculty that maintains the continuous intelligent supervision controlling all the dynamic activities in the living cell and the cessation of which signifies death and decay.

We know that the self-replicating system used by the LS introduces, over time, increased complexity and orderliness into the copies (offspring organisms). That is one variance between the LS and any other phenomenon we have encountered in our world. The following informal exercise is designed to persuade you (if indeed that is still necessary) that indeed this aspect of Life constitutes a singular exception to the law of preservation of entropy (The Second Law of Thermodynamics) insofar as the information aspect is concerned.

Self-Replication As An Engine Of Increased Complexity:

Special circumstances characterize the relationship between energy and information in the living system under self-replication conditions (case 3 above). There are three distinct results that can arise within the LS when biological self-replication occurs. In each instance described below, the amount of energy used in the biological reproduction processes can be assumed to remain constant for all three cases and all energy audits consistent with the 2nd law. Thus, energy considerations can be eliminated from the following discussion—only orderliness, in terms of organism complexity need be seen to come into play as a variable.

1] Biological Replication Leads To Degradation:

If the offspring copy (organism) is degraded as a result of the deleterious effects caused by a random mutation of a genetic instruction, then the result is greater disorder, and entropy (both from the information and energy aspects) is preserved. If the offspring fails to survive, the gene pool where complexity accumulates is unaffected.

2] Biological Replication Is Neutral:

If the consequences for an organism of a random genetic change are neutral and the effects benign, then for the sake of simplicity we can assume that the copy is equivalent to the original and not worse. Thus, there is no change in entropy due to disorder. However, as we shall see, even neutral genetic changes can skip generations and dramatically affect future offspring; genetic change that can be expressed dramatically both positively and negatively. But for the moment, we will disregard these possible influences. For our present purposes, entropy is preserved by virtue of the energy considerations alone (same as the first case above). In other words, we will assume that more energy is spent in the replication process than can be accounted for in the energy budgets for the individual replication stages even though there is no negative change in the information aspect. Thus, in this case while orderliness is preserved (neither increased nor decreased), some energy is irretrievably lost. The effects on the gene pool can be considered neutral, subject to reevaluation according to whether latent changes emerge as positive or negative contributions to the species genome in the future.

3] Biological Replication Leads To Increased Orderliness:

The third case is at the heart of the whole issue: Here we consider the circumstance where a chance mutation expresses itself as an increase in complexity that confers increased fitness and eventually leads to new evolutionary opportunities in later generations. But, the fact remains that the amount of energy required to reproduce this more complex organism is no more nor less than that required to reproduce the organisms described respectively in the above two cases. In all three examples, genetic changes are unpredictable in both occurrence and quality and their influence on the gene pool is due only to chance. Thus, each has an equal opportunity to contribute negative (detrimental to survival), more complex, or neutral (neither good nor bad), influences to the resultant offspring organism. In all cases, it is the change to genetic information that precedes expressed changes in the physical complexity of an organism. Thus, increase in complexity and order as ascribed to the genetic information of an organism must be in terms of, and limited to, how any changes to that information is expressed in its owners physiology. In other words, in all three cases the results could produce <u>greater</u>, <u>equal</u> or <u>less</u> disorder, all for the same expenditure of energy. Thus, in this, our third case scenario, we have a situation where the same constant amount of energy has been expended in the copying process plus a little bit extra to account for chemical "friction" or heat energy entropy losses. But, out of those three distinct possibilities, somehow the system wide result over time is an unaccountable increase in complexity and thus orderliness that completely overshadows the energy consideration. Now, this phenomenon could be dismissed as an anomaly in a small corner of the planet, (or the universe, for that matter) balanced by an equal or greater number of more chaotic organisms elsewhere. But we know that not to be the case. Over time, the LS within its planetary habitat has become more complex in both qualitative and quantitative terms. And this is achieved at no additional cost of energy. The energy side of the ledger has no effect on complexity. It is merely the cost of replication without regard to the quality of the result. Thus the same energy would be spent, for example, whether evolution saw fit to produce less complex organisms, slightly more complex organisms or the millions of greatly more complex species we find all over the planet today, as compared to the past. Yes, the sun's energy is fueling the copying and becoming more entropic as a result. But that alone cannot satisfy the overwhelming tendency to greater order that the LS exhibits over time. These kinds of activities and results seem to occur exclusively within the sphere of biological life and in two distinct directions: 1) qualitatively—as the results of the evolution of more complex species, as well as 2) quantitatively—as increased "non-living stuff" is being processed and organized into more complex "living stuff". If it were totally left to the laws of probability, logic dictates that changes to blueprints as complicated as those of the organisms of the LS must be detrimental vastly more often than an improvement. This takes into account the fact that there are, indeed, vastly more opportunities for chance changes that can spell disaster than improvement. Then, the conditions in our first case above would apply and entropy would be seen to be preserved. And, if that were the usual condition, then we could expect the system to tend to degrade with time and eventually grind to a halt. Then, of course, we would also be faced with the prospect that under those limiting circumstances, the LS would have never gotten sufficiently off the ground to attain a cumulative level of complexity that could later have the opportunity to degrade according to 2nd law imperatives. At the very least, under currently interpreted dictates of the 2nd law, the LS should have "locked in" in terms of complexity to a level where the forces that tend toward increased complexity reach some optimal or saturated level and become balanced by forces sufficient to stem the LS tendency toward greater complexity; a balance between convergent and divergent forces. Accordingly, how do we account for the fact that the absolute reverse is so—that judging from the fossil record, evolution seems to be "defiantly" divergent? The answer surely lies within the distinctions that define the differences between inanimate chemistry and biology. And undoubtedly, it is these same differences that must account as well for how the second law applies differently to each.

Maxwell's Demon—Better Late Than Never:

There is a classical mind experiment provided by James Clerk Maxwell, the renowned 19th century physicist that has relevance to the above discussions—both with respect to the 2nd law and as well to the increased complexity issue of evolution. We begin with the classical interpretation of the 2nd law at the fundamental level of gas molecules. Imagine two containers connected by a valve, one of which contains a volume of gas under pressure, and the other an empty vacuum. If we open the valve, gas will tend to flow from the filled container to the empty one until the pressures become equal. There is a preferred direction to this process (from higher to lower pressure). But once equality of pressure is achieved, no further gas flow is possible. In fact this closed system can be considered the equilibrium state with no further activity possible at the macro level according to the 2nd law. The temperature of the gas in both vessels will be a measure of the average atomic kinetic energy (velocities) of all the atoms involved at the micro level i.e. temperature is a statistical phenomenon and even in equilibrium, a gas of molecules contains atoms with a range of velocities. In trying to prove the validity of the 2nd law—and entropy in particular—it was suggested back in Maxwell's time that perhaps the law has only statistical validity with respect to atoms, and that furthermore, its validity is only due to the fact that atoms are so small relative to human beings. The implication was that a being the size of molecules would not see a continuous increase in entropy. Maxwell seized upon this and described the following conditions that he thought could violate the 2nd law.

Position an intelligent "demon" (as he called it), the size of a molecule, at the valve connecting two bulbs containing gas at the same temperature. The demon would be instructed to allow fast moving molecules to pass in one direction only (left to right, say). After a while, that bulb would contain atoms with a higher average velocity than the other would and consequently its temperature would have to rise, since temperature is a measure of the average kinetic energy of the gas atoms. Under these circumstances, Maxwell's demon would have created a temperature difference and increased orderliness at the expense of randomness—all without doing work. This would qualify as a violation of the 2nd law. Lord Kelvin lent his support to the idea in 1874 when he suggested that the 2nd law was not an absolute law of nature but rather a human artifact resulting from the relative size of man in comparison to the atom and the law of large numbers.

Ultimately, (mid 20th century) it was shown that Maxwell's Demon couldn't operate for highly technical reasons and grounds—which need not concern us here. Nonetheless, the importance of Maxwell's Demon example for our purposes relates to the *"selection principle"* involved i.e., essentially it addresses the same idea that if you could select between higher and lower energy atoms, or anything else, for that matter, in order to try and remove randomness from a system without investing additional work to do it then, in so doing, the 2nd law can be violated. Well, that is exactly what the so-called "natural selection" process of evolution is all about.

The concept of natural selection works the same way as Maxwell's Demon was supposed to. Instead of a mini-being discriminating between gas molecules passing between containers, natural selection effectively selects which genes will pass into the future and which will not. Those genes that do survive into the future do so because the organisms that possess them are better than the competition with respect to survival fitness as well as their ability to adapt to changing conditions—all functions of the quality of the genes themselves. Those genes that don't "measure up", so to speak, have been stopped in their tracks by an "evolutionary Maxwell's Demon". The fact is that the net result has been an increase in organism complexity over time, which translates directly into increased complexity of the genes. The result is not due to chance but rather to an energy free selection process whose sole purpose results in selecting from a pool of genes having many degrees of freedom (just like gas atoms having different velocities) in the present generation (one of the gas containers) and only allowing certain ones to pass—into the "gene space" of the next generation (the preferred gas container), all without an additional energy investment. Could we not conclude, then, that in our example of the LS—the only example we know of where it applies—Maxwell's Demon has succeeded a little more than a century late, with the corresponding consequences for the 2nd Law? (As stated previously the term "natural selection" is in fact a misnomer—there is no active selective process at work resulting in evolution. Rather, the principles and mechanisms of "adaptive survival" result in establishing anew in every generation the surviving genome of every species which serves as the genetic adaptive survival base for again the following generation—and so it continues).

From Demons To Humans:

Maxwell's Demon raises another important issue—that of the significance of human intelligence and activity in terms of the 2nd law. You will recall that our demon friend was introduced as a way of breaking the logical barrier that prohibits humans from seeing reality at the microscopic level. It essentially acted as our micro representative because none of us could be there in person.

When we casually talk about hypothetical perpetual motion machines and their prohibition according to the 2nd law, we forget the fact that machines are the products of human intelligence. In fact, the only reason the principles of the 2nd law came to light in the first place was in connection with the efficiencies of steam engines—it had nothing at all to do with any innate understanding of entropy or complexity. When Rudolf Clausius coined the term "entropy" in 1865, it was in relation to the investigations carried out by Sadi Carnot and Lord Kelvin of heat energy exchanges between the sub-systems of machines. The fact is that still today the usual introduction to the 2nd law and entropy continues to be in terms of the limitations that nature imposes on man-made machines, and the fact that additional energy must be provided (in terms of fuel) to overcome entropy energy losses due to friction—as well as periodic work in the form of maintenance against normal wear and tear to counteract the natural tendency toward entropic breakdown and disorderliness. Indeed, our machines run out of fuel and do break down unless we intercede—by adding fuel and changing warn parts as needed—and herein resides our whole point. What is "human intervention" in these circumstances, if not "intelligent control" extended from within the LS—in order to interrupt the spontaneous tendency of all systems towards the equilibrium state (the state of lowest energy and greatest disorder)? Since human intelligence is a direct result of the increasing complexity phenomenon characteristic throughout the LS, the creation and operation of machines by humans is merely an extension of that very same LS phenomenon. As such, machines of human design can be considered to be external non-biological extensions and manifestations of the LS itself. And, we can argue that the fueling and maintenance of our machine creations is also an extension of the same intelligent controls that intercede and prevent the randomness universally ubiquitous to non-life from encroaching upon all life processes, thereby sustaining their non-equilibrium states. The moment we neglect to keep up the intelligent controls that maintain order within the subsystems of our mechanical machines, they will spontaneously head in the direction of equilibrium and eventually cease to function as well—no differently than what happens when the intelligent controls that fuel and maintain (keep alive) LS biological subsystems cease (as occurs in the death of an organism). In both cases, spontaneous changes will occur through irreversible processes until the equilibrium state is reached. In that respect, the carcass remains of a "road kill" and the remains of a rundown and abandoned automobile have a lot in common. Similarly, the intercession of human intelligence in the operation of mechanical machines has a ready parallel with the intercession of the intelligent controls responsible for the operation of biological machines. Considering that human intelligence is a product of the results of evolutionary processes within the LS, these can serve as an explanation of the principles involved. In effect, there is a direct connection that begins with intelligent controls in individual cells and extends up the evolutionary ladder through multi-cellular organisms—where more complex levels of control are required to coordinate the activities of individual cells into a cooperative whole. It continues unbroken to the LS pinnacle characterized by human technology that can exercise the levels of control to the extent they permit the creation and operation of complex machines external to, and at great distances from, the biological framework of the LS. The ultimate example to date is the launching into space and continued control of manmade machines that are poised to leave our solar system. The irony is that whether we appreciate the fact or not, we effectively relinquish our intelligent control over these space machines when they are no longer accessible for maintenance and repair. From that moment on, it is only a matter of time before spontaneous changes through irreversible processes will cause a machine to malfunction and eventually cease to function altogether. The process of physical degradation will then continue until the ultimate random state we call equilibrium is reached, no matter how long it takes.

Implications for Life:

Thus, unlike natural processes, it is not energy alone that randomly promotes the behavior of the LS—it is only the intelligently directed energy that can and does support the existence of the LS in all of its complex manifestations. This is well illustrated in an example given previously: All the sunshine in the world shining upon a vessel containing carbonated water (H_2O plus dissolved CO_2) will not produce energy conversions nor complex carbohydrates unless the intelligent photosynthesis conversion apparatus is there to mediate the reactions. Once in place, the photosynthesis subsystem proceeds efficiently and tirelessly directing the sun's photon energies into the production of energy-rich compounds that can be used system wide to power all LS activities. The whole process is controlled from start to finish. There is nothing random about it. This state of affairs represents neither chance occurrences nor long shot coincidences. The point is that before energy can be applied effectively within living biological systems, the intervention of intelligent energy conversion sub-systems must be present to direct and coordinate the complex activities involved. It is this same intelligence component that is responsible for overcoming and eliminating randomness, which itself accounts for the fact that the LS does, indeed, defy both the odds as well as the natural tendency towards chaos and disorder. In so doing, it circumvents important provisions of the 2nd law, as it is currently constituted. But most importantly, in the biological system of life on our planet, this occurs because information and intelligence is in place and precedes the controlled funding and application of energy as well as all of the dynamic activities characteristic of bio-life. If, indeed, this is the case for LS activity, then most importantly, the same must be true for the very OoL itself. Information and intelligence had to be in place (to overcome randomness) before the phenomenon could begin. How did it get there? There is only one possible answer—its called "rational design".

As a parting thought on the ubiquitous influence of the laws of thermodynamics on all processes in the universe we inhabit, we defer to the wisdom of thermodynamicist Henry Brent, who paraphrased the first two laws as follows:

First Law "You can't win—you can only break even."
Second Law: "You can't break even!"

Intelligence—A Many Splendored Thing:

In the next chapter, we investigate the nature of LS system intelligences (< not a typo). We shall come to realize before we are through that LS intelligence is only an umbrella term, which tends to disguise the existence of its many forms—operating, as they do, in a kind of concerted hierarchy of functions. We shall discover, for example, the existence of a primary level of intelligence, operating at the fundamental biological level of life (within the PdP) that even precedes the information and intelligence encoded in the genetic instruction library. It is to be found within the very form of the genetic code language and is very much implicated in the success of evolution. We have already found intelligence at the species level within the system's sophisticated use of distribution statistics that permit species to anticipate biosphere changes, adapt accordingly, and thus be able to control somewhat evolutionary destiny. And, of course, we find many examples at the LS level, within the system wide feedback checks and balances that characterize the interactions across all species. As a consequence, it will become evident that such concepts as information content, orderliness, and complexity take on a whole new meaning and significance within the context of biological life. We are again reminded that this state of increasing complexity characteristic of biological systems is contrary to every known natural phenomenon. Then again, we are not making the case that the LS is a natural phenomenon, are we?

[1] Israel Journal of Chemistry: 1992 Vol. 32 p369
[2] Geology: Vol 10, p458
[3] Smithsonian Institution Journal, June 1970 p6
[4] The Cosmic Blueprint: Paul Davies, p6
[5] Chemical Principles: Harper & Row, p 418-424
[6] Chemical Principles: Harper & Row, p 418-424
[7] Smithsonian Institution Journal, June 1970 p6
[8] Nature of the Physical World: p 74
[9] American Laboratory 10/82, p88
[10] Elements of Chemical Thermodynamics for Advanced Students of Physics: p 99,100
[11] Time Arrows: Scientific Attitudes Toward Time, 1984, p113
[12] Thermodynamics and Statistical Mechanics: p 155
[13] American Scientist, Vol. 65, p409
[14] Biosystems: Vol 1, p259
[15] Encycl Britannica (CD 7 Electronic Edition)
[16] An Introduction to Biology, p 466
[17] Time's Arrow and Evolution, p14
[18] Physics Today: Vol 25, p 28
[19] Natural History, Jan 1996, p10
[20] Nature: 16 Mar, 1995, p 227
[21] Exons, Introns and Talking Genes; Basic Books, p 61

12. The Information Level of Bio-Life

"The most exciting phrase to hear in science, the one that heralds new discoveries, is not Eureka! (I found it!) but rather,
"hmm…that's funny…"
—Isaac Asimov (1920–1992), Science/Science Fiction Writer

The Arrow of Information Flow, Dogmas, and the 2nd Law:

It was once thought that acquired skills and knowledge could be inherited by offspring. The chief proponent of this notion was 18th century biologist Jean Baptiste de Lamarck. In fact, his name is used as a coined phrase (Lamarckism) to evoke the idea of inheritable acquired characteristics. By the mid 20th century, biologists had come to believe that the function of genetic information is specialized only to instruct the order of amino acids in a polypeptide chain in the protein manufacturing process. As such genetic information is thought to flow in only one direction: from the DNA genetic library in the cell nucleus to the ribosome "machine tools" that translate the genetic recipe-like information into peptide chains that—when folded—turn into functional proteins. The implication is that there is no way for novel positive physiological attributes of organisms to feed back and inform the genetic library that a particular trend in a physical trait is beneficial to the organism, and therefore to adjust those genetic instructions to favor and retain it in future generations. Nor should novel talents or abilities feedback directly to effect the genetic information inheritable by descendant generations. The common wisdom suggests that only the survival of a mutation of the encoded information within the genetic library of an affected organism and of its offspring within any species will determine the ultimate future of such expressed random genetic changes. The flow of genetic information has a direction: from genetic information contained in DNA > to transcribed and edited information in RNA > to the translation into physical proteins, where the information is expressed. Information cannot flow in the other direction i.e., from physical proteins back to genetic information. There have been found rare exceptions to this "dogma" of sorts within the ability of viruses to reverse transcribe mRNA into DNA. And, an effect whereby mRNA molecules can execute their developmental functions in cells distant from where they were initially transcribed has implications that suggest genetic changes occurring in any cell at any time in the life of a cell may be inherited[1]. This potentially new paradigm for some gene expression patterns could reverse the common wisdom in the sphere of molecular biology. Lamarckism may yet return to haunt us.

But, this *"Central Dogma"* (a phrase coined by Francis Crick) principle of information flow in the cell represents, as well, an important piece in the OoL puzzle. The Central Dogma, in effect, describes a specific application (the functioning of biological genesis) of what is probably a more general and universal logical relationship between any conceivable contrivance (of human derivation or otherwise) and the instructions for its design, construction and operation—a relationship that flows directly from our 2nd Law entropy deliberations of the last chapter. We wish to introduce a general and universal principle (of which the Central Dogma of biology represents but a specific instance), as it relates to any contrived machine or system in the universe (a product of any intelligence whatsoever)—a principle we shall call: the *"Universal Dogma of Information Flow (UDIF)"*. In so doing, we want to set the stage for the introduction of (and hopefully the acceptance of) the idea that other intelligences may, indeed, be operational within our universe and consequently, logically allow for other examples of intelligently designed systems—where the energy and informational components of entropy can move in opposite directions. In other words—the flow of design and operational information from genetic library to organism operational form and function within the LS (the Central Dogma) may in fact reflect but a single example of a fundamental and universal principle—the UDIF—that allows the reversal of the association between energy and information as understood within a traditional interpretation of the 2nd law. In all natural inanimate (uncontrolled, random) systems, a change of state is characterized by a necessary increase in overall entropy; energy is irretrievably lost followed by the resultant state of greater system disorder (information loss). We already know from experience with human designed systems that intelligence derived design and control information must precede and be in place prior to the application of energy for machine construction and operation. The same can be said to be true in bio-life systems as well with respect to genotype information encoded in DNA that defines the physical phenotypes when expressed. Thus, the cause and effect roles of energy and information, under such circumstances become effectively reversed. Using the only two examples of intelligently controlled systems (human designed and bio-life) as our guide, we can generalize the concept of "the application of energy and matter for the creation and operation of complex systems by first processing information through intelligent systems", and formulate a self-evident and universal rule which might be stated formally as follows:

"The Universal Dogma of Information Flow" (UDIF):

In the universe we know, design(ed systems) must derive from (be preceded by) information; information from intelligence; intelligence from prior intelligence;…etc.

This is directly related to the fact that in all intelligent systems, information is disentangled from (and must precede) the "controlled" application of energy required for its (the information's) physical expression. All else is randomness (uncontrolled) and subject to the conventional 2nd law "energy-information" entanglement.

Another way of putting it (and expanding its relevancy):

"In all intelligent systems: 1] design information must precede realization (physical expression of the information), and 2] operating information (instructions) must precede operation".

The above axiomatic principles, if you will, express in general form the idea that you must split up the information and energy aspects of 2nd law entropy as it applies to specialized systems such as the LS. We can go further and state that the UDIF allows us to actually reverse the cause and effect relationship between energy and information in such systems. By effectively establishing the primacy of information as the causal agent and logical precursor to the application of energy for its expression in all <u>intelligent systems</u>, the UDIF effectively solves the "2nd law violation" problem with respect to the LS. The UDIF effectively validates the principle that design, construction and operational instructions must precede the introduction and controlled application of energy necessary to produce the form and function of any physical machine—including biological machines. We have always known that it applies universally to man-made systems and contrivances; now we have reason to include biological systems as well.

A Definition of Life in Terms of the 2nd Law of Thermodynamics:

The above premise suggests an effective definition for life in terms of the 2nd law of thermodynamics:

> LIFE *is any system where the information (order) and energy components of entropy are disentangled such that the former component can decrease while the latter component always increases.*

The only constant in the order-energy equation with respect to entropy is the energy component—it is always seen to increase, regardless of whether the system is random or intelligent. This simply acknowledges that energy change losses cannot be avoided and are universal. The fact that order can increase, and is seen to do so in intelligent systems—because of the intelligent application of both information and energy—is not really surprising. It is the introduction of intelligent control that effectively removes from the system equation the random chance component—that ubiquitous quality universally characteristic of all non-intelligent (and therefore uncontrolled) phenomena.

The Nature and Source of Intelligence in the Universe:

Our main challenge at this point is to validate the existence of intelligence (the source of all design information, according to the UDIF) as a distinct and primary quality or state in the universe and not simply a manifestation derived from random chemistry (i.e., intelligence evolved from abiogenetic origins). Let us not forget that there is only one example of intelligence in the universe of which we are aware: bio-life, which gave rise to human intelligence, which can design things. Some would include the universe itself (including the behavioral attributes of matter, energy and the laws of nature that govern how they interact in the space-time continuum) as embodying some kind of universal intelligence, which gave rise to bio-life (however that occurred), but we could consider those kinds of sentiments to be metaphoric at this point. Now, it is interesting to note that how you consider the occurrence of the OoL on our planet will color how you define and view intelligence. Supporters of a creationist OoL argue that there is a primary intelligence in the universe they attribute to God, that is responsible for any and all other manifestations of intelligence—including bio-life, and human intelligence in particular. Supporters of abiogenesis must argue the exact opposite—that intelligence is nothing more than a manifestation of complex biological systems within the LS, and that any intelligence we can describe effectively derives from the inherent order to be found within the complex rules and laws that direct cause and effect within our universe. According to this point of view, human intelligence and any other examples of intelligence we can imagine can be nothing more than the products of chemical evolution— itself derived from complex but random chemical processes; that intelligence is nothing more than our way of describing some interesting behavioral characteristics of human beings and other species, and that there is no evidence of any other kind of independent intelligence to be found in the universe. I believe we can demonstrate otherwise.

The case is made that the term "intelligence" is defined in terms of human thought processes and therefore has a built-in restriction on how it should be considered. As such, if we are to search for other manifestations of intelligence outside of these restrictions, at the very least we should first examine and define those characteristics of human intelligence that will serve as a kind of guideline and permit us to seek it out elsewhere. We begin with a formal definition as provided by the *Merriam-Webster's Collegiate Dictionary—10th edition*: For the sake of brevity (and relevance to our discussions), we have edited the lengthy list of human activities that qualify as intelligent and have distilled the definition down to its essence:

> <u>Intelligence</u> *(the dictionary definition): the ability to learn or understand; the skilled use of reason;* <u>*the ability to apply knowledge to manipulate one's environment*</u>*; mental acuteness; an intelligent entity; comprehension; information, news; the ability to perform computer functions…*

Within this definition framework, we can begin a process of depersonalizing intelligence from its egocentric roots and expand its meaning and application to include some fundamental characteristics of the universe in general. Our goal shall be to try and extrapolate examples of human intelligence activity (the milieu that defines intelligence) to a generalized and universal principle that could lend additional weight to our UDIF by pinning down the very source of intelligence in the universe. Of immediate interest is the reference to "the ability to apply knowledge to manipulate one's environment". The implication is that left alone, the environment of interest will remain static, in its natural state and subject only to the dictates of the 2nd law. The ability to manipulate "unnaturally" one's environment is attributable to the application of intelligence.

Let's take a simple example of a child's game: "pinning the tail on the donkey". A poster showing the form of a donkey, minus its tail, is posted on a wall. Each child takes its turn to be blindfolded, is spun around a couple of times to disorient him/her and handed the cardboard tail with a pin attached. The child deprived of sight, then attempts to place the tail as close to where the tail of the donkey belongs in the image. The object of the game is to see which child will come closest to pinning the tail on the anatomically appropriate location. The winner gets a prize. What lessons can we draw from this example? First, there is little skill involved since all of the contestants are blindfolded and disoriented before they proceed. Thus, any given result relies strictly on chance with no opportunity for the exercise of intelligence. Typically, after all of the children have had their turn, the results of many tails stuck on the wall reveal the absence of any predictable pattern and should represent some form of random distribution of points, possibly centering on the one desired locus (where the tail should go). The only reason the points will congregate in the general desired direction is due to the encouragement of the sighted onlookers. Lets us now change the conditions slightly: one of the children wants to win the prize so badly that it is tempted to cheat by altering the blindfold so that it can see exactly where to place the tail—and proceeds to do so. What has changed? Obviously, the ability to see the desired destination provides information that can be processed by the intelligence of the child—what was a random chance of success for the blindfolded child, unable to exercise its intelligence, has turned into certainty of success for the sighted child able to use its intelligence. And if every child cheated, we could expect that every trial would have succeeded and instead of a random distribution of pins on the donkey "map" we would see all of the pins converged upon a single targeted point. Thus, human intelligence and its ability to "manipulate its environment" essentially translate into turning random chance into certainty when all of the sufficient and necessary information is available—as exemplified in the above example. Can we logically draw any conclusions with respect to some basic concepts that can be generalized? Let's look at what we have so far:

We have seen that under certain conditions, randomness prevails in the absence of intelligence, and certainty is assured with the application of intelligence. We have seen that intelligence (seeing) essentially involves the ability to process information (the desired location). It allows us to choose a single desired event to occur among many possibilities. Without the intervention of intelligence, under ideal conditions, any one of the available choices has an equal opportunity to become reality. Intelligence permits certain choice—non-intelligent permits only random chance. The only conclusion is that within human affairs, intelligence is what separates certainty from random chance. Our next challenge is to find a way of expressing this conclusion in both qualitative and quantitative terms—in order to universalize the principles involved.

Intelligence In Terms of Its Qualitative and Quantitative Attributes:

We have seen that invariably, the application of intelligence results in the ability to improve the probability odds of some phenomenon occurring over the probability of it happening randomly and purely by chance. This relates directly to the dictionary definition in terms of "the ability to apply knowledge to manipulate one's environment". "manipulate" implies "choice" over "chance"—no different than: pinning the tail on the donkey is a random process—with an infinite number of chances for failure when a person is blindfolded and unable to apply intelligence to the search, and certainty when the blindfold is removed and intelligent processes are brought to bear in choosing the one successful site. So far, so good. Let us now extend the above principle to identifying the rolls on a single die in order to simplify both the quantitative and qualitative principles involved.

We shall undertake two sets of trials. Each trial shall comprise several rolls of a single die. In each trial, you roll the die and I have to identify the face that comes up each time.

TRIAL 1: I AM BLINDFOLDED AND UNABLE TO SEE THE DIE:

You roll the die. I cannot see the top face and therefore I have to take a guess at what it might be—anywhere from 1 to 6. My chances of guessing correctly the top face of the die is no different than predicting correctly the top face before the event actually takes place: 1/6.

In general terms, the probability that a specific event will occur, out of a quantity of "n" possible event states having equal probability of occurring by random chance, is inversely proportional to the total no of such possible states, or 1/n.

Pr = 1/n

where, **Pr** is the random probability, and **n** is the total number of possible event states.

TRIAL 2: THE BLINDFOLD IS REMOVED SO THAT I CAN SEE THE DIE:

Obviously, everything has changed—I can call correctly every throw of the die because I can read the top face. Thus, the chances of an intelligent observer correctly identifying each roll of the die are certain every time. It makes no difference how many event states there are—I will succeed "n" times. We can state this as a mathematical expression:

Pc = n

where, Pc is the probability of certainty.

From the above two simple expressions, one thing becomes clear: quantitatively, the probability of certainty (Pc = n) is the reciprocal of random probability (Pr = 1/n). What these simple mathematical expressions convey is the fact that the degree of randomness, Pr, depends upon the value of "n" (number of random states) but that regardless of how many random states there are Pc is always its reciprocal. This is due to the fact that no matter how the odds against something occurring increase (the probability of a group of events occurring is arrived at by multiplying the probabilities of each respective event), suitable intelligent intervention can reduce the odds to certainty every time. As "n" increases, the amount of intelligent intervention (quality as well as quantity) may have to increase as well—perhaps as a way of offsetting the increased number of random states.

Thus, certainty is a function of intelligence (intelligent intervention) and random chance is a function of arbitrary randomness (the lack of intelligent intervention). The obvious conclusion we must draw with respect to the connection between intelligence and randomness, therefore, is that the one is the qualitative antithesis of the other. As such, we can now pose the question: Could an entity—randomness, give rise to another entity—intelligence, that is demonstrated to be its reciprocal quantitatively and its antithesis qualitatively? Put another way that has relevance to the OoL question: in the light of our discussions above, is it reasonable to conclude that the intelligence evident within the LS—at both the micro and macro levels and culminating in the distinct variety apparent in human behavior—could possibly have derived from a purely random source, as the abiogenesis paradigm implies?

The Ultimate Intelligence Source

The UDIF raises the all-important question: If intelligent application of information separates random events from non-random events, and must precede its non-random expression, what is its source?" The suggestion here is that neither the intelligence nor the information itself can derive from random events, because neither exists in that environment. And, there is no practical point in deferring the origin of intelligence to the natural laws of nature because they (the 2nd law, for example) are the very sources of the spontaneous tendency towards the equilibrium state and greater randomness (increased micro states)—and in direct opposition to the very orderliness that characterizes intelligence. And, even if a semblance of organization, perceivable as increased information did begin to emerge as the result of some random set of circumstances, surely the tendency of spontaneous change toward the equilibrium state according to the 2nd Law would persist in the end. Thus, our UDIF can serve to enunciate the principle that only intelligence can give rise to other intelligence—this in virtue of the fact that if intelligence must precede intelligent expression, then it could not itself derive from randomness. Our Universal Dogma stipulates the primacy of intelligence for all non-random events (e.g. systems, machines and organisms). In so doing, wherever we find evidence of a non-random nature (life systems, for example) we must look to intelligence as a defining root characteristic, separate from and prior to any consideration of energy audit. This has significant importance for justifying the dis-entanglement of the energy and information aspects within the concept of entropy—when dealing with intelligent systems. As we have demonstrated, there are certain instances that give rise to positive entropy when energy is the cause and information change is the result (all non-intelligent systems) and other cases that give rise to negative entropy where information becomes the causative agent that must precede the application of energy—resulting in greater complexity. Our only examples of this phenomenon to date: human design, and bio-life.

While a formal proof of the validity of such a proposition as the UDIF may be elusive, we may have to rely for its validation on the indisputable fact that, like so many other laws of nature that cannot be absolutely proved at this time (like the 2nd law itself), it is consistent within the logic of the reality we experience. The UDIF can be considered axiomatic in all instances of human-contrived design; where we can trace the progression of information always leads to the validation of the UDIF. The only problem we encounter is with respect to that singular phenomenon of biological life. We are neither in a position to track the flow of its information back to the very OoL, nor are we familiar with the intelligence-derived information that a UDIF insists must have preceded it.

In the case of life-information flow, Crick's Central Dogma addresses exclusively the operational instructions within the cellular system and is based on the empirical evidence alone. The operational (living) cellular machine does not function, and therefore cannot exist, without those instructions in place, because what you would be left with is no more than inanimate chemistry and we already sense (even if some of us—doctrinaire supporters of SAb in particular—seem to want to downplay the fact) the very real limitations of chemistry devoid of life's directing instructions. When such information, or the lines of communication for such information, ceases to exist in a living cell, it dies, whereupon spontaneous changes cause it to revert its "liberated" constituent components back to the equilibrium state—pursuant to the entropy provisions of the 2nd law. Therefore, a very first living entity, under a SAb scenario, simply in order to be able to function, would have had to have had within it a semblance of intelligent control that could direct its basic chemical operations under the complex conditions of life— conditions that do not exist in non-life; this, prior to any consideration of any kind of ability to evolve and adapt. In addition, no matter how simple you postulate that first life entity, you still require a set of feedback control mechanisms with logical operators that can compare the error differences between actual states to the control states hard wired somewhere in physiological memory. This is universal in bio-life and without exception; otherwise control of repetitive functions that ultimately must lead to the complex operations involved in the timing and performance of self-replication could not transpire. The point is that the information that comprises these instructions is separate from the physical entities they serve, and as such must precede them. Which brings us right back to the life-nonlife interface issue, which can be considered in two ways:

1) The physical interface that separates life from non-life, and

2) The historical chronological interface that delineates Earth planet history "before" and "after" the OoL.

In the first case above, the qualitative difference is explained by the existence of the informational database and the intelligence that mediates all biochemical activities. The second case requires the explanation of the source of sufficient and necessary information and intelligence that gave rise to and promoted the survival of the living state in our planetary biosphere some 3.8 billion years ago, and without which only randomness and non-life would have continued as before (and as usual throughout the rest of the inanimate solar system). We can assume that the pre-life biosphere conditions represented nothing extraordinary in terms of the existence of some kind of natural resource from which intelligence could develop. It becomes obvious, therefore, that if the source of such intelligence could not derive from the fledgling biosphere itself (from within the random states of its chemical constituents) then it had to have been imported from outside. This is the message and conclusion that the UDIF forces upon us, underscoring, as it does, the primacy of intelligence and information and their precedence over the physical living organism entities they control. Again, because we cannot look for the illusive source of such intelligence within the known natural order as reflected within the laws of nature, (because they promote the preponderant universal convergence toward the equilibrium state, leading ultimately to the "heat-death" of the universe as it winds down), therefore the intelligence that characterizes life on our planet must have been imported as an integral part of its phenotype vehicle—the primitive system of life implanted here billions of years ago. This is exactly in agreement with our Rational Design Hypothesis.

Two Different Worlds—One Convergent, The Other Divergent:

And, throughout these discussions, we must not blur the very real differences between the organized laws of nature that dictate the interactions between inanimate matter and energy throughout the universe, and the controlling organized intelligence that allows for the mediation and interpretation of the informational data bases within the LS. The many levels of intelligence associated with biological Life on our planet have driven it incessantly towards greater complexity over its history. As such, the LS can be described as "divergent" and expansive—growing incessantly in terms of both physical biomass as well as in terms of diverse complexity.

In every other respect (Life is, after all, a part of our universe), the universe is convergent and organized to go in only one direction—from hot to cold, from high pressure to low pressure, i.e. from lower entropy to increased entropy—always spontaneously seeking the inevitable ultra-equilibrium state, described above as its "Heat Death" state of maximum entropy. As the name implies, no further significant activity can be contemplated.

We are now in a position to augment the dictionary "egocentric" definition of intelligence with a generic definition – one applicable to any system:

> *Intelligence (a generic definition): System capacity to **counteract entropy**, differentiate information from randomness, and **affect** "choice" over "chance".*

Time—Sooner or later:

You will have noticed that there is no direct mention of a framework of time, within which the universe becomes more entropic—only that things in the universe generally go from a less entropic state to a more entropic one. While we may not be able to pin down an absolute value for the progression of time, its flow and direction is implied within the direction the universe is heading with respect to its observance of the entropy provisions of the 2nd law. The fact is that because of the universal applicability of this law of entropy, physicists have come to define the direction and the very nature of time itself in terms of entropy. The direction of time is said to parallel the chronological increase in entropy of the universe.

The question could be raised, as to whether our Universal Dogma (the UDIF) applies to all of the dynamic processes in nature, i.e., is there any suggestion within the UDIF that implies that there is a body of primary information controlling the functioning of the universe and its dynamic processes that could be construed as the primary source of the sufficient and necessary information from which biological life could derive as well? The answer is an unsatisfactory: "Not necessarily so", because the universe unfolds in the only one way it can and in only one direction,—according to the provisions of the Laws of Thermodynamics that define and describe it. The First Law demands that the total of mass-energy in the universe remain constant. The Second Law demands that the attribute described as "entropy" increases spontaneously until the universe reaches an equilibrium state, no matter how long it takes. Our Universal Dogma need not be implicated here, because all of the dynamic activity of the universe, while organized—from the conversion of energy into matter and the consequential creation of space-time, to the formation of galaxies and stars—can proceed without additional intelligent control. Such activity can be considered to fall under the 'spontaneous change' umbrella that derives from the 2nd law and leads entropically in only one time direction—from states of greater organization to less organization—all proceeding towards equilibrium (and, again, finally toward the "Heat-Death" of the universe). We can argue that as the universe expands and becomes less dense, there is a steady increase in entropy with the concomitant loss in organization of its constituents—in the same way that such a loss of organization occurs during the conversion from the solid phase of matter to the liquid, or the liquid to the gaseous. There is no controlling intelligence evident and none required throughout the process. Since its big-bang inception, it is proceeding on its own, in the only direction it can, like some kind of wound up spring uncoiling. We may, indeed, question what started the whole process going. That will always remain enigmatic. But, perhaps, even the Big Bang birth of the universe can be considered to be only a step along a convergent path towards its equilibrium state and that even the so-called Heat Death of our universe could be considered as just one step along the same way. While we casually like to describe the laws of nature, as we know them, as having come into existence simultaneously with the universe we inhabit, there is nothing to support the notion that matter, energy and indeed intelligence are uniquely attributes of our particular universe. They could logically transcend any such limitations. As such, our laws of thermodynamics and particularly the 2nd Law of entropy could transcend such limitations as well. The point is, that the life of the universe we know may logically be considered to be just a single stage in a larger supra-cosmic journey, characterized by a convergence toward some ultra equilibrium state that transcends the life of our universe. The only seemingly contrarian monkey wrench in the whole scenario seems to be the enigmatic existence of biological life on our planet and its apparent disregard for the entropy provisions of the 2nd law (as presently interpreted).

Of Chickens and Eggs:

Our UDIF, as stated, remains, after all, a limited application of the "chicken and egg" question—limited in virtue of the necessity for the information to precede its expression, regardless of the form of that expression. In life, the genetic information must precede its expression and eventual self-replication, particularly because it is the information itself that constitutes the master plans of those very capabilities. Also, it is the genetic information that provides the design and operational instructions which the physical biological machine entity will fulfill—until such time as it is deprived of that information and/or the lines of communication within a given organism cease to function. And, in reality, it is only this informational database that gets passed on, and survives to instruct and control the continuation of future generations, and the ultimate survival of the LS. Of course, that database, the genotype—like any database we are aware of—must reside in a physical (or chemical) medium of some kind, which brings us right back to the phenotype where the copying process occurs. This leads us directly to the question: Which came first—genotype or phenotype?

When invoking a Universal Dogma as it relates to the LS, the only really interesting discussion centers on the point of origin of life—before the phenomenon of evolution could come into play. Of course, it is understood here that we are regarding evolution as a phenomenon that is an integral part of biological life and not something that preceded it i.e., there is no proof of the existence of any other kind of evolution, nor in particular any kind of natural "chemical evolution" that SAb would have us believe preceded and led directly to biological evolution. It is a given that after the OoL, there was never a lapse in intelligent control of the system. As such, our discussion centers on that which separates life from non-life (its controlling information) and the fact that its primary intelligence had to originate separate from that which it is to control. This would be consistent with the von Neumann self-replicator analogy where the controlling information tape would first have to be in place before the system would self-replicate. Why should these same conditions not apply within a biological self-replicator—and in particular the first one(s) to come into existence at the OoL? This is the essential inspiration for our "Universal Dogma" (and laterally for the Rational Design Hypothesis we are developing). While admittedly the term "Universal Dogma" does sound somewhat pompous, its application can be considered axiomatic (and therefore dogmatic) in all instances (e.g., human designs, with only a single argued exception—the LS, a non-human design). This highlights the question as to why biological life should not be included together with all the other operating systems (all products of intelligence) of which we have knowledge. We would suggest there is only one reason—because it is also the only known phenomena where we cannot actually trace the source of its design and operational information. Should that fact alone suppress its inclusion with all other designed systems? For our part, we feel completely comfortable with the argument that the LS being an integral part of the universe behaves totally in accordance with its special kind of state (an intelligently controlled system), characterized by its informational data base that precedes and controls its form and function, and permits it to "go against the gradient of entropy", as it were. It is worthwhile remembering that as long as a human-designed machine is fed fuel and worn-out parts are replaced (by its intelligent operators), it can operate indefinitely—seemingly contrary to the 2nd law. Thus, energy alone is not the issue. Similarly, the LS comprises biological machines that are able to fuel themselves and repair themselves. The only discernable difference is that instead of humans controlling these functions as occurs in all human designed machines, these functions are intelligently controlled automatically from within the biological machines that comprise the LS (no system-external intelligent operators required).

LIFE—ANOTHER KIND OF STATE?

One of the great perpetual challenges faced by intellectuals seems to be how to adequately define that special kind of state that comprises life's animate living condition and its processes as distinct from the inanimate and non-living state of the rest of the known universe. It is not too late in our discussions to ask that enigmatic question: What exactly is Life? "Enigmatic", because despite our vast databases dealing with every aspect of biological systems, any attempt to make a list of simple criteria to precisely define bio-life seems to run into problems. For example, most biologists would list at least growth, reproduction, response to stimuli, and metabolism. However, there are living things that do not meet all of these criteria (mules cannot reproduce), while such non-living things as fire appear to meet all. Crystals and viruses also seem to fall through the cracks, somehow. And, it seems that the more sophisticated we become with respect to our understanding of the processes of the universe in general, the more confused becomes our ability to delineate the interface that separates those two states. Modern disciplines such as complexity theory, chaos theory, A-life, quantum theory and the like all seem to introduce novel concepts that, more often than not, cloud the issues within which we seem to be perpetually searching for an adequate definition of life. We have developed above the idea that life systems can be defined in terms of the dis-entanglement of the energy and order aspects of entropy. Within this backdrop and the ideas raised within these pages we shall continue this important process of shedding novel light on the concept of life that can help contribute to our search for a much needed adequate definition. We know the following:

1] Biological and non-biological processes share the same characteristic behavior of their constituent atoms and molecules (within the universal rules of chemistry). But,

2] Living processes are divergent—giving rise over time to increased numbers of more complex molecules. In sharp contrast, non-living processes are convergent, tending towards greater disorder and equilibrium states (despite the so-called "chemical evolution" concept). Furthermore,

3] There appears to be a well-defined physical interface between the form and function of biological life processes and those of non-biological processes. As interfaces go, we might have difficulty in actually describing the logical characteristics in terms that empirical measurements could nail down (assuming they could be taken in the first place). However, in physical terms with respect to its form and function, there is no difficulty in acknowledging the cellular environment as the sufficient and necessary environmental circumstances within which biological living processes can operate and without which they do not. The living cell is the physical location where all biology occurs and the PdP indeed is the smallest common denominator and the minimum physical state that can create and sustain the rudimentary functions of life. And, the actual physical interface separating life from non-life is the cellular plasma membrane that encloses biological cells, (appearing in two distinct variations—prokaryote and eukaryote). We can go further and define the biological cell as the physical boundary that can incorporate within itself the minimum quanta of physical and logical complexity that can operate as life. Life thus becomes a "quantum state" of biological complexity within which the life processes can function and below which they do not. Thus, the interface between life and non-life can now be described as a boundary or barrier that separates two distinct levels of complexity; one occupied by the life state and the other by the non-life state. In addition,

4] There appears to be a logical interface separating life and non-life directly tied to the 2nd law: living processes appear to be less consistent with our traditional understanding of the entropy provisions of the 2nd law and non-living processes appear to be always consistent. Thus,

5] Any classification of life within our universe must incorporate within itself both:

a) a suitable descriptive reference to the unique physical interface that both defines and separates (interfaces) a particular life-form from its inanimate environment (e.g., its PdP) and,

b) a suitable universal descriptive reference with respect to the 2nd law (e.g., entropy disentanglement) that all living systems share and non-living systems lack.

Our thought processes have now moved beyond the single example of LS we experience—one that requires no accurate working definition (because there is non other to compare it to)—to the universal concept of life systems that can serve as a litmus test for any suspect system we may encounter. With respect to the 2nd law, we have developed the idea above that what differentiates bio-life from non-life is first, the dis-entanglement of the energy and informational aspects of entropy in the LS and the fact that while the former increases in all systems, the latter decreases in the LS. The last remaining question is whether this same criterion can be extended to any life system. Well, the answer, of necessity, must incorporate both good news and bad (less than good). First the bad news—we don't know because we have never encountered any other life but our own kind and therefore we have no way of knowing what kind of alternatives there could be. The good news is that we have created a description of a living system (life) that incorporates a universal law of nature—the 2nd law—and one that ideally suits our own LS. By extending that description into a definition, we can do no wrong because definitions by their very nature are logically infallible. Thus, we can now appropriately define any system that incorporates the dis-entanglement of its energy and informational entropy components such that the one decreases while the other increases—as a LS (life).

Therefore, with respect to the origin of life, the issue now becomes—what set of circumstances can start such a process? What is the source of the first quantum of complexity to cross the barrier separating the two levels of complexity—life from non-life? How do matter, energy and the intelligent systems that control them become quantified into the complex state we call life? At present, the only mechanism we are certain of is for inanimate matter at the lower non-life complexity state to become organized and energized by being "pulled" through the complexity barrier into the life-state by living things above and already there. (In contrast, SAb, within the context of this scenario, would have us believe that the first such living entity was "pushed" across the complexity barrier from below through the intervention of some universal complexity rule.) With respect to other higher levels of complexity and complexity states—while the process of quantification begins at the boundary separating life from non-life—we can envisage additional higher levels and states of complexity. For example, the divergence of the single-celled into more complex multi-cellular organisms could possibly represent the next level of complexity. And the ability of organisms to "think" may represent again another further up the complexity scale. Of course, human egocentricity would reserve the highest complexity state we know of to the thought processes of the human brain, and its own ability to design and create organized systems of its own. In each instance, we could consider species as discreet and quantified complexity states, with no "averaging" of species complexity states apparent. Thus, the difference between our closest relative—considered to be the chimpanzee—and us is represented by a thorough complexity barrier that separates the two species, no less than occurs between discreet quantum energy levels in quantum mechanics.

A "Quantum" Definition of Life:

The use of the term "quantum level" to define that proverbial line in the sand that separates life from non-life is particularly appropriate in the sense that the term "quantum" itself conveys as well a logic "state" (similar to discreet energy states in quantum theory) that is both quantified and indivisible. In quantum theory, an electron can occupy only integral energy states that are effectively separated by unoccupiable barriers that serve as quantum interfaces. In the case of life and non-life, it is the interface between the two—however large and whatever its underlying characteristics—that provides us with the parallel sense of an unoccupiable barrier similar to the interface separating electrons from higher occupiable energy levels. A thing is alive or it is not. Our definition of life above, in terms of 2nd law entropy, delineates clearly the living state from the non-living state. And physically, that translates into the LS PdP defined earlier.

Thus, we can define the "life-nonlife" interface as a quantified logical barrier in terms of 2nd law entropy, and its corresponding PdP LS physical manifestation with its cellular enclosed environment— being the minimum quanta of physical and logical organization that is both sufficient and necessary to qualify for the existence of biological life. Less than that certain minimum quantum level of complexity disqualifies a biological process from being "alive", and renders it subject to the normal application of the 2nd law. An overriding characteristic of a living system then, is its ability to organize more and more inanimate matter and energy and subject it to the inherent intelligent controls characteristic of such systems. However, life quantification only takes place during cellular reproduction under PdP conditions—when and where the minimum complexity required for partaking in independent cellular existence can be replicated. Once quantified into a living cell, the organized cellular entity can behave according to its quantified complexity state of being—characterized by its ability to continue to drag up sufficient material and energy from the non-life level at the interface barrier and chemically organize it into new quantified states of complexity. Again, below that complexity level, the 2nd law applies in its traditionally understood form. At the life complexity level, living states can and do operate according to different rules with respect to entropy, which have been detailed above and in Ch 11.

The quantum definition of life goes hand in hand with the UDIF (Universal Dogma of Information Flow) discussed earlier. (It also represents the inspiration for the 'Quantum Theory of Evolution' we shall be developing toward the end of the next chapter.) The minimum quantum of complexity required to raise matter and energy to sufficient complexity to enable it to cross the interface barrier into the life complexity level can be recognized as the sufficient and necessary information that must proceed system design and operation. i.e., information (quantum of complexity) must precede (must form a combination with matter and energy to turn it into) its physical expression (the living cell).

As a parting thought on the subject, you might consider that the UDIF is less arrogant as a principle than the Central Dogma. The Central Dogma, after all, could have been proven patently false by future empirical data. Dogmas by their very nature should not be subjected to that kind of uncertainty. In fact, as it stands today there is reason to believe that the Central Dogma is less dogmatic in virtue of the discovery of exceptions with respect to RNA which can act—under special circumstances—in both capacities: as information carrier as well as enzyme. The UDIF, on the other hand, as stated is effectively an axiom.

The above gives rise to one more little detail that is implied by our Universal Dogma. If information must have preceded the physical phenomenon of life, then where did the first information set reside just prior to the OoL? The information must have existed somewhere—within some medium. Man-made information is stored in a variety of places—as design drawings on paper, in the silicon chips and magnetic discs of computers, in the memories and imaginations of human beings. If all the varieties of information that life requires to function (structural, operational, housekeeping, reproduction, etc) preceded the physical entities that were the progenitors of all life on the planet, then where was this information stored just prior to its introduction at the OoL? In human-designed machines, the information derives from a designer. The implication from the RDH vantage point is that prior to the OoL the system intelligence must have existed within another intelligent physical entity—the would be LS designer. What is the nature of that other entity that must have served as the medium and source of the information that gave rise to the first living things on the planet? No matter how primitive the first life on the planet may have been, the sufficient and necessary information that served as its operating instructions to control its chemistry had to have come from somewhere—just before the "switch" of life was turned on (no different, in principle, from the informational instruction tape source for von Neumann's hypothetical self-replicator). Just stay the course; for eventually we must address this critical "origin of design information and the intelligence that must have preceded it" question.

For now, let us jump forward and address the form and function of the intelligent data processing systems of life—the genetic information encoded in DNA. How does the LS convert genetic information into the instructions that control its chemistry—allowing it to operate intelligently against the information gradient of entropy, which a traditional interpretation of the 2nd law imposes upon the rest of the inanimate universe?

DNA—The Informational Molecule:

Just how the genetic information encoded within DNA is transcribed and translated into the operating instructions of life and become expressed as the physical entities we call organisms is the stuff of molecular biology. The intelligence incorporated throughout the scheme is nothing less than pure genius and the envy of any design engineer. How it works is simplicity itself and yet logically sophisticated in the extreme. We will explore the principles and the mechanics of execution of the processes that take pure information from the genetic library and express it as the physical proteins that make up the physiology of every organism of life—past, present and future.

In 1953, James Watson and Francis Crick figured out the double helix structure of the DNA informational molecule from the X-ray photographs of crystals prepared by Rosalind Franklin of King's College, London. This led, eight years later, to the deciphering of the Genetic Code—the relationship between the composition of the DNA molecule (**D**ioxyribo**N**ucleic **A**cid) with the information encoded within, and the composition of physical proteins. Once the language of genetic instruction became known, this knowledge led to the establishment of molecular biology. Since that time, we have learned a whole lot about how life's instructions get translated into biological activity. If the cellular PdP is the heart of the LS, then truly, the information encoded in the cells DNA is its proverbial soul. The DNA molecule is the carrier within its atomic structure of all hereditary information. All the instructions required to direct the Life processes (e.g., development, growth, metabolism) of each and every organism is encoded within the microscopic bundles of DNA that are housed within the nucleus of every single cell of that organism.

Those bundles of DNA informational molecules that encode the genetic information are called *Chromosomes*. The genetic blueprints of the cell and the intelligent component of life is written in code along lengths of coiled DNA molecules, much the same as speech is encoded in the magnetic tape of a cassette recorder. That's where the comparison ends, however, as the information storage capacity of molecular DNA has no correlation within our experience. It is a molecule, after all, and if the DNA that encoded the human genome were uncoiled and stretched out, the DNA in a single human cell would reach one meter in length. This figure is not just an idle metaphor but is arrived at mathematically: there are 3 billion basepairs in the human genome; each twist in the DNA coil takes up 10 nucleotides and extends 3.4 nanometers along the length ($3.4\text{x}10^{-9}\text{x}3\text{x}10^{9}/10 = 1.02$m).[1] This is normally compacted considerably forming millions of tight coils around a core made of proteins filaments called *histones*. The histone core itself is coiled and twisted into the chromosome structures shown in photographs taken through the electron microscope that we have all become familiar with. A study of this marvelous bit of packaging reveals that the histone protein surface has a path of positive charges that precisely match the pattern of negative charges along the DNA double helix. In this way the positively charged histone molecules attract and bind to the negatively charged DNA to form the incredibly condensed DNA library present in each and every living cell. Just accessing one particular part of this coil upon coil of encoded DNA molecular tape—in order to read the information and transcribe it into a useful instruction the cell machinery can work with—is in itself a marvel of information handling and retrieval. It is thought that the histone scaffolding behaves somewhat like an accordion, relaxing and permitting the DNA coils to separate when a particular segment—a genetic instruction—needs to be copied, and then bunching up again after the copying is complete. But physical descriptions only tell part of the story.

Before the completion of the Human Genome Project, it was thought that the genetic library of a human being contains of the order of 100 thousand genes, each of which coded for a single instruction, protein or enzyme. The total set of genetic instructions, which direct the functioning and replication of an organism, is referred to as its *genome*. We are now informed that there are only between twenty and thirty thousand genes that comprise the human genetic library. If all the information contained within the DNA located in the nucleus of the human cell were to be transcribed on paper, it would contain of the order of 1 billion words comprising 3 letters each and occupy the equivalent of roughly five thousand volumes each containing 500 pages. That's a lot of paper—for only a microscopic dot's worth of DNA. And there is an identical 5-thousand volume library worth of information in each of the body's thousands of billions of cells. But the genetic content of human DNA—that which actually codes for proteins, accounts for only roughly 8% of the total information contained there. The balance, as much as 92% of the information stored in human DNA, is considered by biologists to be superfluous (and referred to casually as "junk DNA"). That amounts to only 400 of the 5,000 volumes worth of equivalent information in the genome devoted to genetic instructions for life and the remaining 4,600 volumes devoted to what? We shall have need to investigate this remarkable situation further and will do so in Chapter 13.

Without a doubt, the storage of information within the DNA molecule is the kind of miniaturization computer engineers can only dream about. The best information storage densities they have managed to come up with is the equivalent of 0.65 Gigabits (billion bits) per square inch on commercially available magneto-optical disks[2]. As much as 8 Gigabits per square inch densities are anticipated in the future, equivalent to half a million double spaced typewritten pages. The informational content contained in the sub-microscopic nucleus of a single human cell, by contrast, amounts to ten times as much. It is also worthwhile noting that each cell nucleus, with the exception of the germ (sex) cells, contains two full 3 billion basepair sets of information—the contributions from both parents.

An Alphabet of Four Letters:

The genetic information is encoded in the DNA molecule (a polymer) as a series of bases running up and down a ladder-like structure, twisted into a "double helix" shape. Picture a ladder that has a number of rungs running its full length. The sides of the ladder provide the structural-repeating framework, and are made up of alternating sequences of sugar and phosphate molecules. The rungs of the DNA ladder called "base pairs" are composed of pairs of nucleotide units that serve, as a kind of variable genetic alphabet comprised of four letters. The four letters of the DNA alphabet are themselves composed of two sets of complementary nucleic acids called "purines" and "pyrimidines" physically attached to each other through chemical bonding. The ends of the rung like pairs attach to the sides of the ladder-like structure—also through stronger chemical bonding. The actual "information" units are the base pairs that are strung along the DNA ladder similar to information encoded sequentially in a computer tape or floppy disk. Instead of magnetically encoded bits of information, the information encoded in DNA appears as chemical basepair data. It is this series of basepair "letters" of the genetic alphabet that gets read and translated into physical action within the cell.

The four chemical letters are designated a, t, g, and c, which stand for the names of the four nucleotides bases: Adenine (a), Thymine (t), Guanine (g) and Cytosine (c). Physically, a pairs always and only with t, and g only with c. Thus g and c can pair only as "genetic alphabet letters" g-c or c-g. Similarly t pairs only with a (t-a or a-t). This exclusive "complimentarity" is at the heart of the copying of a genetic message from anywhere in the huge chromosomal library of information, as well as the reproduction of the whole library when the cell reproduces itself. When DNA replicates during cell division, the ladder like structure unzips along its length. One side with its half basepairs goes to each of the new cells being produced. The procedure permits each half to reconstruct its corresponding other half by gathering from within the cell the missing complimentary components to make up the complete DNA molecule. In this way the DNA acts as a repository of information that gets passed on from one generation of cells (and organisms) to the next in a continuous link between parent and offspring— between the past and the future.

Transcription is the process whereby one gene's worth of instructional information is extracted from the DNA library and transferred to the translating machines of the cell—the *ribosomes*—to be read and interpreted. The ribosomes process genetic information, translating it into working instructions for assembling all the different kinds of proteins necessary for the cells existence and operation. It is a truly fascinating set of procedures, exquisite in its logic and extraordinary in detail and miniaturization. It works like this:

Think of all the genetic information in the DNA chromosomes as a collection of cassette tapes like the ones you listen to on your tapedeck. Each chromosome is represented by one of those cassettes. When the cell machinery calls for a working copy of a genetic instruction (e.g., one that codes for a particular protein), there are mechanisms in place that can search and find that particular gene wherever it happens to be in the total database of chromosomes. That's like searching your tape cassette library for a particular song on one of the tapes. Once the beginning and end of the portion of DNA containing the desired gene is identified and marked, a copy is made—not in DNA but in RNA, a slightly different nucleic acid. Think of the RNA copy of the required gene, one that is of interest to the cell at this particular time, as a smaller cassette on which is recorded only a single song. It is the disposable RNA copy that leaves the nucleus of the cell and is used as a disposable set of working instructions by the machine tools of the cell.

Editing Out the "Junk":

But wait a minute. We previously mentioned that the vital genetic information is not continuous within the DNA but also contains introns (intervening sequences)—the so-called "junk DNA". It seems that the actual instructional messages, the genes, are encoded piecemeal throughout the stretches of DNA, interspersed with the longer coded introns that seem to have nothing to do with the genetic instructions. This junk DNA is also copied faithfully into RNA and must be edited out. The results, following the editing process, will leave only the pure expressible instructional information, called "exons" (expressed sequences) encoded in a different chemical format known as messenger RNA (mRNA).

Using a music cassette as an example, before the editing process takes place, it's as though you were listening to your favorite song on a tape player and every so often you would hear interference comprising gibberish phrases (junk) of different duration. But, it's not as if the junk was recorded over the song as occurs when someone inadvertently records over a previously recorded tape. Because, wherever a junk portion ends, the song picks up exactly where it left off. The whole song remains intact if you can get rid of the junk. So with a pair of scissors, you proceed to cut out the junk and splice together the many pieces of good stuff you are left with. Now you have a complete and continuous recorded song minus the junk. This is precisely the analogy explaining how genetic instructions are edited and transcribed intact unto a tape of mRNA. Of course instead of a pair of scissors, the cell uses the appropriate enzymes especially adapted to the job of editing DNA information. It is only following the editing process that the precise instructional mRNA is permitted to leave the nucleus in order to function as an effective "working blueprint" for the production of proteins.

Translation—A Language of Three Letter Words:

The mRNA instructional tape is now transported to the cell's manufacturing facility where it attaches itself to a *"ribosome"*. Think of the ribosome as a very special kind of tape player that not only "reads" the recorded message, but also carries out the instructions as they are played. Just as a taped set of voice instructions comprises a group of word sounds edited and transcribed onto a cassette tape, a genetic instruction comprises a sequential pattern of three-letter "words" composed of basepair "letters" (**a**, **t**, **c**, and **g**)—copied and edited from the DNA original unto a tiny mRNA molecular tape (**t** becomes **u** in mRNA). The ribosome is the chemical tape reader where genetic information gets read and is translated into action. Again, every basepair along the mRNA molecular tape represents a letter in the genetic alphabet. A succession of three such basepairs forms a genetic word called a *codon* that has a simple straightforward meaning. For example, if the chemical word spells out **c-a-g** (represented by the complimentary basepairs: **c̲-g; a̲-u; g-c**), then the ribosome looks for the amino acid glutamine, (the first letter, representing a single base underlined above, of the complimentary basepair is sufficient to designate a letter of a codon). Similarly, codon **g-c-g** represents amino acid alanine. And so it goes for each and every one of the only twenty amino acids, whose varied combinations form the chemical building blocks of every single protein in the LS—regardless of whether it forms part of a cloverleaf or part of a neuron within a brain. A distinct three-base codon signature represents each amino acid. The permutations permit as many as 64 different 3-base codon combinations (4 x 4 x 4) and indeed there is redundancy within the code. For example, both the codons **a-g-u** and **a-g-c** represent amino acid serine, while four codons represent glycine, leucine and threonine respectively. Also, the signal to the ribosome to "stop" (adding amino acids to the chain) is represented by the codons **u-g-a**, **u-a-a** and **u-a-g**. The amino acid methionine (**a-u-g**) begins each protein building procedure. The cellular ribosome is a biological "machine tool" whose job description is to read and translate the codons encoded within the linear mRNA molecular information tape sequentially (one at a time) and assemble the corresponding amino acids into a co-linear chain. The physical chain of distinct amino acids so assembled is called a polypeptide—with each amino acid occupying the same relative position in the chain as its designated codon within the mRNA template.

Intermediaries called "transfer RNA" (tRNA) deliver individual amino acid building blocks to the protein synthesis site on the ribosome. A tRNA molecule carries both an amino acid and the three specific nucleotide bases that form its complimentary anticodon (like adjacent interlocking pieces of a puzzle). The ribosome first aligns and matches a single codon from the mRNA information tape to its complimentary anticodon of an available tRNA molecule. The attached amino acid is then freed from its superfluous tRNA vehicle, and takes its designated place (occupying a strategic position) within the growing amino acid chain—just like beads strung on a string. The mRNA then moves along the ribosome three base positions and reads the next codon. The assembly process, called *"translocation"*, is repeated over and over, resulting in the elongation of the growing polypeptide chain. The process continues until the ribosome reads a "stop" codon (there are three) whereupon it concludes its operation, tidies things up, and releases the finished polypeptide chain of amino acids into the aqueous environment of the cell. Now the dynamics of the characteristics of the individual amino acids come into play as positive and negative charges associated with their individual atoms impose an order in the way the linear assemblage twists and folds as each reacts with others and water molecules within the cell environment. What becomes apparent in all this is the co-linear nature of the genetic code. In other words, codons are determined by the position of the first base in the mRNA sequence and a new one representing the next amino acid in the chain appears at every third position along the mRNA tape. It's like the genetic version of the Morse code, without spaces between words. As with the reading of any information sequence (e.g., left to right in English) mRNA is read and the polypeptide synthesized in a specific direction and orientation (from the "amino terminal, designated as "5'-hydroxyl" to the carboxyl terminal, designated as "3'-hydroxyl"). There are no punctuation spaces between codons. Therefore, establishing a proper "reading frame" is critical. Obviously, any change in the order of mRNA bases (by the addition or deletion of a base) within the reading frame would throw the entire mRNA sequence out of proper alignment at the point of change. This could have disastrous results, particularly if it alters a critical protein that is strategic to the function of the organism.

Protein Synthesis—The Universal Tool Machine:

As implied above, the final outcome that can be expected from a polypeptide chain that folds into a protein represents not just a simple accumulation of the characteristics of the individual amino acid piece parts. It comprises the confluence of all of the characteristics inherent within the positive and negative charges and the distances between these charges that culminate in the three-dimensional structure that defines an individual protein. Thus, every synthesized protein represents a distinct set of emergent cumulative attributes evoking a profound sense that the resultant whole is indeed greater the sum of its constituent parts. The amino acids alone and individually represent nothing more than potential pieces of a complex puzzle. Putting that puzzle together involves not only the fitting together of individual component pieces, but also making those pieces available for assembly as and when required. Unlike any puzzle you may have labored over, the polypeptide chain itself provides no hint as to its final protein characteristics—even after its assembly by the ribosome as a linear sequence of amino acids. These emerge as a combined function of the characteristics of the individual amino acid molecules, together with the consequences of their relative positions within the polypeptide chain. As the chain twists and folds in three-dimensional space within the aqueous environment of the cell, the result is a protein having unique physical and chemical characteristics. Then, to complicate matters considerably, no protein is fabricated without a functional purpose. That is, any protein—as complex and as elegant its production may appear—must fit into the greater puzzle called an organism, where its presence serves some complex and essential cog within an astonishingly complex machine. To put this in proper context, the simplest bacterial organism we know of comprises close to one thousand different proteins and the human organism comprises upwards of one hundred thousand—all required to function smoothly and together. Truly an extraordinary process to both understand and appreciate.

We cannot help but be impressed with the sheer—almost infinite, flexibility of a system that can call upon itself to produce all kinds of complex and versatile three-dimensional biological structures. All the more so when one considers the form and function of the complex universal ribosome machine tool—itself composed of proteins—that is responsible for assembling all of the different combinations among only twenty kinds of amino acid piece parts. The fact that the assembly occurs linearly—in essentially a single dimension—but turns out three-dimensional protein results is astonishing. But, how that is accomplished is itself extraordinary. Mutual attraction or repulsion of polar or non-polar groups in the side chains (R groups) of the amino acids determines the "conformation" or configuration of a protein.[3] The polar have positive or negative charges in their side chains; the non-polar repel the water in the cytoplasm in which they are immersed but are attracted to each other. Some parts of a peptide chain containing 100 to 200 amino acids may form a loop, or helix; others may be straight or form irregular coils. The terms "secondary", "tertiary", and "quaternary" structures are frequently applied to the configuration of the peptide chain of a protein. A nomenclature committee of the International Union of Biochemistry (IUB) has defined these terms as follows: The primary structure of a protein is determined by its amino acid sequence without any regard for the arrangement of the peptide chain in space. The secondary structure is determined by the spatial arrangement of the main peptide chain, without any regard for the conformation of side chains or other segments of the main chain. Both the side chains and other adjacent segments of the main chain, without regard for neighboring peptide chains, determine the tertiary structure. Finally, the term quaternary structure is used for the arrangement of identical or different sub-units of a large protein in which each sub-unit is a separate peptide chain. It is from this complex production system, based on simple principles, that emerges the specialized protein products that make up all of the subsystems of the universal machine-like organisms that comprise the LS.

From Information to Proteins:

By way of summarization and clarification—ribosomes read codons along the mRNA genetic instructional tape and link amino acids together like so many beads on a string. The amino acid positions match precisely the positions of the corresponding codons as read off of the mRNA. And the mRNA is an edited copy of a corresponding portion within the DNA informational library. Now, once this chain of amino acid peptides is completed (the exact sequence of amino acids is formed) the resultant polypeptide molecule is released into the aqueous cytoplasm of the cell. Again, it is as yet not a protein. It will only become the desired protein substance when it has folded itself into its three dimensional shape that represents the structure having the lowest energy level. It's as though the long chain had hinges along its length, permitting it to twist, bend, and fold in a variety of directions and configurations. As the chain of amino acids starts to fold—one twist and turn at a time, it is the bonding forces between adjacent side-chain pieces attached to the amino acids that interact and determine the progression of folding as well as the ultimate shape that results. The process is aided by the effects of thermal agitation that continually jostle the structure as it twists and folds, until the best fold results in a stable enough configuration such that further thermal motion leaves the molecule relatively undisturbed. To a large extent it is just one example of the 2nd law imperative of a system in disequilibrium (one-dimensional polypeptide chain of amino acids) spontaneously seeking its equilibrium state (folding into a three dimensional protein). One can imagine how complicated a procedure this can be as the number of amino acid links involved increases. As an example, the protein cytochrome, involved in electron transport during cellular oxidation, is a single polypeptide composed of 104 amino acids. The hemoglobin molecule is again more complex a structure, comprising three distinct polypeptide chains that must fold in such a way that they all fit together in three-dimensional space. Like all proteins, its properties are both a function of its spatial architecture as well as the resultant electro-chemical properties. We expect its form to be complex considering how it must function as a biochemical switch, alternating in transporting a carbon dioxide molecule from a cell to be expelled in the lung, exchanging it for an oxygen molecule, and dropping it off on the return trip back to the cell. It's a neat trick and just a single example of the multitude of neat biological tricks proteins are called upon to play within the LS agenda.

Again, the production of proteins according to precise instructions carried out by cellular ribosomes is truly an amazing process, both in its simple logic as well as the intricate expression of detail. While we can readily appreciate how the whole operation has to be exact in order to insure consistency of result, we cannot help wondering how such a complex programmed cellular machine tool came about. Like photosynthesis—the engine that powers the cell—ribosomes had to have been there from the very beginning of biological life, otherwise you don't get proteins. While pondering whether such a device could arise naturally, consider as well where the whole genetic coding system might have come from. These are two very separate entities—the intelligent machinery that carries out the instructions, and the detailed instructions that control all of the operation. They are as separate as the telephone book that contains the access information (telephone numbers) as opposed to the intelligence built into the phone system and the equipment (switches, computers, amplifiers etc.) that actually does the information processing. The system intelligence would also have had to be there from the very beginning. Both the hardware (transcription equipment and ribosomal translation equipment) and its operating intelligence (form and function of the genetic code) have to work hand in hand to obtain the kind of consistent precision required in protein production. Yet having said that, if the system, as a whole, is too precise, evolution won't work.

Mutations Revisited:

From the above, it is conceivable that a replacement of one single amino acid with another in a lengthy polypeptide sequence might have little effect on the function of a protein. This—so long as the substituted amino acid occupies a non-crucial position within the three dimensional protein configuration—one that would not adversely affect the collective bonding forces that define the shape and function of that protein. This kind of error could easily creep into the genome of an individual organism and would not be "noticed" as long as the change had no significant effect upon the functioning of that particular protein.

Conceivably, a number of such benign replacements could occur that could set the stage for the "straw that breaks the camels back". Imagine, if you will, a further replacement in the polypeptide chain at a chance location by an amino acid that had the effect of materially altering the shape of the resultant protein. Now the cell has a new product, which it can or cannot use. The cell also has to do without the original called for protein that the new one has replaced. One of three conditions can ensue:

1] The replacement turns out to do a better job than the original;

2] The replacement is neutral and has no immediate effect within the role it is called upon to play. That is to say that if it is a structural protein and the change involves a minor shape change that has no ill consequences—then cell life goes on as usual while the changed protein waits for evolution to find possible new uses for its additional novel attributes;

3] The change is a no-starter having disastrous consequences upon cellular activity and survival and the "error" is immediately culled out of the species genome, in virtue of the inability of the effected organism to reproduce offspring. But, this disaster will only affect the offspring of one organism and thus have negligible impact on the LS. Remember, many copies (organisms) of the previously neutral amino acid substitution stage are out there waiting for a genetic change that will result in a "step 1]" (beneficial) outcome for their offspring.

Survival of Genetic Information:

As we have previously described, the information provided by the genetic library only accounts for the superficial sequential placement of amino acids. That precise information will be passed on to future generations only if the physical organism survives long enough to pass on its genetic instruction library to its offspring. Failure to reproduce (for any reason) is tantamount to eliminating from the species gene pool any trace of that organisms uniqueness, because its distinctiveness resides solely within the unique combination of genes that gets expressed respectively, in every individual organism. An overriding reason some organisms never have offspring is a matter of fitness (as well as bad luck) that results in the inability to survive long enough to reproduce. The species gene pool at any moment in time, then, represents the sum total of the incremental genetic contributions of individual organisms. And what are these if not the offspring of previous generations. Thus, the gene pool composition is changed and reshaped continuously and incrementally by the additions and subtractions made to it by the presence of the surviving offspring of those previous generations. Naturally, the more widespread any gene appears within the species, the greater is likely to be its influence and contribution to species survival, in the present or in the future. By the same token, relatively new modifications to genes in individuals will have to prove themselves as significant survival enhancements or remain neutral awaiting further modification that will improve their chances of becoming assets. In any case, any such modifications will have to survive the test of time, i.e., survive through to future generations.

The Genetic Code—The Universal Language of the LS:

This system of encoding, transcribing, translating and replication of information is universal within the LS, regardless of the size (number of DNA base pairs) or the quality (actual message) of the encoded information. In fact it's essentially the same for every protein, of every living cell, of every living organism on the planet. And, no matter how diverse the organism design, each cell carries out DNA replication, transcription and translation in exactly the same way. A protein is the product of one or more genes' worth of information in the form of a recipe written in nucleic acid (DNA or RNA). This universality of information encoding, decoding and copying lies at the very heart of the LS. The LS, in effect, is a ubiquitous information handling (storage and processing) system wherein the libraries of genetic information continually change in order to accommodate new structures and strategies for survival (of species). How these changes to the genetic libraries occur and the frequency of random changes statistically allowed within a species genome lies at the heart of the SA (species attribute) distribution within a species and consequently—the evolution phenomenon (as discussed in chapter 8).

What emerges from our discussions above is the fact that living things owe all of their dynamic activity to the processing and expression of the stores of genetic information encoded in their DNA libraries. We consider the universal format and coding schemes of the genetic library to be of prime importance for these processes as they represent a single possibility out of many possible alternatives that could have been employed for accomplishing the task (see SE steps 3 and 4 in chapter 5). As such, we shall look for strategic design advantages within the universal format of the genetic coding scheme for possible contributions to LS form and function at a primary system intelligence level that might provide clues to a possible motivating choice for this particular one.

In the pages that follow, we shall be delineating the different kinds and levels of intelligence that characterize the form and function of the LS. We do so in order to gain an accurate appreciation of how different kinds of applied intelligence define in a precise way exactly the limits and capabilities of the system. At the same time, it will become evident that some of these transcend the processes of evolution, i.e. are not subject to change because they are fundamental at the LS primary and defining level and therefore must precede evolution (are part of the PdP of life). In the same way, a bat, ball, and bases are primary components in the definition of the game of baseball, which transcend any future evolutionary variations in how the game may be played. In the analysis that follows, it will become clear that it takes more than just an injection of outside energy to account for the local negative entropy (greater order) exhibited within the form and function of the LS. And in particular, it will become abundantly clear that the 2nd law alone cannot account for the complex coding scheme that is at the heart of the intelligent system of life. Deferring to the 2nd law fails miserably to provide a proper justification for such exquisite complexity, in my view, and would constitute a more contrived explanatory hypothesis than the views expressed herein. William of Occam, indeed, would have a field day with this one.

Mediums and Messages:

We have come to appreciate that if you look at a protein and its job description, you will find no correlation with the raw data that serves as the genetic instructions involved in its creation. The instruction itself only provides a series of codons that code for a specific recipe of amino acid building blocks and conveys nothing related to form or function of the end product. And like a basic cooking recipe, we really don't know what the end result will be until the ingredients are put together in such a way that they can express themselves. The recipe of ingredients—merely symbols on a page, tells you nothing of the taste, color and texture of the end result. All the less so if you cannot read the raw data or are unfamiliar with the ingredient characteristics. Similarly, the shape, and therefore the possible function of the resulting protein only emerges after the assembled polypeptide chain of amino acids folds in three dimensions, as it seeks its equilibrium state (state of least energy). Again, that shape is a function of the collective actions inherent in the forces of attraction and repulsion associated with the individual amino acids, particular to their unique sequence. In effect, the genetic information has no knowledge of the consequences of the instructions it provides, being simply a linear template of symbols. If this is the case, then where does the real intelligence of the LS reside? The answer is that the "system" itself is the "intelligence" of life. If this phrase has a familiar ring to it, it parallels the Marshall McLuhan concept of "*medium*" as "*message*". McLuhan proposed that the "grammar" of electronic technology directly corresponds to the human central nervous system and that the characteristics of a medium such as television—much more than its content—determine what a viewer will experience. As regards the LS, we might make the comparison: the characteristics of the genetic coding system, and of the individual amino acids it codes for, more than the information content itself, determines the form and functional characteristics of the LS. Before I get pounced upon for invoking such a blatant relationship, let me qualify my correlation. The low-level genetic data templates that form the information content within DNA are totally useless, unless and until the intelligent system edits, transcribes, and translates the sequence of arbitrary chemical symbols (the nucleotide bases) into the sequence of amino acids that forms a polypeptide chain. Then, it is up to each individual amino acid building block within the chain to exert its unique electro-chemical influence. The resultant protein is thus determined by both the inherent attributes of each amino acid component and, just as importantly, its position relative to every other in the sequence. The first part of the process—the sequence of bases that yields information in the form of linear arbitrary symbols—is typical of many human designed systems.

The Nature of Genetic Information:

The genetic information, written as a string of information bits forms a linear template analogous to a map, except most maps, as we know them, are two dimensional. A topological map is a scaled down representation on paper of the physical terrain it represents. It provides the location, relative to each other, of major features such as roads, lakes, rivers and valleys. If you can locate one feature on the ground, and that same feature on the map, because the map matches the terrain, you should be able to pinpoint any other location. With only minor differences, DNA and RNA convey genetic information in much the same way. Instead of being two dimensional, and written on paper, however, the genetic map is a linear representation written, as it were, in the string of chemical basepairs of the molecular medium of DNA and RNA. These represent the sequence of amino acids—its primary structure—that makes up a linear polypeptide chain. Only when folded, does the protein emerge as it's three-dimensional conformation, having all of the desired (and expected) characteristics. Some parts of a peptide chain may form a loop, or helix; others may be straight or form irregular coils. But, again, if the amino acids themselves did not exhibit their own specialized attributes, the system would not work because such templates conveys no information on how folding is to occur—only the sequential location of amino acid links on the polypeptide chain. Folding only happens later.

a) Information and Context

In fact, any sequential representation—whether of the order of components in space or events in time—comprises, in effect, a one-dimensional map. Humans use one—dimensional maps all the time. Take the example of placing a telephone call.

A telephone number written on a notepad tells you which numbered buttons to push in sequence in order to reach one of billions of possible phones on the planet. The sequence of telephone number digits on paper is effectively a one-dimensional map of arbitrarily chosen numeric symbols. It indicates the precise chronological sequence of keypad buttons to push in order to produce the progression of discreet tones that define, for the telephone company routing equipment, the signal path required to connect you to the party you wish to call. The phone equipment processes each button-tone in the order received. There is no intelligence, per say, in the number symbols themselves. The intelligence resides in the way the system exchange interprets the simple act of a user pushing a set of numbered buttons on the phone keypad. The system is so set up that it interprets the low level information that the caller uses to initiate the call (the telephone number) and processes it through a series of intelligent and sophisticated sub-systems that ends up as a completed connection anywhere in the world.

Each digit in the sequence represents a button to be pushed on the keypad, much the same as each nucleotide basepair represents one of three symbols that defines an amino acid. Similarly, each button on the keypad, in itself, has little influence. It is the cumulative order in which all the designated buttons are pushed, in sequence, which determines the resultant characteristic of the phone connection end product. Similarly, it is the order of all of the base pairs that determines the sequence of amino acids of the protein end product. In both cases, the sequences of symbols themselves, whether in the DNA or in a phone number must be used in a specific and restrictive way particular to their respective systems in order to initiate a chain of events that results in the system specific results. The point is, that while they represent the sufficient and necessary information required to initiate appropriate action from and within their particular systems, the sequence of arbitrarily chosen symbols themselves have no intrinsic informational value and are meaningless and totally useless in any other context. Again, without the intelligent system that knows how to interpret the sequence of symbols and mediate in a meaningful way, there is no information. And, the same goes for the LS as well as telephone communication systems. The point being that whether or not a sequence of symbols contains information is directly dependent upon the existence of an intelligent system that can process the symbols as relevant information.

b) Colinearity—A One-to-One Relationship:

To clarify further, the genetic instruction does not tell an amino acid how to behave when it is joined to other amino acids, in the polypeptide chain. The genetic instruction for any given protein is, in effect, a linear "template map" representing a polypeptide chain. It is nothing more than a genetic telephone number, (if you replace nucleotide bases by numerical digits), indicating only the physical position of the amino acid elements in sequence space and only has meaning for a ribosome. Similarly, the numerical sequence of a telephone number only has meaning for the telephone communication system. Templates, by their very nature, comprise a map representation in one medium corresponding to the positioning of elements in another. There is a term coined in molecular biology to reflect this fact. We say that the genetic basepair information encoded in the mRNA tape is "co-linear" with the amino acid positions of the polypeptide chain being expressed. In other words, if you can read the codon triplets sequentially in the mRNA tape, you will know the sequence of the amino acids. Again, this tells us nothing about the architecture or biological characteristics of the protein that will result. That is a distinct function of the resultant amino acid chain—part of the system intelligence, as it were. The colinearity of the mRNA triplet codons with the amino acid sequence only establishes the template relationship between the two. Position for position, the one reflects the other. But, it is from the combined influence of individual amino acids, including characteristics determined by their particular sequence in a linear polypeptide chain, that emerges its potential biological role as a three-dimensional protein.

The relationship between genetic information, its linear sequential format and the protein that results, is indicative of the versatility inherent to such map or template informational formats. This linear and low-level information format is an important design feature of the LS. And indeed, like the example above, this kind of format is universally applied in all kinds of man-made systems as well. We will now examine different aspects of such systems in order to determine whether the LS is using this format in additional ways. There are some interesting surprises in store.

The Nature and Versatility of the Linear Information Format:

A) SEQUENTIAL INFORMATION FORMATS:

Maps come in many forms and in one, two or three dimensions. We have seen examples of the first two above. As for three dimensions—what is an architect's mock-up of a future building if not an accurate three-dimensional "map" of the architecture? Element for element the model reflects a scaled down mockup version in three-dimensional space of the real thing. But our interest is in some of the special ways that linear map sequences, or templates similar to DNA basepair sequences, can be used to convey information. In addition to the telephone-dialing example above, advanced technology provides other interesting examples of sequential information processing we have become familiar with.

Electronics engineering uses a serial sequential format to broadcast TV signals that map the resultant picture in two dimensions on the television screen. However an additional control signal is tagged along with the picture transmission to indicate where one line on the TV screen ends and the next line down begins. If we could slow down the process we could actually see the signal scroll across and down the TV picture tube much the same as word-processing text scrolls, line by line, down a computer screen. By processing the signal at a sufficiently rapid repeat rate, and projecting the electronic stream onto an image retentive glass screen, the eye (the brain, really) is fooled into thinking it is watching a two dimensional picture. In fact what is appearing on the screen is a sequence of pixels (smallest single viewing element) of varying brightness and color for each dot location on the screen. But the system is designed to match the screen retention characteristics of the projected pixel images upon the phosphorus-coated screen to the brain's ability to visually and mentally process the data resulting in the illusion of a two dimensional TV experience. Here again we have an example of streams of data, which have no intrinsic informational content except within the specific context of the systems that can process the information. In another example, cinematography uses the same retentive characteristics of sight and mind to fool the eye into believing it is experiencing a seamless moving image. The point is that all information is contextual—requiring an appropriate intelligent system able to process and therefore use that information.

There is an analogy here to the linearity of sequential genetic information and its relationship to the folding of proteins. In both cases the information to be processed (DNA in the case of the LS) provides only a one-dimensional (linear) mapping sequence whose resultant interpretation is a function of the system (LS polypeptide folding characteristics). The point here is that the sequential information-mapping format is versatile and can serve in a variety of ways. As in all the above cases, the raw information (telephone number, TV signals, or nucleic acid basepairs) is translated into a collinear counterpart (dialed number, rapidly scrolled pixels or polypeptide chain). In effect, that is the definition of a template—"something that establishes or serves as a pattern". Outside of their limited context, the actual information elements (digits, pixel information or basepairs) are meaningless. In this respect, templates comprise lower grade information, indicating only positions of elements and requiring sophisticated interpretation hardware (or wetware in the case of the LS) to give it meaning. Let's now examine how additional intelligence can be added to sequential information systems in order to expand their versatility and usefulness. Let's go back to our telephone keypad example.

The form of the raw information (information to be entered into the keypad) can be enhanced in order to expand the system function. For example, instead of asking you to memorize a telephone number some enterprising businesses provide catch phrases in written language whose sequence of letters are collinear with the sequence of keypad entries required to connect you to them. Dial 1-800-callATT is one such example used by the American Telephone and Telegraph Company to help you remember their phone number. In this case an additional level of information is placed in the coding system that is transparent to the machinery of the telephone company. This additional level of information is designed into the information template sequence in order to engage the additional intelligence of another system—that of the human mind. It is easier to remember "callATT" than "1155188" because the intelligent human mind can associate both the reason for the telephone number together with the collinear phrase that translates into the required dialing sequence. And just to remain consistent, the sequence "callATT" would be just as useless as the "1155188" unless you know how to read as well as use the phone, and understand beforehand the duel nature of the symbols as slogan and telephone number. Both numbers and letters produce the same results, (a phone connection) however; one set of instructions (phone number expressed as letters of a word) contains an additional level of information than the other. In fact, the keypad composed of numbers and letters can be used as a coding device with numbers replacing letters in a word. In electronic phone answering systems known collectively as "voicemail", the caller may be asked to punch in the letters of the last name of the party one is trying to reach. The system then matches the keypad sequence to the location of that person's phone and automatically routes the call accordingly, and if she is absent, you will be asked by a recorded message to leave—a recorded message. Thus, the telephone keypad can be used in the dual capacity: to convey sequences of tones, which the central office interprets to complete a call; or can be used as an intelligent interface with another intelligent system—the human brain.

For the ultimate use of the sequential informational format we don't have to look very far, for it is the very essence of language itself.

B) LANGUAGE—SINGLE DIMENSION MAPS OF SYMBOLS:

It so happens that human languages are universally written in one-dimensional sequences. What is a sentence if not a sequence of words? And what are words if not a sequence of letter elements (or pictographs). While our aim here is not to involve ourselves in the complexities that attend the subject of language, syntax, and the like, the simple point we are making is that the same information format that comprises the one-dimensional genetic mapping of protein amino acid sequences is the identical format used in human language. (We shall have occasion later on to wonder if that is mere coincidence.)

The point could be made that a word composed of letter symbols is a kind of linear map of the sequence of those letters. And that's all it represents if you don't understand the meaning of the word. So too is a sentence a template of sequential word elements. This really becomes obvious when one looks at a foreign language composed of strange alphabet elements. Even if you don't understand how to read or write Chinese, you can still copy a sequence, element for element, letter by letter, by using it as a template. In fact, its only value to you might be in the beauty of the calligraphic symbols that for others represents meaningful language as well. What you are copying is only the form. Without the key to its interpretation and understanding, that is all the sequence represents. With understanding comes the meaning and the thoughts that inspired the language residing within the sequence of letter symbols and words. In SE terms, within the human mind resides the system intelligence that is able to read and understand the meaning of the sequence of symbols that comprise human language.

A template map is a physical thing whereas the interpretation of the information it codes for is a system phenomenon. Language is a complex mental construct of sequential sounds and/or visual elements that code for and represent interpretable ideas. The sequence of coded arbitrary alphabet symbols constitutes the totality of the information. Interpretation results through an intelligent mind that effectively works in reverse to decode the information—resulting in mental images that provide meaning that approximates, more or less, the meaning of the mental images and ideas that inspired the encoded linguistic information in the first instant.

The point is, that a sequential list of the alphabet symbols that constitute the written language of virtually all human communities can be considered to be a one-dimensional collinear map-template that defines the physical relationship and location of those alphabet letters relative to each other. Similarly, we have seen how a sequential list of the chemical alphabetic symbols that defines the placement of amino acid building blocks of proteins relative to each other also conform to the one-dimensional collinear map-template. It, therefore, would seem to follow from the above that both sequential systems should be able to convey the same kinds of information. In fact we presently and routinely use the letters of the English alphabet to represent the sequence of amino acids that make up the chain of amino acids that fold into proteins. For example, the sequence: ARG—ARG—TRP—GLN—TRP—ARG—MET—LYS—LYS—LEU—GLY is a case in point. It accurately represents the amino acid sequence in the polypeptide chain that folds into the protein "lactoferricin"—an antibiotic peptide. Using the single-letter designation (according to Table 12-A), the sequence assumes the form: "r r w q w r m k k l g", the human language equivalent of a genetic word. If we can use the English alphabet to represent a genetic sequence, can we also use the genetic code alphabet to compose a message understandable to humans? Why not? The fact is that there is no logical impasse that prevents the four-nucleotide symbols from also being used as the letters of a non— genetic language alphabet—in much the same way the genetic code spells out three base-letter codon sequences representing each of the twenty amino acids. Since we have indicated that the information in DNA repository medium is collinear with the amino acid sequences they code for, we can in fact use the letters of the twenty amino acids to actually write a message that could be encoded in DNA. Let's do it. Table 12-A lists each of the twenty amino acids universally used as the building blocks of proteins on our planet.

TABLE 12—A

	Amino Acid Symbol	Codon (Written in RNA)
Alanine [ALA]	A	gcu; gcc; gca; gcg
Argenine [ARG]	R	cgu; cgc; cga; cgg; aga; agg
Asparagine [ASN]	N	aau; aac
Aspartic Acid [ASP]	D	gau; gac
Cysteine [CYS]	C	ugu; ugc
Glutamine [GLN]	Q	caa; cag
Glutamic Acid [GLU]	E	gaa; gag
Glycine [GLY]	G	ggu; ggc; gga; ggg
Histidine [HIS]	H	cau; cac
Isoleucine [ILE]	I	auu; auc; aua
Leucine [LEU]	L	uua; uug; cuu; cuc; cua; cug

Lysine [LYS]	K	**aaa; aag**
Methionine [MET]	M	**aug (always starts a gene)**
Phenylalanine PHE]	F	**uuu; uuc**
Proline [PRO]	P	**ccu; ccc; cca; ccg**
Serine[SER]	S	**ucu; ucc; uca; ucg; agu; agc**
Threonine [THR]	T	**acu; acc; aca; acg**
Tryptophan [TRP]	W	**ugg**
Tyrosine [TYR]	Y	**uau; uac**
Valine [VAL]	V	**guu; guc; gua; gug**
STOP [SToP]	stp	**uaa; uag; uga**

Nucleotide bases: **u** = Uracil; **c** = Cytosine; **a** = Adenine; **g** = Guanine
Note: "t" replaces "u" in the medium of DNA

To the right of each is the English alphabet symbol followed by codons that code for that amino acid within the DNA. While most amino acids can be represented by several codons we shall designate only a single codon in order to make our point. From the twenty letters of the English alphabet that represent the twenty amino acids, lets see how the genetic code can be used to create a meaningful message within the DNA information library of any cell: (As in the telegrams of old, punctuation does not exist and must be spelled out.) Let's try the message:

WARNING *STOP* PLANET WITH INTELLIGENT LIFE *STOP*

Like any child's introduction to coding games, we simply have to consult the above table to determine which amino acids the letters in the message respectively represent: Tryptophan codes for W, followed by Alanine (A), Arginine (R), Asparagine (N), Isoleucine (I), Asparagine again (N), and Glycine (G). The above sequence of amino acids effectively spells the word "WARNING" in the genetic language. All we have to do now is to consult the Table once more to determine the corresponding sequence of three-letter nucleotide bases that represent individual amino acids in the chemical alphabet of the genetic code. Stringing together the nucleotides corresponding to the three-letter codons represented by the amino acids will result in the representative RNA sequence that stands for the letters of the message. Thus the English word "WARNING" can be written chemically in the nucleic acid of RNA as:

Amino Acids:	W	A	R	N	I	N	G	*Stop*
Bases:	"ugg	gcu	cgu	aau	auu	aau	ggu	uaa

There are no spaces between chemical letters written in RNA. In practice, none are required, as it is understood that each successive three-letter combination represents an amino acid. Replacing uracil (u) by (t) provides the equivalent information in DNA. The actual word "Warning" would be written:

tgggctcgtaatattaatggttaa

The codon taa at the end of the word above represents the "stop" punctuation and could, if necessary be placed between each word in order to prevent confusion. The same procedure would apply to the rest of the message. Obviously, you can't write the actual letters **t, a, c** or **g** in a molecule. Actual chemical representatives called purines (the **a** and **g**) and pyrimidines (**c** and **t**) act in the same capacity in the medium of chemical DNA as do English letters written in ink on paper. The underlying principle is the same everywhere, including the medium involved in skywriting. You use smoke to write the letters because the medium is the air. Every medium has its advantages and limitations. When you want to write in the medium of nucleic acids (DNA or RNA), you use suitable chemical letters of the alphabet such as purines (**a** and **g**) and pyrimidines (**t** and **c**).

A similar exercise in communication was undertaken between the two winners of the Nobel Prize for medicine in 1958. Max Delbruck sent a telegram to George Beadle at the Nobel ceremony in Stockholm that contained a string of 229 letters, which formed a coded message. Delbruck arbitrarily assigned each of the letters **a, b, c, d** to a DNA base and used the sequence of three bases to correspond to a letter in the English alphabet. The cryptic notation when translated produced yet an additional cryptic message: "I am the riddle of life. Know me and you will know yourself".

The point is that the same one-dimensional template medium used by the LS can contain both kinds of information:

1] template mapping of collinear sequential elements such as genetic information in the LS;

2] interpretable non-genetic language written in the same nucleotide alphabet symbols that can serve as information and be "read" by intelligent beings.

To our knowledge, humankind is the only intelligent life form that can claim any kind of language capability that transcends the severely limited modes of communication that any other earth-bound species may possess. This should not be interpreted as a triviallization of the widespread use of communication skills that have evolved among a myriad of species. The point is that these non-human communication skills are not in the same league as the language capabilities innate in humans.

Humans are the only species on the planet that engage in spoken and written language; design and operate communication systems. In fact, we are unaware of any other source of language in the universe. Yet here we are being confronted by an intelligent system, that which comprises the LS that includes an information library together with an extraordinary information processing system that has the capability and the capacity of containing language other than genetic information. It might be a good idea at this point to review what the characteristics are of manmade information systems before we try to tackle the only non-human created information system we know of that is somewhat analogous to our own—the DNA information library. It is somewhat astonishing to discover an information system that can convey language in an alphabet just like we do—one that predates humans by billions of years and has only come to light within the last fifty. Perhaps there is an unappreciated common thread that links the two.

Generic Information Systems:

We are, all of us, familiar with information systems. They include mechanisms that can process and use information. The highest level of communication among members of the LS must unquestionably be that which finds expression within the language skills developed by humans. The use of language is universal and permits the exchange of abstract thought in addition to all the other information processing that evolved as part of survival skills. Not satisfied to be limited by the talking or shouting distance afforded by verbal communication, hand signals, or the blowing of horns at a distance, man has developed first the oral and then the written language of symbols that reflect, in a sequential mapping fashion, information that could be communicated to others of his species.

A) COMMUNICATION SYSTEMS:

Communication systems are meant to bridge the distance between two or more intelligent beings. Probably the earliest form of human long distance communication involved memorized information that a runner or rider on horseback or camel would carry between a sender and receiver. Eventually written messages raised the level of efficiency of communication as both the secrecy and quantity of information could increase. It probably also saved the lives of countless messengers that no longer had to be sacrificed in order to insure such secrecy. A leap forward into the 20th century finds civilization transformed by electromagnetic radio technology—the ultimate in long distance communication spanning not only the planet but also beyond as mankind explores its planetary neighborhood.

Regardless of the simplicity or complexity of communication systems, they all have elements in common. One of the most productive schematic models of a communications system emerged in the late 1940s, largely from the speculations of two U.S. mathematicians, Claude Shannon and Warren Weaver[5]. When they put forth their principles of information theory[2] some fifty plus years ago, the aim was to provide mathematical laws governing the transmission, reception, and processing of information. As radio, telephone and Teletype communication channels became more crowded and technology more complex, a theoretical basis for communication technology in general was required that would apply to any and all information systems humans could devise (that was, after all, the only information systems we knew of). Little did they realize that those same principles might be applicable to the "mother" of all information systems—the only one humans cannot lay claim to having engineered—the information system comprising the genetic libraries of life. Let us examine the main points behind Shannon's information theory and see how they apply to human designed information systems and how those same principles could, in fact, lie at the heart of the spontaneous mutations responsible for evolution within the LS.

Following a number of revisions the "linear" model, as it came to be called, emerged, comprising six constituent elements: (1) a source, (2) an encoder, (3) a message, (4) a channel, (5) a decoder, and (6) a receiver. In some communication systems, the components are as simple to specify as, for example: (1) a man on the telephone, (2) the mouthpiece of the telephone, (3) the words the man speaks, (4) the electrical wiring along which the information (now electrical impulses) travel, (5) the earpiece of another telephone, and (6) the ear and mind of the listener. The linear model is seen to include both source (man on the telephone) and receiver (the mind of the listener), as well as the mediating hardware (and software) that intefaces between sender and receiver.

b) Entropy, Negative Entropy, and Redundancy:

Another concept, first called a "noise source" but later associated with the notion of entropy (the same principle derived from 2nd law of thermodynamics), was imposed upon the communication model. Entropy is analogous in most communication to audio or visual static—extraneous influences that degrade the integrity of communication and distort the message for the receiver. It effectively is understood intuitively as the amount of disorder in a system.

Each time a message (information) needs to be converted from one medium to another, or copied in transit, the conversion process is subject to errors due to entropy. Negative entropy may also occur in instances in which incomplete or blurred messages are nevertheless received intact, because of the ability of the receiver to fill in missing details. This can occur through the use of error-correction algorythms or simply the ability to recognize—despite distortion or a paucity of information—both the intent and content of the communication.

Messages (and information in general) are therefore susceptible to considerable modification and mediation. Entropy distorts, while negative entropy in the form of error correction and redundancy clarify; as each occurs differentially in the communication process, the chances of the message being received and correctly understood vary. Still, the model remains conceptually static, because it is fundamentally concerned with messages sent from point to point, and not with their results or possible influences upon sender and receiver.

c) Feedback:

To correct this flaw, additional complexity was introduced. The principle of feedback was added to the model and provided a closer approximation of interpersonal human interaction. This concept was derived from the studies of Norbert Wiener, the so-called father of the science of cybernetics. Wiener's cybernetic models, some of which provide the basis for current computer technology, were designed to be responsive to their own behavior; they could audit their own performances mathematically or electronically in order to avoid errors of entropy, unnecessary redundancy, or other simple hazards.

The complexity of a communication system is determined by the nature of the information and the distances and medium characteristics between the source and the destination. Let's look at several examples.

d)Long Distance Communication Systems:

The information and its communicating system must form a total and integrated system even if large distances separate the transmitter and receiver. A radio voice transmission is a case in point. The message to be transmitted must first be encoded from its human language form into an electromagnetic signal that can be radiated using the characteristics of the electromagnetic radio wave medium, that of space. The receiver may be many thousands of miles away but must contain within its design the capability of capturing the radio signal and decoding its information back into its original form, intelligible to a human receiver. For the system to function, both transmitter and receiver must be compatible. But, in fact, the process, as described above, does not really begin nor end there, does it? Because, we haven't even begun to consider the complex human elements in the equation, that served as originator and sharer of the information respectively. It certainly helps if both sender and receiver speak the same language as that of the communicated message. This raises an all-important consideration— that the degree of complexity of a communication system depends upon the distance to, and nature of the interface separating sender and end user of that information. This can be as simple (it's really very complicated) as getting information from my head—the source-provider of the information, into your head—the destination end-user, by means of a pleasant chat (using an interpreter, if need be). And, the nature of the information, and again the distances involved, will determine the architecture of the communicating system that joins the two.

E) INFORMATION SYSTEMS COMPONENTS:

Regardless of the nature and kind of information processing intelligent beings engage in, all such systems have components in common which can be reduced to the following discreet elements:

a) A source of information (message composer),
b) A message to be communicated,
c) A communication system (transmitter-medium-receiver),
d) A destination (message end-user).

The idea is that information must originate somewhere and be sent or communicated somewhere else. An information system comprises mechanisms through which an end user can acquire the information. But invariably, the flow of information through a communication system begins with an _intelligent_ sender at the origin and ends with an _intelligent_ end-user at the destination. The communicating system itself may involve the processing of the information into a variety of intermediate forms, before finally converting it into a suitable intelligible form at the destination.

F) SENDERS AND RECEIVERS:

The point we have emphasized is that the most important components of any communication system are the intelligent entities that constitute the sender of the information and the intended receiver and, of course, the communicated message—the information itself. The sender and receiver are the ones doing the communicating and the reason for the existence of the communication system in the first place. Any communication system simply acts to connect the sender—the source of the information, with the receiver—the intended recipient of the information regardless of the distance and qualitative difficulty of the interface that separates the two. The only experience of communication between intelligent entities we are aware of to date has been between biological organisms on our planet. The key to any such communication must be intelligence compatibility between the sender and receiver. And, regardless of the complexity or simplicity of the system, the senders and receivers that are doing the communicating must ultimately be intelligent entities. While this may seem obvious and even trivial, it is the key to understanding effective communication, regardless of the complexity of the system bridging the distances involved.

Communication can and does take many forms, depending on its purpose. From our deliberations above, we can define the purpose of any communication system as providing access of information to an end user. It follows that regardless of how that end result is meant to be achieved, if the end user fails to acquire the intended information, the system itself has failed. Having said that, it is time to examine a kind of communication system whose design intent is to maximize access to information for diverse and anonymous end users over long periods of time. We are now beginning to close in on the heart of the matter.

G) THE INFORMATION LIBRARY:

Take the case of a library of books or other repository of information. A library comprises diverse information from many sources with many potential end-users. Rather than engaging in complex systems to transmit the information from each originator to every possible end-user, it is the intelligent end-user that comes to the information sources, in order to selectively access specific information of interest. In this regard, libraries comprise a special kind of communication system, but a very important one within our deliberations. They represent a repository of many kinds of information accessible to a variety of end users who selectively take communication of (access) the information as, and when, they need to use it. This concept shall figure importantly in the pages ahead.

H) THE GENETIC LIBRARY—A CASE IN POINT:

The genetic library comprises the informational database used by all of the biological systems of the ubiquitous cell—both prokaryotic and eukaryotic. We have come to appreciate how important the evolution processes are and have examined how evolution functions primarily through the expression of a variety of essentially random mutations (M's and m's) to genetic information. We will soon explore how random mutations to DNA basepairs cause all kinds of changes whose ultimate effect on the phenotype are filtered and to a large extent developmentally controlled from within the LS. Now it is time to delve into the random nature of such changes, i.e., what natural principles are responsible for such randomness? After all, the genetic library of a cell provides precise instructions on everything that the cell may require in terms of both form and function—including its own self-replication. We want to home in on the dichotomy within the realization that such precision of form and function would seem to be at odds with the notion of spontaneous and random changes. What is really happening here and how do we explain this operational dichotomy? The answer is readily at hand if we care to look.

The fact is that as information systems go, genetic information has much in common with human derived information. The same forces and influence in the universe that tend to degrade information (2nd law entropy) applies to the one as much as to the other. As it turns out, the primary source of degradation of all kinds of transmitted information is noise—of one form or another. The sources of noise are varied but have two things in common—they cannot be totally eliminated and they are random in nature. In contrast, information is anything but random—it is and must remain constant and unchanged throughout the processes of composition, transmission, and reception—from source to destination—and therefore can be considered, effectively, to be the antithesis of randomness.

Systems Engineering Observations and Implications for the LS:

In this chapter our case for the RDH assumed an ambitious agenda. At the beginning we established the existence of a dichotomous relationship between 2nd law entropy energy and order. We moved on with an analysis of information and intelligence, the one being the currency of the other, coining in the process our Universal Dogma of Information Flow (UDIF). We demonstrated how the exercise of intelligence in the application of energy to a system changes the rules of engagement with respect to the entangled relationship between entropy energy and entropy order. Using the principles thus developed, our discussion led inexorably toward an important conclusion resulting in a novel definition of the 'life state' as we know it. Most importantly, because our definition of life is developed in terms of a fundamental law of nature—2nd law of thermodynamics—it can reasonably be applied not simply to the specific case of the LS on our planet, but as a universal definition of the generic "life state" anywhere the question arises. We then went on to define the interface separating the life state from non-life in terms of principles that parallel quantum theory, representing the LS as occupying quantum states of biological complexity paralleling the traditional quantum energy states espoused in physics.

We have covered in some detail the principles of how the LS information system operates; how the DNA informational molecule forms a single-dimension template, inscribed with sequential genetic information written in a language of four letters. We followed this up with a detailed description of the principle components of communication systems and the universal attributes that define information systems in general—the intelligent information source, the information to be communicated, the communication system, and the intelligent destination end-user. In addition, we have described the LS as an intelligent system because its component organisms each function under the control of an instructional database—the genetic DNA library, in the spirit of and analogous to the von Neumann model. We have further demonstrated that the genetic information system comprising the genetic library and DNA information storage and processing apparatus could indeed serve additionally as a system for inscribing other kinds of information (e.g. human language) besides genetic.

In the course of examining communication systems we have tried to broaden our understanding of what all information systems have in common and to demonstrate that the LS information system shares many of the same attributes. We shall eventually come to see the LS as a special kind of communications system that is able to exploit the built-in potential for language within its DNA library, in addition to its familiar essential role as genetic library of encoded genetic information. Further, we have made a valid comparison between the human library communication system comprising written words encoded in the medium of books and the LS genetic library comprised of chemical words written in the chemical medium of DNA. Eventually we shall establish an astonishing connection between the ability of the LS to store and process vast amounts of information within its information systems, and two systems engineering properties—that of LS design intent and possible LS end uses.

We have earlier determined that evolution is blind as regards the ultimate form and complexity of the individual organisms that make up the LS system and the future directions these take. As such, we concluded that evolution derived complexity of species form and function, in and of itself, could not be a design imperative of the LS, but rather served in an adaptive role for the long-term survivability of the LS. And thus, if the LS did, indeed, have an over-abiding design imperative, it had to be within the realm of *time*—with a permanent operational presence on our planet being the prime objective. We also gained an appreciation of the fact that each organism component of the LS contains within its cells, miniature information libraries containing incredible quantities of encoded information that comes in two varieties: 1) genetic (exons) that code for genes, and 2) non-genetic (introns) that are considered "junk". We have described how genetic information is accessed from the permanent library written in DNA, copied and edited unto the mRNA template, exported from the cell nucleus and delivered to the ribosome which translates the information into a collinear polypeptide chain of amino acids to form proteins. We have come to appreciate the exquisite degree of control required of these processes. What we have totally failed to address is the role of introns, which comprise fully 92% of the information stored in human DNA. Well, the fact is that nobody knows what they are there for—nor has anyone paid too much attention to the question. The fact is that introns have always been considered a nuisance factor within molecular biology—extraneous junk that is edited out of the working mRNA copies of the genetic "blueprints of life" before they can be put to use by the machinery of the cell. Personally, I have never been able to accept the premise that 92% of the encodable space within DNA can serve no purpose at all simply because it is edited out of the mRNA and never leaves the nucleus of the cell (an important consideration we shall return to in due course).

Moving Forward:

As we progress with our exercise, our intention throughout is nothing less than that all of these discussions shall eventually be seen to contribute to the formation of a set of ideas that culminates in and, indeed, defines the LS as an engineered system and ultimately determines LS design intent. In "smart" engineered systems, designed by humans, the source of the controlling instructions is usually the designer who tailors the instructional set according to the operational requirements and design intent of the system in question. We believe we will be able to make the same kind of statement with respect to the LS, that is: that at the heart of the data processing systems required for Life form and function on this planet comprises a versatile and vast data storage capability that is tailored to function simultaneously in capacities other than the simple processing of genetic information. But, before we will be prepared to draw and reveal any definitive conclusions, there is one additional related level of interest that will impact heavily on the outcome. That involves the nature of the genetic coding system itself, and its remarkable influence on the genetic information it encodes. Our interest shall be two-fold:

1] Does the form of the genetic code influence evolution (yes it does) while it itself remains immune from the effects of evolution; and

2] if so, what is the likelihood that the genetic coding scheme is a contrived algorithm specifically designed to modify and control the results stemming from spontaneous and unpredictable mutations—all part of the function of the PdP idea developed earlier (highly likely)?

The actual coding scheme of the genetic code is indeed independent of the information it encodes and we will show it to be the primary level of logical intelligence that controls the destiny of the LS. SAb would have you believe that the genetic code is just another product of evolution—no different from the development of cellular functions. But, the fact is that the genetic coding scheme precedes the information it encodes and thus must precede as well, a priori, any base pair-manipulation mechanisms for evolution. We consider the form of the genetic code to be an integral part of the biological PdP and operating in accordance with our Universal Dogma of Information Flow discussed earlier. Its origin then must, of necessity, impact importantly on the OoL issue.

Our challenge in the next chapter is to explore the ability of the LS, through the form and function of the genetic code, to place extraordinary constraints on evolution. We shall find that it does so by controlling key parameters that affect the degrees of freedom evolution can have. The extent to which the form of the genetic code can serve to modify the results of evolution and in fact operates as an evolution filter will leave no doubt as to the ability of the LS to control its own "developmental" destiny. To better understand the future of the LS, we must first try to understand the mysteries of its past. Toward that pursuit, in the next chapter we shall be postulating a Quantum Theory of Life—an hypothesis that solves a number of sticky problems associated with evolution. The results of the deliberations in the pages that immediately follow will further fortify the case for the RDH—that the LS is indeed a designed system, possessing the necessary keys to, not only control its own destiny, but also protect and preserve its design intent.

---

*While the term "dogma" has too many pompous and generally negative connotations, we feel its questionable use here serves as a suitable counterpoint to the Central Dogma that preceded it. We have also come to realize that the Universal Dogma, which we shall introduce presently, is more of an axiom (self-evident truth) and not really provable (or disprovable). Dogmas, within their historical religious context, have generally been accepted on faith and not subjected to validation by way of empirical proof. Thus, our use of the term "dogma" can probably be considered more appropriate, under the circumstances, than Crick's application, which has already had to yield to contradiction following empirical analysis.

[1]Science, Vol 294, Oct 5 2001, p 53
[2]A Mathematical Theory of Communication, C Shannon, 1948

13. The Primary Intelligence Level of Life

"Reality is merely an illusion, albeit a very persistent one."
—Albert Einstein (1879–1955)

Degeneracy Of The Genetic Code – A Critical System Intelligence Attribute:

A species (its organisms, really) has no way of knowing, or of predicting, that the biosphere is indeed introducing niche condition changes that must be adjusted to. It has no way of knowing, that it is only the incorporation of changes to its genome, that can permit long term survival of offspring to biosphere changes through the gradual process of evolution. And, unbeknownst to the participants of life, evolution through continuous adaptation is the essential ingredient for the ultimate survival of the system of life. Yet, the processes of evolution begin with, and are fueled by, the spontaneous and random mutations of the DNA bases that serve as the blueprints for the construction of the protein building blocks of bio-life. The contrasts are exquisite, to say the least. Here we have what arguably is the most important adaptive phenomenon responsible for the survival of the LS, evolution - totally dependent upon mechanisms of change to complex genetic instructions that are described as both spontaneous and random. At first glance, one must marvel at a long-term survival process that appears so successful and yet seems to depend totally on the delicate balancing act of permissible chance changes to critical genetic information. Obviously there must exist in place controls that can mediate the effects of both the quantity and quality of the chance mutations that can occur to the genetic instructions of living things - otherwise the only alternative imaginable for evolution would be unbridled confusion; all the more so, the more complex the species. We shall now examine the mutation phenomenon and how chance events are filtered into tolerable results. The reader is sure to come away from this exercise with a renewed understanding and appreciation that when it comes to survival, the LS leaves very little to chance.

The genetic code is described as "degenerate" because it exhibits an interesting curiosity: there is no consistency in the number of codons that identify each of the 20 amino acids. Three amino acids are identified by any one of 6 different codons, five by 4 codons, one by 3 codons, nine by 2 codons, and two by a single codon (Table 12-A). The "'stop'" instruction is identified by 3 different codons. They all add up to 64 possible codon combinations. Until recently, this oddity, while perhaps interesting, had not evoked much attention. But, once we dig below the surface, we immediately discover some not-too-obvious properties that genetic coding degeneracy confers upon the LS at its most fundamental level of operation. As part of our systems engineering analysis of the LS, an in-depth statistical analysis of the effects of degeneracy upon the genetic coding scheme reveals a dynamic program of complex data processing algorithms that impact significantly on the consequences of genetic mutations upon the fundamental nature of biological evolution. In the light of these discoveries, one is inclined to question how and indeed whether the genetic coding scheme could possibly have evolved simply by chance. We are inclined to believe that it is an integral part of the PdP of bio-life and thus predates evolution. Furthermore, we believe we may have inadvertently stumbled upon the logical reasoning behind the choice of this particular genetic coding language over any number of other possible alternatives. As discussed earlier, the system engineering design process involves choosing between alternative ways of creating design solutions. Detailed analysis of the code – its form and function - reveals why it is unlikely it could have evolved by chance, and clearly, why this particular design alternative would have been chosen. As it turns out, the universal genetic code contains built-in mechanisms that effectively reduce dramatically the negative effects of chance spontaneous mutations of genetic information – effectively converting a high probability evolution failure rate into an overall certainty of evolutionary success. We are referring here to nothing less than the raison d'être of the form and function of the genetic code and why it is likely it has remained a constant throughout the history of bio-life evolution on this planet. We shall come to appreciate how essential the very composition and specific degeneracy of the genetic code is - to ensure the certain success of, arguably, that most enigmatic aspect of biological life on the planet: evolution.

The Genetic Code - A Non-Equal Opportunity Amino Acid Substitution Filter:

A] : RANDOM CAUSES LEAD TO NON-RANDOM EFFECTS:

A significant characteristic of the coding scheme that determines the sequence of amino acids that make up proteins is the "collinear" (one for one) relationship between the location of edited DNA base pairs (that spell codon words - 3 bases to a codon) and the specificity of amino acid locations in the corresponding polypeptide chain that precedes protein formation. However, the nature of the genetic code is such that a single spontaneous and random change to a codon basepair in a DNA sequence of code produces interesting non-random effects. To understand and appreciate this remarkable process, we will examine the non-linear relationship between the spontaneous change to a DNA codon basepair, and the corresponding amino acid "substitution error" produced in the associated polypeptide sequence. This non-linearity appears to have direct consequences for species evolution and acts as an *operational genetic evolution filter (OGEF)* that effectively directs which amino acid substitutions are absolutely forbidden, and which amino acid substitutions are permissible. In the exercise that follows, we shall explore the mathematical probabilities associated with such substitutions - probabilities that filter in significant ways the resultant consequences for evolution. Our statistical analysis of the relationship and consequences of random mutations to the gene sequences that code for proteins represents a major departure in the understanding of the significance of the form and function of the genetic code for evolution. There is more!

The compliment of twenty amino acids used as universal building blocks in biological life are seen to fall into two distinct substitution compatibility groups that are graphically illustrated within our *AmAcid Node (AAN) diagrams (See Appendix)*. The AAN diagrams visually clarify and indicate the importance of the amino acid substitution propensities that fuel evolution.

B] THE GENETIC CODE - AS GOOD AS IT GETS:

Let's recap a bit. The genetic code defines how the genetic information encoded in DNA is translated into the proteins that comprise the physical components of biological life. As stated, a gene is typically a partial sequence of encoded DNA (transcribed into mRNA), which serves as a one-dimensional template, which ultimately translates into the sequencing of designated amino acids that make up a polypeptide chain. Upon completion, the polypeptide chain is released within the aqueous environment of the cell, whereupon it folds to become the desired three-dimensional protein product called for by the cell. The sequence of DNA information conversion to protein end product proceeds as follows:

1] A single gene's worth of information is transcribed (copied) from the cell's permanent DNA library into a slightly different nucleic acid called RNA, in which form it is edited. The edited RNA instructional tape now referred to as messenger RNA (mRNA) comprises three-letter chemical words called codons. The mRNA is directed to a ribosome - that can read and interpret each codon in turn as a particular amino acid. The ribosome retrieves and strings together in linear sequence all of the designated amino acids into a polypeptide chain. The chain sequence of amino acids is said to be "collinear" with the sequence of coded information. (i.e.: A gene is like a telephone number that describes which digits to string together as a sequence of tones to complete a call. The information digits of the telephone number are collinear with the sequence of tones input to the telephone exchange that results in a successful connection between any two phones. In the case of the gene, the result is a sequence of specifically placed amino acids that will become a polypeptide chain just prior to folding into a protein.)

2] The language of the genetic code is written in four chemical letters called nucleotides – **a** (adenine), **t** (thymine), **c** (cytosine), and **g** (guanine). **a** connects with **t**, and **c** with **g**, to form complimentary basepair rungs within the DNA double helix information molecule. In the transcribed mRNA version, the **t** is replaced by **u** (uracil). A set of three such letters in sequence comprises a genetic "word", or "codon" that codes for a specific amino acid. There are 64 different 3-letter codons possible using a four letter alphabet (4^3). The LS utilizes only 20 amino acids to produce proteins. Thus, many amino acids are specified respectively by more than one codon - a phenomenon called "degeneracy". There are three chain terminating codons that tell the ribosome to "'stop'" the sequencing of amino acids and that the chain is complete. The single codon that codes for methionine signals the start of the translation process.

Ribosomes function by bringing together and matching mRNA codons to the corresponding *anticodons* attached to transfer RNA (tRNA) containing individual amino acids waiting to be assembled. Thus, the reading of the codon understood to be cysteine (ugc) in the mRNA template is matched to the complimentary anticodon (acg) within the tRNA containing the amino acid "cysteine". The amino acid, so recognized is liberated from its tRNA molecule by the ribosome and attached to the growing polypeptide chain of amino acids. One amino acid after another is so recognized, liberated, and strung together to form a single dimension polypeptide chain.

C] MUTATIONS:

Mutations are the changes that occur to the source information encoded in the DNA (and transcribed into mRNA) that can be carried through to the amino acid recognition and assembly process. An amino acid substituted for another as a result of such a chance mutation to a DNA basepair leads invariably is a protein that is different from that anticipated by the cell. Point mutations, as they are called, are classified as follows:

1] *Missense Mutation*: a genetic "spelling" error that has the effect of substituting one letter of a codon for another, thereby changing an original codon specifying one amino acid to another that specifies a different amino acid. Missense mutations come in two varieties:

a) *"transitions"* refer to the substitution of a chemical purine for its counterpart (a to g or g to a) or a pyramidine for its counterpart (c to u or u to c), and

b) *"transversions"* refer to the switch of a purine for a pyramidine or vice-versa. They come in two varieties – Complimentary Transversions (eg: a to u or u to a; c to g or g to c) and Non-Complimentary Transversions (a to c or c to a; g to u or u to g).

2] *Nonsense Mutation*: a single error that has the effect of changing an original codon specifying an amino acid to a "chain-termination" or "'stop'" codon ("nonsense codon"). This kind of mutation causes premature termination of the reading process and consequently an incomplete polypeptide being released by the ribosome - resulting in a protein most probably lacking biological activity.

3] *Reverse Mutation*: a second error alteration, called a *"reversion"* that serves to reverse the effects of a first such change (two wrongs making a "right").

4] *Suppressor Mutation*: occurring at different locations on a chromosome that have the effect of suppressing the change at another site. These again fall into two categories:

a) *"Intragenic Suppression"* - when the phenomenon occurs within the same gene, and

b) *"Intergenic Suppression"* - when it happens in a totally separate gene. Genes that cause suppression of mutations are called *"suppressor genes"*.

D] THE EFFECTS OF MUTATIONS ON EVOLUTION:

As might be expected, mutations to genetic instructions, that must ultimately express themselves as alterations to the physiology of organisms, are an important source of evolutionary change to species morphology, as well as the source of deleterious errors that gradually creep into the genome of a species. One might think that a species - well suited to its environmental conditions - would, if it could, opt for permanence of form and function once a certain degree of perfection has been achieved. After all, "why fix something if it isn't broken?" However, the external conditions that impose themselves on living things keep changing - so it is essential that offspring adapt accordingly, failing which any species is destined to extinction. As discussed earlier, evolution is the essential adaptive subsystem of the LS responsible for change. That goal is acheived as a result of two distinct operational features:

1] the creation of species attribute (SA) distribution curves within populations which allow a species to anticipate biosphere attribute (BA) changes (as discussed in chapters 8 and 9). These reflect variable differences within the genetic information of individual organisms (genotypes) of all species, which are the direct result of the accumulation of mutations to the chemically encoded information within the DNA genetic libraries of surviving offspring. Once expressed in the phenotypes, this results in variability based competition within and among the organisms of a species as a direct result of the distribution of species attributes (SAs) - the net outcome being the survivorship of the successful.

2] the survival of offspring of each succeeding generation shape anew the SA distribution curves that have the affect of fine-tuning the distribution in the short run, and serve to anticipate any and all directions of external biosphere changes in the long run - which in turn translates into the survival of most species in the short term and the LS in the long term.

Chronologically, of the four type of mutations listed above, we can view the phenomena of suppresor mutations, as the more sophisticated latecomer to the arsenal of genome error correction and control. The reason becomes obvious if we consider an earlier time when genomes were much smaller in data content as well as simpler and contained fewer genes - all of which coded directly for basic PdP physiology and reproduction instructions. Under these primal conditions, when the whole phenomenon of biological life was younger on the planet, the mechanisms of suppressor genes, or of any genes not being both sufficient and necessary, could be considered luxury provisions that would have to come into play much later on when there would be sufficient genome size within which to accommodate these evolutionary refinements. But, at the beginning, some 3.8 billion years ago and for some time to come, the top priority of the LS agenda would have emphasized rapid reproduction with little time or energy (or genetic instructions) for anything else. Having said that, any primitive and strictly unicellular life forms would, of necessity, have required both the genetic changes that fuel evolution and, at the same time, some kind of rudimentary controls to obviate the chaotic consequences that would have ensued, as a result of unchecked mutation errors running rampant throughout the earlier genetic data bases. The missense, nonsense and reverse mutations noted above could well serve the purpose, but only under very limited conditions. These spontaneous kinds of changes to genetic information of the first founder species could have provided the source of variability upon which their future evolution depended, but they had to be of a kind and quantity of changes that the formative LS could live with as well. We are referring to a time in the history of biological life before which sophisticated error correction information processing controls need come into play in order to deal with the long term accumulation of errors that could threaten LS genetic integrity. Nonetheless, we shall demonstrate that the sufficient and necessary controls were essentially already in place within the form of the genetic coding system itself.

Our aim here, is to examine the universal genetic code for clues as to how the expression processes, that convert raw genetic data encoded in DNA into the proteins that provide organisms with both form and function, could have served additionally as effective and efficient genetic error damage controllers, all the while promoting positive adaptive evolution influences. Not only would such an LS subsystem serve to maintain order within the haphazard evolutionary processes, but serve as well, as a guiding influence that could account for the generally successful results we see today. These might even apply to general and major morphological schemes such as multicellular organism shapes and body plans, for example. We will eventually contend that built into the genetic code are algorithmic properties that betray - more than any other LS morphological trait - characteristics that could only have derived from design.

The Genetic Code: An Intelligent Data Processing System:

The genetic code is a remarkable translation and encryption information processing system. Our cursory introduction reveals a fascinating set of characteristics that define it as sophisticated, intelligent and selective. A more thorough analysis we shall be engaging in begins with the examination of the codons that code for each of the twenty amino acids that comprise the building block repertoire of the LS. Evolution is fueled by mutations to the chemical letters that spell out these codons. Those letters (a, u, c, and g) spell 3-letter codons, each of which designates an amino acid. A chance mutation causes a letter written in the language of DNA to change – causing in turn a codon word written in a mRNA to change – causing in turn a change in the amino acid sequence that makes up a protein. If you want to study the effects of mutations, the most thorough way is to examine each and every mutation change possible. There are only sixty-four possible three-letter codon combinations comprising an alphabet of four letters (4^3). Thus, while the task of examining every possible change for each codon may be laborious (3 x 3 x 64 = 576 codon changes to be exact) it is the only way to gain a true understanding of how the form and function of the genetic code deals with mutations. Within those 576 possible changes, one-third each produces transition, complimentary transversion, and non-complimentary transversion mutations. Our mathematical analysis as applied to each of these three kinds of mutations reveals astonishing qualities directly attributable to the form and function of the genetic code. At the end of the day, we shall once again be left to query how it is possible - and indeed, whether it is possible - for such a data processing system – a system that directs and therefore must precede all other biological systems - to evolve from the ambient randomness that is pervasive throughout the natural order of the universe. As we shall see, there seems to be no end of surprises.

Detailed Analysis:

I have singled out one amino acid, Alanine (Ala), as an example of how we will proceed. Table 13-A below describes every possible basepair mutation that the amino acid can undergo. Alanine is defined by any of the four following codons appearing in a mRNA information tape: gcu, gcc, gca, and gcg. Now a missense mutation would have the effect of changing a single base letter to any other base letter. Thus, for example if the first Alanine codon- gcu were to have its first base g mutated to u (chemically, guanine to uracil), the mutant codon would read ucu, and code instead for a different amino acid – in this case Serine. Similarly we can go through every single possible alternate base in each codon for Alanine to determine the resultant amino acid replacement (see Table 13-A below).

Table 13-B in the appendix lists each amino acid together with its codon designations (Polar, Nonpolar, Acid and Basic amino acids are respectively grouped together). Beneath each codon is listed all of the possible amino acid substitutions (9) arising from a single letter alteration out of the three codon letters. For the sake of brevity, Table 13-B lists only the substitution amino acids that result from all possible changes to each codon nucleotide (In Table 13-A below we have elaborated the procedure in the single example of Alanine by listing every possible amino acid substitute next to its corresponding mutated codon). A cursory look at the single-mutation substitution results for amino acid "Alanine, as tabled below, reveals immediately a most astonishing characteristic of the genetic code.

Table 13-A: All Possible Single Point Mutations (9 per Codon) for AmAcid "Alanine"

	Codon	AmAcid	Codon	AmAcid	Codon	AmAcid	Codon	AmAcid
Four Original Codons>>	gcu	ALA	gcc	ALA	gca	ALA	gcg	ALA
9 Possible Mutations	Changed to		Changed to		Changed to		Changed to	
1 >	ucu	SER	ucc	SER	uca	SER	ucg	SER
2 >	ccu	PRO	ccc	PRO	cca	PRO	ccg	PRO
3 >	acu	THR	acc	THR	aca	THR	acg	THR
4 >	guu	VAL	guc	VAL	gua	VAL	gug	VAL
5 >	gau	ASP	gac	ASP	gaa	GLU	gag	GLU
6 >	ggu	GLY	ggc	GLY	gga	GLY	ggg	GLY
7 (no AmAcid change) >	gcc	ALA	gcu	ALA	gcu	ALA	gcu	ALA
8 (no AmAcid change) >	gca	ALA	gca	ALA	gcc	ALA	gcc	ALA
9 (no AmAcid change) >	gcg	ALA	gcg	ALA	gcg	ALA	gca	ALA

For starters, out of the 36 possible codon substitutions that single missense mutations could cause (3 base positions x 3 possible changes x 4 codons), fully one-third (twelve) end up coding for Alanine itself - the original amino acid. Four substitutions code each for Serine, Proline, Threonine, Valine and Glycine (55.6% aggregate) two each for Glutamic acid and Asparagine (5.6% each). That's it! It bears repeating: Out of the twenty available amino acids out there, a missense mutation in any codon for Alanine will result in "synonymous substitutions" where no amino acid change occurs whatsoever - fully one-third of the time, or will specify one of only seven (out of the remaining nineteen amino acids) alternative combinations.

Table 13-B lists the same data as Table 13-A for all codons that encode twenty amino acids plus the "'stop'" codon. It indicates every possible mutation for every codon – a total of 576. Again, the first impression that catches the eye is the fact that 138 out of 576 - fully 24% of all possible single mutations affect no changes at all in the resultant amino acids. This extraordinary occurrence is directly due to the fact that most amino acids are coded for by more than one codon. Thus, any mutation to one codon that results in the substitution of a different codon - but one that codes for the same amino acid - has no immediate biological consequence. Table 13-C is a tabulation of the frequency of substitution for each amino acid. The number of instances where basepair substitutions code for "self" (resulting in no change in amino acid) are emphasized. The bottom line indicates the total number of possible codon changes for each individual amino acid (3 per codon) and the number of consequential amino acid substitutions possible. Table 13-D converts the data in Table 13-C into percentages.

In order to further organize the data, the twenty amino have been grouped according to four significant dissimilar categories – Polar (hydrophilic), Nonpolar (hydrophobic), Acid and Basic. This permits an evaluation of mutations that result in one amino acid changing into another within the same grouping and thus having similar and possibly compatible properties. Table 13-E is a summary of the actual instances and percentages of such substitutions as well as the frequency of occurrence of nonsense ('stop') substitutions. It reveals the extraordinary frequency with which substitutions favour same category substitutions (as high as 89% in the case of VAL).

One important conclusion we can draw is the fact that nonsense mutations (those that code for "'stop'"), while random in occurrence (we never know which codon base will mutate nor to which other possible base), are restrained and therefore limited in their consequences for protein production and organism survival. Within the logic built into the genetic code as shown, nonsense mutations can only occur in mutations to codons of only one-half of the twenty amino acids and in only 23 chances out of 576 possibilities overall - 4% of the time for any given mutation. (GLY - 2.8%; CYS, GLN, GLU, and LYS - 11.1%; ARG - 3.7%; LEU and SER - 5.6%; TRP and TYR - 22%; and of course never occurs for the rest). Other interesting observations reveal the fact that in the cases of mutations to the codons of ALA, GLY, LEU, PRO, VAL, THR, and ARG, respectively, no amino acid substitution takes place at all in fully one third of their respective codon base substitutions. The same synonymous phenomenon occurs in 26% of the time in the case of SER; 22% in ILE; and 11% in each of PHE, ASN, CYS, GLN, TYR, ASP, GLU, HIS, and LYS. In order to put this situation in its proper perspective, consider that if each amino acid would be coded for by a single unique chemical signature, every mutation would have to result in the substitution of another of the nineteen amino acid designations or the "'stop'" codon with the equal probability of substitution of any amino acid for any other (1 chance in 21 or 4.76%). This is clearly not the case with the existent degenerate genetic coding methodology, where the probabilities of one amino acid substituting for another are clearly skewed, or as some might suggest, schemed. The logic built into the genetic code effectively functions to allow many more chance mutations to raw genetic information to be tolerated, because the rate of mutations to genetic information is far greater than the quantity of actual amino acid substitutions, and thus, the probability of deleterious effects that such mutations might cause is considerably lessened. When such substitutions do occur, the field of possible substitutions is drastically restricted to just a specific few. And herein resides the primary intelligence of the genetic code - "selectivity". For, built into the genetic code for all to see is a discriminating process that selectively filters and thereby precisely controls the effects of random mutations to genetic instructions.

In addition to the tabulation of all possible mutation possibilities, we have further delineated mutations specific to Complimentary transversions (Tables 13-F through I), Transitions (Tables 13-J through M), and Non-complimentary transversions (Tables 13-N through Q).

Complimentary Transversions - A Very Special Case of Mutation:

A case can be made that a bias exists for certain kinds of preferential base-pair mutations. This is not really farfetched when you consider that mutations involve the breaking of weak chemical bonds that keep the base pairs in their proper place. Some bonds are weaker than others and more likely to undergo breakage. So, let's assume for the moment that the bonds connecting the basepair combinations to the side-rail scaffolding of the double helix comprise weaker bonds than the strong hydrogen bonds holding the basepairs together where they connect. In other words, if we envisage the bonds holding any base-pair (a-t, t-a, c-g, or g-c) to its DNA side-rails weakening because of some specific event, allowing the integral base pair to come loose from it's rung position within the ladder-like DNA structure, then we can also envisage conditions that could cause the re-establishment of those bonds following the passage of the event in question. However, once loose from its moorings, perhaps there is some likelihood that the integral basepair can, as a result of the event energy, flip and reverse its position and re-attach itself in its complimentary form. That is, if the original basepair was a-t, after re-attachment it could appear as t-a. What I am alluding to is the distinct possibility that many (maybe most) missense mutations result in codons that represent the complimentary base (In the DNA, a becomes t; t becomes a; c becomes g, or g becomes c). If that were indeed the case, then we might have inadvertently stumbled on a possible explanation for the phenomenon of "reverse mutations"- those that serve to reverse the effects of an earlier change. (And, if it turns out that this may not be currently the case, perhaps because there are many more opportunities today for different kinds of mutations in complex organisms, it could well have been the situation during those critical early days following the OoL.) Think of a reverse mutation as nothing more than the repeat of a complimentary basepair substitution along the lines described above - the compliment of a compliment, so to speak, which would effectively neutralize any initial change. (A reverse mutation should not be equated to error correction, however. Error correction involves first the error detection. In contrast, a reverse mutation implies the chance mutation righting a previous mutation.)

Postulating a system propensity towards such complimentary transversions (those that favour their complimentary base substitutions over others) imposes dramatic repercussions upon the already impressive consequences of impartial base substitutions described in Tables 13-A through E. In fact, if it can indeed be shown that there exists a decided propensity for mutations comprising complimentary base-pair substitutions, then you might say that the consequences for evolutionary theory would be considerable, such that the concept itself might have to be dramatically reconsidered. Let's examine what the fuss is all about.

A) THE PREAMBLE:

In order for the substitution of a basepair by its complimentary basepair to occur, it is essential that the basepair flip twice in real space - once for the substitution itself in order that a becomes t, c becomes g or vice versa (left becomes right, as it were) and then again to change the orientation (top becomes bottom) in order to accommodate the fact that the DNA double helix has each rail running in different directions: one going up and the other going down. As an engineering exercise (we are after all engaged in engineering here) what kind of imaginative scenario could we devise that could logically account for a preference for such complementary basepair substitutions? Well, perhaps the physical architecture of coiled DNA could actually act as a stimulus to promote complimentary base-pair mutations. First, bear in mind the fact that the bonds connecting basepairs (two hydrogen bonds link a to t; three link g to c) are strong. Second, consider for a moment the fact that DNA is constructed in the uncoiled condition sequentially, section by section, as a so-called "replication fork" (something like a zipper sliding up or down) progresses along a specific length of DNA. The other chemical bonds thus formed can be considered to be sufficiently strong (and presumably unstressed) in the uncoiled state. But, following construction through the replication process, the DNA is then coiled considerably in the presence of proteins present for the purpose, simply in order to accommodate the shear incredible length of the uncoiled molecule. Unquestionably, during the coiling process, stresses are applied to the bonds holding the integral base pairs in their allotted positions within the double helix DNA coil. These stresses could arise due to the physical displacement of ideal bonding distances during coiling, and the influence of attraction and repulsion forces of adjacent atoms from neighboring molecular structures in the coiled state could conceivably place a basepair in a stressed state of chemical tension (like a coiled spring). So far so good. Once the state of equilibrium holding the basepair in place is disturbed by some sufficiently strong outside force, such that the ends become free of their weak-force chemical bonding to the DNA side rails, the potential energy stored within the stresses introduced by the coiling process might then be liberated, to impart a physical force sufficient to initiate a procedure that might cause the liberated basepair to both flip and turn. Perhaps the forces involved might even be vectored preferentially, to promote the placement of the double-flipped basepair precisely where the re-establishment of the same bonds can occur. Something akin to a "snap-switch" that has two stable physical states. Remember, as far as the DNA structure is concerned, once the basepair double-flips, all the right atoms are in place for the identical bond to recur - only this time the basepair appears as its own transversion compliment. Nothing new need be added.

In support of such a preferential complimentary base substitution - over the substitution of either the other two bases - are the physical and chemical differences that characterize each: First, the a-t basepair is held by two hydrogen bonds and the c-g by three. Second, the length of the a-t basepair is 11.1 angstroms while that of the c-g is only 10.8 angstroms[1]. Third, they have different angles to the horizontal of each base connection: t at 50 deg; a at 51 deg; c at 52 deg and g at 54 deg. These, and the differences in the strength of the bonds involved, would seem to diminish more or less, the probability of a missense mutation involving the alternate basepair, while possibly promoting preferentially a complimentary basepair substitution.

There is also another important consequence for a complimentary transversion mutation described above. Such a mutation would, by its very nature, be immune to error correction repair. Think about it. This is particularly true of this kind of mutation, because the "double-flip" inherent in the complimentary transversion mutation consists, as it does, of each base substituting for its compliment. Because error correction requires the complimentary strand as a true template for comparison, the "double flip" as we have described it, changes both strands simultaneously and similarly. Thus, by its very nature, a complimentary transversion mutation appears, for all intents and purposes, not to be an error at all - since all the DNA components involved are in their prescribed position and alignment. This would suggest that when such a mutation occurs it becomes undetectable to any error correction mechanisms. Transverse mutations thus are not subject to correction, become permanently fixed in place, and can only change as a result of a chance reverse mutation. Of course, all mutations, including transverse mutations must pass the ultimate test - "trial by survival". A mutated genotype is only as good as the phenotype it expresses. Thus the survival into the future of any such change will always depend upon the survival of the expressed phenotype long enough to reproduce offspring. Now, it's time for a reality check!

The above is only an engineer's imaginative scenario, put forth simply to logically qualify the existence of physical and chemical conditions that could possibility favour genetic mutations resulting from complimentary basepair substitutions. We have a reason for promoting this point of view, which shall become apparent. It is by no means an attempt to describe accurately what actually occurs, in what is one more example of a biological phenomenon whose complexities are only just becoming appreciated. But if this, or any other mechanisms, can be shown to preferentially promote complimentary basepair transversions, then we arrive at a state of affairs that would undoubtedly shake-up our whole understanding and appreciation of the intimate connection between the genetic coding scheme and its extraordinary influence on the reality of evolution. The stage has now been set for us to examine what happens under conditions where complimentary base pair transversions are favored.

B) THE DATA:

Table 13-F is similar to Table 13-B except it limits itself to only complimentary transversion base-pair substitutions. Similarly, Table 13-G is the counterpart of Table 13-C comprising a tabulation of the individual amino acid frequencies. The data is converted into percentages in Table 13-H with additional refinements and detail. Finally, Table 13-I consolidates the information in a number of ways. The consequences of the analysis can only be described as sensational. How sensational can best be appreciated using graphic techniques. If a picture is worth a thousand words, then the production of a diagram that can indicate graphically the fascinating relationships between amino acid codons and the transversion substitutions they code for is indeed a worthy enterprise. We have created such a group of schematic diagrams – one for each type of mutation (Complimentary transversion, Non-complimentary transversion and Transition mutations respectively).

c) The AmAcid Node (AAN) Diagrams:

During the course of our statistical analysis of amino acid substitutions we were delighted to discover that the data has yielded relationships between amino acids that are prone to schematic representations along the lines of "Feynman diagrams" (graphic representations of the interactions between subatomic particles in the realm of small-particle physics originated by physicist Richard Feynman). If we designate each amino acid as a node, and draw a line connecting it to every amino acid resulting from a complimentary base substitution of each of its codons, we find the twenty amino acids divided into two distinct AmAcid groupings - one comprising twelve amino acids and one made up of eight. Figs 1a and 1b indicate all of the single complimentary-basepair transversion relationships that exist between them. What is at once startling, is the implication that amino acids from one group (Fig 1a) never substitute directly for an amino acid in the other (Fig 1b), no matter how many complimentary point mutations take place within the codons of each amino acid group. From the data, we have generated graphic AmAcid Node (AAN) Diagrams associated with each of the other two kinds of mutations as well (Non-complimentary transversions represented by Fig 2a and 2b and Tansitions by Fig 3a and 3b. The AAN diagrams each render an astonishing visualization of how the genetic code assigns a specific position to each amino acid within mutation space. For each of the three types of missense mutations, the amino acids are seen to separate into two exclusive substitution groups (AAN diagrams Figs 1 to 3). These schematic AAN diagrams boldly display - in ways that leave verbal descriptions woefully inadequate - how this kind of coding system could serve to prevent non-compatible amino acid substitutions, thereby reducing drastically the probability of "negative" amino acid combinations - ones that translate and express themselves as undesirable or non-working proteins, with expected disastrous morphological consequences over time. In addition, it is not inconceivable to suggest that this kind of genetic coding system could also favor specific mutation results.

One predictable consequence for the processes of evolution would be the likelihood promotion of organism offspring reproductive success resulting from the existence of an inordinately large "neutral" gene-mutation space. Thus, it is conceivable that the ability of the genetic coding scheme to effectively alter the probabilities of mutation expression, serves, as well, to guide the evolution of LS species in directions of greatest LS survival enhancement, all the while minimizing the rapid accumulation of questionable morphological mutations. Also, we can surmise how such a coding scheme might have served the all-important roll of directing (that might not be too strong a term) species variability before the advent of sex by permitting many changes to genetic library information - while nullifying the consequences of accumulating deleterious effects on phenotype expression for long term LS survival. We are now in a position to appreciate fully the reality as stated earlier that the form of the genetic code effectively constitutes nothing less than a strategic *Operational Genetic Evolution Filter* - positioned to both prevent negative and promote positive evolutionary results. One fact is certain - this is not simply a random or impartial coding system for amino acids. This recognition will become further reinforced once the additional realization sinks in that within the chemical characteristics of the DNA medium lie additional propensities for particular kinds of mutations. Consider the case of so-called "nonsense mutations".

D) "NONSENSE" MUTATIONS AND LOGIC GATES:

If we examine AAN diagrams Figs 1a and 1b, it would seem that the "'stop'" gateways (3 per diagram) might represent opportunities to join the two AmAcid groups. In fact they are anything but gates – more like solid brick walls. There is no possibility of any connection whatsoever because of the incompatibility of their 'stop' codons. The three 'stop' nodes in Figure 1a comprise both the "uaa" or "uag" codons only, whereas the three 'stop' nodes in Figure 2 comprise the third codon for 'stop' – "uga" only. As such, there is no way for any kind of Complimentary Transversion interaction between any of the amino acids in Figures 1a with those in Figure 1b. Figs 2b and 3b indicate no "stop" nodes to consider in the other types of missense mutations.

If a mutation causes the substitution of a "stop" codon where previously there existed one calling for an amino acid, it is called a "nonsense mutation" and for good reason. Chances would seem to be indeed slim that this kind of mutation would survive long enough for a successive corrective mutation to occur? The 'stop' instruction is just that - a signal to complete there and then the amino acid chain. For the protein involved, it means that some of its essential components would be missing and the probability of total failure of function could be assumed to be high. Conversely, a 'stop' codon that mutates into a codon for an amino acid might well serve as a bridge linking two adjacent genes by the substitute. The substitution of a 'stop' instruction by an amino acid at an adjacent node could thus act as a logic "'AND'" gate - an effective mechanism for the adding together of two adjacent genes - thereby opening the door to an impressive array of consequential possibilities for evolution. With the addition of a second proven and successful gene linked to the first, a novel protein configuration can be tested. The addition of the second gene to the first would represent a genuine challenge and opportunity for LS evolution to consider utilizing the unique chemical and physical characteristics represented by the two-protein combination. As a parting thought, we could speculate that this mechanism whereby the "'stop'" codon mutates to an "'AND'" gate could well represent the pathway for the development of proteins comprised of two or more polypeptide chains. Within the immunoglobul group of proteins, all have the same basic molecular structure, consisting of four polypeptide chains linked together by chemical peptide bonds. It is known that each chain is produced separately, is coded for by different genes, and that the four chains only become joined in the final immunoglobulin molecule. Perhaps the chains came together via such "AND" gates.

The AAN diagrams Figs 1a and 1b offer additional glimpses at relationships among amino acids that are not otherwise apparent. Within Fig 1a we immediately sense the importance of LEU and ILE as substitution amino acids. Each is a preferential replacement for six other amino acids (out of eleven). Also, LEU, TYR and LYS serve as effective "'AND'" logic operators able to replace "'stop'" following their complementary transverse mutation. In Fig 1b, ARG occupies an obvious position of influence as it replaces five other amino acids (out of the seven). Additionally, LEU serves as an effective mutation gate in its own right separating five amacids in the lower left of Fig 1a from the six in the upper right. Next comes SER, which replaces four. Here, SYS, SER, and ARG serve as effective "'AND'" logic operators when replacing "'stop'". What is revealing is the inordinate influence that a handful of amino acids have within the substitution scheme that serves as the basis for evolutionary change. The AAN diagrams also provide a sense of the chances for "reverse mutations" to nullify previous mutations. Because of the stringency of the mutation pathways that define possible substitutions, subsequent mutations to a codon should have a higher incidence of reversing a previous substitution. Also, it appears that the chances for reverse mutations to occur among the influential amino acids as described above are much greater than for the rest. The diagrams provide as well a quantitative feel for such prospects as indicated by the number of nodes each amino acid is connected to and the probabilities associated with each.

Further examination of the AAN diagrams provide additional insights into the filtering capabilities built into the genetic code. We discover, for example, that the permissible substitutions as graphically portrayed, incorporate a decided measure of substitution compatibility. Fig 1a, for example, strongly suggests that non-polar LEU could well be an acceptable substitution for nonpolar AmAcid nodes VAL, PHE, ILE and MET. Polar GLN and basic HIS are each represented by only two codons and account for only 11% of LEU's complementary transversions. Similarly, LYS might be an interesting replacement for ASN, ILE, and MET. Whether this is in fact so, only the molecular biologists will be able to confirm. It is known that Met has a unique role to play as a polypeptide chain initiator. As such, its replacement by LEU, ILLE or LYS due to a complementary transverse mutation of its single codon would have the effect of joining two adjacent genes on a chromosome by any of these three. Unquestionably, the AAN diagrams convey the existence of a very special logical arrangement geared particularly toward filtering and channeling toward specific directions the effects of spontaneous transverse mutations. If our speculative assumption turns out to have validity - that transverse mutations are preferred (or once were) in the overall scheme of things, then unquestionably, we have discovered what must be considered to be a major influence upon both the nature of biological evolution and the course of LS evolutionary history. In truth, only the empirical evidence will be able to validate whether that assumption has some basis in fact. At the very least, our findings should lend considerable support and comfort to the developmentalist tradition. For the time being, we simply cannot ignore the implications within the possibility of the existence of categories of polypeptide chains and their resultant proteins that can, and do suffer change as a result of spontaneous mutations - but only according to the severely limited scope of substitutions defined by the AAN diagrams. Additionally, we cannot rule out the possibility that conditions were such, early on after the OoL, when a greater preference for complimentary transversions might have existed – that might have served to give initial structure and direction to LS evolution.

E) TRANSITION MISSENSE SUBSTITUTIONS:

While we have argued the case above in favor of complimentary transversions and their preferential effects on evolution, other kinds of mutations are possible and a similar treatment can be presented reflecting "transition switches" of one purine for the other (a to g; or g to a) or one pyramidine for the other (u and c). The results are summarized in Tables J to M, and the resultant Feynman-like AAN Diagrams appear as Figs 2a and 2b . Again, the data betrays the almost uncanny intelligence built into the genetic code. Interestingly again, the 20 amino acids are divided into two groups - in this instance 15 and 5 amino acids, respectively - the one having absolutely no connection with the other, not even through a '"stop"' node. Fig 2a does exhibit a single 'stop' node that becomes an ""AND"" gate for joining two genes, using TRP, GLN and ARG as a potential bridge. However, the Transition mutation AAN diagram makes abundantly clear that no matter how many transition mutations occur consecutively, never can any single transition mutation replace an amacid from Fig 2b into one in Fig 2a or vice versa. The transition AAN diagrams offer some additional insights. Among the most obvious is the fact that fully 66 out of 192 possible switches actually code for the same amino acid (34.4%), including 4 out of 9 "stop" codons (44.4%), as compared to 34 out of the same 192 for complimentary transversions (17.7%). Also, only 5 amino acid switches result in nonsense "stop" codons (compared with nine).

F) NON-COMPLIMENTARY TRANSVERSIONS:

Among the Non-Complimentary transversions, two distinct groups emerge comprising fourteen and six amacids respectively (AAN diagrams Figs 3a and 3b). Again we are left to marvel at the complex relationships they portray and wonder at their ultimate significance.

G) CASE IN POINT – SICKLE CELL ANEMIA

There exists an interesting linkage between amino acids VAL (valine) and GLU (glutamic acid) as depicted in Complimentary Transversion AmAcid Node Diagram Figure 1a (no such relationship can be found in the other AmAcid Node Diagrams). Within human physiology, this relationship plays an important role in the genetically transmitted blood disease - "sickle cell anemia". This condition occurs in individual born with an abnormal type of hemoglobin called "hemoglobin S", instead of the normal "hemoglobin A". The only difference between the two is the replacement - at a specific site in the normal hemoglobin protein molecule - of amino acid GLU (represented by codons gaa or gag), by amino acid VAL (represented by codons gua or gug). This very small (microheterogenious) difference – whereby the middle GLU codon nucleotide "a" mutates to "u" specifiying VAL - is both sufficient to allow embryogenesis to go to completion, yet endow its organism with cells that are destroyed by the body faster than normal blood cells. In addition, these cells are misshapen and can become trapped in small blood vessels thereby reducing or blocking blood flow, resulting in potentially life-threatening conditions. The AmAcid diagram clearly indicates that fully 33% of the complimentary transversions mutations that occur to GLU codons result in its replacement by VAL. Sickle cell anemia in humans can now be appreciated as the product of the strong propensity for GLU to mutate to VAL through the process of complimentary transversion mutations, which in turn is directly attributable to the built-in genetic coding scheme.

H) CONSEQUENCES:

While gene pool composition comprises the effects of the genomes of multitudes of individual organisms, the fact of evolution and how that comes about cannot be divorced from the influences of any built-in mechanism or algorithmic influence that interfaces between the causes (basepair mutations) and the effects (expression of genes). As our data tables and AAN diagrams indicate, there is much in the way of cleverness built into the form and function of the genetic code that counters once and for all any suggestion that random basepair substitutions lead only to random results that only natural selection can sort out. Because the mediating influence of the form and function of the genetic code serves to "filter" the results of random basepair mutations to an organism's genome in advance of natural selection, it may well represent - together with the concept of species biosphere attribute anticipation (SBAA) introduced earlier - the major authoritative influence on evolution, serving as nothing less than an operational genetic evolution filter (OGEF).

The ability of the form and function of the genetic code to filter the effects of random mutations to DNA base pairs - represents an astonishing measure of LS internal control over its destiny. The extent of the intervention as laid out in Tables A through Q and graphically portrayed in AAN diagrams 1a through 3b speaks volumes. They make recognizable the scheme and logic that directly impacts on the major dynamic long term activity of the LS: its evolution in the furtherance of its long term survival. They demonstrate clearly that the consequences of random mutations – the currency of evolution - are channeled in non-random directions. As such, the results could well be predictable; one day we may be able to interpret the effects of random mutations on evolution – much in the same way we are trying to learn how genetic mutations cause disease.

The AAN diagrams raise one additional important consideration. It relates to their very existence in the first place and the fact that two separate groupings of amino acids could arise within each of three very different mutation schemes. Unquestionably this area of inquiry deserves more consideration as well as investigation. Scientists are always in pursuit of symmetrical relationships within the mathematical expressions that describe interesting phenomena. Symmetry implies, as well, recognition of beauty of form arising from balanced proportions, the incorporation of simplicity and elegance within a jumble of mathematical symbols, equations and any kind of raw data in general. In their own way, these AAN diagrams represent and explain - graphically and elegantly - the wholly unexpected relationships between diverse amino acids and the dynamics that dictate probable amino acid substitutions. This would all be simply an intellectual curiosity – symmetry and elegance notwithstanding - if it were not for the obvious and significant implications for the processes of evolution.

Of Hox Genes and The Big Bang of Evolution

It is highly likely that whole categories of proteins must have developed as a direct result of the relationships outlined in the AAN diagrams. They, together, may well represent the principle framework through which successful evolution at the molecular level operates. And, even if its influence may have been diluted over time as a result of other, perhaps evolved, evolution mechanisms making their mark, it still represents a logical thesis for validating what has to be considered the major controlling influence on the early evolution of life structures and forms. A strong case can be made that its effects must be felt across the whole spectrum of evolutionary influences and results - such as parallel evolution, homologous evolution, punctuated evolution, and the like.

The evolution filtering effect built into the genetic code is applied at the molecular genotype 'information' level. It expresses itself through the transcription and translation of the raw genetic information encoded in DNA into the corresponding emergent physical characteristics at the phenotype 'form and function' level of physical proteins. As such, it must bear much of the responsibility for the development of some of the universally apparent species attributes such as the bilateral symmetry architecture of nearly all multicellular species. It could well be that this ubiquitous bilateral phenotype configuration originates inevitably as a result of the mutation dynamics implied and articulated within the AAN diagrams above. It is known that certain gene clusters serve as pathways that serve as the master controllers of embryonic development and regulate the formation of body patterning plans[2]. One, known as the Hox (homeobox) gene cluster, regulates anterio-posterior patterning in most metazoan species. It plays a crucial role during the early stages of embryonic growth, helping to organize the organism body into a front, middle and hind region. It is known that invertebrates have only a single group of hox genes; almost all vertebrates have four such gene clusters, each on a separate chromosome[3]. There have been discovered more than a dozen such gene groups, variously (and curiously) labeled, "Wingless", "Hedgehog", "Dishevelled", "Per" - some of which are important in organism development, and others that perform housekeeping, clocking and other cell functions. The point is that these gene groups represent fundamental genetic schemes that are found in common throughout whole genus and taxa groups. It would seem highly unlikely that their development could avoid the consequences of the evolution filtering dynamics that the form of the genetic code imposes - as graphically demonstrated by the AAN diagrams.

More than one hundred and fifty years ago it was suggested that arthropods (e.g.: crabs, lobsters, spiders, flies) and vertebrates are similar but inverted forms of each other. It wasn't until 1995 that it was demonstrated that their dorso-ventral axes are fabricated as a result of related but inverted sets of proteins. This kind of inversion symmetry suggests more than just some happenstance event and could just be compatible with the kind of operative framework implied by the AAN diagrams. There are all kinds of other fundamental phenotype patterns, mechanisms and genetic schemes found among diverse species that suggest a common genetic origin. At a biology conference held in Boston in November 1995, entitled "Patterns of Life", discussions included the possibility that the basic processes governing the development of all metazoans are the same. The evolution of "multi-gene" families and particularly "super-gene" families (genes related by sequence but not necessarily related in function)[4] might have been promoted as a result of the preferential influence of the form of the genetic code as well. Perhaps, the same can be said with respect to the whole phenomenon of the Cambrian explosion, described as biology's Big Bang, and characterized by the sudden evolution of a multitude of multicellular creatures that gave rise to nearly all of the major zoological branches. Back then, some 650 million years ago in the early Cambrian geological period, it is thought that in a relatively short time frame, almost magic-like, the basic body plans of virtually the whole animal kingdom, including insects, worms, clams, fish and ultimately humans. Regardless of whether the Cambrian evolutionary phenomenon was explosive or a steady stream, researchers looking for a solution to the mystery surrounding this unique frenetic evolutionary activity might do well to ponder the relationship, which we have described herein, between data processing at the genetic level and the possible resultant directions of evolution at the species level. As suggested above, perhaps this same phenomenon could account for the concept referred to as "punctuated evolution" and other instances of the sudden and unexplained appearance of new species and of new kinds of life forms. The question we would raise is whether any such cases can possibly be independent of the direct consequence of propensities built into and arising from the form and function of the genetic code, as delineated and represented within our AmAcid Node diagrams.

The fact we would ask you to keep in mind is that evolutionary change among the exclusively asexual reproducing eukaryotic species that existed more than two billion years ago was first and foremost a consequence of the substitution of one letter of the genetic alphabet with another ("M"s) and, how that substitution might have affected the recipe of the proteins involved. It was only after the introduction of sexual reproduction that additional evolutionary mechanisms (as replication errors within the "m"s) could supplement the single basepair substitutions that, until then, had accounted for most genetic change. It must be remembered that during that long period of transition from anaerobic to aerobic respiration, and before the protective ozone layer had become effective, it could be expected that the rate of point mutations would have been much higher - reflecting that fact. In other words, all the while that the "m" kinds of mutations associated with mitotic sexual reproduction had not yet begun to influence evolution, the "M" kinds of point mutations sparked by unimpeded ultraviolet energy must have been significant. This must have also been the time when basic evolutionary patterns were being laid down prior to, and in anticipation of, the much later Cambrian evolution explosion. This would have been the context within which the form and function of the genetic code could exert its early manifest influence on the future course of biological evolution.

Within the concept of the logic ""AND"" gate - that could conceivably turn a "'stop'" instruction into a connection between the end of one gene and the beginning of an adjacent gene - lies an interesting explanation of how a single mutation can promote the combined expression of two totally independent genes. Because the data processing procedure at the heart of the LS filters the effects of all such substitutions, a strong case can be made that, at the very least, the results of the process - variation leading to adaptive change - cannot escape the consequences of the way this information processing functions at the PdP level. Again, it is important to stress that because of degeneracy in the genetic code, novel changes to genetic information need not immediately express themselves as some haphazard and random morphology, but can be stored in many instances as potential future changes (within synonymous mutations) that are exclusively selected and directed through subsequent mutations via the built in filtering algorithm(s) that forms the genetic code. Thus, it follows that any emergent and dominant physiological characteristics shared by all members of kingdoms or phyla, for example, could conceivably be the result of a well executed primary intelligently fine-tuned algorithm as exemplified and portrayed within our AmAcid node diagrams. Such a mechanism would certainly take into account the respective qualities and compatibility's of the amino acid building blocks the information codes for - together with the 'preferred' emergent properties inherent within specific groups and combinations of linked amino acids.

Homology vs. Analogy:

One of the most fascinating aspects of evolution inquiry concerns the similarities that exist among the phenotype attributes of diverse species. Homologous features among diverse species are considered to have a common genetic origin. The term "divergent evolution" is used to describe the phenomenon of two or more species that originate from a common ancestor. The classic example concerns the diversity of the wings of birds. The smallest species of hummingbird flaps its wings at a rate of 80 per second while those of the flightless emu don't flap at all. Biologists consider that the wings of all bird species have a common genetic evolutionary origin, possibly dating back to a dinosaur capable of flight - the enigmatic Archaeopteryx. Its rare fossilized specimen provides compelling evidence that birds are closely related to, and probably are direct descendants of, small theropod dinosaurs.[5] Similarly, the forelimbs of cats, bats, humans and whales are homologous because they are considered to have a common genetic link.

The much more interesting phenomenon that is more difficult to explain concerns analogous structures among diverse species - structures for which there is no common genetic link. The term "convergent evolution" describes two unrelated species that share similar "analogous" traits. Thus, the fins and body shapes of sharks, penguins (bird), and porpoises (mammal) are analogous because they are adaptations to swimming. Take as an example the wings of flight of insects, birds and bats. They are considered to be analogous, reflecting the fact that each developed totally independently to accomplish virtually the same function (flight). In fact, a cursory examination of the wing construction of each immediately sets them apart. The delicate often-transparent wings of insects contrast in so many ways with the feathers of birds and the skin wings of mammalian bats. Whereas all bird's wings comprise feathers and shapes that reflect relatively miner modifications to the basic flight mechanism of birds, their relatively cumbersome form and structure could be considered totally useless to serve the needs of comparatively weightless insects. Thus, there is considered to be no common genetic link that could account for all wings. The same can be said for the existence of eyes among mammals and octupii. They are analogous in virtue of the fact that they serve essentially the same purpose (seeing), yet no common genetic link is considered to exist. The classic explanation evolutionary biologists seem to agree on is that analogous features not only can be explained by natural selection but in fact tend to prove the effectiveness of natural selection. Since natural selection is considered to be the arbiter of what survives within the realm of biology, the survival of analogous features among diverse lifeforms speaks to both the efficiency as well as consistency of natural selection in its ability to home in on effective strategies for survival. The fact that wings have developed analogously among insects, birds and bats is seen to imply that natural selection 'knows' how to pick and choose, as it were, the best phenotype features for competitive survival regardless of origin. Their very resemblances are seen as indicative of the ability and tendency of natural selection to select optimal phenotype formats within biological evolution space, arriving, as it were, to the same practical conclusions, albeit from radically different directions. Analogous traits are said to arise because each species has independently adapted to similar external ecological conditions (e.g., the characteristics of air as a medium for flight) or lifestyles.

But, the most compelling example of analogy must be the similarity of lifeforms evident among the placental and marsupial mammals. Each lineage has made similar evolutionary changes following their divergence from a common ancestor. This evolution of similar adaptations is credited to their respective ancestors having encountered comparable environments, and is referred to as "parallel evolution". Astonishingly, the mammalian wolf has its parallel marsupial counterpart. While most evolutionary biologists would simply include such parallelism as falling under the all inclusive umbrella influences of natural selection, this argument appears to fall short of the mark when we consider the long view of evolution. By the long view, I refer to the concept that many evolutionary biologists hold - that if the tape of evolution history could be rewound, the likelihood that it would replay in exactly the same way would be probabilistically extremely implausible for all practical purposes.   This view was argued elegantly by Stephen J. Gould, evolutionary biologist. Because the equations that describe evolution contain so many dependent and independent variables, and because of the linear nature of that history, it is considered that the likelihood of each and every one of those variables repeating itself in exactly the same sequence is close to nil. And because even the minutest variable change becomes amplified as it carries forward generation after generation, evolutionary history is as unique an expression of its infinite number of minute influences, as is the history of human civilization. Neither would be expected to replay itself in exactly the same way twice. So much for determinism, it would seem. But, if that be the case, an argument can be made that you can't have it both ways. For, the concept of parallel evolution could conceivably be considered to be at odds with the concept of evolution repeating itself. As such, if the replay of sequential evolution is considered unlikely, why then should the concept of parallel evolution be any less so? What is parallel evolution if not the repetition of evolution – simultaneously, but in a different place? How do we resolve this inconsistency? The answer, we believe, lies within the influence of the evolution filtering aspects of the form and function of the genetic code during , what we refer to as , the "formative period of biological evolution".

Aerobicism, Multicellularism and Sex – Three For the Same Price?

We would describe the "formative period of evolution (FPE)" of biological life on our planet as beginning with the OoL approximately 3.8 billion years ago, and ending just before the expansion of eukaryotic evolution into the multicellular format, some 2 billion years ago. Accordingly, the FPE preceded multicellularism as well as sexual reproduction, and represented the approximate full transformation of unicellular eukaryotes from anaerobic species to oxygen-loving species. Can we ascribe the conversion of the planetary atmosphere to one having oxygen as its major component as a primary cause of all three (aerobicism, multicellularism and sex)? Definitely so in the case of aerobicism – but what about the other two? Or, is it merely a coincidence that all of these watershed transformations occurred approximately at the same time? The engineering mentality does not take kindly to multiple coincidences - especially the juxtaposition of three of the most monumental evolutionary changes to confront the LS as a whole. Casually ascribing a common cause is quite another matter. Let's try the following scenario on for size:

1] At the OoL, a variety of unicellular eukaryotic species were implanted on our planet thereby "seeding" the then aqueous environment of the planet. These would have comprised hearty varieties of fast reproducing species whose respective genetic libraries would have comprised: 1) the basic eukaryotic PdP genetic format common to all species (described previously); plus 2) one of a wide variety of additional (but optional) genotype formats spread among the implanted founder species. Included among species would have been a variety of photosynthesisers whose express function in the scheme of things was to terraform over time the extant atmosphere from one devoid of oxygen to one where oxygen would become a dominant component. Thus, the genotype of any such included species would comprise the following formulation:

$$G1 = (PdP) + g1$$ where,

G1 = total genetic library,

PdP = genes that code for the constant operational "primary design platform of biology", common to all species, and not subject to evolution.

g1 = an additional add-on genetic program (specific and different for each respective species) subject to selection by survival and upon which evolution could apply to future generations.

Thus, all of evolution (including during the FPE described above) applies only to **g1**. The principle mechanism of evolution during the FPE would have been point mutations, upon which the form and function of the genetic code would have acted as "evolution filter", as described above. The effect of such an evolution filter, acting upon the **M** type mutations to the "g" components of the genetic libraries of participant unicellular eukaryotic species over the period of close to two billion years would have paved the way for each of the monumental changes that were about to occur simultaneously. But, the timing of the three events would have relied upon an external trigger mechanism from the biosphere, such as a significant change in the oxygen level of the atmosphere reaching a critical threshold. The conversion of the atmosphere from no oxygen to significant oxygen was a slow and gradual process, having to await the oxidation saturation of all exposed iron bearing minerals before an excess of the gas could appear in the oceans and atmosphere. This also afforded sufficient time for the gradual evolution of aerobic species. At the same time, the evolution filtering effect within the form and function of the genetic code (an integral part of the PdP) would have permitted the LS to lay down evolution formats - channels of evolutionary directions likely to be successful in the future expansion of biological life within the tailor-made conditions of the planetary biosphere. In this way, the LS was equipped to both anticipate and modify future biosphere conditions and provide as well explicit directions to species evolution. Thus, while oxygenation may have been a necessary prerequisite toward multicellularism and sex, it was in fact the major component within the larger scheme to create compatible planetary biosphere conditions that promote the future thriving of the LS. The FPE would have laid down the necessary groundwork prior to the completion of the oxygenation of the atmosphere – allowing for an effective bedding-in period of the LS following the OoL. The FPE was the necessary first crucial stage of LS acclimatization that would set the stage for the future expansion of the LS in successful directions. We maintain that the phenomenon of parallel evolution represents confirmation of that hypothesis. In fact, this is the only way one can really justify the existence of the concept of parallel evolution. It all started with the evolution filtering capabilities of the genetic code within the PdP of all introduced species - together with the inherent preprogrammed evolution formats respective of each species - that the LS can try out. Whatever formats worked were conserved and passed on; whatever did not were discarded (their species became extinct). This suggests a radically reduced role for natural selection.

We would argue that because it preceded all else (the expression of genetic information), the form and function of the genetic code could not have evolved - it had to have been in place prior to evolution, precisely in order to act the way it does: to control the consequences of spontaneous mutations, on the one hand, and to provide compatible direction to evolution, on the other. If the LS can be said to be dependent upon evolution for its survival over time, then it is inescapable that successful evolution itself can be said to have been helped and guided by the form and function inherent to the genetic code - together with its built in relationships as portrayed within the AAN diagrams. The question now arises as to what kind of mechanisms might give rise to a preferential imposition of one kind of mutation over another (e.g., transversional over transitional)?

Plausible Operating Scenarios

We have observed that the three possible kinds of point mutations are: 1) Complimentary Transversions (complimentary purine to complimentary pyramidine); 2) Transitions (Purine to purine; pyramidine to pyramidine); and 3) Non-complimentary Transversions (Opposing purine to opposing pyramidine). Each comes with its own AmAcid Node Diagrams that provide strict "mutation rules." Thus, depending upon which type of point mutation occurs, will also determine which set of mutation filter rules apply. The question arizes whether any one of the three can be shown to occur preferentially and thus predominate evolutionary strategy?

One such possible scenario might well consider, for example, the effects of the bombardment of the planet (at the beginning of the metazoan period, or the Cambrian explosion, for example) by radiation of one kind or another that could theoretically serve to trigger preferentially one of the modes of mutation described above over the others. I'm suggesting a very physical phenomenon that would see particular energy particles (e.g., radioactivity, cosmic, x-ray, ultraviolet, etc) interacting with the DNA molecular genetic medium supporting the four nucleotide bases, in such a way as to promote one kind of point mutation over the others - dependent only on the nature of the interactions involved. The preferential weakening of specific susceptible bonds, for example, could result in the preponderance of one kind of mutation over the others. Another scenario might consider whether specific original founder species, implanted on the planet at the OoL, could have been programmed respectively to mutate preferentially under one of the three AAN diagram regimes. This would have offered the advantage of the three mutation alternatives competing for evolution success - one of which might be more successful at producing adaptations compatible with the fickle biosphere particular to our planet. Think of the three mutation schemes as broadening the palate and scope of evolutionary possibilities, while at the same time eliminating the majority of dead-end possibilities that indiscriminate and haphazard point mutations could be expected to produce. On the positive side, each of the three schemes may have been designed to selectively impart a different but definite direction to the evolution of offspring that ultimately resulted in, for example, the founding of different kingdoms or different major structural representations within the LS.

Alternatively, the three kinds of evolution strategies might have been programmed to operate sequentially – each in turn, and designed to come into play at specific times, or when external conditions were "right". For example, during a first phase (the FPE, perhaps) one AAN strategy out of the three might have been able to provide a preferential advantage for ensuring rapid expansive growth of the LS under asexual reproductive conditions and anaerobic metabolism, while oxygen levels were rising. The increase in oxygen in the oceans and ultimately the atmosphere might have caused the end of such a first phase, marking the beginning of a second mutation strategy (triggered perhaps, by the new protection from ultraviolet rays afforded by the newly created ozone layer). This phase could have lasted until the end of the Precambrian era, let's say, with the invocation of the third strategy that might have signaled the so-called Big Bang of evolution some 650 million years ago. By that time, the LS would have been sufficiently "bedded-in" and ensconced - population wise as well as geographically - across the vast expanse of the planet, to allow the freeing up of prior restrictions leading possibly to a resultant free-for-all and open evolutionary strategy - all the while under the filtering effects afforded by the form and function of the genetic code.

These speculative discussions on "mutation strategies" we have engaged in above are simply meant to both sensitize and stimulate the reader to consider the developmental potential that exists within the LS, i.e., all of the different kinds of evolution strategies that can eminate directly from the LS itself. Another goal, of course, is to free the mind to consider logical alternatives to the abiogenesis evolution paradigm that simply passes off evolution as the result of chance mutations of genetic information that are inherited, tested by natural selection, and then passed on to future generations. Our analysis of the form and function of the genetic code and the conclusions derived therefrom has opened up the prospect that chance indeed has considerably less influence within the broad scheme of evolution and that the LS is amply equipped to engage, on its own, in some very real and effective strategies that both control and filter any and all chance mutations that occur. Perhaps the LS does exhibit deterministic characteristics after all!

An Ounce of Prevention...

The form of the genetic code, within its capacity to direct which base switches will be expressed, serves not only as an evolution filter, but acts as well within the capacity of an error "prevention" mechanism. This ability would have proved essential in the early days of primitive lifeforms on the planet. It accomplishes this important task by preventing more than the absolute minimum of expensive errors that could spell doom to primitive species. In so doing, it allows a greater proportion of the accidental changes to genetic information to result in integral offspring that can then be tested by competition for survival followed by reproduction. Thus, error "prevention" as an unappreciated phenomenon represents in our scenario a proactive process integral to the adaptive selection strategies that serve LS.

In contrast, the much heralded natural selection mechanism of Darwinian evolution is, in fact, a passive phenomenon defined by results that are both undirected and observed only in hindsight.

Active error correction mechanisms are usually thought of in terms of the existence of complicated and expensive genes and structures within the genomes of organisms. In modern cells, excision repair and the initiation of DNA synthesis are part of a complex set of available proofreading and error correction tools, including DNA polymerases and enzymes that can be brought to bear to neutralize and reverse the damage to genetic information brought about as a result of rare failures in the replication process. It is estimated that the occurrence of single base mutations vary somewhere of the order of once in every 10 million to 100 billion replication events . Error correction can function efficiently and expediently because of the double stranded nature of DNA, whereby each strand can be used as the information template to repair the other. As discussed above, simultaneous changes to both complimentary bases - as might occur in complimentary transversion mutations - would tend to bypass such error correction provisions. But, if the priority of the LS in the early days was rapid expansion and acclimatization, then explicit and dedicated error correction mechanisms might have represented a waste in resources and complexity, the system had little room for and could ill afford. Proactive error prevention, however, built into the way the genetic information codes for amino acid codons, and without the need for superfluous biological mechanisms specifically devoted to such functions, would have constituted a sufficient and necessary design provision requiring no additional energy nor resources - all the while allowing specified changes to genetic information to fuel evolution. It's really quite perfect, when you come to think of it this way - isn't it?

Now Add Variability

But, one of the greatest advantages the genetic code affords evolution, is the ability to introduce variability within the genotypes of early asexual genomes, while leaving the phenotypes relatively undisturbed. In virtue of the degeneracy of the genetic code, identically expressed physiology within organisms could result from the expression of different genetic information. In other words, different organisms within the same species could have the same protein structures down to the minutest detail, and yet many of their amino acids that make up the same proteins could be coded for by different codons written in their genetic libraries, due to genetic code degeneracy. As a result, such variability within the DNA informational content of identical organisms could endow them with latent and potential variability that might find expression later on as other missense mutations occur, particularly with respect to later substitutions. Take, for example, two identical organisms having the identical amino acid, Serine, in the same physical location in an important protein - one that is coded for in their respective genes by a different codon. In the one organism, that codon might be ucu. In the other, it might be agc. Now a subsequent missense mutation to the same base locations of each could alter ucu to ccu (Pro) in the one, and agc to ugc (Cys) in the other. In this way identical clones could produce substantial physiological differences in their offspring if the location of the respective amino acid substitutions are significant - potentially introducing important differences in the functions of their respective proteins.

The consequences for variability becomes clear, as the degeneracy of the genetic code introduces parallel opportunities for phenotype "fitness" (differences in SA's) available for adaptive selection to process.

The Genetic Code as Double Threat *(Evolution Filter and Error Prevention)*

Because the form of the genetic code can act as an evolution filter at the primary information level, the LS can continually offer up new and novel non-random genetic variations that can be expressed as survival potential at the operational level of species form and function. Many of these survive to become events within the population distribution curves that comprise SA's (species attributes) discussed previously. In so doing, each species continually fine-tunes its physical composition in the frenetic race to maintain compatibility with the niche conditions of the external biosphere of the planet that apply to it (BA's). This, I may add, is accomplished without any help from "nature" (the external environment). And, because a species can, and does, effectively control within certain limits the variety and numbers of member organisms it produces at the macro level, through the distribution of SA's, the LS can anticipate the direction BA's are moving. It perpetuates itself by ensuring that there are always survivor organisms and species available to carry on the LS process. Unless you confuse "anticipative readiness" on the part of the LS, with "random selection" from the natural and blind biosphere, there is no selecting going on here at all. It is, in fact, "survival" - pure and simple.

The results of our analysis of the genetic code and the relationships delineated within the tables and AAN diagrams, represent an astonishing revelation, and acknowledgment as well, that the form and function of the genetic code can be interpreted in only one way: as the primary strategic evolutionary mechanism, emanating, as it does, from the LS itself, and rivaling in importance, the traditional role of the process evolutionary biologists refer to as "natural selection". But it doesn't 'stop' there. The genetic code not only "directs" evolution - it also acts to prevent evolutionary disaster. "Prevention", where possible, always precedes "cure". As stated, the form of the degeneracy within the genetic code, also serves as an error prevention mechanism, by channeling evolutionary change at the primary information level, in non-random and promising directions, reducing the necessity for follow-up error correction measures in the process. One important consequence of this resides in the logic - that any preventative measure must emanate from within the system involved (in our case, the LS). Contrast this with errors that must be addressed and removed after the fact. In the case of Life, it is the non-survival of the unfit organisms, in virtue of their inability to reproduce, that accounts for the elimination of genetic mistakes within the organisms of species, by the process of error elimination, after they occur. Surviving offspring have only bought themselves one more generation within which their genes must prove their worth all over again. Thus, checks and balances are required to ensure and maintain optimal populations of viable mutated offspring just in order for evolution to operate. This likelihood goes back to the notion that blind changes randomly applied to data base information that control complex replicating machines should logically have a statistically low chance of success - particularly so the more complex the machine. Thus, any built-in mechanisms that can improve the chances that mutations will be tolerable to offspring organisms so they can survive to reproduce future generations and serve as potential for successful future genomic evolutionary change, can be viewed as - not just desirable, but pretty well mandatory. This - just for the system of evolution to work at all. The form and function of the genetic code is just such a mechanism and, we maintain, an internal prime determining influence of LS survival over time.

This highlights as well the major difference between "LS survival"- something organisms are programmed to do in the ultimate service of the LS survival agenda, in virtue of efficient subsystems operating from within the LS - and "natural selection"- something that simply cannot happen in the absence of any evidence that "nature" is programmed to "select" anything. This enigmatic, if descriptive, label has served the cause of abiogenetic SAb since its inception at a time when the chemical soup theory was the only OoL option - in defiance of religious Creationism. I suspect that when naturalist biologists were looking to replace the traditional theological source as the "selector" (savior, if you will) of those destined to live, "selection" for survival was accordingly attributed to anonymous "nature", and hence the grossly misleading term, "natural selection" was unfortunately coined. But, with the introduction of a contemporary RDH as a 5th OPTION for the OoL, we believe the time has come to re-examine what the process we casually refer to as "natural selection" really is about, to determine whether the term has any real meaning at all. The point we are driving home is that in our view, the evolution mechanism referred to as natural selection is, ironically, neither *natural* nor *selective*. This, in virtue of our demonstration of two compelling LS survival mechanisms (species adaptation and operational genetic evolution filter) that emanate from within the life system itself. Again, just because the label (natural selection) was bestowed upon the phenomenon a century and a half ago, does not confer upon it monopolistic legitimacy to the exclusion of all other possibilities. In time, the term could quite possibly be revealed to be nothing more than metaphor and cliché.

As a parting thought on the subject, the intelligence built into the genetic code represents a prime example of the complexity built into LS form and function and provides more than just personal intuition for the justification that the LS does indeed function against the tide of 2nd law entropy.

Transition Fossils and Punctuated Evolution

One of the strongest arguments posited against the concept of evolution concerns the issue of the "missing fossils" that should bridge the evolutionary gaps separating related species. Because evolution postulates continuous changes to phenotypes that are supposed to confer greater fitness upon offspring, it is considered that incremental transitional changes should logically be present in the fossils within the strata studied by paleontologists. The fact that there exists a paucity of such transitional fossils is considered by creationists as an embarrassing omission that Darwinists have at times been at pains to explain. Modern paleontologists are quick to assert that many transitional fossils, missing in the time of Darwin, have been found and that the fossil record is "spotty", at worst. It is a fact that excellent fossil evidence exists that shows, for example, the transition from reptile to mammal and from land mammal to early whale. Perhaps more difficult to understand might be the hypothesis of "punctuated evolution"- meant to explain the relative rarity of transitional forms, as well as why speciation appears to happen sometimes relatively quickly, gradually, or in spurts. Well, perhaps an explanation for punctuated evolution can be found within the context of the genetic code depicted above as evolution filter operating according to the data and AAN diagrams that describe the "non-random" consequences for phenotypes of "random" genotype basepair mutations.

The AAN diagrams give a clear visual description of the relationship between random single basepair mutations and the resulting non-random consequences for evolution. Thus, they, together with the tables they represent, have the effect of connecting the two distinct partners of evolution: genotype (where random mutations originate) and phenotype (where the non-random consequences are expressed). They also afford a unique opportunity to help us visualize a solution to the "spotty transitionals" problem refered to above that seems to have eluded definitive explanation to date.

Evolution and the Missing Transitional Fossils

The key to understanding the reasons why transitional fossils are not found is simple: it is because they do not exist. Neither must they exist because phenotype evolution does not, and need not (and in many instances cannot) occur incrementally - it occurs as discrete "quantized" levels of phenotype expression. That is why "incremental" phenotype transitions are not found within the fossil record. The question then becomes: if evolution is some kind of quantum phenomenon how do you get from one quantum level of phenotype expression to another? This is not as difficult as it may seem. The answer resides within an understanding of the specific conditions that allow a genotype to be expressed as a viable phenotype. In fact, the same phenomenon of phenotype quantification also explains how complex organs arise. Consider the following:

A Quantum Theory of Evolution (QTE)

The quantum theory of evolution (QTE) begins with the acknowledgment that the integral viability of an organism depends on the intimate relationship between the information encoded in its genotype and the expression of that information in its phenotype. To the extent that the final successful result can only occur under very specific sets of conditions associated with genotype and phenotype respectively, one can consider each to be "quantized" with respect to meeting whatever conditions that will ultimately yeild a successful (viable) outcome. Any genotype that can result in the expression of a viable phenotype can be considered to be a quantized genotype.

Any given organism (a combination of genotype and phenotype) can be considered to be a "quantized organism (QO)" in the sense that reproduction of a new generation cannot occur unless an accurate copy of the genotype of the parent is produced which can then be expressed successfully into the phenotype of the next generation. Accordingly, we can go further and define individually the "quantized genotype (QG)" and the "quantized phenotype (QP)" as the two partners in the process, each able to contribute, repetitively, to the production of a viable QO. The production of a viable QP becomes a direct result of the expression of an integral QG resulting in a viable integral QO. From the above, it becomes obvious that every QP is the result of the expression of a QG. Thus, by definition every QG leads inexorably to the expression of a QP.

Evolution depends upon changes introduced to genotypes that express themselves as respective phenotypes. We know that within the many attempts at reproduction a good number of them fail to result in a viable organism, as a result of either a faulty genotype (one that fails to meet the minimum QG conditions) or faulty phenotype (one that fails to meet the minimum QP conditions) or possibly both. Of course the only real test of any resultant QO is the survivabilty of the effort. But, if a viable QO depends both upon a QG and QP, there is no question that the evolution process is much more forgiving of changes to genotypes than to changes to phenotypes i.e., there exist many more integral QG's within a species gene pool than QP's. Accordingly, every individual QP can be the result of a great many possible QG's. This fact flows directly as a consequence of the AAN schematics discussed above. Since 64 codons code for 20 amino acids (plus 3 "'stop'" codons), it is obvious that an identical QP can be expressed by many differently encoded genetic sequences – all yeilding identical amino acid sequences and therefore identical proteins. This fact alone presents an ideal opening move in the quest to unravel the mystery surrounding the missing transitionals. But, there is more.

Polymorphism defines the variations to be found in the genomes of organisms of the same species. When such variations derive from the change in single basepairs, it is referred to as a "single nucleotide polymorphism" or SNP (in humans, there are in the order of 3 million SNPs, which comprise about 90% of all polymorphisms in the human genome). Also, it has been determined that single amino acid substitutions in peptide sequences usually do not alter enzyme activity.[7] Apparently, the ability of a gene to express an active enzyme does not require an exactly specified amino acid sequence – a variety of close approximation configurations can be functional. In contrast to structural proteins (muscle, nerve, membrane etc,), which have critical amino acid sequences, enzymes act as intermediary catalysts that enable - but themselves are not required to enter into - biological reactions to occur. As such, their operational specifications permit wide acceptable tolerances for amino acid substitutions within which they can carry out their intended tasks (more or less) efficiently. The net result is that many variations to enzyme protein amino acid compositions represent a rich potential for future evolution activity - none of which need affect present QP viability. This provides an additional secondary level of basepair substitutions (coding for changes to amino acids) in the genetype, which effectively remain viability neutral (where a change in the amino acids of enzymes represents no fundamental change in the viability of the phenotype).

Thus, genetic neutrality derives from either of two possibilities: 1) Synonymous substitutions where the replacement of one codon for another codes for the identical amino acid. In such cases QP's are identical despite differences in QG's. and/or, 2) the actual replacement of one amino acid by another, as dicussed above (in accordance with the permissible changes dictated by the AAN diagrams) resulting in the expression of slightly different, but non-critical proteins. Thus, different QG's produce slightly different QP's, which accounts for variation among the viable organisms of any given species. The significance of the first possibility above is that synonymous substitutions afforded by genetic code degeneracy multiply considerably the number of compatible QG's that can be expressed as identical (but not cloned) phenotypes. The significance of the second is that many nonsynonymous substitutions to innumerable enzyme genes, within complex organisms, can remain both differentiated and neutral within their respective phenotypes over many generations. In either case, all it takes for a non-neutral event is an additional change to some strategically located basepair in a gene that causes a change in a strategically placed amino acid in a strategically important gene sequence within a QG that expresses itself as a fundamental change to a QP, for interesting things to happen. One of two possible outcomes of such amino acid change(s) is possible: either it is expressible as a viable offspring (QP) or it is not. But, in many such cases, the expression of a modified genotype is attempted. I use the word "attempted" to highlight the reality that many strategically significant changes (basepair changes to important genes) cannot be expressed as viable organisms because of inconsistencies somewhere along the complex pathways of expression that prevent the continuity of the process and lead to a non-viable result (unquantized phenotype). This understandably occurs because embryogenesis involves a multitude of processes and mechanisms in sequence and in parallel, each of which must occur with the utmost precision in order for the successful expression of subsequent events. The implication here is that there exists a critically precise set of sufficient and necessary conditions (biological requisites) that leads to QP organism reproductive viability. The corollary applies as well – quantum organism viability cannot occur if all of the sufficient and necessary critical procedures for successful reproduction cannot proceed. Because successful phenotype viability is quantized, all of the "intermediate" formats (those not meeting these exacting conditions and cannot occur through the reproductive expression process) are doomed to failure. In QTE terms, they are simply genotypes that fail to meet the "quantum" test and therefore cannot be express as QP's. Conversely, the genotypes of every viable organism are quantified into unique combinations of genotype codons that can achieve full reproductive expression so long as they can pass all of the technical procedural requirements that lead to viable biological form and function.

And, therein lies the solution to the mystery of the missing transitional fossils. They effectively exist as potentially expressible QP's within unique QG's awaiting mutations to strategically placed codons that have previously undergone synonymous mutations. For some reason(s) a genotype that would express itself in what we would describe in hindsight as a transitional phenotype cannot and does not reproduce. The reasons must obviously relate to the issue of genotype quantization and the fact that the genotype in question fails to meet its quantum criterion. But there are many other genotypes in the species gene pool with potential for various degrees of phenotype change – some with the potential to leapfrog beyond transitions we might describe as incremental. Most importantly, when such a successful "quantum leap" expression occurs – whereby an "advanced" QG results in a leaped-forward QP, the species attributes of interest in such an offspring QO would most likely confer some significant survival related traits – traits that might well improve organism reproduction success. In time the improved model (fitter) phenotype would supplant its less adapted contemporaries as its SA's become significant toward species survival – albeit a somewhat different evolved species. And in very special cases, the differences between an organism and its QP offspring may be sufficiently extreme as to not only render the new generation fitter than its contemporaries but also qualify it as occupying different genetic and phenotypic quantum levels (QG and QP respectively). The leapfrogged difference genetically and physically that results between parent and offspring under such extraordinary conditions could well represent the sought-after missing transitional developmental levels of species, punctuated evolution, the development of complex organs, and, indeed, could even account for the formation of new species.

On a strictly logical level, the quantification of evolutionary results serves to actually prevent the kinds of chaos that would certainly ensue if it were possible to express as phenotypes each and every incremental transition represented by the genotype. As complex as the existence of multitudes of species within the LS represent, there is an abiding sense of perceptible order throughout all of its complexities. This clear division between species speaks directly to the concept of quantification. We can easily imagine how all of that order would collapse if there were not fixed in place the quantum effect within evolution - to effectively separate species. The combination of quantification within gene-space that expresses itself as quantification within phenotype-space well serves that purpose.

Incremental changes to genotypes <u>do not</u> directly translate into incremental changes to phenotype expression, because of the quantification of sets of sufficient and necessary conditions for reproductive viability. While the degeneracy of the genetic code has the effect of expanding the pallet of future phenotype modifications in very limited directions, as a restrictive evolution filter it cannot avoid a critical role in promoting the successful quantification process(es) of phenotype expression. It is all a question of the potential within the genomes of a population of a given species (due directly to the built-in logic within the AmAcid Node schematics) for evolutionary divergence within the permissible range of such possibilities. We argue that this is fed directly by a small but specific set of permissible mutations to critically situated basepairs.

The offspring that do get expressed as viable phenotypes can retain the sub-critical genotypes in neutral form (as described above) until in some generation, critical mutations appear that propel the emergent phenotype into a newly successful quantum level of complexity resulting in successful reproduction. This scenario strongly invokes the premise within chaos and complexity theory, that small and seemingly infinitesimal changes (such as critical mutations to neutral basepairs) have a way of becoming inordinately amplified down the long sequential process of genetic expression that leads inexorably to phenotype species attribute (SA) emergence.

Conclusions

The QTE, together with the form and function of the genetic code (operating, as it does as an "evolution-filter" at the molecular level within the PdP of the LS) can account for some puzzling phenomena as diverse as punctuated evolution, and the so-called missing transitional fossils – the latter responsible for directing permissible mutations, and the former controlling which genetic compositions will translate into viable phenotypes. As stated above, the combination of both is sufficiently versatile to even account for the evolution of complex organs - only feasibly viable combinations of incremental change, get expressed. Admittedly, the prospect of some new highly sophisticated organism popping up within a phenotype is a statistical longshot, however, given a sufficiently large species population and enough generations for the developmental incubation of genetic schematics, and somewhere, sometime, we can expect all of the right, if unlikely, conditions to come to fruition.

The QTE readily explains how random mutations within the genotype can generate the highly organized biological structures that form the LS. Together, the evolution filtering characteristics of the genetic code operating at the information level, and "biosphere-attribute (BA) anticipation" aspect of "species-attribute (SA) distribution", operating at the macro organism level (discussed in Ch 8) - all represent powerful evolution-controlling LS subsystems. We have demonstrated how they respectively shape and influence in tandem from within the LS, the directions and consequences of evolution for the survival of the LS. Having done so, we believe that our challenge - to show that the LS independently controls its near and long-term primary function of survival (adaptive evolution), by controlling all the key aspects of evolution at its fundamental levels of operation - has now been met. This achievement effectively eliminates any responsibility on the part of the external biosphere for long-term LS survival and defers all of that responsibility to the LS itself. So long as the sufficient and necessary conditions can be met for LS operation (which includes a wide spectrum of acceptable biosphere conditions), the LS will continue to survive and function according to its design intent by continually adapting to changing conditions. Any influence the biosphere seems to exert on evolution derives from the unpredictability of changes to biosphere conditions. As demonstrated, the LS comes fully equipped to meet such challenges – by adapting to whatever surprises the biosphere can spring.

The big questions now are: "What possible use could such a system - the LS - serve?" And, from the RDH viewpoint: "For what possible purpose was the LS designed and implanted on the planet Earth?"

---

[1] Molecular Biology of the Gene: 4th Edition; The Benjamin/Cummings Pub Co;inside back cover

[2] Nature: Nov 23 1995, p331

[3] Science News: Feb 3 96, p74

[4] Molecular Biology of the Gene: 4th Edition; The Benjamin/Cummings Pub Co;p 891

[5] Enc Britannica (Electronic Edition)

[6] Molecular Biology of the Gene: 4th Edition; The Benjamin/Cummings Pub Co;p 340

[7] Molecular Biology of the Gene: 4th Edition; The Benjamin/Cummings Pub Co;, p 226

14. A Question of Purpose

"The difficulty lies, not in the new ideas, but in escaping the old ones, which ramify, for those brought up as most of us have been, into every corner of our minds."
—John Maynard Keynes (1883–1946), Economist

The noteworthy significance of our separating the LS from its planetary biosphere, from the very beginning of our exercise, was to try to dispel any automatic notion that the LS is merely a product of it. The conclusions drawn in the last chapter validate that intuition. Our position has been all along: to try and maintain an open mind with respect to the bottom line premise of SAb—which maintains that the LS is merely a cause and effect product of planet activity. In fact, what our investigation has demonstrated is effectively the contrary—that the relationship between LS and biosphere approximates one of "parasite and host". In support of this theme is the extraordinary pliancy with which the LS is able to interface the biosphere at the level of the PdP. This has permitted it to alter over time system form and function, not just to enhance its own survival, but seemingly, as well, to preferentially take full advantage of extant biosphere conditions. In fact, LS survival and thriving depends largely on being able to exploit an extensive range of necessary and available raw resources of the host planet. Furthermore, over its history, bio-life has demonstrated impressive versatility in its ability to radically manipulate biosphere conditions as would be expected of some long-term system survival program. And, while acknowledging a certain amount of "give and take" between biosphere and LS in the effects of one on the other, the LS unquestionably has the only stake in the process. Its very survival depends (for the moment at least) on its continued presence on the planet. Thus, while the external conditions of the planetary biosphere shape and influence LS evolution—including the extinction of species—the undeniable fact remains that because the LS is implicated in influencing many of those external conditions, the argument can be made that whatever independent influence the biosphere exerts may, indeed, be largely mitigated by the LS presence. At the very least, the biosphere cannot totally escape some of the effects and consequences of LS activity.

Lovelock's *Gaia hypothesis* supports the premise—that LS and planetary biosphere are in fact different aspects of a single phenomenon, described as "symbiotic". From the RDH point of view, we argue that the relationship can more accurately be described as *"parasitic"*, with the initiative deriving exclusively from the LS, as it appropriates the resources it needs from the planet in the furtherance of its single objective—survival. Indeed, it is the LS that manipulates its biosphere conditions and not the other way around (the biosphere can only affect the direction of evolution by way of changing BAs, but not the PdP of biology itself). And despite some popular current skepticism on LS survival, I am fully confident that the system will always be able to respond in innovative ways to any challenges to its survival. The biological LS, as a generic system of survival, would seem to have the capability of doing the same on any suitable planet that it can terraform and make hospitable to its basic biological needs. And if, one day, the planet Earth becomes less able to serve the requirements of that survival, is there any doubt but that some technologically capable LS member organisms may wish to abandon this largely exhausted planet and strike out into space in search of some other planetary habitat that can be exploited? The RDH argues that a precedent for such a colonization has already taken place—that the OoL on our planet is no less an example of LS colonization than NASA's planned projected colonization of the planet Mars. We would provocatively suggest that the participants in both colonizations derive from the same biological LS—only from different time periods and by different representative species.

A Turning Point:

Our exercise so far has comprised (with some interesting side issues included) the reverse engineering of the LS towards the quest of delineating its system "form" and "function" (Systems Engineering steps 5, 4, and 3 as described in Chapter 5). I believe we are now ready to draw some conclusions with regard to the lessons learned in these pages, all pointing definitively to the "identification of LS objectives" (SE step 2), followed by the possible "problem" or "mission" statement (SE step 1) that the LS existence was designed to address.

None of us joins the search for "the significance of the existence of bio-life" without bringing along a lifetime's worth of "bias baggage". This includes tons of cultural dispositions derived from exposure to religious and philosophical "values" imposed on each one of us by the particular society from which we derive. The fact that every individual places their very own individual stamp of interpretation on the shared cultural experience of their peers means that the particular composition of any human being's body of thought and intellectual biases, as well, is essentially unique. For these reasons, it is best to proceed slowly and methodically toward the "grand finale" of our exercise. This is important in order to recognize when we overstep the boundaries separating science from philosophical speculation. The search for the OoL is heading into its final phase. We begin this phase with some conclusions that follow directly from the work we have covered so far.

LS Form and Function:

"The _form_ of the LS is as follows: Life on our planet is an integrated system of evolving species, organisms and indeed cells based on the biological PdP operating along the lines of the universal self-replicating machine defined by John von Neumann. The PdP of life _functions_ as both protective housing and medium for a repository of information within its DNA molecules. LS form and function are capable of transcending both time and space through the process of self-replication and adaptive evolution. As such, there is no logical restriction that can be placed on the type of information that can be included and stored, along with genes, within the same DNA information medium. Indeed, at present we have identified two distinct types of information included in DNA—labeled exons and introns. There is nothing that prohibits the inclusion of a third distinct body of information, what we shall be calling "extraneous information (EI)" encoded within informational DNA.

LS Objectives

"The only plausible objective the above description of the Life System can allow is as follows: to serve as an "information time capsule" for the preservation of a body of extraneous information (EI). In pursuit of that objective, the LS operates as a sophisticated and efficient informational storage, copying and preservation system designed to function over great periods of time. _That is all the LS is good for, according to a logical assessment of the over-abiding characteristics of its form and function. Consequently, that is all that it does!_

The LS design intent, as represented in the above statements, reflects the fact that the LS functions as an effective perpetual information library, able to make new and perfect copies of it's vast stores of genetic and non-genetic information—both subject to entropic degradation over time. Such degradation, resulting in large part from spontaneous mutations to DNA basepairs is characterized as the raw material that leads to evolution of the system phenotype in the former, and the source of signal noise, in the classical Shannon information theory sense, requiring error correction, in the latter. The unique design of LS features permits the information to overcome and transcend the degradation and entropy considerations typical of man-made copying and preservation procedures. Thus, the LS is nothing more than an information repository and preserve—an information storage library for a body of EI, pure and simple. This is its Design Intent. As stated, _that's all it is "good for"._

Use & Purpose:

The SE analysis of the LS has delineated it's generic design intent as revealed within its Form, Function and Objectives as follows:

A Self Replicating Library of Extraneous Information (EI) within the

<u>*Molecular Medium of DNA, housed, protected and preserved within an evolving biological Time Capsule—the ubiquitous LS Eukaryotic Cell and its biological primary design platform (PdP).*</u>

We shall be taking this generic description as the starting point for determining the answer to vital question 1: What is the actual use, or particular mission, if any, that a "designer" might have had in mind in order to put this specific system to work on our specific planet? Before we start speculating on that thorny subject, let's begin exploring the EI concept we have introduced above by asking some obvious questions that come to mind and result directly from the SE analysis we have concluded.

a) *The DNA Library Metaphor:*

Could the same sequential DNA informational tape that contains an organism's genetic instructional library contain, as well, an extraneous body of information that stays within the sanctuary of the nucleus of eukaryotic cells and never gets transcribed into messenger RNA? Could a body of such supplemental EI, indeed, be encoded within the DNA using the same four-letter alphabet that encodes genetic information? Since we have already answered this question in the affirmative, in virtue of the message coding exercise of the last chapter, we are then faced, as a consequence, with a whole menu of additional intellectual challenges and possibilities.

We casually refer to the *"genetic library"* that is contained within the coiled bunches of DNA molecules within the chromosomes of every organism. We have already considered that there was no reason why that same library cannot contain within a body of <u>extraneous information—that has nothing to do with genetic instructions</u>, but is written using the same basepair alphabet as used for coding genetic instructions. In other words, if there is sufficient room within the DNA of organisms, then the LS could indeed serve as the protective library and medium for a body of supplemental information encoded in a compatible language readable by any intelligent reader capable of decoding the information—much like a library of books available to anyone capable of reading the language in which they are written.

In this respect, the PdP of the LS contains its own "time capsule" which in virtue of its survival over vast periods of time, can conceivably serve as an elaborate medium capable of housing and preserving two totally separate libraries of information—one genetic and expressible, and the other totally uninvolved with the form and function of biology. This supplemental library of information could, theoretically be readily available to an intelligent user—not just over thousands of years, but as we have come to appreciate—the billions of years marking the history of the LS. This leads inexorably to the two most tantalizing questions: what kind of EI could be contained in such a living library—which we have dubbed "The Virtual Living Library" (VLL) and for what possible use? Let us not be oblivious to the huge bonus contained within the answer to the first question. Within conclusive evidence of the existence of such a VLL resides the illusive holly grail of our search—none other than the incontrovertible proof of design we have been painfully looking for. For, if ever we can determine definitively that such EI does indeed exist in DNA and gain access to a translation that reveals it to contain such content that could not possibly have been naturally derived (i.e., could not possibly have self generated nor be the results of evolution), then the consequences that flow from that impressive bit of discovery shall be quite extensive, as well as extraordinary—don't you agree? Ironically, the proof the LS is a contrived and designed system may well rest upon the research and evaluation of DNA by information theorists and not at all upon the efforts of molecular biologists.

b) *What Purpose Could It Serve?*

The living organisms of the LS, in this respect, can serve as the carriers of two kinds of information:

1] The **Genetic Information (GI)** that serves as the instructional tape, a la von Neumann—the encoded LS genotype that expresses itself within the form and functioning of the phenotype; and

2] A body of *supplemental* **Extraneous Information (EI),** encoded in the same manner (same 4 nucleotide letters of the genetic code) within LS DNA and the actual purpose for which the information time-capsule-containing LS could have been designed, jump started, and put in operation on this planet.

The EI can be preserved together with, but separate from, the system genetic operating information within the DNA of organisms' cells and passed on with it, in relay fashion, as both are copied to the cells of succeeding generations. Significantly, the body of supplemental information never gets transcribed into RNA and, significantly, never leaves the nucleus of the cell. Not all copies (organisms) survive, but that is not the objective. There are enough copies out there that permanence (within sufficient numbers of surviving organism copies through replication) is virtually assured over the life of the LS on the planet. The LS, then, could serve as the permanent library of such a body of information that has survived intact since the OoL on the planet, nearly 4 billion years ago.

c) *Boiling It Down:*

Our analysis to date permits the notion that Life could serve as a repository of supplemental and extraneous information riding "piggy-back"—together with the genetic instructions for Life within the DNA of it's component organisms, and insulated and protected from the planetary external environment within every eukaryotic cell's nucleus. As the DNA is replicated and passed on to succeeding generations, both kinds of information are copied and passed along to offspring much the same as digital program and data information files are simultaneously copied to computer disks.

In communication systems terms, we would describe such a system as follows:

1) The DNA molecule is the medium that contains the information written in the alphabet of nucleotide basepairs within its double-helix architecture.

2) All the rest of biology—species, organisms, proteins, behavior, etc. represent the expressed manifestation of the LS physical plant (phenotype) that encapsulates, protects, and ensures that all the information (genotype and EI) transcends the dimensions of both space and time; -

Space: by producing many copies across the whole of the planet, thereby making the library both permanent as well as very accessible; and

Time: by incorporating the information library within a system of self replicating von Neumann—like universal machines that replicate both themselves and their genomic operating instructions within the DNA medium, together with the EI library the system was designed to perpetuate and maintain. This type of information system would be analogous to the library "communication system" example discussed earlier. But, before we get too carried away with our speculative scenario, let's backtrack a bit and entertain, within this line of thinking, some of the options that might be relevant in the light of what we have discussed previously.

d) Logical Possibility of EI:

We have seen how DNA is sufficiently versatile to incorporate both genetic template information that is collinear with the order of amino acids in a polypeptide chain and also code for additional information in the form of a written language of some kind—information that never leaves the cell nucleus but gets copied and passed on to daughter cell nuclei—ad infinitum. Under the circumstances, DNA is the logical place to look for a supplemental body of extraneous information. Most importantly, and again—if we find it, and if we can decode it—we will have also found the incontrovertible evidence we need to virtually prove Rational Design.

A "Virtual Living Library (VLL)" of Information:

There is nothing in principle to preclude the above possibility. And, while we have no idea about the nature of such information, if it exists, nevertheless we know that its form could be in the same sequential format as genetic information. That is to say that theoretically any EI encoded in the DNA could take the form of a single dimensional sequence—the same kind of template information that genes code for, but meant to serve a totally different purpose outside of LS genetics. Thus, while not coding for codons that represent amino acid sequences, this information could conceivably be in the same form and even act as some kind of analogous map or template. But in fact, as we have seen, there is no reason to impose limits upon the quality of any information that could be encoded within the LS informational library system. We have previously described the versatility of the sequential single dimensional format (from telephone numbers to human language to television signals). For all we know, the EI could be in the form of a sophisticated language written (encoded) in the variable groups of nucleotide base pairs and not requiring the use of a system of codon triplets that are exclusively useful for designating the anticodons attached to tRNA that translate into amino acids. Certainly, the four-letter nucleotide DNA alphabet is no limitation to language flexibility. Computer language comprises only two language elements: 0 and 1, which forms the binary basis for all computer programs and word processing in all languages. Without question, neither the language of DNA written in four such elements, nor the biological operating system itself pose any limitations on our hypothetical (and fanciful) premise. The point is that I do believe we can feel quite comfortable with the concept of the LS serving as an information copying and preservation system for a body of EI, which can include, as well, the Virtual Living Library (VLL) we have suggested. Again, it is a logically acceptable possibility.

We have now passed through the door that leads to a novel but distinct reality: that of the definitely logical capability of biological life serving as a utilitarian entity together with its possible logical function. Remarkably, in so doing (finding a purpose for the LS) we have nailed down and validated the LS as an object of design study. In effect, we have validated the legitimate basis (after the fact), of invoking the SE analytical approach to the study of the LS. Whereupon, we began the exercise envisioning the SE analysis of the LS as an intellectual catalyst (those are the words we used), this intellectual approach has proved itself to be not only valid, but also consistent within the best tradition of the SE approach. For, the reverse engineering procedure we have engaged in has, indeed, led to the elucidation of a logical problem statement that is consistent with the form and function and both short and long-term objectives of the LS—that can be seen to follow a consistent design pattern that could prove to be "intent". The problem statement (step 1) that logically follows is:

"To design and create a system to contain a permanent library of information capable of surviving indefinitely within a continually physically tumultuous venue (in our case the planet earth)"—is consistent with LS form and function. Now we will deal with the issues that flow as a natural consequence of this possibility, not least of which concerns the reason the LS may have been placed here (i.e., its actual intended use). But, before we do…

The Location of Extraneous Information:

Question: Where could we expect a body of EI to "hide itself" within the genome of an organism? Wouldn't it have to be separated from the information that codes for genetic instructions, if only not to contaminate the one by the other?

Solution: Immediately we find an ideal location for such information: the so-called "junk DNA" of the intervening sequences called Introns. You will recall that before a genetic instruction can be transcribed into mRNA to be read and translated by ribosomes, an elaborate editing process is invoked to separate out the introns dispersed throughout the length of DNA that begins and ends a gene. The resultant mRNA genetic instruction "tape" is only then sent forth out of the cell nucleus to a cell protein manufacturing facility to be translated into the production of proteins. It may not be entirely coincidental that these introns also never leave the nucleus of the parent cell. Even when copied and handed down to an offspring cell introns remain exclusively within the nucleus. As far as molecular biologists can discern at present, introns seemingly serve no clear biological purpose. Yet, these mysterious streams of basepair sequences represent a great majority of the genomes of most organisms (except bacteria, which have none). More importantly they get faithfully reproduced along with the minority information that codes for genes whenever an organism reproduces. The introns would seem the logical first choice of medium location for a body of EI that could serve as a Virtual Living Library (VLL) referred to above. This idea—the existence of a VLL within the introns of DNA—raises an important issue concerning information integrity within DNA.

Maintaining VLL Information Integrity:

What use is an EI preservation system, as represented by the LS, if the information (Introns) is different in every component (species) of the system as a direct result of chance mutations? Mutations to DNA information are a LS requirement—to fuel evolution—upon which the long-term survival of the physical system itself depends. Mutations to exons modify the expression of genetic instruction and must pass the test of organism survivability to be retained over generations. Mutations to introns, on the other hand, seem to be preserved specifically because they do not affect expression within the phenotype. Put another way:

What good is a VLL within the introns of DNA unless such information could be accurately copied from generation to generation and across species, throughout the system in both space and time? Most importantly, how could such information, which forms the majority of the information in the DNA of many organisms, escape the chance mutations to genotypes that the adaptive evolution of phenotypes depends on? This is more than just an idle question considering the fact that we know there exist extensive variations within the introns of human DNA. In fact, it is these same variations upon which depends the operating principle of so-called DNA fingerprinting. It is considered that because introns are not directly involved in structural genes, mutations that occur are not subjected to culling by adaptive selection, as are most changes to structural genes. Consequently, mutations to introns are considered to be conserved and have come to represent a source of genomic variation that identifies every individual organism as unique. The consequences for the notion of a VLL within introns are real and serious. How can you have an information library where the information contained in the books is subject to typos (chance errors) on a continuous basis? Let's look at the issues.

It must be assumed that if a body of extraneous information, the VLL we refer to, exists in the genomes of certain organisms, that the information must have been there within founder species since the inception of life on the planet and that if fidelity of the copying of that information is essential, then the LS must incorporate specific subsystem(s) to insure fidelity success. In other words, while biological evolution depends upon chance mutations to the genetic instructions for life that produce the distribution of variables (species attributes) within the population of organisms, this very mechanism would spell doom for any information library whose data integrity is expected to survive intact over billions of years. This is a serious issue that lies at the heart of our present premise. Here again, we can draw upon our own experience as designers to envisage a solution to the accuracy issue. The answer of course is *"error correction"*.

Introns form over 92% of encoded DNA in humans. It has been determined that the approximately 3 billion base pairs that comprise the genetic library of every human cell is equivalent to 5 thousand volumes of information (500 pages each)[1]. Thus, of the order of 4500 such volumes actually comprise introns. Perhaps the VLL we refer to above comprises just a fraction of the total introns (say just 500 volumes of error corrected, error free and protected text), which could be subjected to the same kinds of error correction processes as genetic DNA. This would leave the remaining (in our example—4 thousand volumes) introns subject to mutations and the variations upon which DNA fingerprinting so depend upon.

All computer functions depend upon error correction algorithms to insure the accuracy of results. While computers can accomplish billions of calculations per second, a distinct error rate introduction can be arrived at statistically that determines the limitations in terms of accuracy. (Interestingly, information theorists refer to such information degradation in terms of "entropy".) That's why computer hardware and software designers incorporate sophisticated error monitoring and correction mechanisms that restore and maintain accuracy in their results. Pity the world banking system if that were not the case. Electronic transfers in the billions of dollars are commonplace and continuous 24 hours a day, seven days a week and would all grind to a sickening halt if the mechanisms that ensure accuracy could not be relied upon. At the other end of the application spectrum are the computer monitoring of life dependent medical processes from diagnostics to treatment, and space shuttle launch and activities—all dependent upon secured information accuracy over time. The point is made: if humans can do it—from compact discs to computer discs—certainly the biological production of true copies of DNA encoded VLL should be technologically possible in a manner that precludes the effects of chance mutations, (upon which the rest of the encoded genetic information is subjected to). Let's examine some of the possibilities for a differential error correction scheme—one that allows errors to genetic information at a controlled rate, while preventing such occurrences to a body of permanent protected data. One immediate solution comes to mind.

Differential Error Correction:

It is not an unreasonable assumption to consider that any kind of mutation to DNA basepairs must leave evidence of the kinds of damage incurred—that might even serve as clues to what was there before. While such clues might be partially and selectively ignored in the case of exons, where mutations are required to drive evolution, they could serve to guide built-in error correction mechanisms to effect necessary repairs to render the encoded information true. Enzymes that can home in on particular recognition sites along the DNA molecule in order to access particular genes and the like are already in place. In an analogous way, we can conceive of specialized enzymes that can act as error detection sensors—that have the ability to either repair the physical damage that mutation errors must entail, or mark the sites for other repair mechanisms to target.

It is known that some bacteria have remarkable abilities to recover from the ravages of dehydration stress. The results of such stress can cause massive DNA fragmentation that demands some form of appropriate and expedient remedial procedures for survival. The challenge is to reassemble, intact, chromosomes from hundreds of detached fragments. It seems that the "Deinococcus radiodurans" bacterium harbors within itself the necessary recombination pathways capable of restoring its DNA library within 12 to 24 hours following fragmentation. They rely upon the existence of a double chromosome structure (duplicate DNA strands) intertwined in virtue of so-called "Holliday" junctions that maintain precise alignment of homologous base pairs—that can serve as repair templates for each other. The assumption is that at least one undamaged DNA duplex is always available to serve as the template for the damaged one. Just how good a repair mechanism this is, is confirmed by the ability of this bacterium to recover from potentially lethal ionizing radiation in doses of up to 3 million rads, that can shatter its chromosomes into hundreds of fragments. The existence of similar and other types of DNA error repair mechanisms—able to cope with the occasional expected mutation errors that tend to alter encoded information within intron DNA—becomes conceivable in other species. Studies of yeast cells, for example, have been shown to be remarkably predictive of the human system. Furthermore, the mechanisms that effect excision repair in bacteria work in essentially the same way in all eukaryotic cells.

It is known that cells incorporate sophisticated mechanisms that can delay the completion of cell division until error correction measures have been implemented successfully.[2] For example, in eukaryotic cells, a gene called "p53" can sense the first signs of damage to chromosomes and can delay the cell from engaging in any further activity until the damage is repaired. It can detect and repair mutations caused by radiation or other environmental agents. Consequently, "p53" can obviate an error in one cell generation from passing on to future generations. So important is this gene to human health, that its disruption is considered to be one of the earliest and most critical phases in the multi-step development of cancer. Within the context of the RDH, so-called defects in "p53" could assume an additional level of importance. In addition to its normal error correction role, it may in fact harbor the ability to signal an individual cell for self-destruction should error correction measures fail to maintain VLL information integrity. In other words, if for any reason the system can't self-repair a faulty component (a cell whose VLL information is corrupted), then that cell could be sacrificed. In that context, cancer disease might simply be an extension of the same self-destruct mechanism to multicellular organisms as a whole. Under these circumstances, what medical researchers assume to be defects in "p53"—leading to cancer disease—could logically act in the capacity of a fallback program that targets for destruction any organism that fails to respond to its error correction remedies. Understandably, under such a speculative scenario, the physical library (phenotype) becomes secondary to the integrity of the information (VLL encoded along with the genotype) it contains.

Thus, we envisage error correction subsystems capable of first, recognizing the different kinds of information contained in DNA and second, capable as well of being applied differentially (controlling the rate of mutations in exons or allowing none at all in a specific intron repository). Error correction would thus accommodate both the nature and purpose of preserving information fidelity from the very OoL—whether that information be encoded in the genes of exons or within the non-genetic coding intron regions of DNA. With the advent of sexual reproduction, error correction could assume a more sophisticated role—for both genomes, as well as the VLL.

The Nature of Sexual Error Correction:

We shall now continue a discussion, begun earlier, of the ongoing debate among evolutionary biologists over the issues surrounding the introduction of sexual reproduction within the LS. You will recall that two options are being considered as the instigating root cause: *error correction* and *variability*. While each had arguments for and against, there is no question on which side of the debate we will lend our support. Error correction wins hands down. Supporters of the RDH would argue that, while the error correction argument currently waging in the scientific arena restricts itself to the issue of error correction of genetic information, within our particular context there is no reason the debate should remain so restrictive. Besides, if error correction is considered to be applied to the genome of an organism as a whole, then the introns, of necessity, have to be included in the procedure. We might argue further, that the genetic instructions for sexual reproduction could have been there from the beginning, (included within the genomes of implanted eukaryotic species at the OoL), lying dormant and only programmed to become operative when certain targeted internal and/or external trigger conditions would have been met. There are very interesting aspects within the sexual reproduction process that render it the ideal error correction subsystem, not just for genomes but particularly where absolute fidelity of information is repeatedly demanded (e.g., the hypothetical VLL within the introns).

During the process of organism sexual reproduction, you will recall that the offspring daughter cell contains twice the number of chromosomes necessary to contain all of the genetic instructions. Each full set derives one from each parent organism. Then, of course, choices are made that lead to the selection of one chromosome or the other containing the alleles that will express themselves in the offspring that convey characteristics of each parent. What significance can this have with respect to the introns? First, we can assume that both sets of parental chromosomes should contain identical sets of introns, where bodies of EI would be thought to reside. After all, we are referring to a library of information that must remain accurate and error free through countless generations. Thus, wherever the EI resides within the introns of DNA, those intron sequences in each parent's chromosomes would have to be identical and error free. But, we have a problem with this proposal: the mechanisms that permit limited chance mutations of exon sequence bases would seem to cause the same kinds of errors within intron bases. Chance mutations cannot be selective in the base changes they make and really "don't know" the difference between introns and exons. Mutations introduce errors at a calculable rate that affects the basepair sequences of all DNA, irrespective of the information encoded therein. The fact that introns are dispersed throughout the exons (since introns outnumber exons by a wide margin, this should be stated in reverse) would tend to support this principle. So how could sex introduce error correction of introns only, while effectively ignoring mutation errors in exons? It's really quite simple:

The exons of each parent are somewhat different to begin with, as this is the essence of variability introduction and maintenance within the species. The particular introns of our interest, however, supposedly carriers of a repository of constant non-genetic information, must remain identical from generation to generation and from organism to organism in a given species. This could be accomplished through the application of some kind of continuous, zero-tolerance, error correction sub-systems—operational throughout the history of the LS. Thus, we can make the safe assumption that intron error correction in any generation must simply take into account only those errors that have crept in since the last error correction, which occurred only a single generation ago. These would consist of the M's and m's of the previous generation. Consequently, selective error correction of the introns afforded by sex might comprise, first: the detection (and marking) of the infrequent and rare mutations of intron DNA basepairs, and second: correction through a comparison of the basepairs contributed by each parent. Each can thus serve as the correction template for the other, comparable and analogous to the repair and error correction roles that duplex fragments serve as correction templates for bacterial DNA described above. The chances of both parents having errors in the identical basepairs would have to be rare indeed. Thus, so long as there exists, between the two sets of introns, a complete error free copy of the VLL, then we can conceive of an error correction mechanism whereby an intact sequence serves as the template wherever and whenever a mutation occurs in the corresponding basepair sequence.

Zero Tolerance Error Correction—Where and When?

The ideal time for zero-tolerance error correction of VLL information to occur would be immediately following sexual fertilization, when the intron basepairs of both parents come together as single sets. Then the effects of error correction would permeate throughout the DNA of any subsequent cells of the new organism, including the sperm or egg of the offspring when its reproduces offspring. So, at the time of fertilization, we have two genomes that merge into one—where the genes within the exons appear as distinct alleles with their slight differences. In contrast, the intron sections of a VLL have no such allele characteristics and are nearly identical (except for the spurious and infrequent basepair errors that occur in the somatic cells of the previous generation). Thus, only basepair error mutations that have been introduced within a single generation (in the time between reproduction of parent and offspring) must be corrected. As an example, let's take a sequence of 1000 basepairs of intron information and assume an arbitrary error rate of one basepair per generation per organism. Thus each parent contributes, on the average, a single error randomly dispersed through the their respective matching one-thousand basepair sequence of intron DNA—an error that must be removed from the genome of the offspring prior to its replication. The key to error correction in our scheme is as follows:

If the two parent genomes described above are made to line up, one next to the other at their corresponding basepair locations, the chance of an intron error appearing at the same basepair location is small indeed. The chance of that happening is the product of the chances of error in each case: $1/1000 \times 1/1000$ or one in 1 million. An error correction mechanism must simply detect the fact that a given basepair combination in one DNA strand is an error. Then, the corresponding strand contributed by the other parent, having no detectable error at that location, can serve as the template for correcting the error. In this way, each copy can serve as the error correction template for the other. The net result, when all works well, is two error free copies. However, in our specific example, there is always that one in a million chance that two errors will crop up in the identical intron basepair locus of both parents' copies. Under such conditions, the problem can easily be solved by targeting the faulty cell for self-destruction or failing which, will be solved assuredly in the next generation where the odds of such an unfortunate alignment recurring in the identical base pair become staggering.

As regards entropic degradation of such information over time as a result of the nearly infinitely repeated copying process, we can allow our experience with the copying of digital information to guide us: every digital copy is as true as the original—byte for byte; and applies equally to the LS—base pair for base pair.

Kinds of Information and Selection of Species:

The versatility of the information system that comprises the LS permits us to conceive of the many ways it can be utilized for the purposes described above. Because there are so many species that form the LS, many of which are distant genetically from each other, the possibility exists that different families or classes actually contain different quantities and kinds of non-genetic EI. This would not be inconsistent with our proposal that when life was introduced to the planet, it had to be seeded with numerous species of eukaryotic microorganisms—to satisfy the "evolution principle"—each theoretically able to have been programmed with a different VLL—the offspring of each having survived to the present. The good news is that we do have, at present, the tools to analyze intron sequences for their non-random and language composition. To this effort can be brought the disciplines of information theory and cryptography. Only that kind of investigation could confirm the probability of the propositions we are suggesting within the context of our SE analysis of the LS.

Considerations and Consequences:

Following the enunciation of the form, function and the possible objectives of the LS in the previous chapter—all resulting from the readily available facts, we have, above, explored speculatively the possible purpose that such form and function could serve. In reality, arriving at an answer to this controversial question in this chapter involved a simple move—the splitting up of the information contained within the DNA molecule into two distinct categories: genetic information that can be expressed biologically and EI that can serve as a VLL. But, as in the game of chess, it is within the simple moves that lie the solutions to, and the ultimate success of the game. Again, we are not unappreciative of the fact that the issues that we have dealt with in this chapter are controversial at best, but based on reasonable notions, we believe. In balance, we feel they are both logically possible and defensible. And, that is about as much as we can expect at this juncture of available knowledge (on the content of intron information stored in the DNA of most species genomes). So long as that knowledge remains enigmatic, we shall continue to remain in the dark as regards the possible significance of introns within the realm of biology—and even less so about any role it may possibly have within the RDH realm of purpose, or raison d'être, for the whole phenomenon of Life on our planet. For the moment, we will have to contend ourselves with the satisfaction that the LS, indeed, could serve as a preservation time capsule for a body of extraneous information we have designated as a VLL—a possible purpose we have been seeking in answer to vital question no 1. We did make the point earlier that from a SE point of view, the above conclusion, while admittedly speculative and indeed a stretch of the imagination, does indeed satisfy the only criteria that logic permits: If you can define the basic unit of bio-Life as a self-replicating information molecule, then the ideas presented above are not only compatible with this definition but appear to offer a perfect match with LS form and function.

Nevertheless, despite the above attempt at validation, we openly acknowledge having crossed over the line separating scientific fact from speculative best guessing. But, in so doing, have we also crossed the all-important line that separates fact from fancy? The fact remains that introns, comprising an inordinate quantity of conserved non-genetic data, do exist. This is no fabrication, but fact! Currently, our finest molecular biologists are totally in the dark as to any purpose they may serve. The best they can suggest is that introns may represent ancient information that is no longer useful to their organisms. Still, they haven't a clue as to why so much "junk DNA" has been conserved and must be replicated at tremendous biological expense into every single eukaryotic daughter cell. Indeed, why has this junk DNA not gone the usual way of biological discards exemplified within the phrase: "If you don't use it, lose it!" The inability of the scientific establishment to shed meaningful light on this single glaring anomaly within molecular biology demands novel ideas and approaches. Our roll, as we see it, is to try to deal with the facts in as rational a way as possible. In the process, we have had no hesitation in trying to fill in the gaps as we have encountered them. This is to be expected in any challenging intellectual exercise, including the occasional stretch of imagination. Some of the best hypotheses begin this way. Our imaginative solution to the mystery of biological life, its origin and function involves taking all of the anomalies together, working with the facts, and then constructing a model that satisfies as many as possible. In the process, it is inevitable that we sometimes have to acknowledge ignorance as to which of the pieces of the puzzle is a perfect fit and which is somewhat forced. Nevertheless, the important exercise is the process itself. Just the examination of the whole puzzle, then its individual pieces, and the illumination of the issues, questions, and anomalies as they reveal themselves represents a positive and worthy exercise, in and of itself. So, in answer to the question of whether we have "crossed over the line separating fact from fancy", it is difficult at this point to say for sure. I will leave the reader to contemplate that one as we prepare to enter even more controversial territory with our follow up quest for the "holy grail" itself—the elusive system "mission" or intended use that could help qualify the RDH as the "Best-Buy" of origin-of-life hypotheses.

One of the smallest DNA containing chromosomes in the human body is Chromosome 21. Astonishingly, most of the code is "meaningless junk DNA" as reported when gene researchers finished decoding its entire length. The journal Nature described Chromosome 21 as "a genomic desert". "Large swathes of Chromosome 21 appear to do nothing". The DNA in Chromosome 21 "rambles on through 7 million base pairs that contain just a single actual gene". It is suggested that some of these pieces may have been conserved since before multicelled organisms evolved one billion years ago. For my money, I think a good place to start to look for non-genetic extraneous information encoded in DNA would be human Chromosome 21.

In the final analysis, it will be up to the information theorists to initiate studies that could confirm the existence of the abundant esoteric informational data the RDH predicts is contained within the introns. In fact, such studies have already begun and we trace their progress in the next chapter. The results of such research, we are convinced, will provide the incontrovertible evidence of the rational design of bio-life we are seeking. Understandably, any progress in such research leading to definitive determination of introns informational content is absolutely critical to our whole RDH thesis. For, while the superficial physical attributes of the LS can arguably be the product of evolution, any non-genetic information found within a genome logically couldn't, because esoteric information, itself, cannot be the product of random chance—it can only be the product of informed intelligence. The fact remains, that all esoteric information must be the antithesis of randomness—by definition. Thus, any proof of the existence anywhere within DNA of non-genetic information, written in any language—understandable or not—will constitute sufficient proof of LS design and consequently comprise the complete validation, as well, of the RDH. Of course, if none is found, we may have to rethink our premise.

Approaching A Critical Phase:

We have now reached an important point in our SE inquiry into Life. Having addressed and proposed the solutions to the primary questions 5 through 2, which have yielded the design intent, we are now ready to consider vital question number 1: What specific purpose (as opposed to the generic "what its good for" described above) could such form, function and objective serve? What is the specific problem statement that the design intent is meant to address? We know full well what such a LS is good for—now we want to know why it was placed here and what it actually accomplishes i.e., its precise mission statement. By simply putting these questions, there is a sense that we are getting to a critical phase in our inquiry, and simultaneously and inexorably approaching intellectual arenas that smack of wild speculation. We prefer to refer to this phase of the exercise as freethinking in order to generate interesting ideas. Again, we still want to proceed cautiously.

In arriving at the solution to the identification within the LS of vital SE step 2 (the "identification of LS objectives") we have simply described and then drawn conclusions following our interpretation of the empirical evidence. But, it is important to appreciate that throughout, we have gone out of our way to not cross over that delicate line that might address design motives or objectives. Our role has been limited to an exploration of the RDH option, based only on the search for evidence within LS form and function—evidence that could persuade any objective juror that the design option—after reviewing all of the facts offered into evidence—makes compelling logical sense. Until now, the OoL option "trial" has dealt only with the facts (LS form and function), and the laws of nature (basically the 2nd Law of Thermodynamics). Now the "logic trial" will place us squarely inside the realm of motive—translated as specific "purpose" a designer might have had in mind for perpetrating the LS—and the serious philosophical implications involved. While proposing the RDH and all of the inherent implications as a possible 5th option for the OoL, we have, until now, pretty well stuck to describing the overwhelming circumstantial evidence threatening SAb and the justification for subjecting the LS to SE analysis. In the process, we have had to deal with some sticky problems in regard to evolution and have thrown our weight fully in support of those who clearly see a violation within the current interpretation of the relationship between the LS and the entropy provisions of the 2nd law of thermodynamics. We have even suggested a way to circumvent that violation, by disentangling the energy provisions of entropy from the informational disorder provision that the LS refuses to recognize. So, while we have utilized SE methodology to unravel the questions of life definition, its form, function, and objectives, we have as yet not directly addressed the "delicate" questions that implicate specific "purpose" and "use" for the system design intent as delineated above. Even as we proceed with care, we have finally arrived at that point in our inquiry when all of that is about to change.

Why, some might question, are we bothering the attempt at all? Why not simply end the exercise here and now—after the reasonable and objective case for rational design has been presented. In effect, we have already "let the chips fall where they may". One answer is that it is human nature to try to go the distance—despite not knowing where we will end up if we continue our intellectual journey into the uncharted waters. But, the most important reason for venturing into unfamiliar intellectual territory is the curiosity of what may lie ahead—the very real hope of discovering new realities, or answers to important age-old questions—that could contribute to human understanding and enlightenment. That is what awaits us as we seek the designer's mission statement inherent within the OoL by rational design—"the 5th option". We shall be relying on the logical consequences of the RDH to guide our search. Regardless of one's intellectual or emotional position, what makes this whole exercise irresistible, is our intention to make good on the promise, made at the very beginning of our exercise: that the RDH is testable. That very notion imparts relevancy and provides us, as well, with the intellectual license to proceed unintimidated into the uncharted but tempting waters that await just ahead. As a pre-requisite, we shall first consolidate the ideas we have developed so far pursuant to the formalization of the Rational Design Hypothesis. We do so in order to build a solid foundation we can lean on as we explore the nuances inherent within the discussions of LS design purpose—its mission statement.

---

[1]The Dragons of Eden; Carl Sagan

15. The Rational Design Hypothesis (RDH)

*"What I am going to tell you about is what we teach our physics students
in the third or fourth year of graduate school... It is my task to convince
you not to turn away because you don't understand it. You see my physics
students don't understand it... That is because I don't understand it.
Nobody does."*

—Richard P. Feynman (1918–1988), Physicist

What is an hypothesis? The dictionary definition includes the following:
> *"1. A set of propositions set forth as an explanation for the occurrence of
> some specified group of phenomena, either asserted merely as a provisional
> conjecture to guide investigation (working hypothesis) or accepted as highly
> probable in the light of established facts. 2. A mere assumption or guess."*

Thus, an hypothesis is the formulation of a set of ideas to account for the facts on the ground, in the process of trying to solve a mystery. It tries to tie together a bundle of available evidence by creating a model of reality that can account for that evidence. The result usually represents a new way of looking at old ideas. In the light of our investigations and the SE analysis conducted in the previous chapters, we are ready to formulate an hypothesis based upon the conclusions derived from that study.

The Rational Design Hypothesis Concept:

The whole complex system of biological life we find on the planet Earth today is the direct product of the deliberate seeding of the planet with unicellular organisms by a technologically advanced alien civilization some 4 billion years ago. To date, the LS is the only identifiable evidence we have available that can shed light on the nature of its alien designer civilization. Interestingly, within this context, the LS is the only common link that connects two satient entities—the alien intelligence that designed biological life, and human intelligence that is the direct product of it.

Both bacteria (prokaryotes and/or archaebacteria) as well as unicellular eukaryotes would have been included in the seeding program. The bacteria were meant to multiply quickly and serve as the initial source of food energy fueling the considerably more complex eukaryotes, until such time as the planetary atmosphere became clear enough for photosynthesis to function*. Accordingly, the RDH postulates not only that the LS is the product of design, but also that the LS was implanted on the planet fully operational and with a variety of built-in subsystems designed to promote system long term survival.

Let us now turn our attention to some technological considerations that would be involved in the design of LS components on the microscopic scale.

Nanotechnology—Engineering at the Molecular Level:

Richard Feynman (born 1918, died 1988) has been described as the American theoretical physicist who was probably the most brilliant, influential, and iconoclastic figure in his field in the post-World War II era[1]. On December 29, 1959 he delivered a memorable lecture at the annual meeting of the American Physical Society at Caltech. While all of Feynman's lectures have been described as memorable, this particular talk shed light on a future discipline that at the time could only be considered science fiction. Less than fifty years later scientific conferences on "nanotechnology" occur with regularity.

Nanotechnology, as the name implies (nano = a billionth) is the concept of designing and building things literally from the ground up. The ground, in this case, refers to the basic building blocks of matter—atoms and molecules. Applicable research typically involves characteristic dimensions that are less than one thousand nanometers (millionths of a meter). Computer chip technology involving sub-micron lithography is currently able to produce line widths that are less than one micron (one millionth of a meter). As impressive as that may seem, the lithographing of microscopic lines has its fundamental limitations—for example, it will not permit the construction of semiconductors in which individual "dopant" atoms are located at specific crystal lattice sites. A whole new "post-lithography" technology will be required if computer chip designers are to continue the exponentially improving trends in miniaturization. And, that's where nanotechnology comes into the picture.

Nanotechnology involves working directly with the atoms themselves. Eventually, when properly executed, the technology is expected to:

1] Allow us to build things from the atoms up—requiring a degree of atomic position control, such that every atom appears in its appropriate location;

2] Allow us to build almost any structure that is consistent with the laws of physics and chemistry in detail—down to the very last atom, and most importantly;

3] Allow us to reduce manufacturing costs to the level of the cost of raw materials and energy.

With respect to the first point, at present, we are only beginning to understand the difficulties inherent in manipulating individual atoms to specific locations in three-dimensional space. However, it is fairly easy to envisage important developments in the area of position control, considering the already successful implimention of techniques that gave rise to tunneling microscopy (ability to "feel" the location of atomic sites). As for the second point, Feynman suggested, in his original talk, that the principles of physics allowed ("do not speak against") the possibility of maneuvering things atom by atom—"all we have to do is make parts go where we want by "putting" them where we want".

Number three on the list implies the notion of self-assembly—a technological concept that has a familiar ring to it. Another way of describing it is "self-replication"—arguably the primary defining feature of our biological LS and the kind of activity that, at present, only biological machines (organisms) can do. Somehow we don't think of biological self-replication in terms of manufacturing or production costs. We simply accept the fact that organisms are produced, they survive only so long before they die, and that as a result biological life is cheap, all because it happens all by itself. On the other hand, humans have been keen on exploiting this biological phenomenon by organizing food "factories" in the form of agricultural farms and the raising of poultry and livestock in conveyor belt style manufacturing facilities. Effectively, these operations have reduced the manufacturing cost of food to the level of the cost of raw materials and energy (use the sun and the energy is virtually free)—precisely what nano-technologists hope one-day to achieve. Of course, it is understood that nano-technology is expected to expand the scope of production to include more than simply designs derived from within the LS. Hopefully, tiny machines will result that will be able to intervene at the molecular level in all kinds of diagnostic and manufacturing processes. Then again, we could draw some parallels with biotechnology using biochemical principles in the production of all kinds of chemical products. But, what better way to achieve nano-technological goals than to simply re-program the genetic instructions of suitable organisms to produce the required end results—atom by atom. This also has a familiar ring to it—we call it genetic engineering.

One wonders how nano-technological self-replication is going to be achieved. Considering how little progress has been made in the effort to understand the essence of self-replication in biology—where the phenomenon is literally seen to occur—one could be excused for being somewhat skeptical about the chances of achieving success in non-biological areas of self-replication research. On the other hand, we might do well to refer back to John von Neumann's self-replicator discussed earlier. If we could design and build one such system able to perform a task that could also copy itself, we would have the potential for producing systems that exhibit both precision as well as low cost. While von Neumann concerned himself with the intellectual concept and not with size, the goal of nano-technology is to design and create self-replicators on the sub-microscopic scale—compounding the challenge considerably.

Undoubtedly, the piece-de-resistance of Feynman's lecture (for our discussions, dealing as they do with methodologies for qualifying our RDH) was within the nature of the poignant example he raised. At the very beginning of his talk, Feynman provokes his audience with the ironic question: "Why cannot we write the entire 24 volumes of the Encyclopedia Britannica on the head of a pin?" The balance of his lecture discusses the physics involved, followed by a discussion of the technological possibilities. He concludes that there is nothing that stands in the way of writing the entire encyclopedia on the head of a pin. The area involved (1/16 inch across) provides ample room allowing each of the little print dots of the fine half-tone reproductions of the encyclopedia to contain within its area as many as one thousand atoms. He suggested that if the size of each letter could be reduced by a factor of 25,000—in the form of raised letters on the pin—it would be easy enough to read using 1959 know-how. Apparently, the technological limitation back then was not in the reading—but in the writing.

Nanotechnology and Biology:

We find it both interesting and ironical that Feynman invoked an information density example for his preview lecture on nanotechnology nearly a half century ago. At the time, computer designers were already taking advantage of the size-reduction advances in both transistor and chip technology. Miniaturization (effectively positional control) was really all there was to consider; there was no practical need then and, therefore, no thought of considering a self-replication provision that is occupying the thoughts of present day nanotechnologists. The irony derives from the fact that Feinman unkowingly helps the cause of RDH by demonstrating the association of key elements common to both the RDH and nanotechnology: 1) Feynman chooses the head of a pin as both an interesting and practical place to write large amounts of retrievable information, as a way of predicting future cutting edge technological feasibility; The RDH says that it has already been done—not on the surface of the head of a pin, but in a much more efficient location—within the basepairs of DNA. 2) Feynman's challenge is how to achieve the miniaturization of writing within a medium density he defines as 1000 atoms per pixel bit (the reading of it being a non-problem). The challenge faced by the RDH is the exact opposite: how to read the information already written (and encoded)—not on the head of a pin (a comparatively easy task) but within the chemical strands of DNA encased in the nucleus of a cell, where the miniaturization comprises orders of magnitude smaller (only 50 atoms per bit of information). But, the ability to identify individual letters written in DNA is actually the least of our problems—the Human Genome project attests to that. More to the point will be the challenge of sorting out and translating those sequences of basepairs within the non-genetic databases encoded in DNA introns—a feat which we are counting on to validate the RDH—the 5th OPTION for the OoL.

The association with biology does not escape Feynman's attention—he does take as his prime example of high-density information, what he refers to as: "The marvelous biological system"[2]. He acknowledges that enormous amounts of information are required for the implementation of biological processes within life and that it is all contained "… in a very tiny fraction of the cell in the form of long-chain (nucleic acid) molecules …".

The Marvelous Biological System—According To Richard Feynman:

Richard Feynman:

> "The biological example of writing information on a small scale has inspired me to think of something that should be possible. Biology is not simply writing information; it is doing something about it. A biological system can be exceedingly small. Many of the cells are very tiny, but they are very active; they manufacture various substances; they walk around; they wiggle; and they do all kinds of marvelous things—all on a very small scale. Also they store information. Consider the possibility that we too can make a thing very small which does what we want—that we can

manufacture an object that maneuvers at that level!"

The above quotation, in a nutshell, captures the essence of our ambitious enterprise. Feynman's inspiration "to think of something that should be possible" followed by: "Biology is not simply writing information; it is *doing something* about it" touches a resonant chord within us. While we may differ on what it is exactly that biology is doing he makes the point inevitable—biology is indeed "doing something". The RDH makes the point: that "something" may also actually be what he thought it ought not to be— information simply written and stored as a body of supplemental and extraneous information; a virtual library written in DNA not in order to do something (that's what the genetic component of DNA is there for) but simply there to be found and decoded and read for its own sake. But more to the point: by including the biological as a prominent example of information storage density achievement within the same landmark lecture concerned with how designers could accomplish information storage on a much coarser scale adds considerable legitimacy to the arguments put forward within the RDH. When we update the 1959 "nano" mindset to present day nano-technology concepts, that realization becomes all the more significant. Nano-technology effectively represents the logical link joining the macro ideas of John von Neumann (who answered the challenge of self-replication in machines) put forward in the 1930's, to the micro ideas expressed in Richard Feynman's classic lecture of 1959, to our proposed RDH hypothesis working at the encoded DNA molecular information level in the new millennium— all melding together in a grand transcendence of concept and technology. von Neumann described the concept of universal replicator based on two essential components—an idealized 'universal constructor' controlled by a 'universal computer'. Richard Feynman discussed idealized concepts in overcoming the difficulties in manipulating and controlling things on a scale of atoms. Separately, these two academic giants tinkered intellectually with futuristic ideas that would impact on present nano-technological concepts of methodologies for constructing miniaturized machines, atom by atom. The role of our RDH in this threesome is to press home the idea that, as happens so often, once again human innovation will have to take a back seat to historical reality on a grand scale; that we have really discovered nothing new; its all been done before—ironically, art trying to imitate life, 'literally'.

Nanotechnology = OoL Methodology:

Nanotechnology is indeed the key to understanding the principles of LS design. We have defined the PdP of life as the idealized self-contained eukaryotic cell. This PdP of biology is nothing, if not a prime example of everything nanotechnologists are hoping to achieve. The biological PdP incorporates within itself all of the critical concepts and components that scream out that here we have the results of manipulation and position control on the smallest of scales, that can be self-sustaining, reproduce as necessary, and do all of those things we believe we will one day be able to replicate (no pun intended) within small contrivances of our own design. We have already begun the process. What is genetic engineering if not nanotechnology as applied to the biology platform? Molecular biologists are in effect engaged in retrofitting existent biological machines either mechanically—by adding to, removing from, or altering their physiologies, or through reprogramming—by modifying the genetic instructional libraries (genes). The trick in biological manipulation is to do so without destroying the operational PdP in the process. When done successfully, the results are impressive. Of course most of the nano-biology being undertaken is funded and geared toward the lofty goals of improving the human condition—increasing food production, neutralizing pests, and restoring and extending health to ailing human phenotypes.

If the aim of nanotechnology is the study of how to create tiny mechanical machines, then its counterpart in biology is microbiology—the study of already existing microorganisms. During the course of studying bacteria as pathogens, the aim is to identify their differences—in both form and function. In an uncannily parallel sense, one-day nanotechnology may permit humans to create nano machines—also having differences in form and function. Let's look at that again—micro-organisms that have been around for close to four billion years, and nano-machines we hope to design and create in the future—can you really define a meaningful difference between the two? That assessment—that we can identify such obvious symmetry between nanotechnology and biology—should indeed encourage our confidence in the premise of a Rational Design OoL. The advent of nanotechnology, and all of the promise it represents, heralds a new appreciation of the potential for human created tiny mechanical creatures that can themselves manipulate and control phenomena on heretofore unimaginably small scales. It also underscores the obvious relationship between that technology and microbiology. Accordingly, is there any logical reason we should not consider molecular biology and microbiology simply as branches of nanotechnology.

For the purposes of our specific exercise, the promise of impressive advances in nanotechnology in the near future can offer as well renewed hope for discovering a solution to the challenge of biological OoL design methodology. Consider that nanotechnology allows us, for the first time, to relate, in logical and meaningful ways (intuition aside) this new technology (itself the product of human culture) to the logistics implicated in the origin of bio-life—until recently considered beyond the pale and scope of human understanding. The nanotechnology mindset can provide scientists with a new and relevant context within which to consider the OoL question. They need no longer constrain their thinking of the origin of the life-state phenomenon as uniquely a natural and bottom up SAb phenomenon. The aim of nanotechnology is to take raw molecular resources from the environment and organize and direct them in such ways as to create artificial machines and systems that could not derive naturally. Now simply apply von Neumann's self-replicator model to the nanotechnology arena scale and what do you get? We call it the Rational Design Hypothesis.

In another twist of irony, we are now able to predict the form and function of an idealized nanotechnological machine—one that humans someday hope to be able to design and build—in terms of the biological PdP, an exemplary such entity that has existed on our planet for close to four billion years. The PdP of life—comprising the generic eukaryotic cell—represents in every realistic way what nanotechnologists hope to achieve. Using the same basic structure and equipment (atoms and molecules), they hope to produce machines which can be tailor programmed to produce an infinite variety of end products, positioning one atom at a time, and then manipulating those products into precise positions. Well, isn't that what ribosomes do in the construction of the protein constituents of cells? Don't they receive their programming from sequences of mRNA, one codon at a time, and blindly assemble polypeptide chains, one amino acid at a time? The net result is a protein of one kind or another that is transported to wherever it is required within the micro-cell, or accumulated and stored in appropriate miniature containers until it can be shipped to a desired location.

Take one such protein as an example: an enzyme referred to as *F-ATPase* that looks, uncannily, like a tiny engine—with parts that resemble pistons and a drive shaft. It operates by spinning an actin filament counterclockwise, just like a propeller. Its actual biological function is as a sub-unit of a larger enzyme (ATP synthase), spinning and cranking out ATP—the universal biological energy molecule that fuels all biochemical processes in cells. The characteristics of this biological engine are extraordinary by human engineering standards. Its output torque is very high—equivalent to a man rotating a rod 150 meters in length. And, the rotation rate can be ratcheted down depending on the load—similar to the changing of gears "as a good motor transmission should". This tiny engine is miniature, even by molecular biological standards—less than one-tenth the size of the molecular motors that drive bacterial flagella. For the time being, and until it can be put to practical use, the team of scientists studying this molecular scale engine plan to show off their skills by creating some "moving toys" by inserting it between a bacterial flagellum and a plastic bead.[3] Compare that with an example of biological form and function—the external plasma membrane of the cell is outfitted with a variety of embedded specialty proteins which can serve, variously, as channels, gates, alarms, detectors—sensors of all kinds that serve to preserve the protective internal environment of the cell (e.g., by helping to maintain potassium levels against osmotic pressures) as well as tailor the generic cell according to its intended function. How's that for the intelligent and skillful application of nanotechnology—and devoid of human involvement, to boot.

The important lesson here is that the construction of all nano-biological machines—of which these above are just two examples—involves the precise positioning of individual atoms and molecules, one by one—just what nanotechnology is all about. Therefore, it no longer requires any great stretch of the imagination on the part of supporters of any of the other OoL options to appreciate the logic of OoL by design—now that the concept has effectively become more logically palatable, all because of the advent of nanotechnology.

Scientific Relevancy:

The 'piece de resistance' of our exercise resides in the fact that the Rational Design hypothesis, as described in these pages, is testable. So, no matter what the reader's impressions are so far with respect to the case we are making in defense of rational design; whether you have, indeed, been influenced by our arguments against SAb, or remain unimpressed with the concept of the LS as a utilitarian construct—the fact that we can put the RDH to the test should certainly attract your attention. This very fact—that the RDH is testable (and therefore falsifiable)—fulfills the basic scientific criterion that renders it, at least on a legal technicality, as the only relevant OoL hypothesis according to standard scientific protocol. The fact is that each one of the other OoL options can only suggest, but never really prove, its validity. Their respective fates invariably must be decided by default, if and when any of the competition can somehow claim some breakthrough achievement that awards it with an undeniable level of scientific acceptance. This is the basket in which the RDH is prepared to place all of its eggs.

Anybody can propose a theory or an hypothesis about virtually anything, and the guarantees of freedom of speech (wherever they do exist) will protect that person's right of expression. The frequency of this kind of intellectual phenomenon (the proposing of all kinds of theories) seems to occur directly in proportion to the inability to test the ideas in question. Put another way, the number of diverse theories and hypotheses enthusiastically proposed, that are intended to explain complex phenomenon (as well as the many strange and curious ideas, real and imagined, that seem to pervade people's concepts of reality), seem to be inversely proportional to the verifiability of those ideas. And many of these seem to stick around beyond their usefulness, refusing to go away simply because of the fact that no one has been able to prove them false. Astrology, psychic, and so-called paranormal phenomenon as well as the innumerable superstitions and urban myths many of us have grown comfortable with are the kinds of unproved notions that refuse to go away because people choose to believe in them. Many of these can simply be relegated to the science fiction file and probably explain more about human nature and less about the reality they purport to elucidate. However, science imposes some tough criteria upon new ideas that are claimed to describe important phenomena in a new way. That criterion, of course, revolves around the testability of any such novelties. Can the newly espoused notions be repeatedly tested—in a valid scientific way—in order to be, a) proved in a relevant and satisfactory manner, or more importantly, b) disproved? The idea here is that if new ideas (they crop up like weeds) cannot be tested, they immediately fall into the category of ideas that are held by belief, and lack the essential qualifications required of them in order to be acceptable along scientific standards, until such time as a suitable experiment can be devised. Most importantly, it is the peer review, by a critical scientific community across all the relevant disciplines, which will ultimately determine the validity of any new theory or hypothesis. But, actual acceptance can only be achieved after it has been put to the test. Untested theories fall into two diverse categories which have an important distinction: 1] ideas that are not testable, under any conceivable conditions, and 2] ideas that are testable—but must await the development of appropriate, and heretofore unavailable technology for a suitable test to become available. Traditionally, religious dogma and ideas that require negative proof fall into the first category. For example, how do you devise a test that disproves the existence of mental telepathy? You can't, any more than you can prove that UFO's don't exist, or that extraterrestrial intelligence doesn't exist. A lack of positive evidence in support of the existence of any of these phenomena need not necessarily preclude their physical existence. But, absent any such positive evidence must render these notions, regardless of their popularity, as untested ideas held by belief alone.

As for the second category above, there are many examples of hypotheses having a scientific basis that were unprovable at the time they were suggested in virtue of the fact that the technology required to test their efficacy was then unavailable. Only with the advent of new techniques and sufficiently sensitive equipment could experimental procedures be brought to bear on ideas awaiting verification—followed by validation. And, only then could their importance become appreciated, and form part of the ever expanding fabric of the universally accepted scientific database of information. Or, by the same token, the removal of a persistent idea by showing it to be scientifically false could clear up an intellectual logjam that may have stymied progress in an important area of science—so long as experimental contradictory proof remained unavailable. From a culturally pragmatic point of view, testing is important in order to update and remove questionable ideas, and create intellectual vacuums. Also important, is the ultimate passing of an older generation of scientists, so that many of their outdated (and sometimes career self-serving) ideas can pass with them. Whatever the mechanisms, it is essential, as well as inevitable, that new fields of opportunity open up for younger minds willing and able to challenge and test old dogmas, and offer novel approaches to test old questions. It is equally essential that they be unencumbered by the perpetuation of untested but entrenched outdated paradigms. That's what scientific progress is all about.

Most importantly, the scientific method for acceptance of new ideas demands that experimental proof be repeatable and not just the results of one-time occurrences. Repeatability is essential to eliminate experimental errors at best and experimental fraud at worst. Only after experimental results repeatedly parallel prediction, can new ideas take their place in the scientific jigsaw puzzle that purports to be reality. I use the word 'purport' to make the point that even after experimental results point the way to acceptance of new concepts, in science, the whole picture of reality is never known—only a limited glimpse, at best. Therefore, as new experimentally derived parts of the puzzle are continually put in place, the only guarantees that accompany the acceptance of these new ideas are tied to the provision that the door to further revision always remains open. Thus, all facets of scientific knowledge and fact are contextual and subject to amendment, if and when new data is presented that even remotely bears on the subject matter. The ability of science to continually update and question the relevance of recent as well as old material represents the beauty of the philosophy of science. The fact that scientific reputations can be made overnight (don't ever underestimate the motivation of self interest) by both the presentation of new evidence, and also by challenging successfully older ideas, virtually guarantees that ultimately the system stays relatively honest. Defying reputation, influence, prejudice, philosophy, ideology and doctrine, the scientific method is the only universal creed that demands of its adherents, at every turn, to remain open-minded, impartial, critical, and that they question everything. Indeed, no other system of culture goes out of it's way, to such a degree, to implement the checks and balances that are inherent, in order to remain aloof from the excesses and weaknesses characteristic of human nature. Couple the desire for excellence with the human trait for recognition, and open up the field to anyone competent and willing to play the game, and what do you get? You get competition to unseat questionable ideas, and the continuous introduction of new ways to see old phenomena. The exponential increase in the publishing of innumerable scientific papers and abstracts annually, in all kinds of media and journals, attests to the above, and supports the premise that the scientific method has no equal when it comes to uncovering the secrets of nature—from the subatomic level to the cosmological.

We are truly living in an age of knowledge and information access. Consider that it took thirty-one years (1907 to 1937) for "Chemical Abstracts" to publish its first million abstracts[4] describing newly discovered chemicals. The second million took eighteen years. The most recent million took just one and three quarter years. As individuals, few of us have really come to grips with the implications of the knowledge explosion to which we are witness. Besides the practical implications for the dissemination of new ideas, the avalanche of such information and its increased availability can only result in the further reliance upon the well of scientific knowledge (in contrast to the more traditional sources), to illuminate reality—to the extent it is describable, and therefore understandable. In our own way, we are contributing to the process by utilizing an "applied scientific", (i.e., "engineering") approach in search of a solution to the OoL mystery. However, it is the testability of our thesis, as discussed in the next few pages, which will indeed set the RDH—the 5th OPTION, apart from the competition.

Testing—One, Two, Three...

Before the advent of the RDH, the problem with any OoL hypothesis has been the virtual inability of any of them to be tested for verification. This is considered, not to be a problem of methodology, but rather the nature of the problem itself (they simply fall into the category of untestable ideas described above). Supporters of SAb, PS and DPS, all science-based efforts, are quick to point out, and rightly so, that the event happened too long ago, and probably under conditions that would have obliterated evidence of such a delicate nature. To complicate matters further, they can argue that those conditions under which the OoL occurred must have been so special such that the phenomenon quite possibly occurred only once. Thus, they consider that only circumstantial evidence (hardly proof at all) of the origin event is logically possible under such restrictive circumstances. They therefore proceed in the only conceivable way left open to them—by hypothesizing how the OoL might have happened. How, for example, could you test for SAb? Even if nano-biologists would manage somehow to invoke in vitro some kind of self-replication activity from raw chemicals, that is still a long way from proving that that is, indeed, how it might have happened naturally and without help billions of years ago. SAb supporters can still be expected to hang their hats on the results of such a contrived laboratory experiment as validation of the principle of SAb and conclude that the case for the SAb OoL can be closed—for all practical purposes. But still, no right-thinking scientist should accept that kind of event as proof positive that, indeed, that is how it happened. And, as we have alluded to time and again, the only thing that an in-vitro demonstration of the contrivance of self replicating molecules from ordinary chemicals could prove, is that it can be done by intelligent agents—in this case, biochemists—and exactly how the RDH says it happened. The question then remains as to whether a successful exercise of this kind would really end up making the case for abiogenesis or, in fact, end up proving the feasibility of the RDH. Ironically, the in-vitro nanotechnological assembly of the components of life and the subsequent jump-start of the processes of life essentially comprise the kind of OoL scenario that the RDH postulates. We simply contend that somebody else beat us to it—by some 3.8 billion years or so. Thus, rather than proving SAb, such an experiment would actually be serving the cause of RDH instead.

How about Panspermia? Would the discovery of spores or other biological entities in meteorites offer up the necessary proof for validation of the idea? Even if this material could be shown to be uncontaminated by terrestrial life and manage to sprout into living and reproducing organisms on its own, it is doubtful that this would lead to a satisfactory conclusion that the OoL mystery had finally been solved. Problems relevant to the establishment of a viable LS beginning, with very limited stock and under very limited and happenstance conditions, would persist. Even if such seeds of life could survive their voyage, how do you explain their extraterrestrial existence in the first place and then their ability to evolve? Have they simply spontaneously self-generated elsewhere and then had to endure an arduous journey through space to get here? Our chief umpire in these deliberations—William of Occam—might prefer SAb for that reason alone, to obviate having to survive a journey through space. But our main concern here is that there is no conclusive way to prove Panspermia. Directed Panspermia is an even more difficult proposition. Unless some ancient and fossilized mechanical spacecraft or pod happens to be discovered, containing equipment for keeping organisms alive for extremely long interstellar voyages, the unlikely premise will remain a dead issue. Then again, if some day in the future we manage to overcome the time limitations presently imposed on deep space travel, we may want to have another go at DPS. Of course, by that time, the whole question of DPS may simply be an academic curiosity if the mystery of the OoL has already been solved.

Creationists, one would think, have no problem with testing for obvious reasons. Regardless of the approach creationism relies purely on tautological statements whose logic belies the need for tests. Rarely does that kind of debate proceed beyond the intellectual challenges and exercises posed by a particular limited set of esoteric texts, whose contents are considered to be the only permitted reference data. Somewhere within may be found "truth" according to varying interpretations—however, truth devoid of hard evidence will continue to fall short of the critical standards imposed by science. For their part, religious adherents need only rely on subjective experience as their sufficiently acceptable standard for the validation of their thesis. That is not the end of the story: Creationists not only believe that all creatures are the products of design but are prepared to go to great lengths to defend their opposition to the very notion of mutability—one of the cornerstones of the theory of evolution. Evolution—both chemical and biological—is the cornerstone of the SAb OoL option and supporters eagerly defend their cause utilizing a host of scientific data and imaginative hypotheses to bolster their case. One would hope that by now, a clear winner in the evolution debate, still raging since Darwin's day, could be declared—on the evidence alone. However, such is not the case. Creationists declare emphatically that no one has ever seen biological evolution at work and that, in fact, it is nothing but an illusion. Evolutionists respond that the results of biological evolutionary processes are unmistakable, that many of the mechanisms are understood and that the fossil record represents nothing if not the recorded history of species evolving. Can the same data—available to both sides in the debate—be interpreted in such diametrically opposed ways? Is there a realistic way to test evolution such that the results appear incontrovertible to all? Judging from the negative reactions to the arguments put by both sides so far, it would appear that the issues are more complex than appears to the casual observer. And, the same can be said for the OoL question—how, indeed, does one assess what kind of evidence is sufficient and necessary to prove one OoL option or another? Incontrovertible proof does not seem to come easy. If evolution, a contemporary phenomenon, cannot be proved beyond a shadow of a doubt, how much more difficult must it be to prove abiogenesis—an event that dates back billions of years and relies not only on biological evolution following the origin of life, but depends even more so on prior chemical evolution as the engine required to drive abiogenesis? There are important principles involved and the RDH has much to contribute that can help to clear up many of the misunderstandings that characterize much of the ongoing evolution debate. We can make this claim because the RDH accepts the basic principles espoused by each side—OoL by design and biological change through evolution. We shall also take advantage of these discussions (issues that divide creationists and evolutionists) to highlight, as well, the fundamental differences between Rational design and creationism. Because the two issues, OoL and evolution, are so intimately linked, it is important to revisit and deal effectively with the evolution question within this context before addressing the complex issue of test criteria as it applies to OoL according to the RDH.

Evolution vs Design:

The RDH principle differentiates between species that have evolved from an ancestor, and the original founder species the RDH postulates to have been designed. The former is considered the resultant product of continuous adaptive changes to species phenotype beyond the PdP level in response to changes within the genotype. The latter is considered to be an essentially constant and immutable phenotype expression of an equally constant genotype (our PdP concept) with a built-in adaptive subsystem responsible for and capable of all of the potential biological changes labeled evolution. As stated, creationists advocate a vastly more restrictive definition of biological design, with immutability of species stated as their prime position. Of course, what looks like design to creationists and supporters of rational design alike is argued by the opposition to be nothing more than the product of evolution. Without wishing to get more embroiled in this kind of debate than absolutely necessary, it is important for us to delineate precisely the differences between the RDH and creationist positions. Creationists (and anti-evolutionists) claim that:

1] Evolution has never been observed.
2] Evolution violates the 2nd Law of Thermodynamics.
3] There are no transitional fossils that could prove incremental change over time.
4] The theory of evolution implies that evolution proceeds by random chance.
5] Evolution is only a theory—it has never been proved.
The RDH response is as follows:

1] Evolution has never been observed?

Evolutionists point to examples of experimentally created species of Drosophila (fruit flies) in the laboratory. They claim as well to have observed the origin of new species in the wild. More to the point, they can claim that the number of observations supporting evolution is impressive; that biologists define evolution as change in the gene pool of a population over time and that as slow as that rate of change may appear, it is sufficient to produce all of the diversity of living things from a common ancestor. In reply, anti-evolutionists are adamant that genetic variation is nothing more than dominant and recessive genetic traits that appear and vanish in successive generations within populations of organisms, and that all possible changes or variations within a given population are limited to those inherent traits. As far as the RDH is concerned, the question of whether evolution occurs too slowly to be observed is of little consequence. From our RDH OoL perspective—discussed extensively in these pages—biological evolution is an essential design component within the PdP of biology—through mechanisms totally controlled from within the LS—responsible for short and long-term adaptation to changes in the biosphere. Thus, rather than viewing evolution as an obstacle to the concept of design (as Creationists do), the RDH takes the opposite view—that without adaptive evolution as an inherent part of the design, there can be no long term survival of the LS.

2] Evolution Violates The 2nd Law of Thermodynamics?

We have discussed in detail the LS and evolution and the relation of each to the 2nd law. Here we simply wish to draw attention to the fact that SAb relies on evolution as the responsible agent for first: the appearance of a very first abiogenetic chemical self replicating entity, and second: the development of this chemical phase forward in time to its ultimate biological phase. Creationists (and many scientists as well) see serious obstacles to the very possibility of the occurrence of both these phenomena and as violations of the 2nd law. The RDH wholeheartedly agrees on both counts. But then, Creationists adopt a rather curious stance with respect to evolution. They extrapolate their denial of chemical evolution to include biological evolution even though the fossil record is replete with ample positive evidence, and dating techniques establish with little doubt their origin in antiquity. They thus waste away the credibility of their 2nd law arguments as they properly pertain to any chemical abiogenesis event by trying to carry the same argument forward through to cellular biology as well. Unfortunately for them, it just doesn't wash. As previously discussed, the RDH insists that evolution can only exist as a biological phenomenon (within the exclusively cellular environment); that it adheres to the strict energy provisions of the 2nd law; but that the 2nd law must be reinterpreted in order to account for the increase in LS complexity in both space and time. Thus, the RDH draws an important distinction between how the 2nd law imposes different results with respect to energy and state of order insisting they are two independent and separate domains. Within the purely chemical realm of random atoms and molecules, the 2nd law imposes a ruthless control over both system energy and information, reverting any temporary increase in complexity back in the direction of equilibrium and minimum energy state. In stark contrast, it is within the exclusive and protective cellular environment—where all biological reactions occur—where the 2nd law provisions of energy and information effectively split in two: the energy constraints of the 2nd law are preserved, while the information provision is freed from any 2nd law energy entropy constraints. This split occurs in virtue of the fundamentally unique characteristic conditions that impose from within the LS—where chemistry is intelligently directed by and under the management of an information database. This intelligence acts as a mediating interface that permits the expression of genetic information for the construction of physical organisms from inanimate chemical building blocks. The RDH claims that it is this unique controlling intelligence phenomenon that affords the LS the ability to achieve the following two specific and distinct results—both of which technically violate the 2nd law as presently interpreted: The first allows the LS to maintain within its constituent components (organisms) a constant state of disequilibrium thereby rendering any biological activity independent of traditional 2nd law constraints. The second permits the increase in system order in both space and time, both qualitatively and quantitatively—characteristics unique to a LS.

3] The Case of the Missing Transitional Fossils?

Used historically by creationists to deny evolution, this argument is characteristically weak in that over time, more and more fossils have been discovered and studied, filling in many gaps. Also, the fossil record is being supplanted in importance by the molecular-biological record that can provide accurate clues to linkages that both join and separate lineages, and as well can serve as a relative time line providing chronological order. Rather than helping the anti-evolutionists, the missing-fossils argument has become somewhat of an embarrassment for them. To bolster their cause, some Creationists go on the offensive and suggest that the punctuated evolution hypothesis, proposed by Eldridge and Gould, has been formulated simply as an excuse to explain gaps in the fossil record. For all we know, punctuated evolution may indeed be the accurate explanation for a certain paucity of transitional fossils. The RDH has suggested (in Chapter 13) as a possible explanation for missing transitional fossils the novel concept that there exists a very real divergence between total genotype information within a particular species and the information that actually gets expressed as phenotype—this in virtue of the special characteristics (degeneracy) of the form and function of the genetic code. That is to say, that very real differences in genotype do not all translate into differences in phenotype. As a result, in any given generation, the introduction of critical mutations to any genotype regardless of how they derive can produce uniquely inordinate changes to the expressed phenotype. In any case, the very existence of the fossil record provides ample and clear supportive evidence for the existence, as well, of extinct species and their undeniable relationship with the physical genealogy of extant species. Evolution, according to the RDH, for all intent and purposes is alive and well. We do, of course, reserve our right (a right already amply exercised) to have fundamental differences with both Darwinists (and neo-Darwinists)—many of which have already been discussed—as to the operational principles that drive evolution.

4] The Theory of Evolution Says Evolution Proceeds By Random Chance?

Random chance certainly plays an important part in the operational mechanisms that permit certain aspects of evolution to operate—such as random mutations and the position of SA's of individual organisms in SA distribution curves. But like any dice game system, regardless of what random numbers come up, dictated only by the laws of probability, the rules of any game are so structured as to direct, in game-specific ways, how the random dice throw can only be applied, through the direct intervention of a player, according to constraining rules that ultimately yield non-random results. The random numbers permit the game to progress—the rules of the game dictate the choices of how the random numbers must be applied. Similarly, we have shown in detail in the chapter on evolution how a random change in the nucleotide letters produces results that are non-random in attempted application (phenotype expression) and that an ultimate non-random selection process occurs through survival. Changes to genotype either end up being, inheritable and therefore successful, or are not and halted in their tracks. We have shown through our statistical analysis of all possible mutations within the genetic code how there exists a primary level of intelligence built into its form and function. This study yielded the graphic "AmAcid Node diagrams" which plainly indicate what the rules of the evolution-by-mutation game are, demonstrating clearly how the form and function of the genetic code acts as an evolution filter. The implications are just as clear—random changes to genetic information lead to non-random results. Thus, evolution is no hit and miss random enterprise at all. If it were, the system would spend an inordinate amount of energy and time only on wasteful experimentation and probably not be able to survive long-term biosphere changes. Evolution does involve a constant state of preparedness as represented within the interactive distribution curves that comprise a multitude of species attributes (SAs). Even so, because future conditions cannot be predicted at all, all species tend to lose the long-term battle of "biosphere attribute anticipation"—the ability to produce future generations that can adapt to the unknown long-term conditions of their respective environmental niches. It's not unlike playing a chess game where you have to think several moves ahead and try to anticipate any and all of your opponent's potential moves. When done successfully, one can plot in one's mind an opponent's anticipated series of moves, and then calculate an opposing series in reply that will meet an anticipated threat. Now, species don't plan for the future—their members can only deal with the present. However, within the distribution curves of species attributes exist the potential—according to the laws of probability—for both some kind of effective biosphere attribute anticipation of future change as well as one very powerful additional evolutionary weapon—the ability to cast new offshoot species that can act as additional players within the competition for survival. All such competition serves admirably the ultimate survival—somewhere on the planet, and by all the available means at its disposal—of the biological system of life we call the LS.

5] *Evolution Is Only A Theory; It Hasn't Been Proved?*

Evolutionists respond by clarifying what scientists mean by the technical term "evolution". One such strict biological definition is "a change in allele frequencies over time"[5]. This, of course, tends to limit the phenomenon to sexual species where there are alternative Mendelian characters from which to choose (one contributed by each parent). In fact, as we have stated time and again, we consider evolution to be an umbrella term that includes not just the results of adaptive change, but as well all of the mechanisms—some well known and others less so (including some as yet unknown)—that come together to permit the biological participants within the LS to adapt over time to changing biosphere conditions. Thus, even though certain specific operational features may be questioned as to the importance of their contribution within the overall scheme, and others may be doubted entirely, the consequences are nevertheless clear.

One could argue that the "theory" of evolution is somewhat of a misnomer—there is no single theory but rather a single set of results. Certainly, science doesn't claim to know everything about mutations, natural selection, genetic drift, genes, DNA, and all of the interactions and operational features that ultimately culminate in evolutionary change. Thus, various theories that purport to tell and describe a part of the story of evolution are currently on the table. Some are more precise than others—some are most likely not accurate at all. But, the concept of evolution, in terms of biological change and survival results and as the adaptive phenomenon of the LS in the global sense, is no theory at all—it is simply a definition of what must happen and does happen—change, without which the whole system of life on the planet would ultimately grind to a halt.

Rational Design vs Creationism:

So where does that leave us? Again, the Creationists believe all of the above propositions to be true; the evolutionists believe them to be false. In summary, the RDH takes the position that proposition 1 is irrelevant to the debate—the speed of evolution matters not; proposition 2 as presently interpreted, is both half true (with respect to entropy order) and half false (with respect to entropy energy)—according to the RDH the 2nd law must be reinterpreted to take into account the anomalies associated with life phenomena. Proposition 3 is probably true to some extent—which opens the door to some kind of punctuated evolution. Propositions 4 and 5 are patently false. Evolution is plainly a fact of life.

We have now elaborated precisely on the fundamental differences between Design by Creation and Rational Design. The former accepts all species to have existed from time immemorial in their present form and therefore requires none of the adaptive provisions that evolution can provide. Thus, Creationist design extends to each and every species extant on the planet. The latter insists that only the primary design platform of biological life is designed, and that included within the design are all of the operational features required to effect the inheritable changes and adaptations evolution is responsible for. Completing the tour is SAb, which extends evolution back to a hypothetical chemical phase supporters believe to be responsible for the abiogenesis of biological life from ordinary chemicals. Thus, while Creationism and RDH agree that SAb is impossible (and therefore that chemical evolution is a fantasy), SAb and RDH agree that evolution, as an umbrella term, is responsible for biological adaptation and the origin of biological species (with one exception—we differ on the origin of the original founder species). Ironically, Creationism and SAb have only one thing in common—neither hypothesis is testable. That leaves only the RDH with something more than mere speculation.

The Nature of Incontrovertible Proof of Design:

The Rational Design Hypothesis—the 5th OPTION, is in a class by itself. It is probably the only OoL hypothesis that could expect to discover within the LS, as it is presently constituted, some kind of hard proof to validate itself. Because, once you find proof of design that you can buy into, you then inadvertently resolve the OoL mystery as well. Problem solved! And even if the technology for discovering such proof were lacking today, we could expect to find that incontrovertible proof of design in the future, as that technology improves. However, at the very least, the present state of knowledge should be able to reveal, if only in a circumstantial way, evidence of design intent that can be convincingly shown to be derived from outside of the parameters of evolution by natural selection. The big question remains: what kind of proof of design could possibly satisfy supporters of SAb? This is not an idle question but at the very heart of the whole OoL controversy. Supporters of SAb have had a lot of experience, some bitter, in dealing with these kinds of questions since Darwinian evolution came on the scene. They have answered every creationist design challenge with arguments that explain away the numerous examples of seemingly irreducible biological complexity—as nothing more than the accumulation of incremental changes due entirely to micro-evolution over periods of time. For example, in the classical case of the "eye"—requiring the simultaneous working together of all of its complex parts, each fitted specifically to contribute a single end result called sight—the organ has been logically reduced to a series of evolutionary changes, culminating in an exquisitely functional seeing apparatus; the whole being nothing more than the sum of its individual evolutionary parts. Other equally intricate examples of biological intricacy (such as how the explosive defense apparatus of the bombardier beetle could have developed in a piecemeal fashion) have had to endure similar patterns of SAb logic. But protesters just aren't buying it. Still, under the circumstances, one wonders out loud whether any kind of evidence offered of design, albeit rational, can sway supporters of SAb and, if so, what evidentiary criteria will turn skeptics into believers?

In truth, there is only one kind of evidence that is incontrovertible, and truly not subject to any kind of refutation. The discovery within the primary design platform of biology (the eukaryotic cell) of a written label that advertises who the designer is and where the design originated; that or its equivalent should satisfy any juror. The RDH contends that there might be such incontrovertible evidence to be found within the extraneous information (an external label, if you will) encoded within the chemical medium of intron DNA. By definition, this kind of information can only derive from a source external to the system of biology. We make this assertion simply because the LS design definition (life is a self replicating information molecule) permits such information to exist in addition to and along side the genetic information encoded in DNA. If such EI were to be discovered somewhere within the junk DNA, then the evolutionists can make no claim on logical grounds that this information could possibly be derived from evolution—regardless of the methodology. And, the only logical source of an intelligent non-genetic message written anywhere in DNA would have to be derived from outside of the system itself i.e., the intelligent designer of the LS. The beauty of this kind of evidence is that any such message, regardless of location or origin within the LS, represents virtual apriori proof of LS intelligent origin—that of an intentional alien mind. As such, in defining the introns as the repository of extraneous information within the medium of DNA, our challenge turns to how to investigate and evaluate any such information located there. The following will go a long way towards a solution.

Testing—Where to Begin?

Let's say that our arguments in these pages have remained within the bounds of logical possibility and that the LS quite possibly could serve the purposes as outlined. How could we, in fact, prove it? An obvious solution comes to mind. We have made the case that the LS can serve as a time capsule for the preservation of a body of extraneous information. If we locate it and prove the existence of such information—some readable and understandable message that could only derive from outside the LS—would that indeed be the sufficient and necessary proof we are looking for? Would that discovery, as well, comprise the logical proof that the LS is a contrived and designed phenomenon? I should think so and can think of no possible refutation of such claims. The question now becomes: Can we test the introns contained in the genomes of organisms to determine whether they indeed contain "meaningful" information of a non-genetic nature? We are not talking about just any kind of data but rather the kind whose very existence within the DNA medium of a living cell can only be explained as coming from alien sources. We want to exclude, of course any encoded data whose content might possibly have derived from evolved genetic information. Thus, if we could find such information that could only derive from a non-biological source then wouldn't that constitute sufficient and necessary proof of the major thesis we have presented in these pages? The next question is how could we go about doing just that? How do you 1) find and identify as such a body of extraneous information, and 2) having found it, be able to analyze it for meaningful information not derivable from biological mechanisms and finally, 3) having made that determination, go about translating the language in which such information is written so that we can attempt to interpret its content? The fact is, that, indeed, as we write, a host of mathematical algorithmic procedures either exist, or are presently being developed that will facilitate the task of language revelation of DNA intron sequences; indeed, a case of truth seemingly stranger than fiction.

Revelation Science:

A) THE HUMAN GENOME PROJECT:

The challenge now becomes how to recognize and decipher the information contained in intron DNA. This is more than simply of interest to the RDH model. It is part of the ever-important quest on the part of molecular biologists and others to shed light upon the mystery of introns—their existence as well as their data content. The quest must be viewed in the larger context—as an integral part of the continuing *"human genome project"*, the gigantic worldwide scientific effort to unravel the information contained within the genetic library of the human species.

The huge funds allocated towards decoding the sequences incorporated within the 3 billion basepairs library has been responsible for the development and invocation of a variety of DNA data search techniques. These have sped up the daunting task of delineating every single basepair on the way to mapping of every gene. While all of the organized efforts have been aimed exclusively at genetic information, theoretically nothing prevents their application towards deciphering the intron information as well. Of course, at present, most efforts are aimed exclusively at comparing and aligning genetic sequences, with little reason to address the non-genetic sequences of introns. In fact, a major challenge in the work is to weed out the introns from the exons (the "junk" from the genes)—the wheat from the chaff, as it were. Of course, if our contentions are valid, we will find major differences between the two kinds of information found in exons and introns respectively. This fact has apparently not been totally lost on the part of a small but growing minority of human genome researchers and associated information theorists who have begun to examine the information characteristics of any and all data to be found in DNA.

The genome project has spawned the development and invocation of a variety of novel and ingenious techniques to help speed up the task of recording genetic sequences, on the one hand, and making sense of the information, so it can be put to practical use, on the other. That objective has spurred the development of all kinds of hardware and software whose aim is to reduce the amount of time required to complete the task. These include fast comparison programs, such as "BLAST" (which can compare one thousand sequences per second), and data compression methods in the application of factor analysis, principle component analysis, correspondence analysis, multidimensional scaling, distance geometry, and more recently a technique developed by M. van Heel referred to as "sequence space projection"[6], just to name a few. The aim is to reduce complex data to a simpler form while minimizing any loss of information. The result is an organized genetic database that can be rapidly searched using the "DARWIN" (Data Analysis and Retrieval With Indexed Nucleotide/peptide sequences) retrieval system.[7] As monumentally important to medicine and genetic research the success of the human genome project is expected to be, it could very well turn out that the techniques developed for this research will make equally important contributions to the ultimate disclosure and significance of the information in the other 92% of the human genome that comprise the introns. When the time comes to turn their attention in that direction, and the analysis results become known, we would not be totally shocked by the discovery and revelation of the kinds of extraneous and supplemental information that could only have been placed there by a would-be designer of biological life. Astonished?... definitely! Surprised?... not really. And, perhaps the motivation on the part of molecular biologists to turn some of the attention to the introns might stem from the sheer infatuation with the subject, alluded to above, or perhaps we can just count on old-fashioned curiosity—that mainstay of scientific inquiry. That curiosity will no doubt encourage some to tinker and "play" with newly acquired knowledge and techniques in order to "see what else it is good for" and to consider how and where else it can be applied. Scientific ingenuity often extends beyond the strict confines of the profession, occasionally even turning the results of cutting edge research into gamesmanship.

b) SOMETHING TO PLAY WITH:

A relevant case in point is the exercise reported in Nature magazine (entitled "A Word In Your Protein"[8]) by G. Gonnet and S. Benner of the Institute for Scientific Computation and Institute for Organic Chemistry, Zurich, in which they attempted to match the entire 20 volume Oxford Dictionary

(572,728,830 characters) against the entire SwissProt protein sequence database. Using the English alphabet single-letter codes for amino acids, they have searched for the longest word spelled out in the sequence of a protein in the protein sequence database (not unlike our simple example in Chapter 12). The result of the 23 minute computer search yielded two words of nine characters: a) "hidalgism"—from the 9 amino acid sequence 247-355 of the integrase enzyme of bacteriophage lambda (histidine, isoleucine, d(aspartic-acid), alanine, leucine, glycine, isoleicine, serine, methionine), and b) "ensilists"—from a sequence within the PRRB protein from E-coli bacteria. As the authors are quick to point out, not only are these the longest strings appearing in both the English and protein languages, but also probably rank as well among the top nominees for the most unusable pieces of information in both biochemistry and lexicography. The DNA information library seems to have a magnetic appeal for anyone engaged in its study. Now, these kinds of frivolous word games are not the type of intron analysis we were suggesting above. After all, the names of the twenty amino acids are arbitrary and so too are their first letters. So, using them as the basis for decoding information in DNA is quite useless. What this trivial example makes abundantly clear, however, is the fact that sequences of DNA codons that designate polypeptide amino acid sequences can and do evoke more than just genetic interest. More to the point, anyone who becomes intimately familiar with these sequences cannot help but immediately recognize an analogy between sequences of DNA basepairs, and sequences of letters that form the basis of human language.

Not to be outdone, David Jones, Dept. of Biochemistry and Molecular Biology, University College, London, took it upon himself (this is hardly a sanctioned activity) to perform the same exercise, but expanding the human database to include 1.3 million words from ten European languages plus Esperanto, and came up with at least four nine-letter words and a couple of ten-letter words, using the same word-game principles. In an article (in a serious science journal) entitled "More Protein Talk"[9], he spoofs this kind of international race to discover the longest peptide-word as a source of misplaced national pride. (A kind of "genetic-linguistic-scrabble Olympics".)

Gonner and Benner, and Jones' participation, in turn, caught the attention of Stephen Harvey, who wrote a subsequent letter published in Nature magazine headlined, "Hidden Message"[10], in which he builds on their efforts and describes the application of his own "Sideswipe" algorithm to the task. His efforts have been rewarded with the discovery of two ten-letter words. He even concedes that this activity, on his part, is not directly related to his work. (The inference is that he did it for the fun of it.) His letter also references other articles that deal with techniques for the systematic analysis of biological sequence data. We are not unappreciative of the irony inherent in the title of the piece, "Hidden Message" as a stark reminder that these kinds of informal exercises belie important characteristics shared by both genetic and human-like systems of encoded communication. The RDH, indeed, is all about exploiting these similarities in the fulfillment of its self-appointed mandate. While Gonnet, Benner, Jones, Harvey, et al seek non-existent and randomly formed hidden messages written in human language within protein sequences, our interest, of course, is in searching for possible meaningful messages within alien derived extraneous information that may exist—encoded within the "non-coding" introns. We have still to move on from playing games to serious scientific analysis when it comes to the introns. Let's consider the issues involved.

c) Recognition First—Then Meaning:

It can be considered a "given" that any non-genetic message information library encoded within the DNA of organisms would be in a language, unfamiliar to any human. How then can we hope to recognize, no less share, in this kind of hypothetical information. It is one thing to find an ancient tablet upon which is inscribed some strange text written in an alphabet of a lost language of some archaic civilization. The very discovery of such a unique artifact immediately begs further investigation, including its publication in academic journals, so that language specialists and historians from every institution of learning become aware of its existence. The hope is that someone out there in academia may be able to shed some light on its origin and composition. And it is quite another to attempt to do the same using the biological medium of DNA as your data source. Ironically, our problem, beginning with recognition, in a sense derives from our over-familiarity with both the medium (DNA) and the alphabetic form of information (the four nucleotide letters of the genetic code) encoded in nucleic acids. This is further complicated by the fact that specialists in such matters have already pronounced their recognition of certain intervening sequences as non-relevant "junk". In other words there is no surprise in finding the same 4 letter basepairs within inexplicable DNA sequences that are known not to code for genes and, therefore, of little or no use to biologists. In fact, introns represent a nuisance for molecular biologists and thought to have only nuisance value, as well, for the LS reproductive process. Thus, they have pretty well made up their minds that intron DNA represents vestiges of discarded information along the path of evolutionary history and that there is no real percentage, at this time, in pursuing the matter of introns any further—particularly when we've only just begun the serious work of decoding genes. Accordingly, there would be great irony in the discovery of a message from a would-be designer encoded in throw-away junk DNA—analogous in some small way to the discovery of a rare Da Vinci manuscript among discarded vintage engineering drawings of the Florentine public works department. Accordingly, the RDH proposes that it no longer makes sense to treat introns simply as unrecognizable molecular biological fossils. The challenges involved are: first, be able to recognize encoded text, if it exists within introns, and second, be able to translate any text found. However, perhaps we shall presently have the necessary tools to accomplish both.

d) Testing According to Zipf's Rule:

In the early 1950's a linguist, George Zipf developed mathematical mechanisms with which to analyze languages. He determined the relationship between word rank and word frequency.

Most information sources produce a message that consists not of a single choice but of a sequence of choices. The writing of English sentences can be thought of as a process of choice: choosing a first word from possible first words with various probabilities; then a second, with probabilities depending on the first; and so forth. According to information theory—this kind of statistical process and, indeed, all information sources are thought of and referred to as stochastic processes. By measuring the frequency of words in long texts in several languages, Zipf discovered a remarkable mathematical relationship that transcends all languages. Thus, if the most common word in a lengthy sample of text had a frequency of 10,000 occurrences, then the tenth ranked most common word would appear 1000 times (one tenth as often) and similarly, the 100th ranked most common word would appear roughly 100 times. This remarkable phenomenon has been shown to be true of any language and thus has become, in effect, a kind of universal litmus test for language itself. Zipf's rule might serve our purposes well.

Printed English is a type of information source that has been studied considerably. By playing a kind of "Twenty Questions" game, suitably modified, with subjects trying to guess the next letter in an English sentence, it can be shown that the information rate of ordinary written English is not more than about one bit per letter[11]. This phenomenon is a result of the very unequal frequencies of occurrence of different letters. For example, "e", "t", and "a" are very common in English, while "z", "q", and "x" are infrequent. With respect to pairs of letters, th is very common and qz rare. The same can be said for the existence of frequently recurring words, phrases, and so on. This body of statistical data related to a language is called the "statistical structure of the language". If all 26 letters and the space in English had equal frequencies of occurrence (i.e., each had probability 1/27) and the occurrence of each letter of text was independent of previous letters, the information rate has been determined to be log 27, or about 4.76 bits per letter. Because, in fact, only one bit actually is produced, English is said to be about 80 percent redundant. The redundancy of English can be demonstrated by the fact that a great many letters can be deleted from a sentence without making it impossible for a reader to fill the gaps and determine the original meaning. For example, in the following sentence the vowels have been deleted yet it is still readable.

"Ths sntnc hs n vwls."

As might easily be deduced, the fact of redundancy in language plays an important role in the field of cryptography.

Surely, the intron basepair sequences within the DNA of various species could be subjected to similar linguistic analysis to determine if Zipf's Law and others like it apply. In this case, because hypothetical word size is indeterminate (there are no spaces or evident punctuation that separates base-pair letter combinations of different length), the analysis could proceed by dividing up the continuous DNA basepairs into recurring basepair "words" or patterns of arbitrarily different lengths and determining their frequency of appearance. Computer analysis should afford numerous ways of subjecting introns to such investigation in order to determine whether Zipf's linguistic laws apply. At the very least, this kind of analysis would be able to compare introns to exons (genetically coded DNA) to determine if, and the extent to which, their patterns are similar or totally different. If introns are simply discarded genes, as some suggest, we should expect such a computerized analysis to yield many similarities. If, on the other hand, the introns can be shown to be radically different from the exons—which, as we have already seen, are merely telephone-number-like encoded sequences—then either they must be shown to serve some heretofore undetected genetic function within the cell's operating system, or they may, in fact, represent a body of supplemental information such as that described above. If that were shown to be the case, then perhaps this kind of extra-biological evidence would indeed represent a positive test for design. How else could one explain such a phenomenon? Of course, a negative result would not necessarily represent a failure of the basic premise of the RDH. The information contained therein could represent useful data of a different kind.

Two questions come to mind: 1] what kinds of data are we talking about, and 2] Useful to whom?

E) STOP THE PRESSES (BELATEDLY)!

An exceedingly curious and exciting report appeared in the December 5 1994 issue of Physical Review Letters. As reported in Science News (December 10, 1994), let's start with the title: **"Does Nonsense DNA Speak its Own Dialect?"** The piece goes on to describe Zipf-style tests applied to genetic material (information encoded in DNA) from a variety of simple and complex organisms. 37 DNA sequences containing 50 thousand base pairs each, as well as one longer sequence of the order of 2.2 million basepairs, were evaluated according to two **"linguistic" tests. The results were summarized as follows:**

> *"Long ignored as "junk" this noncoding DNA nevertheless carries its own message, says Michael Simons, a molecular biologist at Harvard medical school in Boston. He and his colleagues, working with Rosario N Mantegna and other physicists from Boston University, have found "language-like properties in this junk".*

The scientific teams tested both coding (genetic introns) as well as non-coding (introns) regions of DNA. They explain that <u>codes</u> are different from <u>language</u>. "One mistake and the code will be misread" is how it was stated. "In contrast, because of what linguists call redundancy, the non-coding regions—like all languages—can contain a mistake and still be understood". In fact, molecular biologists had previously begun to recognize the differences between coding and noncoding DNA, and had used these differences to advantage in order to separate genes (coded regions) from introns along unfamiliar lengths of DNA. However, according to H. Eugene Stanley, of Boston University, this work is the first to demonstrate that noncoding DNA sequences represent <u>a structured language fundamentally unlike the coding in genes</u>. "That's quite different from what people had thought", he notes. The feeling is that there's something going on in the non-coding region (introns). Until researchers can translate this newfound language, any ideas concerning their function are just speculations", he adds.

Sounds a bit like science fiction, doesn't it? But, it's not and I didn't make it up. However you interpret this phenomenal revelation, one thing is certain: the time has come to stop referring to DNA introns as "junk". This research has demonstrated that the introns may be expressing a language, and may, indeed, be the supplementary EI that the RDH suggests may constitute the "reason d'etre" for the existence of Life on the planet, and our long sought after design intent, as well. In any case, the fact that these noncoding regions of DNA constitute fully 92% of the human genome should serve to caution us against persisting with a misleading label (junk DNA) that most likely derives from a too hasty assessment of a misunderstood phenomenon—coupled with the impulsive desire to classify it anyway.

Other science-oriented journals have since picked up the story. The March 1995 issue of Scientific American (p24) provided some additional insights into the recent efforts being made to characterize intron information. Mathematicians, applying some of what they have learned about fractal patterns have found, within sequences of introns, what are termed *"long range correlations"*—that the position of nucleotide basepair depends on the placement of other basepairs. This contrasts sharply with the total lack of correlation that characterizes the genetic coding sequences within exons. Additional information theory analyses—performed according to the rules of quantified redundancy in languages as put forth in the 1950's by Claude Shannon—have helped to support and confirm the tests according to "Zipf".

Just as interesting as the findings themselves are the initial interpretations the researchers seem to be at pains to offer. For example, it is suggested that junk sequences (when will they learn?) may be essential to the way DNA has to fold to fit into a nucleus. My answer to that is: "Give us all a break!" You don't have to be a mathematician to question the absurdity within the suggestion that 92% of the information within the (human) genome may be going towards a comparatively mundane geometric folding operation. This is not meant to demean the importance nor the complexity of fitting a seven-foot linear length of DNA within the microscopic nucleus of a cell. But, consider how much less the predicament would be in the first place, if you eliminated 92% of the space problem—by simply removing the intron instructions for the solution that occupy nearly the entire problem space in question.

Since the discovery of the double-stranded helix structure of DNA, scientists have developed powerful tools to help them decipher the information bound up in the sequences of DNA base pairs. A relatively new field of biology labeled "bioinformatics"[12] has been formed to bring together a multidiscipline approach to the tasks involved. Mathematicians, chemists, biologists, physicists, and computing specialists are all part of the bioinformatics team approach to solving the mysteries that reside in DNA information, according to Dr. Hanah Margalit of the National Institute of Health, Bethesda. The coordinated application of numerous fields of expertise toward the greater understanding of the very heart of the LS—the information that controls it all—will undoubtedly shed much needed light on the introns as well. Unquestionably, the possibility looms that their work could, indeed, validate the ideas represented by the RDH as well.

As a parting thought, let the prophetic words of researcher Rosario Mantegna echo in your mind: "We think we've found a language, but we don't know what it's saying". I would like to respond as follows: "Yes, you may very well have found a language encoding a body of extraneous information within the DNA information molecule. More importantly, you may also have stumbled upon the most important academic discovery of this or any millennium." What indeed would be the reaction of researcher Manegna and others if it was ultimately revealed that he was among the very first in recognizing the language characteristics of arguably the most important documents ever discovered—encoded and written within the chemical medium of DNA and deposited for safe keeping by extraterrestrial sources within the intron sequences of the eukaryotic cell nucleus. Could he have inadvertently stumbled upon the "smoking gun"—that crucial bit of incontrovertible evidence that ultimately confirms beyond a shadow of a doubt the RDH? Such a body of EI could well comprise the VLL predicted by the RDH—couldn't it? As we shall come to appreciate in the pages ahead, the importance of nailing down definitively this fact cannot be overstated because, besides the amazement of the disclosure itself, there is reason to believe that the very future survival of the human species may well turn out to depend on it.

While Zipf-like rules may have helped to provide a measure of recognition of the language characteristics of the information content of introns, that is still a long way from being able to discern what any such information may actually contain. But, while we may remain unable for the time being to actually translate intron data into human understandable information, there have appeared on the scene some truly ingenious techniques that can categorize any kind of language text, without having to first reference the actual language in which it is written. Could this development lead us directly to the "Holy Grail" we have been seeking—of determining both the significance of the existence of intron DNA as well the unexpected bonus in the form of a very real potential for understanding its information content?

F) LANGUAGE-INDEPENDENT TEXT CATEGORIZATION:

Undoubtedly a major contribution toward the interest and fascination we laymen have with science is in the way it so often lends vitality to the cliché: "Truth is stranger than fiction". We are exposed to steady streams of media images that convey the essence of biological activity, from animal behavior studies in the wild—much of it unbelievably bizarre—to electron microscopic images of the workings of the cell. Thus, we may be forgiven if, on occasion, our attention is somewhat diminished—a natural consequence of the "Been there, done that!" syndrome that tends to jade somewhat our sense of wonder and appreciation. Even seasoned scientists cannot help the occasional failure to fully appreciate all of the exciting implications within the phenomena they work with—day in and day out—because of saturation exposure. While such overexposure to the sensational tends to raise our wonder expectation threshold to unrealistically high levels, thankfully every now and then a truly amazing bit of news comes along that not only attracts our attention, but serves as well, to revitalize and, indeed, reaffirm that sense of wonder. The following text analysis procedure personally ranks among the best in this tradition.

French patent no. 2,694,984 describes a technique for analyzing any text, in any language and then being able to categorize that text according to subject[13]. Nothing terribly new so far! Many document categorization and retrieval methods exist that rely on using words, sentences and paragraphs for sorting, categorizing and retrieving text. Generally, such programs require a linguist for initial setup and continual adjustments, are vulnerable to spelling variations and random character errors, and are both language and topic specific. What makes this new technique truly novel and exciting, is its phenomenal ability to do all of these things <u>without prior information</u> about document content or language. Its well-defined procedures can predict similarity between any two documents—without regard for language or content, and therefore context, as well. And, if an existing document of known language and content is used as an exemplar, then the methodology also permits accurate predictions of topical attributes of the unknown text. Thus, for example, a text document in Japanese can be compared to one written in French by a technician knowledgeable in neither language and their context can be inferred as it applies to document similarity. When tested against traditional methods at the Text Retrieval Conference sponsored by the National Institute of Standards and Technology, this amazing computer program was shown to perform on a par with some of the best existing language-dependent retrieval systems. It also permits an off-the-shelf computer to compare thousands of documents in just a matter of minutes.

The name of this amazing language independent retrieval system described above is "Acquaintance", and was reported by Marc Damashek, US Department of Defense, Fort Meade. If this computer program truly lives up to its reported expectations, then it has tremendous implications as a possible tool for both the recognition of intron sequences as information text and then the evaluation of content for context. And even if this particular algorithm proves to be not quite up to the task for our particular application, it signals the prospect of improved programs in the near future that quite possibly will be. The fact that the present version has the capability of being able to topically partition a large collection of documents without prior specification of subject matter and no user intervention is indeed an exciting development. And, because of its unique ability to compare two texts for document similarity, based solely on brief reference samples some dozens of characters long, *Acquaintance*-type programs would appear to be the ideal strategic tool for comparing DNA text (an unknown language) with a variety of topical subjects (within known texts and language). Any close correlations might then constitute evidence of text recognition—leading even to the possibility of subject categorization.

What makes this prospective exercise particularly enticing is the prior revelation, as noted above, that introns have already tested positive for language characteristics according to Zipf's rules. Thus, the fact that introns seem to have already passed the preliminary tests for language recognition must be seen as a very positive sign—one that should encourage a procession to the next step. Acquaintance, as presently constituted, together with any analytical improvements that can be expected in the near future, would seem to represent the ideal kind of application tools for testing for any hidden information we suggest may be encoded within intron sequences of DNA. As stated above, such a revelation could, indeed, validate our RDH thesis.

Undoubtedly, there is no turning back now. We believe that information theorists may, sooner than later, find themselves on the brink of a watershed discovery—one that ranks as being in a class of its own. As has occurred in the past, such a singular event could present a unique opportunity for humanity to reevaluate, once again, our place in the universe. If intron DNA research continues as anticipated, the RDH may indeed be tested sooner than I had expected and not that much later than its publication herein. The following provocative piece is included simply to crank your already whetted appetite one more notch for the segment just ahead.

G) MAKER'S MARK:

In the April 1, 1993 edition of the prestigious science journal, "Nature" a letter (to the editor) appeared that would seem to have startling implications. The authors, Michael Dalrymple and Ian Garner begin their comments as follows: "*We would like to present evidence for the existence of a controlling influence in the construction of human chromosome 4 and possibly others.*"

They go on to describe the existence of: "*a puzzling number of near-perfect matches to sequence tagged sites (STS) on human chromosome 4*". They then describe several such examples, and conclude: "*We can only interpret this to mean that <u>man, unlike most other species, was indeed 'manufactured', presumably by some all-powerful deity</u>.*'" They continue: "*This individual must have used standard cloning techniques to piece together chromosome 4 (did he/she use different vectors for different chromosomes?). Despite leaving* *behind evidence of construction, <u>this work is clearly a tour de force.</u>"*

Then, in a whimsical vain, they conclude with: *"The company that sells pBSIISK+ must, presumably, have a license from God to market and sell his vector. One wonders, perhaps, if other well-known repetitive elements, for example Alu sequences, represent the fossil remains of earlier divine cloning vectors."*

What are we to make of the above—the details aside? Well, from a SAb viewpoint, I guess the only interpretation possible is that the above extraordinarily described phenomenon is somehow natural, and possibly only the result of extraordinary coincidence. But, at the technical level, what are the chances of multibase sequences (of the order of 50 bases) of seven different sequence tagged sites being homologous to a multiple cloning site of a cloning vector? Let's leave that one for the molecular biologists to consider.

The truth of the matter is that the implications only really make sense within the context of the Rational Design Hypothesis put forth in these pages. While we respect the passing theological interpretation put forth by the authors for the surprising discovery they have made, our approach, of course, would seek a more scientifically palatable explanation. The RDH serves that purpose admirably well. This suggestion of outside intervention, derived as it does from scientific sources, offers the kind of additional tangible substantiation of LS design that we are, in fact, looking for. It certainly speaks louder (and clearer) than the limited circumstantial demonstrations offered by any of the other OoL hypotheses.

On the other hand, in the example above, we must not over-react by extending their interpretation beyond the authors' limited intentions. After all, the homology phenomenon described above could turn out to be narrowly limited to the antecedents that gave immediate rise to the human species and not before. If that were the case, then this discovery opens up the question of some intelligent molecular-biologist-designer having interceded and modified the human genome in particular, perhaps sometime in the early genetic history of *homo-sapiens sapiens*—as our species has come to call itself. This, in fact, parallels a thesis put forth in a series of *Earth Chronicles* authored by Zecharia Sitchin. His scholarly interpretation of ancient religious documents and archaeological remains leads him to the conclusion that humankind is the product of genetic manipulation by astronauts from an alien civilization from some reclusive *12th Planet* in our solar system. He further suggests that such intervention on our planet began as late as 445 thousand years ago[14] and that human encounters with aliens are preserved in the myths, legends and early writings of ancient human civilizations. Implicated as well are the great historical mysteries that surround the Biblical flood, the Great Pyramids, the massive ziggurats of Mesopotamia, the Exodus from Egypt, the Trojan Wars, the destruction of Sodom and Gomorrah and the collapse of the ancient Sumerian civilization. The introduction of the idea that present day humans are the progeny of some relatively recent genetic engineering modifications, in no way interferes with, nor invalidates the idea of an intelligent designer of the LS—it simply invokes what could be considered to be an additional intervention—only several billion years following the OoL. It also validates and lends additional credence to the whole idea of a preexisting (pre-human) extraterrestrial intelligence that forms the crux of our thesis. Moreover, it certainly reflects on the Drake formula value of "n" greater than 1—an absolute requirement for the RDH to have validity.

Consistency = Credibility:

If ever the day arrives when we can, indeed, verify the recognition of language and determine the content of an extraneous body of non-genetic information encoded in sequences of intron DNA, that evidence alone may qualify as that sufficient and necessary to validate the RDH. So far, progress in methodology appears to be right on track, and intron analysis to date seems to suggest human-style language—a quality shown as well to be importantly missing in exon DNA sequences. As progress-to-date reports go, we really could not expect better, considering the complexity of the task at hand and the extant state of the art.

For introns to have meaning outside of genetics as we propose, the bottom line, from our point of view, would be the discovery of identical sequences of intron DNA within the genomes of modern, as well as ancient, species. In this respect, it might prove useful to examine the preserved DNA of fossilized remains of ancient species—a la Jurassic Park. You will recall (if you read the book or saw the movie) that scientists recovered dinosaur DNA from within the stinger of a wasp that had the misfortune of becoming entombed in a drop of what would become amber. If the introns of that kind of ancient DNA could be compared to the DNA of its present day survivor offspring relative for identical intron sequences, then therein would be one kind of test for the EI the RDH refers to. Then, further testing could reveal these sequences not to be "junk" at all, but a message written in a language meant for an end user. (N.B: We are not suggesting that all of the introns comprise intelligent non-genetic information—only that such may exist somewhere within the vast amounts of introns of respective eukaryotic species.)

If EI can be found encoded anywhere within DNA the immediate questions arise as to what possible extra-biological purpose such information could serve as well as whom a potential recipient might be.

For Whom The Bell Tolls:

Let us address the question of an intelligent "end-user" of such EI. To do so, we will assume, for the moment, that within the introns contained in DNA is a body of EI described in these pages. Who would it be meant for, and what might the nature of the content be? This is, at best, a totally speculative issue, with no evidence of any kind to go on. However, that has never stopped humans from putting forth some guesswork based on intuition of one kind or another—until hard proof becomes available. Of course, if we ever get to decipher and read an intelligent message derived from the introns of some organism, we might not have to guess any further. But, let's begin with the possibilities for the client end user of such information. There are only two possibilities: one direct, and the other indirect.

A) Direct User:

The direct user aspect would reflect a specific utilitarian purpose for visitors to our humble planet. The immediate questions that come to mind are—who, and why? The "who" would immediately raise the oft-discussed mysterious phenomena that are described under the umbrella term of "UFOs" or more commonly "UF-ology". Despite all that is written concerning close encounters of one kind or another over the many centuries of recorded history, the whole subject remains clouded in mystery. I, for one, am not going to enter that debate—and will not even venture a personal opinion on the subject—other than how the idea of visitors from space could impact on the RDH. However, let's face it: the RDH depends on a value of $n > 1$ for the Drake formula. As such, I am personally placed in the curious position of waiting for the positive proof of the existence of any kind of close encounter with extraterrestrial information (ETI)—as derived from reliable witness accounts or any of the various SETI exploration programs—while at the same time postulating a theory of OoL that, you might say, absolutely relies on the existence of ETI. But, the curiosity of the position in which I seem to have placed myself is not really one of conflict. The belief in ETI (in virtue of the RDH) does not necessarily impact on the veracity of UFO reports of such encounters. That is, with the evidence available to me at this time (I have never personally had a UFO experience), a definitive conclusion on the subject becomes difficult. But, in the judgment of many respected investigators, psychologists, scientists, and politicians, something unexplained and special seems to have occurred in at least a limited number of such reported incidents. I will not engage in a vast compendium-like list of reported UFO incidents to shore up an argument, one way or the other (there is no shortage of books on the subject). But, many seemingly rational academics and politicians have gone on record believing that some form of universal (earth bound) government censorship mechanism is in place, whose goal seems to be to try and limit any kind of public awareness of official investigations into certain "UFO incidents", their findings, and conclusions. Whether these kinds of sentiments have validity or simply reflect some aspect of a collective human nature-based hysteria comprises a mystery in and of itself. However, there is a discreet percentage of reported UFO incidents for which ostensibly hard evidence seems to exist, but for which reporting from the governments involved does not. The very fact that governments still consider most of such information as classified and secret, in fact, increases the speculation supporting the existence of administrative conspiracies specifically aimed at hiding whatever facts they may have about specific UFO incidents. The suspicions are further heightened when documents pertaining to UFO events, and obtained under the Freedom of Information Act of the United States, contain numerous blanked out portions that render useless their interpretation. One could excuse such behavior for security reasons; to prevent sensitive information from getting into the hands of one's potential enemy. But the world has changed in recent years with the demise of the cold war, and the release of much geopolitical tension on the planet. Still, this kind of UFO secrecy persists and serves to fuel both rational as well as irrational speculation about UFO and ET based phenomena.

Every now and then, some academic comes under fire for delving into UF-ology. Take the case of Pulitzer Prize-winning Harvard medical school professor and psychiatrist Dr. John Mack. He wrote a book in 1994 entitled "Abduction: Human Encounters With Aliens", purported to be based on the testimonies of his patients. While not directly vouching for the content of the interviews, nor espousing a belief in "space aliens", he thought that some unknown traumatic experience could explain his patients' strange memories. While Harvard's medical school decided not to censure the professor, "who studies people who say they were abducted by space aliens", they did tender him an unusual public reprimand—not to let his enthusiasm for UFO research steer him from the path of professionalism. Some of Dr

Mack's colleagues considered this to be an unmitigated challenge to academic freedom. An outsider is left to wonder what perceived harm had been done to Harvard's prestige that would have warranted this kind of publicity. Its only real accomplishment was to draw widespread media attention to the question of aliens from space and the whole UFO question in general, as well as the involvement of a growing number of credible academics in the field.

Enrico Fermi, the noted physicist, when asked his opinion with respect to the existence of ET's and UFO's mused back, a half century ago, with the now classic reply: "So, where are they?" With the exception of those individuals that claim personal UFO experience, the rest of us must deal with the issue in a somewhat ambiguous way. On the one hand we all have a sense that we are indeed being kept in the dark about such things, possibly out of some paternalistic concern on the part of respective governments for our ability to absorb the truth, whatever that happens to be. Or, conversely, some view such secrecy as an extension of the "big-brother" attitude of governments "for the greater good of earthly society" concerned with maintaining calm and order in the face of civil unrest that might ensue "if the truth (whatever that may be) be known". But, while most of us can accept the premise that most of the curious events labeled UFO may in fact be unexplained but natural phenomena, it would seem that there exists a small number of truly fascinating events that appear to uniquely defy any logical and terrestrial explanation. While most of us might be prepared to withhold judgment that might place us on one side of the UFO validity argument or the other, I believe it is safe to say that there is a nagging feeling—even among the most hardened skeptics among us—that something is amiss; that facts are either officially being withheld, or that there is indeed a mystery that requires answers. Either way, questions relating to the UFO phenomenon refuse to go away. This feeling is no doubt aided and abetted by the intuition most of us harbor, that we are not alone in the universe—that there must be life elsewhere. I read somewhere that a survey revealed that as many as 95% of academics, scientists and the like, indeed, believe that we are not the only intelligent entities in the universe. If so, then perhaps our planet could be the object of visits, from time to time, by intelligent aliens. Periodically, scientific reports appear that tend to increase incrementally greater confidence in such possibilities. Take for example the recent confirmations of planet-like bodies in the vicinity of star-like objects in our galaxy. Pursuant to the *"principle of mediocrity (PoM)"* introduced earlier, this discovery would tend to lend credence to the premise that ours is only one of possibly millions of celestial neighborhoods where intelligent life might be found—allowing us to see our planet and solar system as a non-unique kind of event in the galaxy. It is within this context that equating UFO type phenomena with our own brand of intelligence takes on a realistic and logical significance. Couple this with the numerous SETI projects actively looking for the objects of that same mediocrity principle (intelligent life elsewhere in the galaxy) and we have a viable intellectual model postulating the likelihood of the existence of alien lifeforms, the likelihood of alien intelligence and therefore, an accompanying technology as well. Without a doubt, we will have to await the disclosure of the definitive evidence before any logical conclusions can be drawn.

As stated in the early pages of this book, the scientific community has a rich tradition of investigating and searching for ETI, and the UFO phenomena must be viewed within this context. The PoM—applied to mankind's reach outward to the universe as a whole—can serve an important purpose here if it helps us put into proper intellectual perspective the connection between the UFO phenomenon and the possible existence of other intelligent beings (besides humans on the planet earth). The importance to human culture of having a definitive answer to whether "we are not alone" cannot be overstated. The very knowledge of an answer, one way or another would immediately impact on every major question faced by humans—from politics to the OoL. Of course, this is the class of question where the only evidence possible would be of the positive variety. That is, the absence of confirmation of ET, no matter how long we wait can never be taken as proof that it does not exist. In this respect, the lack of positive proof today does not invalidate that possibility tomorrow. However, the PoM does indeed provide the intellectual comfort to pursue the matter as a real possibility—personal intuitions aside.

It is thus inevitable that our attitudes towards ETI should reflect a combination of our rich historical record of humankind's fascination with the motions of celestial bodies in the skies together with the new technologies afforded by modern astronomy that increasingly lay bare many of its secrets. Advances in radio telescopy and computerized data processing capabilities hold out the promise that we will be able to detect and possibly interpret signals from ETI sources, if and when they are received. It is only natural, therefore, that widespread publicity of these progressive efforts should result in heightened expectations for timely explanations from government officials of any reported events that could suggest they already have in their possession evidence indicating that we are, indeed, not alone. And the logical extension of the suspicion that governments are not being entirely honest not only opens up and allows for the distinct possibility that ET's may, indeed, be visiting our planetary shores, but in fact, encourages these kinds of attitudes. It takes no great stretch of the imagination to extrapolate the notion of ET visitors to our planet to the question of how they come and go and—voila—you end up smack in the middle of the UFO controversy. Thus, with a little rationalization, we can freely engage in a logical discussion that includes periodic visitations from non-terrestrials arriving in space vehicles of advanced technology, without fear of outright intellectual reprimand. Anyone who does would be in good and valued company. They have included scientists such as James E. McDonald (University of Arizona, Tucson), meteorologist, and J. Allen Hyena, Northwestern University (Evanson, Ill), astronomer—who, following an appropriate study went on record[15] as concluding that: "...a small percentage of the most reliable UFO reports gave definite indications of the presence of extraterritorial visitors."

UFO's, in short, need not necessarily all be simply the figments of the human imagination or the consequences of hysteria, but could logically include real events, real spacecraft passengered by real intelligent beings from somewhere else, who have mastered how to overcome the distance limitations inherent in space travel. At the very least, it could be argued that keeping an open mind on the subject of UFO's is no more intellectually hazardous or ridiculous than keeping an open mind with respect to religious concepts. Seen from a strictly rational point of view, we can even envisage a future state of the human condition where, given enough time (and the survival of humankind), we humans could conceivably become future UFO's and ET's in our own right, for other life-forms encountered on future manned missions to outer space. For now, there is the curious position of government when it comes to UFOs—what they know and what they don't know and what they choose to keep secret. For starters, if the US government has no knowledge of nor concern for encounters with ETs, then one might question the reasons for the implementation of "Title 14, Section 1211 of the Code of Federal Regulations", (implemented on July 16, 1969 and subsequently repealed on April 26,1991), which make it illegal for U.S. citizens to have any contact with extraterrestrials or their vehicles.

B) EXPLAIN THIS:

As stated, there is no shortage of books that deal with the UFO phenomenon in one way or another; I did indicate that I would not subject the reader to needless exposure to more. However, I will mention briefly three reported incidents—one each from the United States, the former USSR, and England that are exemplary. That assessment stems from the fact that each has attracted the attention of prominent leaders in their respective communities—who, also, are searching for the answers.

The first is probably the most celebrated UFO incident both because of the large number of witnesses involved and the United States government's overt attempts to conceal the facts from the American public. I refer to the celebrated crash of a strange craft and it's occupants in the desert just outside of the New Mexican town of Roswell on July 2 1947. What makes this extraordinary event even stranger is the political dimension it has assumed as a result of the interest shown by the late Republican congressman from the state of New Mexico, Stephen Schiff. He complained in an interview that even he, the then democratically elected representative of his state (at one point he was also the chairman of the House panel that oversees basic research) could not get a straight answer from the US military or from the General Accounting Office of the government of which he forms a part, as to the events that occurred. The fact is that farmer Mac Brazel's property was littered with wreckage following the crash of a strange flying object, comprising a 'metallic, foil-like substance' that was very thin, pliable and unusually tough with obscure markings. Subsequently, a US Army officer, Major Jesse Marcel would describe the material as being like "nothing made on earth". It was reportedly resistant to attack by blowtorch and sledgehammer alike and despite its thinness, could not be creased nor permanently bent, reverting back to its original shape and form. The following day, civil engineer Grady L. Barnett, discovered the actual crash site some three miles away in the desert. He reported finding a disk-shaped metallic craft, about 30 feet in diameter, split open and within which were the bodies of small, hairless humanoids with large heads, wearing gray, one-piece suits. A group of archaeology students apparently showed up on the scene that could corroborate his findings. Recently, a film of unknown reliability, reportedly showing the government autopsy performed on one of the humanoid alien crash victims, was aired in both Britain and the US. Despite assessments of fraud by some, the video cannot help but jolt the imagination of those who witness it. The sight of a strange looking alien-kind of being in the process of being dissected represents an eye-opening, if grisly sight to behold. While human-like features are apparent, there are sufficient differences that definitely conjure up a sense of credibility with respect to the alien nature of the whole affair. For the first several days following the 1947 incident, the local newspaper, the Roswell Daily Record, reported the event, as it was perceived—the crash of a strange alien craft with no survivors. Then, like the plot out of some cheap Sci-Fi novel, the government apparently dispatched its military "hush-up" team to cart everything away and "neutralize" the situation. This included re-editing the original news reports to explain away the event as nothing more than the crash of a weather balloon. Perhaps—just another government exercise in damage control.

Intuitively, I feel somewhat embarrassed to include the Roswell UFO episode within the context of our deliberations. While I must admit to approaching such reports with a characteristic dose of skepticism, I would simply raise two points that warrant its inclusion here: First—how do you explain the unsatisfactory response given an elected representative of the state of New Mexico by the federal government department responsible for such information. After all, the cold war is over and more than fifty years after the fact it is hard to conceive of any kind of proprietary technological information that could possibly be associated with the event, dating back to 1947, that could be required to remain secret. What are we to make of it, when even the congressman of the district where the event occurred can't get a reasonable response for a logical explanation? It has been suggested that perhaps the events at Roswell in 1947 represent the biggest story of the millennium: visits to planet earth by aliens and the successful cover-up of the data, the bodies, and the wreckage. Thus, we detail this event, not only because of the plethora of witnesses and evidence, but just as importantly, because of the apparent effectiveness of the apparent cover-up by the US government, to the extent of being able to stonewall even New Mexico congressman Schiff. Let's face it—this whole story could be dispelled of any shred of credibility in less than five minutes if the US government were to open up its books on the event. Because they don't and until they do, the circumstances surrounding the Roswell event will continue to represent the quintessential UFO event in America.

Another important UFO reported sighting occurred on September 20, 1977, emanating from the town of Petrozavodsk on the Russian-Finnish border. This encounter is significant because over 170 witnesses, including 20 border guards and police stationed near the border with Finland, observed it. The sighting was described as a large glowing object, raining downward beams of light, and then moving off in different directions. It hovered above the town for some 15 minutes and was seen over a wide area during a period of 4 hours. In addition, all radio, telephone, and cable lines became useless during the sighting. Col. Boris Skolov recently revealed that this single event motivated the USSR government to establish a well funded scientific research department—a cooperative venture between the Russian Academy of Science and the Ministry of Defense—dedicated to following up and researching any such UFO sightings and encounters. Their mandate was to both shed light on the facts of such matters and, most importantly, to possibly glean from any such studies any new and unknown craft propulsion technology that might serve Russian military objectives. Dr. Anatoli Akamov was placed in charge of a state funded organization set up to investigate and exploit any new propulsion system based on UFO reports. Here was a UFO research program having all 10 million Soviet military personnel as potential observers. Obviously, the Soviets considered UFOs as more than the mere products of hallucinations.

Lastly, there is the famous incident that occurred on the night of December 27 1980 at the Woodbridge joint British-American airbase in Suffolk England (then, one of NATO's largest stockpiles of nuclear weapons). Strange-lighted manifestations occurred that couldn't be explained. Without going into more detail than necessary, what makes this incident stand out is the fact is that the whole event was recorded on video and film by separate base military personnel as part of their standard procedures of investigation. Where is that video record today? Why is it that despite repeated efforts at access by the media, both the American and British governments refuse to even acknowledge the event? The only official document available is the report by Lt. Col. Charles Halt, USAF, dated January 13, 1981 and some tape recordings of the actual real-time witness accounts. In addition, there is the TV report from both the American and British witnesses attesting to the strange events of that evening, as well as a commentary by Lord Peter Hill Norton, Former UK Chief of Defense Staff in the early 1970's to the effect that "either a large number of military personnel on a nuclear-weapons airbase were hallucinating—and for a nuclear base this is extremely dangerous—or what they say happened, did happen; either way, it is of extreme defense interest to the United Kingdom". Apparently, according to Lord Norton, he has never had a satisfactory rebuttal of that view.

So, how do we explain the cover-ups of and denials of UFO events from the government officials of both the US and UK—two of the most progressive western governments—in ironical contrast to the relative openness on such matters on the part of USSR government officials of arguably one of the most repressive regimes at the time? Which leaves us to ponder: "What if..?"

c) Giving "Away From Home" A Whole New Meaning:

Thus, with the forgoing serving within the context of, and providing some measure of, intellectual legitimacy, so to speak, I shall feel free to speculate on the issues that immediately concern this exercise. For, whatever the real facts are, the UFO issue plays importantly within our proceedings, and the RDH model. Let's, therefore, make the crude assumption that periodically, the planet is visited by galaxial travelers who find themselves far removed from their home base. Within our own historical legacies, we have become familiarized with stories of early seafaring voyagers exploring far from home, in search of new lands, treasure—whatever. Before departure, they would stock their ocean-going craft with all manner of provisions that could hopefully sustain a voyage of uncertain duration. However, on the arrival to new shores, whether inhabited or not, the opportunity would not be missed to explore and search out resources that could refresh provisions—fresh water, fresh game and fruit, and the like. And, of course, along the way they could supplement their planned diets with fresh fish. Numerous historical studies of ventures by ancient sailors have disclosed such journeys into uncharted waters by early Norsemen, Polynesians, adventurers and fortune seekers of many diverse stripes. More often than not, unpredictable winds landed them in uncharted territories even though some may have set out according to the crude maps in their possession for other particular destinations. How handy it would have been, had they, upon landing, had access to a visitor's manual describing the particular locality and providing all kinds of information of value to a voyager far from home. Such an hypothetical manual might include, for example:

1] A general map of the neighborhood, including its position on the globe that could provide some estimate of the direction and distance to their preferred final destination;

2] Local compass adjustment data to compensate for the difference between magnetic north and true north;

3] Availability of nutritional resources, including fresh water;

4] Availability of useful natural resources;

5] Availability of energy resources.

In fact, the early explorers of new continents on our planet could leave home in search of unknown lands without any such manual, in full confidence that anywhere they did find land, they could count on replenishing food supplies from the indigenous animal, bird, fish, plant, and fresh water that could be expected to be found anywhere on the planet their journey took them. They could enjoy such confidence for one very special reason: they never had to concern themselves with "metabolic compatibility".

Now, we ask you to extend that basic idea to space voyagers who—arriving in our corner of the galaxy—would find the need of such a manual detailing available resources essential, and not just a convenience. While the information might be similar to that listed above that would have been valuable for our own early explorers, some fundamental additions and some unique considerations would of necessity, be included. The existence of such a manual detailing information about our planet would be nice for starters, but totally useless if it were unavailable or unreadable. In fact, ask yourself where you would place such a treasure trove of information to insure that it could be readily found, and be readily available over great periods of time? Placing it in any single location on the planet would, over time, subject such information to all kinds of geological degradation and loss, due to volcanisms, erosion, all kinds of continental surface movement, meteorite bombardments, etc. The problem essentially becomes, how to insure that such a body of information, and its medium, if it were to exist, be readily available at a remote location the size of a planet, and retain its integrity, while avoiding inevitable degradation and deterioration over time? We have addressed two critical conditions: availability and permanence—both not easily achieved for a body of information on a remote, desolate and capricious planet.

Now, the problems of availability and permanence have one meaning in the context of seafaring voyagers to distant and foreign shores on a single planet, and another in the context of space voyagers trekking to the far reaches of the expansive galaxy. With respect to nutritional resources, there is, indeed, an obvious advantage when traveling abroad to remain within the confines of your own food chain. For earthlings on the planet, metabolic compatibility is pretty well inevitable. For space travelers, all bets are off.

Space travelers have a different set of problems. First, the concept of food chain does not exist because any planet they happen to set down in, in whatever solar-like planetary system, will invariably exclude them as being incompatible metabolically with any existing food chain—in the remote chance they do find some kind of life to exist there. The incompatibility might relate, perhaps, to differences in the amino acid constituents that make up their particular kinds of proteins, chemical chirality, and so on. So, there is a likelihood that space travelers would, of necessity, require the replenishment of certain basic chemical resources that are, for them, nutrition production related. These might not be obvious, upon arrival on a strange planet (any remote planet might be considered unique and strange), and would require considerable exploration to produce an accurate audit of resources that could be of interest. Most importantly, the distances and time frames involved in space travel are considerably greater. As a result, there is never any time to lose once a decision to set down on any particular locale is taken. In other words, while a voyagers' manual would have been convenient for earth bound seafaring voyagers, it could have been considered a luxury and not an absolute necessity. For space travelers, such a manual of travel and resource information, could be considered indispensable and without which such voyages could probably not be undertaken. Thus, if you have followed my train of thought up to this point, we can envisage the identification and establishment throughout the outer regions of the galaxy, of outposts comprising valuable resources for ET voyagers on the one hand, together with the availability of the kinds of information described above, on the other. We suggest that the planet earth could well be such an outpost. Our resources are plentiful comprising the full compliment of elements that make up the periodic table plus an abundance of complex chemicals and in particular an abundance of available water, from which both oxygen and hydrogen can be extracted. As for the voyager's manual we have described above, I'm sure, if you have followed my drift up to now, you have figured out where I'm leading you. What better location to preserve such a body of information over great periods of time than within the chemical medium of DNA located in the cells of an indigenous biological LS—designed and placed there for just that purpose. Such information might even include instructions on how to modify the chemical composition of our particular kinds of amino acid based protein building blocks in order to render them compatible with the respective metabolisms of ET visitors. The LS provides both of the critical conditions listed above for such a visiting voyager's manual: permanence of information integrity over great lengths of time, and availability—within the DNA of any cell (plant or animal) you come across. All an ET visitor would have to do is access the information library and read it. How neat it is.

D) TOURIST INFORMATION?

Thus, we can imagine a space traveler passing through our part of the galactic neighborhood, targeting the Earth-planet outpost for a "pit stop" with the knowledge that an LS database had been established and was available for consultation. Upon arrival, the first order of business would be to take a leaf sample from any green vegetable organism (why bother to mess with squishy animal DNA) and load the sample within the reading mechanism of a DNA reader that could be presumed to be standard issue on such galactic space craft. This would be analogous to our loading a roll of microfilm in a microfilm reader; orienting it, focusing and reading the table of contents for the information you are after. In the former case, the reader-detector would focus on the introns where such information would reside. No use in reading exons that code for LS genetic information; that's like reading the programming information that renders a CD-ROM operational, instead of the useful informational database contained within the readable files. The beauty of having the LS serve as a database is the universal availability of the information across the whole of the planet so that no searching is required. Another great advantage is that the method of LS preservation guarantees its integrity for voyagers over the complete period of time that the planet will remain accessible (3.8 billion years, so far).

I have considered the plant leaf as the ideal format for an intron-reading machine. The leaf is ideal because of its ease of accessibility and compatible characteristics in general. On the macro level, the leaf has a two-dimensional consistency that offers convenience of size and handling. In contrast, animal life must be hunted, caught and more than likely destroyed in the process of obtaining a reasonable cell sample that would be compatible with the reading machine. Also, flesh is messy. Of course, we know that the first land plants were not available until the Silurian period of the Paleozoic era, only some 400 million years ago. This means that for most of the time before then, the EI was only available from the oceans in wet and unicellular format. Then, EI access would have been only minimally less convenient and would have involved the deposition of a unicellular organism upon a microscope-like slide for viewing and the reading of its intron messages.

E) INDIRECT USER:

The indirect user of the ET information encoded in DNA referred to here is the system itself. No, I'm not alluding to the LS transcription and translation execution of its genetic instructions written in the exon sequences of DNA. I suggest that in addition to a body of EI directed towards ET space travelers might be a separate text strategically placed there in the unlikely but possible evolution of an intelligent LS species on the planet Earth itself—one that could conceivably develop the technologies to access, recognize and decipher such information.

Think of it this way. The LS was placed on the planet as an information time machine for the limited and restricted purposes of ET travelers described above in this chapter. The characteristic of the system that allows it to survive under tough and uncertain conditions over a period of billions of years is the built-in adaptive capability of evolution—whose purposeful responsibility for LS survival is predictable according to the RDH, but whose specific directions, at any given time, is unpredictable—in a certain sense. I say "in a sense" because while the precise outcome of the evolution process is indeed uncertain, the LS does tend towards the direction of increased complexity. The system produces, over the long term, more complicated species that, according to our Quantum Theory of Evolution discussed previously, occupy discreet quantified biological states. The tendency toward complexity does stall from time to time as a result of catastrophic physical assaults upon the planet, as well as other fundamental changes of biosphere conditions over time—conditions that tend to scale back the forward push to complexity. The five great extinctions briefly referred to in these pages attest to this reality. But, the LS tendency towards greater complexity does have the potential of eventually producing a species that can achieve such a high plateau of complexity, so as to place it in a different category from both it's antecedents, as well as the co-species that share the planetary biosphere. This species could, in theory, and over time, develop the intelligence and technology to control much of it's habitat and, eventually gain a unique ability to, indeed, comprehend the circumstances of the existence of the system of which it forms a small part. Included would be an understanding of many of the laws of nature, and insights as to how the universe evolves and functions. What I have described above is indeed an exceptional state of LS reality—yet one that has, indeed, come to fruition as "us", the human species. Call it good fortune, an accident, or fate, but here we are—intelligent survivors of the interplay of external biosphere conditions and LS evolution. And, according to the raison d'être of the SETI philosophy and implemented search programs there is a betting chance that we may not be alone in that category. Thus, while humans may simply be the product of a pedestrian biological information system—as the RDH considers the LS to be—nevertheless, humanity and other such evolved intelligent life forms, whose planetary habitats may be distributed throughout the galaxy, may each represent a kind of resultant, longshot possibility—the intelligent products of an evolution capability. As such, we can further imagine a scenario whereby under certain specific conditions an intelligent product of the evolution process, within its respective LS, could qualify for special and exemplary consideration (according to the prescriptions of certain applicable galactic protocols) within the family of other ET civilizations. However, before this elevation of status could possibly become acknowledged as such, there could be expected to be some kind of sufficient and necessary qualifications to be met—perhaps within the realm of intelligence and technological capabilities in order for the rules of such a protocol to come into play.

What better test of such achievement on our part than a demonstrated ability of human technology to access and decipher information contained among and within the intron information library of its genome. The rewards of such a technological achievement would be instantaneous—the instant access to a treasure trove of information specifically awaiting any LS species capable of accessing it. Such information encoded in intron sequences of DNA might possibly disclose, for starters, that the achievement itself qualifies our lifeform, according to some kind of galactic rules that pertain, for full fledged membership into the galactic community—entitled to "all of the honors, privileges and prerogatives" relevant to that newly acquired status. There is no limit to the quality and importance we might attach to information that could be included within such a body of EI (meant for us if and when we could access it). We could conjecture, among other things: a] protocols of acceptable galactic behavior; b] advanced methods of communication (some kind of advanced beacon, perhaps) required to notify others out there that we have come of age and have opted to take our place among them (we may have already received such signals in the past without appreciating their significance). As such, we would be entitled to every consideration that attends such status (welcome to the club, so to speak); c] the full set of operation manuals (perhaps complete with diagrams) describing the LS biological system and how to preserve it under oppressive biosphere conditions. This might shave many centuries off the time required to complete the original medical and molecular biology research programs we are presently engaged in. The inclusion of such information would be justified following the logic—according to the designer of all such systems: "They (meaning us) have finally figured out how to read (the introns of DNA). Why should they have to reinvent the wheel? Let's reward them for their achievements." Consider it a lollipop prize given to a child for having figured out how to tie its shoelaces.

I am the first to concede that the foregoing scenario comprises nothing more than an exercise in imaginative speculation. But, if the forgoing procedure appears frivolous, it is not totally futile. Another way to look at what we are doing is within the context of attempting to conjure up an exemplary way of putting the form and function of the LS design to good use—the illusive "design intent" (in the pursuit of purpose and use) we have been seeking. But, the reader must concede, as well, that once the LS form and function became clear as a possibility, (self-replicating extraneous information library, according to the RDH) what followed was not untypical of the engineering mentality—the consideration of how to put such a valuable bit of technology to good use. Engineers do it all the time. Our brainstorming of possible LS design intent is not much different from data storage experts imagining how to replace the more primitive microfilm data storage technology by the more efficient laser-based CD technology. As it turns out, both LS DNA and CD-ROMs are useful wherever large libraries of information must be available and searched. Today, CD-ROMs are used to make available in compact form the telephone numbers of every phone in the United States. Auto mechanics use them to access quickly any part of any system of every automobile ever produced—no longer having to find and thumb through the printed equivalent. They can then print out a cheap working copy. From multi-volume encyclopedias to complete medical databases, CD-ROMs provide reliable, quick and easy information access, cross-referencing and facile retrieval. If you want some database stored on CD-ROM, you produce an original in digital format, from which virtually limitless perfect copies can be produced. This product of human technology serves as an ideal analog for a DNA intron version of an hypothesized EI database. It is universally available on the planet in limitless copies—within the introns of eukaryotic cells (for only the cost of raw materials—according to Richard Feinmann's nanotechnology model). We have suggested two highly imaginative possibilities as to who could benefit from such stored non-genetic information: ET visitors to our planet as the primary user; and under restricted conditions, a terrestrial based species—if and when it meets sufficient and necessary qualifications.

There is no reason that both beneficiaries could not be simultaneously accommodated—ET's on a regular and ongoing basis, and the human species, as a test of two equally important achievements:

1] First, and obvious is sufficient technological expertise simply in order to access the information;

2] Second, and less obvious, but particularly special is the necessary achievement of survival of our species from self-destruction at the hands of our own technologies long enough for the access technology to become available.

In the light of the above scenario, our species may have arrived at an unprecedented (and unappreciated) crossroad in our history. On the one hand we are arguably on a fast track toward self-destruction; on the other hand, we are on a technological fast track toward accessing and decoding the information in DNA. Ironically, we may, indeed, be unwitting participants in a crucial race between self-destruction and, if we survive, a future of unparalleled enlightenment. Perhaps only random chance will determine which road our species is destined to follow.

Conclusions: *Where Do We Go From Here:*

"Science has no boundaries—so long as it remains within the realm of logic and the laws of nature". Within those guidelines—the remembered words of a respected university professor—"There are no limits to where the imagination can take us in the pursuit of answers to difficult fundamental questions". There is no doubt in my mind that I have strictly abided by the rules while at the same time allowing the imagination to soar. In the process, we have established important links that connect real facts and have called upon the imagination to logically fill in only the missing pieces of the puzzle. Thus, we have formulated the Rational Design Hypothesis as a testable 5th-option solution to the OoL problem. It is the direct consequence of our subjection of the LS to a classical reverse SE analysis. Regardless of one's view on the sufficiency of our case for rational design, or even its merits, the exercise itself has yielded some fundamental intellectual dividends—most of them unintended at the start. Our analysis has yielded the LS form and function at a number of technical levels—the macro, micro, energy, and information as well as an in-depth understanding of the LS subsystems responsible for adaptive evolution. In the process, we have introduced a number of important concepts including:

1] the impenetrable "chemistry-biology interface"—the barrier that separates the inanimate world from biology;

2] the biological primary design platform of life (PdP) that is constant and therefore exempt from evolution;

3] how mutations to genotypes designated as M's and m's can only affect evolutionary add-ons to the PdP leaving the PdP intact;

4] the Quantum Theory of Evolution—which explains how incremental changes in the genotype produce only quantized phenotype results;

5] how biology controls evolution by anticipation—species attribute distributions (SA's) anticipate changes in biosphere condition attributes (BA's);

6] the Equivalency Principle of evolution which equates the effects of biosphere attribute (BA) changes that better accommodate the species attributes of certain segments of the population, to changes to population species attributes (SA) that become closer synchronized with the corresponding environmental BA's;

7] the exceptional form and function of the genetic code as a vital "evolution filter" and the mathematical tables that clearly demonstrate the phenomenon;

8] the all important AmAcid Node Diagrams that serve as genetic mutation maps—illustrating the mutation relationship of adjacent amino acid nodes and consequently demonstrating the reality of the genetic code as evolution filter;

9] the fine-tuning of the 2nd law of thermodynamics to include biological life by disentangling the entropy-energy element from its entropy-information counterpart;

10] a simple mathematical proof indicating intelligence to be the reciprocal of, and therefore the antithesis of, randomness— thereby rendering the former as unlikely to have been derived from the latter;

11] the introduction of a novel generic definition of the life phenomenon in terms of a law of nature—the 2nd law of thermodynamics;

12] a Universal Dogma of Information Flow, which demands that within intelligent systems (such as bio-life) "information" must precede any energy considerations required for its expression;

—just to name a few.

Our SE analysis to date amounts to the facts of biological life that lead to a design hypothesis, as well as the purposes such a design might serve. If this were a murder mystery, we would describe what we have learned to date as the *evidence* of the events that form the mystery, together with the *motive for the events having taken place.* At the beginning of this exercise, we suggested that the issue of LS origin of life by design must be separated from the issue of the origin or nature of a would-be designer. That allowed us to focus exclusively on the OoL question. Now that we have achieved our goal of establishing the RDH, we are prepared to reconsider the 'origin of the designer' challenge.

The RDH represents not just a testable hypothesis, but also a model of reality as it concerns biological life on the planet earth. As such, like any model that purports to represent an accurate picture, it is fair game to demand of that model how its acceptance might affect in particular some of the major human cultural issues that it relates to. In other words, if the results of testing end up validating the RDH, then what are the consequences for life on the planet, and most importantly for humanity, as we grope in the dark for solutions to some very serious problems we face. Because some of those consequences, of necessity, could have enormous impact on our future as a species—just at a time when many believe that we have lost control over human destiny—time may be of the essence, to the point where we may not in fact have the luxury of sufficient time to await such results.

♦It is widely considered that prokaryotes and eukaryotes are descended from the same "progenitor", the common ancestor of both. While the RDH rejects that idea out of hand, there is also the implication therein, (which the RDH does indeed accept) that prokaryotes and eukaryotes are contemporaries.

1Encyclopedia Britannica: Richard P. Feynman
2There's Plenty of Room At the Bottom: Richard Feynman (Internet download)
3Science News: Mar 22 97—p 173
4Science: 13Oct96, p 247
5Five Major Misconceptions about Evolution: p4 Mark Isaak (Talk.Origins Archive)
6Nature: Vol 353, p 388
7Science Vol 256, p 1445
8Nature: Vol 361, p121
9Nature: vol 361, p694
10Nature: Vol 362, p300
11Encyclopedia Brittanica, Electronic Edition1997
12Scopus Magazine—Hebrew University of Jerusalem 1995/96p16
13Science: vol 267, p843 10 Feb95 [265]
14The Wars of Gods and Men; Zecharia Sitchin, p345
15Encycl Britannica Electronic Edition'97: "Unidentified Flying Object"

16. Loose Ends

"It is often stated that of all the theories proposed in this century, the silliest is quantum theory. In fact, some say that the only thing that quantum theory has going for it is that it is unquestionably correct."

—Michio Kaku (1947–), Physicist

The last chapters of any book that espouses new ways of looking at reality are a special place. They can provide the author a final opportunity to plead his case after having reviewed the "testimony" of all of the preceding chapters. The final three chapters of this book serve essentially as closing arguments for the RDH option—chosen to both summarize, and clear up any real or imagined weaknesses that may still remain in our case. Of course, they are also an opportunity to tidy up any loose ends left dangling along the way—a kind of clearinghouse where the author can address any unresolved issues, questions, and contradictions. In that respect, these should probably be the longest in the book in virtue of all of the functions they must perform. There is an acknowledgment, nevertheless, that in the journey of inquiry such as ours, the very notion of a final chapter and thus of an end to such an ambitious exercise, is illusory. If anything, the end of our particular effort represents but a way station, in the never-ending quest for discovery, observation and understanding of the difficult issues we have been addressing. We begin this phase with a summarization and reminder of what our focus has been throughout this exercise.

Our Mission:

The mission of this work is an attempt to read between the lines of what is known about a system we call "life", and to provide a personal best guess solution as to its origin and presence within the universe we inhabit. This mystery effects every one of us because of the fact that while each biological lifeform—the organisms that make up the LS—is made of the same building blocks that comprise the rest of matter in the universe, the biological format seems to represent a special and possibly extremely rare phenomenon. Our OoL quest is intimately tied into our attempt to understand the significance of its existence. During the course of our exercise, we have combed through much of the available information on the subject, and have tried to synthesize a picture of reality employing best guess techniques to fill in what is missing (nothing really new here). Hopefully, as we approach the end of the task we have set out for ourselves, the many complex layers that comprise an integrated picture of our collective reality emerges—like an onion, each layer providing a basis of support for the next. And, even when some layers are less well defined than are others, hopefully, there is sufficient integrity within the configuration as a whole that manages to hold the structure together. In the end, we want to come away recognizing the objective onion for what it is. That is what we have tried to do with the OoL question—by removing the smoke and mirrors—to reveal life for what it truly is, what it is doing here, and finally trying to best guess how it got here.

Our exploratory exercise is a novel variant of similar efforts, its prose style reflecting more of an engineering mentality as opposed to a purely scientific one. The systems engineering mentality searches for the same telltale clues within the same maze of facts and hypotheses as any other, in order to get a feel for, and be able to extract the emergent and understandable phenomenon-wide significance of what is occurring. Engineers tend to want to view and explore things using a multi-disciplined approach and from the top down. This approach is particularly attractive as applied to complex systems and has proved itself particularly helpful here. There are no more complex or more far flung systems than biological life. Scientists generally approach complex questions from the bottom-up and according to specific disciplines. While general differences in the investigative techniques adopted by scientists and engineers may appear to be subtle and perhaps trivial with respect to the results they hope to achieve, we would suggest that when it comes to OoL, technique and approach assume an importance all their own. Engineering, after all, is applied science, and its success or failure is normally measured directly by the extent to which it solves actual problems. When it fails, the truth usually comes as a brutal and expensive reminder of the fallibility of its practitioners. The expression "back to the drawing board" says it all.

The 5th OPTION, in effect, is one engineer's interpretation of reality, as he perceives it. It is a synthesis of both subjective personal experience tempered by an engineering mind, together with the objective evidence gathered by others—in the search to find order in the confusion and sometimes chaotic state of what is known and perceived about bio-life. And while it does not claim to be scientific research per se, it is a rather game rational attempt to read between the empirical lines that the players of science and philosophy have been reciting on the many performance stages of human knowledge. In that respect, this book tries to simplify and make order out of the myriad of complex interpretations mankind has conjured up throughout its history to account for, what I believe, are in fact simpler truths than most of us imagine, many of which are open and understandable to anyone willing and able to engage in the exercise. Other apparent truths become more difficult to comprehend in virtue of the fact that their often contradictory nature lie beyond the horizon of our spheres of experience, and beyond our current abilities to understand as well. Such is the ambivalent nature of the universe itself, where we are able to find simple truth in terms of that which we can understand together with ambiguities that represent secrets we must struggle with simply to put in words, no less try to describe. Therefore, we may be forgiven if in many of the discussions we have already engaged in—and others that follow—we appear to incorporate a significant degree of freethinking speculation. But, all such instances simply reflect our limited collective abilities to just describe, no less come to grips with, the very abstract nature of the critical issues involved—issues that supposedly add up to explain the circumstances of our existence. It is within this tenuous framework of reality itself that we are proposing the RDH option as a solution of the OoL mystery. Still, despite all of our efforts we are fully cognizant of the fact that controversy will continue to plague any design hypothesis—as rational as it may claim to be—simply in virtue of the specific complication represented by the designer issue. Despite the fact that we went to great pains at the beginning of our exercise to delineate "evidence of rational design" from the "intelligent source of rational design"—as two separate and divisible concepts, I am fully aware that the "designer" question will just not go away. We realize fully that the designer question can no longer be ignored and, in fact, must be addressed with the same dispassionate and logical objectivity as the rational design question, if only for the sake of maintaining RDH credibility. In fact the "designer" problem is every bit as much a bottom-line problem faced by the RDH—as much as the chemistry-biology "interface" problem faced by SAb.

Addressing the "designer" question is a risky adventure, to say the least. Obviously, if we are going to be bold enough to tackle the designer issue we shall feel fully entitled to exercise the greatest intellectual latitude in the pursuit of such an illusive goal. Rest assured that we shall not abuse the privilege and that such investigative license we may exploit shall remain logically consistent with the nature of the issues we will raise.

The "Origin of the Designer" Problem:

Way back in Chapter 4, we went to great lengths to explain and validate the separation of the issue of "design" from the issue of "designer" of the LS. In effect, knowledge of the former, logically, need not include knowledge of the latter. A lack of information on the source of design need not hamper in any way the study and analysis of the design itself or, indeed, the search for evidence of design. But, the question of the source of LS design cannot be ignored from the point of view of the very important issue of the "ultimate source of the design intelligence", pursuant to our invocation of the Dogma of Information Flow. The issue can best be described as follows:

Question: What is the possible nature and origin of the intelligence responsible for the LS design as postulated in the RDH?

We have herein postulated a designer hypothesis for the OoL complete with design purpose and design intent. It's primary dilemma and credibility lie within the obvious issue of the ultimate origin of intelligence in the universe that could give rise to an intelligent designer responsible for the OoL on our planet. We may rephrase the inquiry as follows:

> "O.K., you claim that some designer managed to overcome all of the
> difficulties in designing a biological system of life for our planet and
> managed to seed the planet with all of those originating prokaryotic

and eukaryotic lifeforms some billions of years ago. Good! Now where did the designer come from? Isn't the whole problem of origin simplified considerably by the SAb paradigm (which assumes that all of the sufficient and necessary conditions for the OoL are already in place on our own planet) in particular because we have no evidence of any other life beyond our solar system and you cannot discount the possibility that ours on earth may indeed be all that there is? Accordingly, doesn't the RDH simply delay the ultimate question of OoL by relegating its (a would-be designer's) ultimate origin to somewhere else? In the end aren't you faced with the same problems as SAb plus the additional problems of not having any clue as to the conditions on some other world in some unknown star system? At least with SAb we have the "home" advantage. We can play the OoL game in our own planetary "back yard", where we are acquainted with the local rules, our own local biological history within the fossil record, and the specific idiosyncrasies of our own biosphere."

Answer: The logic within the above 'devil's advocate' arguments are, indeed, persuasive and probably represent a most compelling rationalization in favor of abiogenesis over the RDH in spite of all of the obstacles SAb faces. However, let us keep in mind the fact that there are two other OoL options (Panspermia and Directed-Panspermia)—whose support can only be interpreted as rational condemnations of abiogenesis. Cleverly, neither one nor the other even bothers to deal at all—directly or indirectly—with first-cause issues vis-à-vis abiogenesis because of the obvious difficulties anticipated. In sharp contrast, the RDH offers the ultimate solution when it comes to first causes. It also has the most impressive credentials of all OoL options because of the tantalizing fact that the RDH is testable. However, both advantages come at a price: having to conjure up a satisfactory solution to the origin of the intelligence responsible for the design of bio-life on our planet. We do believe the inquiring engineering mind is able to offer some interesting ideas that can help extenuate this most perplexing issue of the design source. But, be forewarned: because of the special nature of the designer question, we shall have to resort to some rather unconventional lines of inquiry and in the process expose any impression that any of us may value of a concrete existential reality to be illusory. The inquiry we shall presently engage in represents, in effect, an interesting side journey on the road that hopefully will culminate in some kind of acceptable "theory of everything" with respect to the LS. The stakes couldn't be higher!

Back To First Principles:

Let's begin with the universe in which the LS finds itself. The fact remains that the biological LS does not exist in some kind of vacuum but is part and parcel of our, at best, obscure universe. We have no idea at present whether biology (as opposed to other logically possible life formats) is a widespread phenomenon, as the Principle of Mediocrity would have us consider, or simply a one-off phenomenon.

But, in order for the LS to exist at all, and in order for us to be able to contemplate that existence—and ultimately its origin on our planet—it is incumbent upon any OoL option to consider within its deliberations the nature of life's existential environment, i.e., the nature of the mysterious universe in which it finds itself. This consideration applies regardless of whether one supports an abiogenetic OoL option or the RDH option. The former must take into account the laws of chemistry and physics—laws that characterize our universe—that might give rise to an abiogenetic result; the latter must consider the primary source of intelligence in the universe (according to the UDIF) that could give rise to a design result. In both instances, we are referring to the respective sufficient and necessary conditions that had to precede the OoL event. For obvious reasons, the question of the source of an intelligence that chronologically must precede human intelligence represents both more complex and controversial issues than those with which SAb must deal. Here we refer to the fact that SAb need simply accept the premise that the laws of nature are such as to promote the evolution of chemistry into a biological LS. (The Anthropic Cosmological Principle attests to the lengths they will go in that quest.) Their remaining task, while difficult, is to demonstrate the evolutionary pathways SAb could have taken on the road from its purely chemical beginnings.

In sharp contrast, the RDH is faced with a totally different set of challenges, beginning with the daunting task—as evidenced within these pages—of demonstrating within the LS itself the evidence of design of bio-life on this planet. Nevertheless, regardless of how we may rate our success in this venture, the RDH must face the all-important challenge—from a purely psychological point of view—of attempting to explain the logistics of the existence of a "primary universal intelligence (PUI)" that would both precede, and could possibly give rise to, the source intelligence responsible for the design of the LS—as indicated in these pages. In the process, we intend to demonstrate that the PUI is also the essential element that satisfies the imperative of the Universal Dogma of Information Flow as it applies to the OoL and, remarkably as well, that forms the essential and fundamental reductionist element within any concept of reality the human mind can comprehend. In order to do so, we begin by taking a critical look at some strange attributes of our universe—characteristics that essentially challenge any meaningful comprehension—characteristics which richly deserve to be classified as "weird".

Weirdness—A Prime Characteristic of Our Universe:

I would suggest that there is no field of human inquiry that has yielded more unsatisfying results (to date), from a purely psychological point of view, than the inquiry into the nature of the universe we inhabit. The principal tools science has enlisted in its search for an ultimate understanding of physical reality are the disciplines of cosmology—the study of cosmic phenomena, and particle physics (also known as high-energy physics)—the study of the constituents of atoms, which together attempt to elucidate with some degree of precision, the true nature of the big picture—that of the universe itself. Let's not forget the most important tool of all science brings to the task, the human mind, which must ultimately interpret the results of any such inquiries. The field of study has progressed in recent years to a stage that literally brings us full circle in our never-ending quest to understand the form and function of our universe. In a twist of exquisite irony, exploration on this grandest of scales, entails detailed knowledge of the most intimate actions and interactions of and between the smallest constituents of matter. Things were a lot simpler not too long ago, when all we had to contend with were the electrons, protons and neutrons that make up atoms. Today, particle physicists have to deal with and explain the over one hundred smaller entities that have been discovered that form an integral part of matter within the framework of the space-time continuum of our universe. Who could have predicted that particle physics would one day have an essential role to play in the understanding of the cosmology of the universe? But, despite all of the seeming progress, most revealing of the often-confusing nature of human knowledge in these areas concerns the many diverse cosmological models that have been developed over the years—with no actual consensus among practitioners in sight. In this respect, there is a recognizable parallel with OoL studies—a sure indicator of how far we still have to go in the quest of mortal humans to gain some understanding of the true natures of both our universe and this system of life of which we form a part, respectively. Along the way, surprises are frequent, and who knows how many more are in store as we await some kind of agreement to emerge. Between the Unified Field Theory—which attempts to describe all fundamental forces and the relationships between elementary particles in terms of a single theoretical framework—and the Grand Unification Theory (GUT)—which comprises a variety of theoretical attempts to unify the "strong", "weak" and "electromagnetic" forces—particle physicists have been kept busy trying to distinguish fact from fiction as they tease apart the fibers they believe form the fabric of our universe. Meanwhile, cosmologists are busy trying to understand the same reality from the other end of the spectrum—where "black holes" and "dark matter" play significant roles as cosmic phenomena on an immense scale. The point here is that each new concept introduced into the game represents a kind of chess move created to solve one problem that creates in turn another conundrum that must be dealt with—at either end of the reality spectrum and everywhere in between. In that respect, and this is the point, OoL studies parallel that of cosmology. The average intelligent person who does not know the rules of the game is presented with different scenarios and descriptions that are confusing at best and, more often than not, probably make no sense at all.

Cosmology is an exemplary instance of our general human propensity toward a comprehension of the greater reality that borders on sheer but wonderful arrogance. It is rare that one can extol the virtues of a human frailty (in this case, intellectual arrogance) whose exhibition generally evokes antipathy. But, in the case of cosmology, and the quest for an illusive TOE (Theory Of Everything), the arrogance is tempered with an understanding that practitioners of the art are precisely in the same position as young children groping to make sense of an adult world that is alien to their limited experience. As such, it is no wonder that many overlapping and contradictory interpretations exist to explain a picture of the reality of our universe that has revealed itself sparingly. But most importantly, what comes as more a disappointment than surprise is that the emerging picture appears to be one that is totally outside of our comprehension. There has been, for some small while, the astonishing realization that while complex equations reflect a certain capacity on the part of scientists to describe an emerging reality within the logic of the language of mathematics, there are a growing number of circumstances that defy anyone's ability to translate those same efficient mathematical descriptions into any other language that makes sense to the human mind. Any attempt to extract logical conclusions from such an effort at translation always seems to end up resembling some badly written exercise in science fiction. Take the simple concept of anti-matter, for example. When physicist Paul Dirac, one of the founders of quantum mechanics, developed the mathematical expressions that would unite QT with that of Einstein's relativity, the so-called Dirac Equation insisted that an electron could logically have a mirror image particle, with a positive charge. In so doing, he inadvertently introduced in 1930 the concept of anti-matter (confirmed in 1932). What happens when matter and antimatter meet? You had better look out, for they annihilate each other and the result is pure energy[1]—a concept quite outside of our daily experiences, yet innocuous compared to some other examples.

Try the following explanations in plain high-school English translated from some of the more credible scientific theories that purport to describe the conditions of the universe we live in:

EXAMPLE 1—QUANTUM THEORY DESCRIBING LIGHT [WAVE-PARTICLE DUALITY]:

"Light photons are particles...well, maybe not really particles, they are more like waves... well, not really—sometimes they act as both... but never at the same time."

In fact, in the words of Niels Bohr "to understand a specific experiment, one must use either the wave theory or the photon particle theory but not both". He called it the *Principle of Complimentarity*.[2] In practice, the behavior of light is best explained using its wave properties when it is traveling through space or a medium (like glass, water or air) and using its particle properties when it interacts with matter. From the human experience perspective of: "take your pick but you can't have both" everyday reality, complimentarity appears quite bizarre and rightly defies our comprehension.

EXAMPLE 2: QUANTUM THEORY DESCRIBING ELECTRONS:

The tiny electron—traditionally thought of as having a definite charge (negative) and mass as it orbits the nucleus of an atom—fares no better. Electrons, too, seem to behave like waves. In fact, electrons have cloud-like properties, in deference to their probability distribution... but "when they act as particles, you can't know how fast the are traveling if you know where they are; but, you can if you don't know where they are." This forms the crux of the *"Heisenberg Uncertainty Principle"*. Psychologically, it fares no better than complimentarity!

EXAMPLE 3: QUANTUM THEORY DESCRIBING EVENTS:

"'Reality', in reality, has only some kind of potential existence which can be expressed as some kind of hazy cloud-like probability mathematical equation called a "wave function" before anything happens...but for something to happen you need an observer to "observe" what is happening...which causes the wave function to collapse, so that something can happen. There is no underlying reality without measurements and measurements are the only reality!" Say again?

EXAMPLE 4: SUPER STRING THEORY:

"Space is made up of superstrings that are so small (one-dimensional, massless strings, 1 divided by 10 followed by 33 zeros cms. in length) that they cannot be detected so we don't even know if they exist, but if they do exist, then they exist in a space-time of ten dimensions...but since we can only experience three dimensional-space plus time in our everyday world, perhaps all of the others are curled up (described as "compactified") and unnoticeable". Good luck!

These might be typical statements by a student trying to explain QT, wave-particle duality, Heisenberg's Uncertainty Principle or Super string Theory to a casually interested friend using plain English. Scientists normally won't even try because when they do, there is a sense that they aren't sure of what is really going on relative to the experiential "real" and personal world we share.

Is It 'Metaphysics' or 'Physics'?

The practitioners of metaphysics have traditionally been charged with investigating what exists and determining what is truly real. They tend to rely on such internally related notions of substance, quality and relation to back up claims that only what is substantial truly exists. However, even they acknowledge that any concrete thing one selects to exemplify the notion of substance turns out in practice to answer and be dependent upon a certain description—which means that it cannot effectively be spoken of apart from its attributes. The conclusion is that substances are no more primary entities than are the qualities and relations that describe them. Some metaphysicians have proposed that it is science that seeks to define what is ultimately real as opposed to what is merely apparent. However, as we shall see, the question of contrast between appearance and reality is by no means peculiar to metaphysics. Physicists attempting to explain the peculiarities between appearance and reality as revealed by Quantum mechanics represents a case in point.

A group of eminent scientists: Einstein, Podolsky and Rosen in 1935 proposed their "local realism" (EPR) hypothesis that attempted to do just that.[3] They argued that common sense dictates that physical quantities whose values can be predicted with certainty before they are measured must have an "element of reality", as they put it. Unfortunately, the physical universe we happen to live in just doesn't happen to necessarily agree with the common sense of curious scientists. And, two recent experiments using space age technology—one by Leonard Mandel at the University of Rochester, New York, and another by Anton Zeilinger, University of Innsbruck—aimed at solving the controversy, both confirmed unequivocally the failure of the EPR hypothesis of the 1930's, rendering the concept of local realism null and void, making the EPR appeal to common sense look like some naive exercise. "The weirdness of quantum mechanics jumps out at you" is how one researcher described the recent work. Take the related paradox involving a concept labeled "quantum teleportation"[4] that takes advantage of the quantum phenomenon in which a single event produces two photons traveling in opposite directions. In Quantum mechanics, such particles are said to be "entangled". Because some seemingly invisible bond ties them together, no matter how far apart they are separated physically; QT demands that the attributes of neither photon can be accurately defined until an observer detects one of the two partners. The ultimate conclusion is that if one of the pair of entangled photons is "observed", thereby "fixing" its polarization from a range of possibilities, then the other photon must assume the opposite polarization simultaneously, no matter how far removed (even to the other side of the galaxy) the second photon has traveled from the first. Let me remind you that this is not science fiction, and yet—it strikes us that it just as well might be. A full six decades following the disagreements over the nature of "existence" that took place in discussions between Einstein and Niels Bohr, a founder of QT, the conclusion that unmeasured physical quantities have only a "potential" existence (with their ranges of possible values described by a haze of probability that drifts about) still stands. According to the equations of quantum mechanics, only when a measurement is actually made, does the "wavefunction" collapse to just a single value. Thus, in metaphysical terms—something (within the range of probabilities) must become apparent (must be measured) before it can become real (for the wavefunction to collapse). The fact remains that from our limited temporal perspective, the universe indeed defies our common sense. As such, ours is, in the view of many observers, a weird universe. Again, it is important to make the distinction—it is not the theory of reality that is weird—what has become clear is that it is the reality itself that is weird. Another way of looking at it, and more to the point, is the undeniable fact that our perception of reality disagrees markedly with an acknowledged greater reality—that which our mathematical expressions tell us, indeed, prevails. Thus, while we cannot help but marvel at our human ingenuity that can invent new methodologies for uncovering the hidden mysteries that define the greater reality of the universe, we have come to realize full well the cognitive limitations inherent in any attempt to actually relate the resultant findings to our conscious world—that which is insulated and filtered through the human mind, and which defines reality within personal experience. In effect, these kinds of intellectual exercises have finally opened up an acute awareness of at least two distinct realities we must accommodate: the one that is personal and intimately knowable to biological beings; the other, mediated only through a mathematical interface—from which we are totally insulated and therefore, of necessity, must remain virtually incomprehensible in any meaningful sense. We could just as well be referring to different universes, for all we know. For the foreseeable future, it shall remain questionable whether there is any practical hope that the human mind will somehow be able to bridge the intellectual interface that separates these two universes, as it were. Ultimately, the only answers in which we may find intellectual comfort may have to derive from the refuge of philosophy. Even science, as exercised by inquiring human minds, may have its limits—elastic limits we appear to be straining.

Is It Real, or Anti-Real?

In a sense, success at understanding reality may ultimately relate back to the relationship between human knowledge and the world, a debate that goes under the umbrella term: "scientific realism" between the realists and the antirealists. The question is whether scientific knowledge does correspond to and truly represents how the world really is. The "realists", can point to our tendency to view knowledge as transparent, reflecting the hard-earned rewards of clever scientists and researchers. The "antirealists", on the other hand, can claim that since science is probably the best knowledge we can have of how the world really is, it is thus impossible to peel back further the curtain that may be separating us from an ultimate reality and questions whether, indeed, science has, in any particular instance, got it right. Regardless of where you stand in this debate, the fact that the very idea of ultimate reality can be questioned is the relevant point to this whole discussion. While no one in their right mind would question their own personal reality—that which defines one's conscious existence—it must be remembered that any LS terrestrial lifeform's reality exists within the very special context of biological reality—a reality recognized as an intelligence rich environment. A flourishing debate among intellectuals of all stripes continues on how we are to assess the relationship between intelligence—a unique characteristic of LS organisms—and the illusive greater reality we sense exists out there. According to science, the heart of the matter may, indeed, reside within the mysterious mathematical expressions that accompany QT. When you get right down to it, QT and experimentation, in essence, force us to question whether any reality is possible if there is no observant intelligent entity available to assess it initially—thereby, in effect, creating reality; effectively making itself happen. Accordingly, reality ends up being—not something concrete—but the individual products of intelligent entities that, in virtue of intelligence itself, can force the collapse of their particular reality wave function. These are the kinds of considerations we shall shortly examine as we continue to set the stage for dealing with the origin of the designer intelligence question.

Quantum Theory to The Rescue?

The Theory of Everything (TOE) is the proverbial phrase coined to imply the sought after but elusive single theory that science hopes will resolve all of the contradictions and paradoxes that presently obstruct a true comprehension of reality within the universe of which we form a part. At present, a number of enduring theories have divided up into various terrain and turf the kingdom of reality as it is perceived by science: Quantum Mechanics Theory, the Theory of Gravity, Special and General Theories of Relativity, and various "models" of the universe, as they have come to be recognized. On their own, each of these theories has contributed much towards providing a possible solution to particular parts of the puzzle that is the universe. The problem is to find a meaningful way to coalesce the conflicts that have arisen between them into a seamless framework. For example, it is the ultimate quest on the part of the science of particle physics to link together in a single comprehensive framework the four fundamental forces: the weak, strong, electromagnetic and gravity, as well as their respective particles: the so-called W, Z, photon, and the graviton. It is considered that once the relationships between all of these can be described and secured, science will have achieved the ultimate quest of physics—the "Theory of Everything". But, if and when the fulfillment of this important and lofty goal is accomplished, will that necessarily conclude the matter? Will human intelligence then consider that an understanding of the reality of our universe has finally been placed within our grasp? Judging from our discussions above, I truly don't think so. For in the course of searching for the TOE we have come to appreciate the fact that even if we do manage to resolve the relationship between all of the forces and their particles, there will always be unanswerable questions that relate to existential issues. There is arguably no greater paradox standing in the way of our comprehension of reality than the dualities that impose themselves within "quantum reality". As previously stated, among these are the dual representation of the basic electron in terms of a particle and wave. Now it is perceived as a point, and then as part of a wave: a paradox. Then there is *Heisinger's Uncertainty Principle* that limits what we can know about an electron;—if you know its location, then you cannot know its momentum—the act of measurement seems to interfere with the measurement. It's a trade-off—you can know precisely one parameter, but not both. While somewhat unsettling, intuitively we can rationalize these questions because the choices are black and white, so to speak. There are no shades of gray in between. You can choose one or another of only two available choices. But, even if we do one day come to grips with some of these duality issues, it would seem that there will always be one fundamental notion deeply imbedded within Quantum Mechanics that relates directly to our deliberations that will always evade total human comprehension: the mysterious "observer phenomenon" that is an essential element of quantum reality. Here, astonishingly, everything is gray. What is an observer and what are the sufficient and necessary characterizations to qualify it as such? This observer phenomenon that defines quantum reality seems to be in a class by itself. It doesn't merely claim to define reality—it is credited with virtually creating reality. The concept that "quantum reality can only be defined by an intelligent observer", whose act of observation effectively makes the observer not only an active partner of any reality that exists but the virtual architect of that reality, rivets our attention. And, this is the point. The fact is that we can draw an interesting relationship between the very real dilemma faced by quantum physicists over this observer phenomenon, and the dilemma we ourselves (RDH) face with respect to the nature and source of the external intelligence that, according to our UDIF principle, had to precede, and be ultimately responsible for, the design and origin of biological life on our planet. Are we having fun yet?

While uncertainty among the attributes of electrons is an interesting scientific study, uncertainty takes on a whole new and personal meaning when it comes to the very meaning of reality in the first place. Heisinger's Uncertainty Principle raises the issue of how the measurement of one attribute prohibits measurement of another. How about taking uncertainty a "quantum leap" further with the acknowledgment, that reality itself cannot exist until an intelligent observer (i.e., a conscious entity) observes, thereby effectively creating that reality. The implication (it is more than just an implication) is that a conscious observer and that entity alone, is capable of changing reality on the fly. It's the quantum version of: "When a tree falls in the forest and no-one is there to hear it, does it still make a sound?" The quantum version runs something like: "In our universe, possible alternative reality choices seem to be made only when there is an intelligent observer there to actually scan the present, and not until then." This curious truth imposes itself mathematically, in accordance with Erwin Schrodinger's equation, where the act of "observation", itself, causes the collapse of the so-called "wave function"—which mysteriously serves to choose and set a single reality from all of the statistical possibilities that the mathematics say existed before. How is this state of affairs to be interpreted? Several scientists have given it their best shot:

In 1957, Hugh Everett III proposed in this regard what has come to be referred to as the "many-worlds" interpretation, which suggests that when a wave function collapses following a measurement by an observer, the universe branches into a number of non-interacting universes. Each of the possible outcomes represented within the wavefunction occurs, but in a different universe.[5] Not very satisfying, is it?

A famous mind experiment was designed by Erwin Schrodinger to provide a "human" visual representation of the strangeness of quantum reality (as well as challenge the mind, no doubt) to explain the seeming paradox it portrays. One can contrive of an apparatus wherein a live cat, shielded from view in a black box is subjected to a lethal dose of poisonous gas. The question is: "is the cat alive or dead?" Then, "how do you know?" And next, "Well, LET'S LOOK IN THE BOX!" Aha! According to QT, the mathematics cries out emphatically that until an observer actually looks inside the box, the "Schrodinger's Cat", not only could be alive or dead, but, in fact, may be neither alive nor dead: a puzzling state of affairs, viewed from the perspective of one's own personal experience. (While it has been suggested that Schrodinger's Cat was his way of highlighting the weirdness within the implications of his mathematical equations involved at the small particle micro reality level, rather than representing an actual and realistic phenomenon at the "cat" macro-level of reality, a satisfactory explanation as to how to realistically separate the two has yet to be offered.) According to QT, the very act of "looking" by the mandatory "conscious observer" makes one of the statistically possible choices actually happen. It makes one wonder how we in the real world, who live our lives oblivious and unconcerned with quantum effects, can comprehend the "twilight-zone" aspect of this quantum reality. In reality, perhaps we can't! But, the mathematics that says it is so has been shown reliable and consistent to this day, with all experimental result; which leads us to ask:

What Is An Observer?

Our concern here is with the concept referred to as the "observer phenomenon" which physicists insist, after careful analysis of the results of their experiments, comprises an integral component within the equation of reality. What defines such an observer—one that can establish the conditions of our reality in the universe? First and foremost among the qualifications for such an entity would seem to be a sufficient and necessary modicum of intelligence—simply in order for it to be able to apply its attention to and thereby witness in some critical way whatever it is that can go on to qualify the procedure as the sufficient and necessary pre-requisite which then results in an interpretation of reality. Does any of this make any sense to an observer-reader of this work? We should note that nowhere in the equations that constitute the quantum wave function are there any limitations on the nature of the intelligent observer—but we are told that it must exist for things to happen. Because quantum physics concerns itself with energy and the particles that carry and transport it, as well as the observer conditions that dictate ultimate reality, we are faced with a relationship that is both curious and bizarre to contemplate, and ends up as our very own reality paradox; of energy and particles on the one hand, and intelligence—which intimately concerns the designer origin question—on the other. Think about it: we are used to treating conscious intelligence as the evolved attribute of the human species that has itself evolved to become arguably the highest complexity rung on the LS evolutionary ladder. In other words, from our own anthropological perspective, it took a lot of trials and tribulations of evolution to finally produce a humanoid species possessing that most unique and valuable attribute we call human intelligence. Within our own experience, we are alone as the possessors of this attribute referred to as "higher intelligence", and have therefore come to think of that quality as uniquely our own. Unquestionably, varying degrees of intelligence are exhibited by all of our fellow species, but only humans have the intelligence wherewithal to discuss these or any other issues. But, our point is: here we have QT shoving observational intelligence—at the most fundamental level of matter and energy—right into our collective faces: the very same intelligence it appears the reality of our universe depends on; this just in order to validate the equations that define the nature of matter, space, and time—the very stuff that comprises the essential scaffolding supporting our own existential reality. As such, for the very sake of reality as we know it, intelligence of the observer variety must have preceded the biological version extant on our planet or anywhere else it may exist for that matter—just in order for our system of life to acquire the environmental infrastructure regarded as necessary and within which it could assume its biological form and within which it can function. In other words, the logic of QT implies the existence of an observer precedent to the existence of the planetary biosphere—the habitat where life originated and took hold. All of which complicates further our ability to understand reality. Then again, why should it be any easier for us today than it was back in the days of Einstein, Podolsky and Rosen? Six decades later, scientific experimentation continues to confirm the weirdness of quantum reality while our own intuitive and common sense understanding of existential reality remains forever steeped in a version better described according to deterministic classical physics. Can there really be more than one kind of reality—one for the inanimate universe and one for intelligent beings? In the light of the above deliberations, does the "many worlds" idea proposed by Hugh Everett now seem somewhat more palatable?

What Is the True Meaning of Reality?

As far as humans are concerned, reality has two distinct aspects to it—one external and one internal. From the point of view of our kind of biological life, the external reality of our universe seems universal and comprises the total theater where it can exist, together with all of the conditions that apply. The internal reality is existential—how we humans perceive the external reality including all of the biases particular to our individual and personal fields of observation. For the purposes of our primary issue—that of determining the nature of the design intelligence that the RDH depends upon to qualify the design option—we are here interested in the former—the external reality of the knowable universe as represented by the physical operating conditions that describe its form and function. We begin with the space-time continuum of the universe; all of the laws of nature (those we know of and those about which we haven't a clue); all of the forces and their carrier particles; all of the particles of matter; all of the galaxies, stars, planets, etc, etc, etc. In essence, what we have described is nothing less than the observable, explorable universe that serves as our external world—that of all biological life on our planet. For all we presently know, biological "us" may be the only witnesses of this or any other world. But curiously, we are reminded that for that external world to exist at all, according to QT, there must first have existed some independent observer—some *other* independent observer—just in order to make possible (through the act of observing) the three-dimensional space-time environment, without which, the likes of biological life, apriori, cannot exist. But the fact remains bio-life does exist—and so does the world it requires to exist in. The conclusions are forced upon us so long as we can still rely on the intellectual comfort of last resort—the rules of logic: Accordingly,

1) An important repercussion of the observer phenomenon of QT is the inclusion of an intelligent observer, as an integral part of the structure of nature, and not merely an evolved consequence of it.

2) Consequently, intelligence is every bit a fundamental part and requirement of the reality of the universe (to qualify as the conscious observer within QT) and not merely a happenstance manifestation of some evolved species.

3) Without the intelligent observer to define event horizons that comprises reality within our universe, one can question whether the space-time continuum exists at all, or indeed, whether anything in the universe can really happen at all.

4) The RDH postulates the Dogma of Information Flow as an apriori statement of fact as it relates to any designed system including the intelligence responsible for the design of biological life on our planet. Therefore,

5) The source of the intelligence required to validate the RDH and the source of the intelligence that serves in the capacity of the observer phenomenon in order to validate quantum reality are one and the same.

Once again, this perplexing situation could and would be discounted completely but for the fact that QT has passed every important test thrown at it in the last three quarters of a century and, like it or not, seems to be here to stay. And our explanatory discussions above could just as easily be discounted completely except for one important fact: no one to date has made even the slightest dent at breaching the logical interface that separates quantum reality from our common sense reality. The only issue remaining that concerns us is: What is the derivation of the common intelligence responsible for both the observer phenomenon that gives rise to the external world, as well as that attributable to LS design. In fact, the answer becomes trivial compared to what we had to deal with in order to arrive where we are. Here we defer to QT, which, in accordance with our discussions above, forces us to conclude and acknowledge the following:

For reality, as we understand it, to exist at its most fundamental level, that quality we define as "intelligence" must be included within the exclusive register of fundamental constituent elements that comprise the foundation of our universe. These include the material elements that make up the constituents of matter and energy and the non-material elements we call dimensions—the three that define space and the one that constitutes time. We make this claim in virtue of the inherent capability of such an intelligence to satisfy the "observer phenomenon" without which reality—and possibly the reality of the elements of our universe itself—cannot exist. As such we suggest that because intelligence can be considered as a non-material component, it should be classified as a "fifth dimension", completing the "*intelligence plus three dimensional space plus time*" continuum. We designate intelligence first among equals in deference to its primacy as a precursor element of the universe, responsible for its very reality.

The universe thus comprises:

a) Five dimensions, all characterized by their non-material ephemeral qualities comprising: (1) primal intelligence (an analog of human intelligence, without necessarily incorporating human limitations); (2, 3, and 4) three dimensional space; and (5) time (of the five, only intelligence might be defined as a comparative constant—the other dimensions are relative);

b) Matter and energy—the actual stuff comprising the material of the physical universe (while the sum total of matter and energy in the universe may be constant, the one is convertible into the other via $E=mc^2$);

c) The fundamental laws of nature that dictate the rules of engagement and the parameters that specify the conditions of interaction of all of the above (these, of necessity can be considered constants of our universe).

Laying the 'Origin of the Designer' Question To Rest:

It is this intelligence (that which we have designated as the first dimension—the very one demanded by QT in order for reality itself to exist—and that which must have preceded our own evolved intelligence) which we shall take as the sufficient and necessary primary intelligence (according to our UDIF), that ultimately gave rise to the intelligent entity that could implement the design and implantation of biological LS on our planet. We do not claim that this "primal" intelligence itself was the instrument of LS design and existence—only that it was the necessary precursor that could give rise eventually to an intelligent entity that is responsible for the design and implementation of biological LS here on Earth (and ultimately responsible for generating any and all other intelligence that may exist in our universe).

Question: "Is it necessary to assume that the intelligence that gave rise to Life on our planet in accordance with the RDH would have had to have the form and function of our kind of biological life (e.g., the human kind)?" This may really be the crux of the whole "designer origin" dilemma. Why should any consideration of the question of a designed biological life here on earth be necessarily linked to a similar process elsewhere in order to account for the origin of the designer? For all we know, it could have—but why assume it? Admittedly, all we can comprehend about life and intelligence is inevitably restricted to our experiences with that of which we humans are the only known example. Nevertheless, logically speaking, there should be no imperative to constrain the designer's form to mere biological characteristics or standards. The only logical definition necessity for a designer of anything is that it comprises the necessary intelligence and technological skills to accomplish the task. Intelligence, in and of itself, can be considered to be that which can create and process information. As stated, if reality in our universe "logically" depends upon its observation by an intelligent observer, then any such reality, a priori, must contain whatever necessary intelligent entity sufficient to fulfill its observer requirement. As our experiences with computer hardware and software increases and as computer capabilities increase as well, we may have occasion to witness intelligence akin to our own replicated in hardware, as opposed to our own wetware. Could human engineers replicate consciousness within computer hardware that could qualify as observers within the requirements of QT? Is there something special about biology such that our kind of intelligence can only exist within its wetware format, or is the biological brain just one of a number of such possible formats wherein intelligent behavior can occur? The fact that we cannot answer satisfactorily any of these questions forces us to allow the possibility of extending intelligent capabilities to other intelligent formats, so long as those formats can encompass the adequate complexities that their kind of existence and intelligence requires. Thus, we can consider the probability for the existence of some kind of intelligence that preceded our own, simply to justify reality within our universe, commensurate with the existence of the sufficient and necessary intelligence required to validate a potential designer of our biological LS. But significantly, this line of reasoning allows us to suspend any necessity for the intelligent designer to have had an evolved biological origin elsewhere within the context of a SAb origin. So, where does that leave us? The fact is we are no closer to understanding the origin or nature of a possible designer intelligence for bio-life—any more than our best minds have an inkling into the true nature of the source of intelligence demanded of the "observer" within the arena of quantum reality. Don't misread our objective in making the above statement as some attempt to compare our problem with that of QT. On the contrary, the case we are making is that the two problems are not just equivalent but in fact are the same problem. There exists a primal core intelligence in our universe responsible for quantum reality and ultimately responsible as well for the design of any systems including bio-life on our planet. We suggest that to attempt to elucidate the issues further, one would have to defer to philosophical contemplation.

One additional clarification is in order: we must differentiate between a core intelligence responsible for reality and design, as opposed to the laws of nature that apply to random processes. Random processes adhere to the dictates of the 2nd law (are entropic in the classical sense), whereas intelligence and its products, on the other hand, can be considered as selective promoters of order by channeling energy in ways that defy those dictates (disentangling entropy energy from entropy order as prevails in living systems) as discussed earlier. We made the case earlier that intelligence is the reciprocal of randomness and therefore could not be derived from it. Therefore it follows that intelligence and randomness each shape the interactions of matter and energy independent of the other—operating, if you will, as separate and parallel influences in the universe. QT demands an observer intelligence for reality to exist, and the resultant laws of nature operate under the abiding rules of entangled entropy—the universe is entropic under the firm grip of the 2nd law. For living systems to exist, the intervention of intelligence is required to disentangle the energy and information aspects of entropy.

Closing The Circle:

Thus, the intelligent designer and its own history need have nothing in common with our kind of biologically evolved species intelligence. It is sufficient for our purposes, simply to postulate its prior existence within the physical universe. This, in order to validate both the conscious observer—an intelligent entity demanded within the context of quantum reality, and which can also serve as the precursor intelligence source that had to have preceded the designer intelligence (according to the UDIF) that could account for our kind of intelligent biological LS. We believe our obligations in this matter end here. Our license to do so derives directly from the paradoxes emanating from QT—which science is able to describe mathematically and substantiate experimentally. Consider the existence of the LS designer intelligence within the same context—an intelligent entity capable of implementing a genetically engineered biological lifeform and placing it on a suitable planet within our galaxy. That is all we need consider, because the attainable proof of design must exist within the design itself. And, that evidence of design is all we need to validate the RDH as the authentic 5th OPTION for the origin of life on our planet. If and when that incontrovertible proof of design is attained, we will then have reason and ample motivation to speculate further, and as best we can, on the "nature of the designer" question. Until then, speculation on the designer question serves no useful purpose whatsoever. In fact, it may well turn out that the achievement of such a body of incontrovertible evidence of LS design may, indeed, also provide the only tangible evidence of the existence of the designer that we may ever have occasion to experience. Again, our bottom line responsibility herein rests with discovering and validating acceptable evidence that will convincingly provide confirmation of LS design—that which we suggest can only be gained from within the design itself, and least of all via an understanding of the nature of the designer. The designer may be logically unknowable—not so the evidence of design we seek.

Don't Just Leave Them Hanging:

Unquestionably, some readers will find themselves somewhat uncomfortable (and possibly breathless) with the line of reasoning we have engaged in above, and for obvious reasons. In contrast with the preceding SE exercise, the "designer" discussion we have engaged in above is nothing but pure speculation. Speculation based on logic, to be sure—but speculation nonetheless. Our only justification, if any is required, is that a casual reading of competitive discussions, both religious and philosophical, that attempt to validate a prior intelligence responsible for putting in motion the universe reveal them all to be intellectually wanting. In short, we are in good company. For, that same kind of intellectual discomfort surely accompanies the many and various anomalies, gaps, contradictions, and discrepancies evident among many competing and questionable hypotheses that attempt to describe reality. The following discussion will serve to highlight the notion that incongruities are a fact of life when it comes to weighing and considering many of the hypotheses and scenarios that purport to explain lofty ideas (the nature of the universe and ultimate reality, for example).

Hypotheses are routinely subjected to intellectual ridicule when compared and confronted with conflicting principles emanating from other related hypotheses. Yet, it is hoped that every hypothesis, standing on its own, will contribute something of value that can at least help to illuminate some of the conflicts inherent within competitive theories. For example, what may seem to be the major conundrum of our RDH from the SAb point of view is easily and quickly dismissed within the religious Creationism doctrine by the invocation of "GOD" as the designer and creator of Life on our planet. The Creationist option even includes the solution for the design and creation of the whole universe, to boot, and thereby, sweeps away in "one fell swoop", as it were, the major difficulties that accompany both the origin of Life and that of the universe as a whole. Quite an accomplishment, on the surface at least, wouldn't you agree? One glaring weakness in the case of religious Creationism appears to be its reliance exclusively on the inconsistent interpretations of a collection of ancient writings to bolster its case. By so doing, the Creationist option reveals itself for the intellectual lightweight that it is. Having made the point, our own attempt to find a rational response to the origin of the designer question places us in no more enviable position—simply because the available data is so sparse. This may be seen as a failure—if instantaneous proof positive for the RDH option is considered the only acceptable result. However, that perceived failure can also be construed as a measure of success if we are given points for coming up with a scenario, however speculative it may seem, that finds a logical way to circumvent the designer problem. This we unabashedly can take credit for—and it has been accomplished without compromising the credibility of our RDH—by linking its bottom line (the existence of a prior intelligence) to that of quantum reality (there is no reality without a prior intelligent observer). No smoke or mirrors— perhaps some imaginative cleverness. Lest the reader consider the designer-origin problem as some kind of fatal flaw for the RDH, we have shown it to be no more problematic than some of the fundamental theories science relies heavily upon to describe the greater reality of the universe. The fact remains that fundamental differences on the subject are as common among hypotheses purportedly based strictly on scientific objectivity, as those based on other methods of inquiry.

Free At Last?

The discussions in the last few pages, and the above conclusions, in our view, take the RDH off the hook with respect to the 'origin and nature of the designer' question. It has become, for all intents and purposes, intellectually irrelevant to our task. For the time being, all we need truly consider, with respect to the designer, is that it had to possess intelligence in order to put into practice the technology associated with the design and engineering of a biological LS. Effectively, we need only look for absolute and positive evidence of design to meet the RDH validity requirements. If we succeed in this limited objective, then all of us—the scientists, the creationists and everyone else can begin together to contemplate, anew, the issues that concern the source and nature of the rational design of the LS. We believe that the authoritative evidence that will do the trick, that which cannot be explained away as the products of evolution exists—not as some kind of physical evidence within physiological biology—but as intelligible and non-genetic related information encoded and preserved within the biological medium that comprises the LS. Ironically, evidence of design is not to be found within the window dressing organism products of evolution, but rather within that which preceded evolution—the translatable extraneous information residing within the intervening DNA sequences referred to as introns—the repository and preservation of which, we suggest, forms the object of the RDH "design intent". We have also been able to infer—from the design itself—certain motivations, purposes, and intentions that the designer may have had in mind.

The same kind of scrutiny, as applied to the universe as a whole would seem to be a more challenging enterprise. We can make this statement in virtue of the fact that there appears to be significant limitations to our ever understanding the true nature of the greater reality of our universe. QT makes the point that all such attempts merely reflect our own limited biological perceptions and prejudices that constrain our scope and understanding. In other words, whatever we do claim to understand, must of necessity, remain within the context of the limitations characteristic of our biological system hardwired intelligence potentials, and the restrictions they impose. But, no such limitations need cloud our abilities to understand the OoL on our planet. The difference lies within the experience we bring to an understanding of each.

In the first case, that which concerns a true understanding of the reality of our universe, the best we seem to be able to come up with is exemplified all too well within the glaring paradoxes and anomalies that comprise QT. After more than eight decades, the real message QT continues to tell us unequivocally is that the human capabilities to both experience and understand this universe in a meaningful way seem to be woefully inadequate. These limitations—characteristic of our hard-wired neural physiology—suggest we are "in way over our heads" when it comes to understanding greater reality issues. The fact that scientists have developed skillful means to describe obscure phenomena that characterize our universe, using the sophisticated language of mathematics, does not equate with an equivalent ability to begin to understand and comprehend all of those phenomena. While the math can indeed serve as a bridge between the reality it describes and the human mind, there exists no effective way to bridge the translation gap that separates that reality from our potential to have knowledge and understanding through meaningful experience. QT makes that point clear enough and brings home, as well, the all too apparent truth that within our universe, reductionism has its limits and we had best get used to that fact of life.

With respect to the second case—that of the mystery of the OoL—it can be said that the opposite is true. The fact is that of all the abilities human intelligence comes endowed with, none is more apparent than our distinct capabilities to imagine, plan, and design solutions to problems. Whether those problems involve survival or how to contrive a tool, a machine, or a musical instrument in order to enhance our living conditions, planning and design is a constant experience of human existence. It has always been so, ever since we have been human. In certain respects, we can argue that this distinct ability to design ways to solve problems is what set apart the human species from our antecedents. Accordingly, I am confident and looking forward to the prospect of testing the LS for proof of design—just as I am confident of what evidence we shall find when that splendid task is undertaken.

A Disclaimer of Sorts:

Some may suspect that I may have done science a disservice by seeming to trivialize the esoteric nature of some of the important discoveries and phenomena they engage in. Rest assured, science can well survive any such incursion. But, in effect, all we have done in the exercise above is to help validate the rational case for the designer option and all it stands for—within the context of a modern day SE approach—and have drawn conclusions from the explainable facts. The bottom line of all of the arguments and deliberations above is a simple one: Until proper computer analysis of the language properties of the information within species genomes is carried out, I maintain that any problems that remain with the RDH concept, including design source, can be shown to fall neatly into the same category as some of the unexplained or unexplainable hypotheses discussed above. This is the only disclaimer I will offer. If scientists can afford to shrug their shoulders when confronted with evidence their pet theories can't explain, then all I ask is a similar forbearance and the same latitude they allow themselves. I promised at the very beginning of our exercise that I would not shrink from my responsibilities in presenting the controversial issues. I believe I have kept that promise. I simply appeal for the same tolerance and the same open mind afforded other controversial ideas.

I believe that the RDH—the 5th OPTION—has now been placed on as firm a logical footing as any of the other OoL options, with the added benefit of testability. At the end of the day, my message to any and all detractors is simple: "Test the introns—all the important answers are to found there". The next chapter will deal with the ramifications for the future of life and humankind in particular, which are direct consequences of the RDH model of the existence and OoL on our planet.

---

[1] Nature: Nov 16 1996, p 223
[2] Fundamentals of Physics: pub Heath, p.712
[3] Science: Vol 270; p. 1439 (Dec 1, 1995)
[4] Science News: Apr 10, 1993; p 229
[5] Encyc Brittanica Electronic Edition 1997.

17. Consequences of the Rational Design Hypothesis

"We turned the switch, saw the flashes, watched for ten minutes, then switched everything off and went home. That night I knew the world was headed for sorrow."

—Leo Szilard (1898–1964), Physicist

The RDH model is more than simply a possible solution to the OoL mystery. The very nature of this option has unique implications for humanity that go far beyond the simple question of origin of Life. In addition to solving some very sticky problems that plague all of the other contender OoL options, the RDH touches upon questions that have enormous importance on many aspects of human cultural values, belief systems and human existence itself. As an alternate model of biological reality, we should not be surprised if the RDH turns out to be ideally suited to providing as well alternate answers to some of the heavy-duty questions that have traditionally challenged humankind. The RDH allows us to deal with these issues from its own unique perspective—one that imposes important new consequences for the future survival of our species and all of the other species over whom we have become guardians in virtue of our self-imposed takeover of the planet, its resources, and environment.

As we expand our familiarity with novel RDH perspectives, what becomes abundantly clear is that there are some inescapable consequences that impact upon the larger significance of the existence of our biological LS within the universe, in addition to the more egocentric issues of more immediate concern, such as the very survival of our species. For starters, the RDH impacts on the question of whether we are alone in the universe (the value of "n" within the Drake equation), the existence of ET (extraterrestrial) civilizations, UFOs, and the uncertainties associated with our ever having close encounters with alien life. As well, the introduction of a rational design model raises the possibility of including within the PdP of biology all kinds of extraneous subsystems, including one in particular that we shall discuss—which could materially impact upon the future survival of the human race. Thus, with the introduction of our new model of reality that the RDH claims to be, we find ourselves obligated to test these peripheral topics and others against that model to determine the impact of the one upon the others. The exercise produces some interesting results, for, indeed, the RDH—if and when verified—will have important implications and some surprising consequences:

For Evolution and Complexity Theory:

We have gone to great lengths in our discussions into how evolution comprises the adaptive subsystem of biology and serves to buy the LS the means of survival over great periods of time. It is also responsible for fine-tuning species offspring to the continually changing environmental biosphere. In stark contrast, supporters of abiogenesis assume a "no holds barred" invocation of evolution for everything—from the self-organization of raw chemicals into the precursor self-replicating molecules that SAb insists evolved into biological cells, to all of the changes responsible for transforming unicellular life into the myriad complex multicellular species that today abound. To validate their hypothetical pre-biology phase of evolution they go to great lengths to try to equate evolution with the same elusive extra-biological universal phenomena collectively known as "complexity"—in order to establish the roots of evolution as predating the OoL. The RDH makes clear that evolution is exclusively particular to biological life, i.e. biological evolution has no counterpart in the inanimate universe. The RDH, in validating the concept of evolution as a contrived sub-system designed into—and in order to serve the needs of—the LS, deprives once and for all both complexologists and abiogenecists any basis for an expanded interpretation of evolution, and the underlying basis for seeking the existence of some "universal rule of complexity" as well. We can make this statement because the vast majority of the literature on the subject of complexity deals specifically with life—whether biological or "artificial". Since evolution is seen as the decisive element common to both, it has become a focal point in complexology for much of the intellectual activity seeking to essentially equate the two—evolution with complexity. Remove evolution from the equation and complexity assumes a considerably more plebeian interpretation; complexity then becomes "anything that can be described as too complicated to explain by traditional means or concepts". We will leave the reader to figure out exactly what diverse and independent phenomena qualify under the complexity banner. The RDH contends that the only example of complexity that exists—one that most easily comes to mind and continues to mystify most of us—is the increase in species complexity within the LS attributed to evolution over time. You will recall that the RDH, by way of the SE analysis conclusion discussed earlier, downgrades "complexity" to a distant second place in favor of "survival over time" as the primary attribute of the LS. Nevertheless, from the above discussions, the RDH is fully compatible with and supports the premise that the evolution of an intelligent species within the perspective of a contrived (designed) biological LS is neither unlikely nor likely, but simply a question of serendipity. Of course, it could happen—given enough time and the right circumstances. The RDH would at the same time add the warning: Given the chance to replay the history of the LS: "Don't hold your breath waiting for it to happen again."

For Quantum Theory:

Quantum Theory demands an intelligent observer—just in order for the "quantum wave function" to collapse. Therefore, we have concluded that the intelligence Quantum reality demands for reality to exist at all must derive from a more certain and primary source—one that emanates from outside of and predates biology. Thus, biology alone is insufficient, and ineffective as a practical source to fulfill the observer imperative of Quantum Theory. Finally, whatever other intelligent source we can imagine, that can fulfill the demands of Quantum reality, we accept that it, too, can also serve to satisfy the RDH criterion for the designer of the LS—pursuant to the UDIF. The ball is now in the Quantum reality court, as it were, to shed more light on the "observer" paradox.

The above contentions elaborate somewhat on the most controversial aspects of the RDH as it relates to a designer of the LS and go a long way towards eliminating or diffusing the argument of "original cause". By invoking the "observer" provision from Quantum Theory, we have demonstrated the virtual futility of trying to bridge any kind of gap that separates the LS designed system from any meaningful knowledge of the intelligence source that must have preceded the design OoL.

For Spontaneous Self-Generation (Abiogenesis):

The RDH serves to not only provide a solution to the OoL problem but more importantly offers a way around the dilemmas faced by SAb. In this respect RDH and its SE approach raise the hard questions that SAb has, perhaps, not given sufficient pause to appreciate. By raising, again, the critical question of (negative) entropy and all of the other interface issues that stand between the living state and the non-living state, RDH forces SAb to reexamine the scope and significance of the impressive interface that separate the two. By analyzing in depth how adaptive evolution can only work with large numbers of species and populations to qualify the crucial distribution requirements for species attributes (SAs)—particularly critical near the point in time of OoL—the RDH serves to focus attention on the weaknesses in the case for SAb. In truth, the appeal of SAb is no different today than it was in the days of Aristotle when the so-called "common sense" dictated a solution to the problem of how life spontaneously originates. The difference between then and now is seen to be in both the quality and quantity of the information and knowledge we have gained that puts us in touch with the intimate details of molecular biology. Thus, the Miller-style experiments, that purport to show how common organic materials essential for life can be formed so easily from the raw chemicals of the planet, simply acknowledge what should almost be apriori under the circumstances. That all these experiments, and all our molecular biological understandings, point to the obvious: if you were going to design a system, that is to be implanted in a remote region, (biological life on earth, for example) don't you think it makes good sense to use comparable component materials, and to tailor your design and construction of that system to the ease of availability of local resources? By the same token, no engineer in her right mind would design any remote system (e.g., the LS) that is incompatible with the intrinsic dynamic environment (chemical and physical) within which it must obtain raw materials and energy to maintain form and function. Where else can you expect to obtain the amino acid building blocks upon which the LS depends if not from the ambient chemistry of the biosphere? All that Miller-type experiments accomplish is to confirm this reality.

If you were to construct a manufacturing facility on a remote planet, would you ship bricks, copper wire, iron pipe and all the other construction ingredients to the site? The cost would be prohibitive and you would eventually run out of replacement parts. The most likely scenario would be to assay a common enough type of planet before hand for its abundance of appropriate materials. Then all you would have to do would be to ship only the design and construction information within the computers that will initiate and control the critical construction processes and operations. In theory, you might ship a single suitable miniaturized von Neumann type universal machine that would be able to construct others from the raw materials already in place on the planet in question. The RDH holds that the original organisms implanted on the planet earth comprised a variety of miniaturized von Neumann universal replicator machines based on a common PdP, whose DNA already included the design drawings, construction manuals, schematics, repair and operation manuals for independent existence and reproduction. And, don't forget—the two major mechanisms of adaptive evolution, as well.

Thus, while OoL scientists attempt to "coax" non-living chemical molecules into living self-replicating molecules artificially in the laboratory—in order to show it could have happened spontaneously 3.8 million years ago—all they may really be doing is demonstrating that an intelligent ET could have beaten them to it and done the same. For, it is a long way from molecular scientists (intelligent beings) doctoring a mix of chemicals and jump-starting it into life-like behavior in the laboratory, to showing how it could have sprung up spontaneously in nature—against the ubiquitous negative gradients—without some controlled help of any kind. SAb supporters are fully aware of the fact—that is why they desperately seek a universal rule of complexity that could get them off this hook. What SAb researchers are accomplishing, in reality, is learning increasingly more about how the LS system functions. In fact, maybe one day, humans will have learned enough molecular biological tricks to be able to pull it off so that we will also be able to create biological life in vitro. And, when that momentous day arrives, that accomplishment will surely be hailed as the ultimate scientific achievement on the part of biologists and taken by many as proof of the validity of the argument in favour of OoL by SAb. In fact, it may well be nothing of the kind and the reality, if known, could prove somewhat anti-climactic. Rather than proving, that the original OoL phenomenon on this planet could have spontaneously self generated by happenstance, all that could be legitimately concluded from such a feat is that we have, at long last, learned the complex procedures that constitute the technology for the contrived generation of life, and how to jump start it into existence—similar to the way the designer of our own LS might have done it, some billions of years earlier. That is a significant difference, and as well, the difference between the 2nd Option—SAb, and the 5th OPTION—the RDH.

For Panspermia:

The RDH, in effect, strengthens the PS argument that Life originated from outer space—but not in the way their supporters intended. In effect, PS tries to solve the OoL problem by waving a magic wand and legislating life into existence. The idea of biological spores of some kind coming from outer space is really just a way out of having to endure a SAb scenario on the planet—an OoL option its adherents obviously view as a near-impossibility—thus circumventing the issue altogether. William of Occam, our perpetual referee in these matters, would undoubtedly insist that PS is just a delay tactic, and simply introduces additional conditions to an already tough challenge. PS effectively avoids the OoL issue altogether by forgoing any kind of life-nonlife "jump-start" interface problems. But, PS turns out to be, as a British friend likes to put it, "too clever by one-half". It raises a whole menu of additional problems in the realm of "arrival obstacles" whose complications effectively tend to push it way to the back of the class. However, PS can derive some comfort from our RDH, in that it can perhaps claim, that the designer randomly "flooded" the galaxy with such spores or seeds of life, a quantity of which somehow overcame the planet arrival obstacles and settled in, for the long evolutionary haul. But, without a provable purpose attached to their story, it would seem to lack potency or any effective meaning, for that matter. In this respect, the RDH may serve PS by providing a much-needed boost within the design intent provision, which PS could conceivably latch on to. Then, PS becomes simply a modified and watered-down RDH. William of Occam might well propose: "Why not just stick with RDH?"

For Directed Panspermia:

Here, we can entertain a totally different reaction. Directed Panspermia could, in theory, dovetail nicely with the RDH. Obviously, the directing of the seeds of life to our planet would entail an intelligent and purposeful intervention. But, why does DP simply stop there? Why not postulate as well, that the seeds of life were contrived to begin with, and directed to our planet with a purpose? In fact, DPS can simply add RDH to the tail end of their story, and imply that what they have really done is to posit the shipment of the LS to our planet, without the designer having to make the trip. In fact, RDH can do the same and claim that a smart way to deliver the designed goods—in this case all the different species and organisms required to seed the planet—would be by means of suitable space vehicles, maybe even little ones. Humanity has utilized unmanned space probes that have landed successfully and have performed diagnostic tests and radioed back the results. There is nothing that would have prohibited the disgorging of hardy varieties of cellular life, in order to try to seed these planets as well, if they so intended—inhospitable conditions for success aside. The fact is, that NASA ensures that any contact (manned or unmanned) with other planets are carried out in a sterile manner, in order to avoid any possibility of contamination that might serve as potential livestock. Of course, DPS stops short of suggesting that any lifeform directed to our planet would actually be designed for some purpose. They imply that the exercise is rather in the form of an attempt at perpetuation of their kind of life form, rather than biological life being used restrictively for utilitarian purposes, as a long-range communication tool or repository of information, as does RDH. Nevertheless, in certain respects, we can describe DPS as an arrival scheme, plain and simple. RDH, by contrast, is not concerned with the exact mode of arrival of life on our planet. We assume it was successful and 3.8 billion years later is still serving it's design intent. DPS offers no way of validating it's simplistic idea. RDH, on the other hand, looks to proof of design, both for its validation, and relevance to the OoL debate.

For Creationism:

Curiously enough, Creationism can claim an affinity with and for RDH. But, if so, it comes with a "good-news, bad-news disclaimer". Primarily, the "designer" aspect of RDH serves as a vindication of an important claim of Creationism,—that all the living things on the planet are the product of a deliberate creative process. It also acknowledges, in a certain sense, the intuitive understanding of our ancestors (and vindication for them as well) that the many examples of exquisite form and function to be found in all living things were derived from a phenomenon that required a superior intelligence to create. This much of creationism is upheld within the claims of RDH. Unfortunately, Creationists continue in their denial of the overwhelming evidence in favour of evolution processes that allow the initial founder species so created to adapt to their environments over billions of years. They have placed themselves in the untenable position of opposing any and all evolutionary change in deference to their belief in a design doctrine within a universe considered to be thousands rather than billions of years old. The RDH can help mediate changes in such attitudes by demonstrating, as our exercise has done, the logic of incorporating the concept of an adaptive evolution subsystem within a designed LS. If, indeed, the assertions of RDH turn out to be valid, the RDH may provide the much-needed impetus to propel Creationism into the 21st century, wrapped up in a new and modern package. Of course, in so doing, Creationism may have to reconsider its message—whose sole purpose seems to be to deny the ascendancy of scientific relevance in its affairs, while it desperately seeks to perpetuate its own anachronisms. Unfortunately, as part of that program, there are those who preach that science is as much a belief system as is religion. While in some philosophical sense their claim may have some justification, in a larger sense this accusation bears more on human nature than institutionalized intent. Nevertheless, the two systems—science and religion—employ totally different sets of logic, which have very little in common. Lest anyone reading this book harbors suspicions as to my own true personal understanding of the differences between scientific and religious belief, let me specify precisely where I stand on the matter.

The Difference Between Religious and Scientific Belief

Science only believes that its methods of inquiry are on the right track. At any given moment in time, the scientific description of reality merely represents a database that, self-admittedly, "attempts" to reconcile the disparate and diverse observed elements of that reality. Also, science acknowledges, that the closeness of fit between that attempt at description, and reality itself, has limitations that stem from 1] the inherent limitations of scientific investigative techniques, and 2] cognitive limitations, inherent in any human attempts at understanding the very nature of reality. Science is well aware of these limitations; it can do something about the first, but unfortunately has to live with the second. That said, scientists can still point to the ingenious and practical uses of their discoveries, and this, in reality, should be the tip-off that science is indeed on the right track (think about it the next time you watch the image of an astronaut space walking on your color TV screen in real time).

Religionists, on the other hand, operate as if, for them, such limitations do not exist. On the first point above—religion claims that its investigative techniques are perfect first time around, and furthermore—that it has an inside track on the nature of reality in virtue of direct communication with the source that created it. Therefore, no further investigation is considered warranted. As regards the second point—religion believes that human intelligence is such that a perfect understanding of reality can not only be understood by all, but that it is subject to discreet interpretation by an enlightened and privileged few. Furthermore, while the study of the knowledge written within its doctrines is encouraged, no further investigation on the fundamentals is considered necessary or tolerated. Many organized religions still warn their adherents against trying to independently interpret religious teachings on pain of condemnation by the powers that be. Don't look to religion to provide much in the way of empirical evidence. That's the bad news.

The good news is that religions obviously serve the legitimate needs of many. Some of their historical contributions to human civilization are magnificent, and for those, I believe humanity owes the collective religions of the world a debt of gratitude. Their original contributions toward civilizing our species outweigh by a long margin the excesses and divisions they have been accused of creating among the world's peoples. The stated goal of all religions has always been to try to tame the so-called "inhumane" qualities that are universally apparent within human nature. The extent to which it succeeds and fails is testament to how difficult the transition from animal to moral human has been historically and continues to be. We are, after all, a 'species in transition'—each of us perpetually trying to keep our genetically hardwired countervailing and intuitive "uncivilized" natures in balance with the unintuitive and civilizing forces all modern societies and civilizations rely upon. For that reason alone, I am comfortable attributing any present civilized behavior on the part of humanity—individually and collectively—to the positive historical influences of religious persuasion, and any failures—as evidenced by the many horrible examples of religious intolerance induced inhumanity—as typical of our retained genetic propensities for violence, anarchy and cruelty. The concept of universal brotherly love must rank as one of religions most positive legacies—its limited application less so. The fact that some of its claims at truth have fallen victim to modern science should not diminish these contributions in the affairs of humans in both the past and present. I, for one, believe firmly that without the invention and intervention of religion within human culture, the moral and ethical concepts that are taken for granted today might well have escaped discovery. I am comfortable with that statement because of the many contemporary examples of barbaric behaviour—on the part of individuals and communities alike -that reveals how easily we can revert to the kind of savagery characteristic of the remaining vestiges of the uncivilized world still apparent today—a human condition that was prevalent not too many years ago. The ease with which we slide into aggressive and destructive behavior and conflict betrays our deep-seated human nature for what it truly is. Our warring ways belie any illusions that the human species has evolved irrevocably from its animal past. Thus, there continues to be a pragmatic role for religion in the affairs of the human species—one that is precise and clear; religions should simply limit their goals toward the mitigation of the human genetic disposition for violent behavior, by providing humanity a moral compass for positive behavior modification.

Scientific belief resides in the concept of "assessment". If you assess, (following observation and measurement) a situation in a certain way and are confident that the observations supporting that assessment are factual and accurate, then you are entitled to "believe" that version of the facts to be better than some other. And if, tomorrow, a new version appears in the literature that presents a closer fit in the overall reality picture that scientists are trying to assemble, then a reassessment of the situation may well be in order. The fact is that, in science, there is no allegiance implied within one's "belief". We come to believe a scientific hypothesis when we feel that it "fits" within the mosaic of other scientific hypotheses better than competing ideas. When scientists believe in a theory, they do so knowing full well that there is no implied permanence to that belief. What is science, if not the continuing search to displace ideas that don't quite fit—with ideas that fit a little better? When scientists do so, they imply that they "believe" the new ideas are better than the old. That is the true nature of "scientific belief".

For The Living System (LS):

The RDH postulates that life on our planet is the purposeful establishment of an information system comprising a "universal self-replicating information molecule". Furthermore, the limited design intent of the system of biological life we refer to as the LS, is meant to insure survival of a body of extraneous and supplemental information contained within superabundant such self-replicating information molecules—over the period of billions of years from the time the LS would have been implanted on our planet, until the expected demise of the planet some billions of years in the future. Easy access to that information is assured, by making it universally available in the DNA medium of eukaryotic-celled organisms everywhere on the planet's surface. If this were indeed so, then built into such a system would inevitably be a host of subsystems designed to maintain and give effect to that limited design intent. We have discussed numerous examples during our SE analysis of the biological PdP in the preceding chapters—including some novel interpretations of how the main thrust of evolution derives from internal subsystems within the LS. But, all of the various subsystems discussed so far have dealt exclusively with functions essential to LS operational performance: metabolism, error correction, reproduction, evolution, maintenance, repair, and the like—subsystems designed to preserve and maintain the LS over time, by perpetuating the creation of organisms and perpetuating as well the integrity of information written in DNA. But, man-made designed systems often include essential safeguards as well, such as 'limiting' subsystems that insure the containment of the system and preventing it from operating outside of the system design intent. For example, human engineered systems habitually contain self-limiting subsystems designed into complex machines in order to obviate unpredictable events e.g., oscillations or cascading runaway effects, which can cause system malfunction or unintended consequences. A typical goal is the reduction of system error amplification that could ultimately destroy the system. A common example of such a self-limiting subsystem in a human designed mechanical system is the so-called "dead man's switch"—which forms an integral part of the accelerator mechanism in a railroad locomotive with an engineer at the controls. Its purpose is to stop a train and prevent disaster if for any reason the prime system controller (the engineer in this case—whose conscious presence is a mandatory part of overall system control) becomes incapacitated (his controlling influence becomes effectively removed from the system) for any reason. The device comprises an accelerator that is suitably spring-loaded that will automatically disengage and halt the train should the engineer let go for any reason. "Better late than never" is both the system and sub-system operational principle. So, while the dead man's switch does not contribute directly to normal system function (efficient passenger transportation) its safety provision provides the necessary insurance against a runaway train and potential disaster, under abnormal conditions. Perhaps, the LS incorporates within all of its intricacies some identifiable self-limiting subsystem(s) of its own.

a) THE INSTRUMENT OF A SELF-LIMITING FEATURE:

We ask you to place yourself, for a moment, in the shoes of the would-be designer of the LS and ask yourself: "Should I, as LS designer, include provisions that would limit the system to its habitat planet?" Within the parameters of the RDH alone among OoL options, this could be considered a fair and logical question. The ideas for consideration are as follows:

Would it be prudent for a designer to incorporate a self-limiting subsystem into an LS design specifically in order to prevent an eventual out-of-control "runaway" syndrome? Such a condition could arise, for example, if units of the LS (viable organisms) somehow managed to escape the limiting Earth-planet-wide biosphere, and threatened to establish a foothold somewhere else—another planet, for example. The possibility of progressive multi-planet contamination over time by LS biological life might well be considered, in the eyes of a designer, as some kind of potential cosmic space environmental peril and something to be avoided at all costs. An analogy would be the provisions NASA has invoked during flights to the moon (manned) and to Mars (unmanned) to obviate the possibility of dangerous exobiological pathogens—if they exist—from contaminating our own planet by hitching a ride back on a return flight. In an analogous way, a self-limiting subsystem, incorporated within the LS, might be designed to restrict LS operations exclusively to its planetary environment and—most importantly— prevent biological contamination outside of its intended host planet—the Earth. Let's elaborate:

Consider, if you will, that the designed LS (similar to numerous other hypothesized contrived biological LS's strategically implanted throughout the galaxy), has been placed on the planet Earth to perpetuate itself in the furtherance of a specific but limited design intent (e.g., as described in these pages). The design team, cognizant of the system strengths (survival over time) and weaknesses (particularly, and ironically, with respect to the potential to increased complexity), might wish to adhere to some extant set of limiting protocols that might serve to define precisely the rules of engagement with respect to the extent that LS biological complexity and any of its unintended consequences (intelligence that leads to technology) be allowed to attain. The designer would be deemed to recognize, that the instrument of extraterrestrial extension of the LS, and the resultant contamination, could only come about as a result of the development of host-planet "gravity-escape" technology, and that such technology could only derive from within the system itself (The likelihood of translocating live material as a result of collision events would not enter into such considerations because of insignificant survival probabilities over the long run and limited range effect).

It's a curious question to be asking, but could the existence of an intelligent species capable of such technology today on planet Earth imply the kind of threat that might be included in such a scenario? Put another way, could humanity at this juncture in its cultural evolution be at a crossroads with respect to its potential role as "contaminator" of: first our solar system, followed by that of our galactic neighborhood? Moreover, and most importantly, could we be approaching a critical point in LS evolutionary history, where some kind of self-limiting mechanism—specifically intended to obviate such a possibility—conceivably, be automatically triggered in order to contain human extraterrestrial exploration? Such a self-limiting mechanism could be designed to come into play predictively, for example, if and when the prospect of the spread of the system beyond the confines of its host planet became a distinct probability; one to be dealt with. If that were the case then so far as the LS and humanity in particular is concerned that time might well be at hand. Pursuing that possibility, we can envisage that at some critical point such a self-limiting LS subsystem could become activated in order to provoke the scaling back of the LS—and specifically to eliminate any species (and its technology) that could represent such a threat. Before we examine the form such a built-in LS self-limiting mechanism might assume, let's first critically examine the present state of human technological "mischief" that could hypothetically qualify our species as a targeted risk and therefore subject to the scrutiny of such a self-limiting subsystem.

b) Potential For Contamination:

Unquestionably, it is the technological aspect of our global species culture that permits the launching into space of all kinds of "space-junk" that, within a certain context, could be considered as having no business being there. This kind of openly questionable activity, left uninterrupted, will undoubtedly continue to escalate over the next decades and centuries leading inexorably to the future wholesale contamination of the solar system. Pollution could range anywhere from space litter floating around in various planetary orbits to microbes or other potentially active biologically material left behind on other planets. Such LS created space junk could in theory, migrate and/or evolve, over untold eons of time—sometime, somewhere, to inadvertently become a full blown LS on some distant planet of some other star system—and all by accident (perhaps this could form the essence of either or both Panspermia and Directed Panspermia, the 3rd and 4th OoL Options, respectively). Think of space contamination as simply an extension of the widespread environmental contamination and pollution we have visited upon our own atmosphere, oceans, lakes, rivers, and forests over the past several hundred years. It is just these kinds of technology-fed misadventures that an LS system "prime directive" might aim to anticipate, control and finally forestall.

Since the launch by the Soviets of the 184-pound Sputnik 1 in 1957, the placement of space objects into earth orbit has literally skyrocketed to the point where there are, today, hundreds of orbiting satellites considered vital to a host of essential services such as communications, defense, weather forecasting, and navigation. In addition, and more to the point, consider the quantities of incidental space "flotsam and jetsam" orbiting our planet—amounting to many thousands of pieces—ranging from lost fastener bolts to large structures, errant and defunct satellites, and launch vehicle parts. And, that's just in our own neighborhood. In addition, humanity has left evidence of its exploration activities on our moon, Mars, and more recently in the neighbourhood of Venus within the solar system. More ominous in significance, are the deep-space vehicles and probes, including the most extensively propelled human fabricated spacecraft—"Voyager 2"—launched August 20, 1977 and poised to leave our solar system for deep space, where it will take tens of thousands of years to travel the distance to the nearest neighboring star. This excursion represents the first ever physical contamination of outer space by an intelligent life form from our solar system (as opposed to data contamination from our radio and TV broadcasts). One fact becomes clear: if there is some prime directive prohibiting contamination and pollution beyond the atmospheric limits of a planet by an LS system (implanted there for specific and finite purposes), there can be no serious denial that the human species has already approached (if not crossed) the invisible line that symbolizes such excess. Not that some cosmic "space police" will be issuing some kind of admonition against further space-environment violations. But, we can envisage a situation whereby the implantation on a planet of a LS, for limited objectives, but with the long-shot potential for the evolution of meddlesome technologically intelligent species, could conceivably incorporate "self-limiting" provisions to obviate just such unintended consequences. These would be designed specifically to confine LS technology-based contamination to within the borders of our native planetary biosphere.

Ambitious human objectives, in the realm of future space exploration, are already being hailed across the planet. While to date, experiments with space technology can be considered relatively primitive, in future centuries space technology will advance in parallel with all the other scientific disciplines. The US has already begun a program aimed at publicizing future manned missions to Mars, foreseeing the day when humans will engage in terraforming the planet in order to create a biosphere hospitable to bio-life. Such a program might actually become a necessity should human activity on our own planet render it sometime in the future as unfit habitat for higher life. We can already anticipate the use of nuclear power as the clean, cheap, compact and extremely efficient replacement for the cumbersome chemical fuel technology currently being used to propel earth stuff into local orbits within our planetary neighborhood. And, it will be nuclear propulsion technology that will undoubtedly one day provide the sufficient and necessary means, to satisfy the human craving for space exploration and discovery, and that will enable us to transcend the limited exploratory excursions throughout our planetary neighborhood with more ambitious manned and unmanned long range objectives. While the human perspective presently views these activities as the natural extension of our long historical tradition of exploring new frontiers, from another perspective these same efforts could well be looked upon as ominous evidence that the LS has achieved the means of its escape from the confines of its planetary quarantine, and that one particular species has the means and every intention of spreading its contaminating influence even beyond its solar system neighborhood. If our own understanding of biological life has taught us anything, it is a deep appreciation for its survival potential under a broad spectrum of ambient conditions over vast periods of time. Thus, a little inadvertent biological contamination in the wrong location, indeed, could have far reaching permanence and consequence. That is precisely what a self-limiting LS subsystem might be calculated to prevent.

Then again, the motivation for including a self limiting LS design feature could be less environmental, and more toward the deterrence of some future menacing LS interaction with other extant galactic life forms, no matter how distant. "After all", the reasoning might follow: "who needs the potential long-term threat of competition (and possibly unpredictable aggravation as well) that a technologically intelligent species (evolved by chance and still loaded with considerable vestiges of 'who knows what kind of aggressive genetic baggage) represents?" As a species, we still harbor vestiges of genetically hardwired behavioral survival tools of a bygone age—propensities that in the modern era have become manifestly self-destructive. While our characteristically aggressive tendencies may, indeed, be ancient— the technological tools we engage in modern behavioral manifestations of those traits have certainly changed—and therein lies the dilemma.

Perhaps, with the advent of nuclear technology, we may have "bitten off more than we can chew". The nuclear conversion of matter to energy is the most efficient energy source available, and possibly represents the only one likely to fuel our species' deep space adventures of the future. Our experience with bombs that exploit this characteristic attest to the phenomenal matter-to-energy conversion ratios made possible according to the Einstein ($E=mc^2$) equation. It is nuclear technology above all else that can lead to deep space adventures that a prime directive could conceivably hope to contain. And because space travel technology would be understood universally by those engaged in it to involve nuclear technology, the development of nuclear science could constitute an important invoking variable in any LS self limiting equation. That is to say, that any species that developed first intelligence, and then nuclear technology (be it mammal, as in our case, or reptile, as it might have been had the dinosaurs not become extinct), could be considered to be a potentially hazardous contaminator of its neighborhood in space—commensurate in importance with the state of its nuclear technology. We could thus conceive of the idea, that a self limiting mechanism meant to destroy a technologically advanced species within a LS, could be considered to be a practical sub-system designed to curb such mischievous LS activities as space travel and thereby eliminate entirely the consequential risks of biological contamination and pollution beyond its planetary borders. The invocation of a self-limiting subsystem would be designed to maintain an effective quarantine of the LS to its planetary habitat.

c) A KIND OF BRINKMANSHIP—GENETICS VS CULTURE:

Has our half-century old space program already exceeded some hypothetical prime directive banning the contamination of space? And, how would a self-limiting mechanism conceivably designed into the LS in order to effect such a prohibition come into play at an appropriate time. Before we proceed with these two questions, I wish to remind the reader once again that these discussions only represent an attempt to explore some of the concepts that are implied within our RDH—in this instance to determine the possible consequences of that hypothesis with respect to the form, function, and feasibility of implementation of a self-limiting LS system provision—one that reasonably could be included within the LS design. Within that context, it will be seen that the RDH OoL model offers an interesting and novel perspective on the acknowledged monumental problems we are facing as a species. For example, at this stage in our history, there is no way to judge objectively the long term effects of the harm we are doing to our planetary environment—notwithstanding dire warnings from some quarters. Thus, any ideas that can shed light on the logistics that may be instrumental in moving our species in the direction of its own extinction—no matter how extraordinarily bizarre it may appear to some at first glance—must be, by definition, a worthwhile endeavor. Ironically, the more one believes in the resilience of LS survival, the greater the realization that continued system survival could actually be dependent on the cessation of human species participation as a species. Then, the reasoning goes, the biosphere, devoid of human activity and no longer under environmental attack, could restore itself over time—allowing the rest of the system species to survive another geological era. You get the point! There are only two possible ways that the dilemma in which the LS finds itself can be removed: either the LS must take measures to eliminate the species in question—the cancer in its midst, as it were—or the species must take control of its own destiny—by substantially modifying or eliminating entirely its questionable activities. Those would seem to be the only choices available. Since we already sense that our species has lost its way—and its future may be in serious doubt, there is some urgency that attends the need to explore any and all variables that may impact on a viable solution to the survival dilemma. Any OoL hypothesis that can help resolve some of the mystery behind the as-yet unexplainable self-destructive human behaviors must be explored fully so that they can be stopped or changed– before time runs out—even if, indeed, the consequences of whatever truth we discover turn out to be stranger than fiction. The reader will soon discover that the RDH contributes some interesting twists of irony to these discussions.

The only plausible way I can think of for the implementation of a self-limiting mechanism—one that activates from within the LS system—would be as a result of the consequence of two or more independent species-specific variables summing in such a way as to fulfill some prerequisite threshold condition. This could conceivably be achieved through the interaction of two critical human "species attributes" (SAs) that would have different time lines: perhaps one having an ancient genetic origin and common to all mammals—what we shall refer to as the "Genetic Variable (GV)", for example, and the other a function of a more recent and distinctly human attribute called cultural development—what we shall refer to as the "Cultural Variable (CV)". The propensity in humans for emotionally fed and hardwired "destructive aggressive" behavior would qualify in the former category and the culturally derived "advanced technological" behavior would qualify in the latter. We refer specifically to the behavioral aspects with respect to each, because ultimately we are interested in the physical actions that are motivated by each kind of variable—which actions if superimposed (occurred concurrently) might comprise the invocation of a self-limiting LS mechanism. The GV has its roots dating back hundreds of millions of years, to the development of our ancestors' primitive limbic brain, something shared by mammals and reptiles alike. The CV, on the other hand, is unique to our species, characterized by tool making and all of our scientific and technological achievements. Thus, we can envisage a graph of two such independent variables with respect to time and a point in time at which the combined sum of their contributed amplitudes exceeds some prearranged threshold. That point in time would serve as the "trigger-arming" moment for the possible implementation of such a self-destruct event. Sounds like science fiction, but stay the course—it gets interesting.

As implied above, the obvious genetic and hardwired attribute(s) that could well provide the aggressive criterion would be any of the emotions—individually or collectively. The emotions are a collective term covering a number of subjective forces whose influences help determine how humans behave, both as individuals within a community, and collectively as communities. They are implicated in the shaping of our attitudes and consequently have a powerful effect on how we make and implement decisions that, because of modern technology, can influence global events. The fact that their genetic inclusion in the human psyche predates our history as a species is probably indicative of their important role contributing to hominid evolution and that of homosapiens in particular. But, it can be convincingly argued that certain aspects of our genetic and hardwired emotional baggage have overstayed their welcome. We are, after all, a species forever in transition. Unfortunately, the very attributes that have undoubtedly contributed so much to our evolutionary success and are continually alluded to in every self-definition of the human condition, seem to have a double-edged quality that may now be turning in upon us. Let's elaborate.

The emotions are responsible, for example, for aggressive human behavior individually as well as collectively. While we placate ourselves with rational reminders (more like excuses) that it is the emotions that make us human and humane, the fact remains that those same emotions—including those that betray our brutal nature—are a legacy of a time when our ancestors competed with the animals and thus behaved very much like them. We have also come to appreciate the fact that the seat of the emotions (in addition to our smell and taste senses) is located in the limbic lobe of the brain, which, as stated, dates back to our reptilian ancestral cousins. In fact, that part of the brain is, indeed, referred to as the "reptilian" brain. As such, we are fully aware that the emotions are a direct link to our animal past, and require intensive education—as every parent and teacher has come to appreciate—in order to become tempered or at least subdued, prior to one's acceptance as a responsible member of any civilized community. All societies have set up laws and customs to protect their members from those unwilling or unable to conform to its version of civilized behavior. In all cases, this element of legal control constitutes nothing more than the attempt at suppression of the natural aggressive and sometimes anarchistic tendencies hardwired into each and every one of us.

The theory of "innate aggression" supported by German animal behaviorist Kanrad Lorenz implies that there is indeed an instinct for aggressiveness and thus humans—individually or as collective societies—are not to be blamed for outbreaks of violence or war; its just part of their true natures. A natural consequence of the innate aggressive tendencies inherited from our forebears is the concept of "militant enthusiasm" which is described in the English translation of Lorenz's *On Aggression* written in 1963. It also forms the substance of the GV referred to above.

> *"In reality, militant enthusiasm is a specialized form of communal aggression, clearly distinct from and yet functionally related to the more primitive forms of petty individual aggression. Every man of normally strong emotions knows, from his own experience, the subjective phenomena that go hand in hand with the response of militant enthusiasm. A shiver runs down the back and, as more exact observation shows, along the outside of both arms. One soars elated, above all the ties of everyday life,*

> one is ready to abandon all for the call of what, in the moment of this
> specific emotion, seems to be a sacred duty. All obstacles in its path become
> unimportant; the instinctive inhibitions against hurting or killing one's
> fellows lose, unfortunately, much of their power. Rational considerations,
> criticism, and all reasonable arguments against the behavior dictated by
> militant enthusiasm are silenced by an amazing reversal of all values,
> making them appear not only untenable but base and dishonorable. Men
> may enjoy the feeling of absolute righteousness even while they commit
> atrocities. Conceptual thought and moral responsibility are at their lowest
> ebb. As a Ukrainian proverb says: "When the banner is unfurled, all
> reason is in the trumpet."

The fact is that no matter how civilized a society may claim to be, with few exceptions its history is rife with conflicts that speak to a savage warring past. Ironically, it seems as though our most civilizing institutions—the entrusted guardians of morality and ethics—acting in the name of religious orthodoxy, or in the name of nationalistic patriotism—seem to be at the very forefront of incitement to "militant enthusiasm" fed by innate raw aggression. Succumbing to paranoia, personal ambition but always with an awareness for their place in history, it is the leaders that bear responsibility for periodically igniting the innate passions and emotions of the populations they claim to serve. Invariably, there have always been countervailing voices of reason—a minority attempting to restore rational self-control—that are drowned out and of no avail. The words of British philosopher, Karl Popper taken from *The Open Society and Its Enemies* have a recognizably truthful tone: "...the history of the world (is) the history of war". In contrast, the popular dictum credited to British Lieut-Col Charles A'Court Repington to the effect that "Those who cannot remember the past are condemned to repeat it", rings somewhat hollow. Despite the fact that civilizations not only remember and recall their lurid history well to the point of fetish, they seem to have learnt little from history that actually serves to modify Lorenz's thesis. In fact it would seem that the history of warfare has traditionally served as a military primer legacy for future generals to emulate. Indeed, the hard-wired emotional attribute that leads to aggression in humans qualifies as the ideal candidate to represent the *"genetic variable"* (GV)—the first essential component of our hypothetical LS self-destruct equation.

The second part of the equation we are constructing is the state of human technological advance—the *"cultural variable"* (CV). Since this part of the mix is the more recent, it becomes as well the most critical in terms of triggering any built-in self-limiting mechanism. We marvel at the advances of the last hundred years, in the application of scientific principles towards the development of broad ranging technologies. The world keeps changing before our eyes faster than we can follow—a natural consequence of exponential scientific and technological advances and their wide-ranging and unpredictable influences on human societies. In the process of trying to accommodate the insatiable needs of runaway population growth—whether for consumer goods, or armaments to allay our traditional paranoid fears from real and imagined enemies—the collective processes of material production continue to exact all the while an increasingly heavy toll on the planetary landscape and biosphere. Massive industrial, transportation and communications networks straddle the globe to serve needs as diverse as the agro businesses that must meet the nutritional requirements of exploding populations, to the military-industrial complexes that consume the lopsided military budgets of nations. Those budgets are also responsible for technological research that strives to impart tactical or strategic advantages through improvements to the tools nations apply in warfare. There is no reason to be hopeful that the competition for strategic parity or supremacy—commonly referred to as an "arms race" will abate anytime soon since the root causes, according to Lorenz, are innate. This national pastime serves to keep the military industrial establishments busy between periods of hostility, by preparing a nation for its next anticipated conflict. There is no conceivable end in sight to this game because it will take many generations for the genetic causes of aggression to ebb and dissipate through incremental processes of human emotional evolution. Therefore, only the very naïve need be surprised or disappointed, for that matter, that over time—as the tools we prepare for war become unlimited in their destructive scope—we, as an intelligent species, have been edging ever closer to the ultimate danger point: our mythological "doomsday", on the critical path to self-destruction.

A significant turning point in human history was acknowledged with the detonation of the first atomic bomb at the Trinity site in the sands of New Mexico in 1944. The awesome power of this primitive nuclear weapon radically altered the outcome of the war against Japan in World War II and changed forever the character of warfare. Until the atomic era, all wars could be contained within the borders of the participants with only minor excursions beyond. Nuclear weapons—their potency and shear numbers—have changed all that. In the short half-century since their introduction, enough nuclear weapons of every variety have been produced (and at devastating costs to the human species on many levels) to virtually annihilate the viable planet habitat of the LS several times over. We hear warnings about the possibility of a catastrophic "nuclear winter" without fully appreciating that what is being referred to is nothing short of the fabled "doomsday" of apocalyptic literature. In the past, aggressive warlike behavior only led to the loss of life and property on a severely limited planetary scale. In the future, nuclear war will not only improve the efficiency in human slaughter and the destruction of property, but has, as well, the novel and crucially important capability of destroying the biosphere niches for all complex species—including our own. Is such a nuclear conflagration possible? Can the fact that we can seriously pose such a question serve as an important clue pointing to an essential ingredient in the makeup of a self-limiting LS subsystem? Definitely yes!

D) NUCLEAR TECHNOLOGY—A DOUBLE EDGED SWORD:

Unquestionably, the field of applied science that demonstrably threatens the existence of the human species is nuclear technology—one that we have experienced in two diverse roles—nuclear bombs that can kill and destroy, and peaceful applications such as nuclear engines for submarines or spacecraft or for generating electricity. One is struck by the contrasts in applications deriving from what is essentially the identical technology—the mastery of atomic energy. The only difference in application between the one and the other comprises how the energy in each case is controlled and applied. In the former, the energy is effectively unleashed in an explosive chain reaction, creating a desired devastation in its wake.

In the latter, the atomic energy is metered out over relatively long periods, converted into other forms, and harnessed for peaceful purposes (e.g., superheated steam that drives a turbine). One can surmise whether there is more to this underlying relationship than meets the eye—or whether the connection is nothing more than innocuous coincidence? Here we have a single energy-conversion technology, serving on the one hand, destructive war, and on the other, improvement in the living condition—two most contrasting sides of human political ambitions—each serving disparate motives and delivering totally opposite results. The former serves our hardwired aggressive natures, and the latter helps us fulfill our collective compulsive need to explore our universe in order to advance human knowledge. An analogy can be drawn between the harnessing of chemical explosives and atomic energy in that both can be used for destructive as well as useful purposes. The compelling difference is in the destructive capacity of a nuclear device—casually referred to in terms of mega tons of TNT. On balance, the case can be made that the most funded and successful research programs into the uses of nuclear technology have not been in the *"atoms for peace"* category. Ironically, the greatest actual nuclear threat to humanity to date derives from an accident at a peaceful nuclear reactor that had the potential to obliterate millions of people. This and other accidents at nuclear reactor sights have fueled the realization that our efforts at harnessing nuclear energy for conversion into electrical energy have produced some glaring failures as one nuclear reactor after another is being shut down for reasons of safety. The catastrophic failure at Chernobyl, in the Ukraine in April of 1986—the worst in the history of nuclear power generation—serves as a painful reminder of just how dangerous a nuclear reactor can become. This case points up the fact that either the operators failed to understand the threats this technology poses or they understood the risks involved but were willing to accept them anyway. The station was relatively new at the time; having come on-line in 1977 through to 1983. The plant consisted of four reactors, each capable of producing 1,000 megawatts of electric power. The accident occurred when technicians at reactor Unit 4 attempted a poorly designed experiment. Workers shut down the reactor's power-regulating system and its emergency safety systems, and then withdrew most of the control rods from its core—all the while allowing the reactor to continue running at 7 percent power. These mistakes were compounded by others, and at 1:23 AM on April 26, the chain reaction in the core went out of control. Several explosions triggered a large fireball and blew off the heavy steel and concrete lid of the reactor. A partial meltdown of the core also occurred. This and the ensuing fire in the graphite reactor core released large amounts of radioactive material into the atmosphere, where it was carried great distances by air currents. Millions of acres of forest and farmland were contaminated and although many thousands of people were evacuated, hundreds of thousands more remained in contaminated areas. In addition, in subsequent years many livestock were born deformed, and among humans, several thousand radiation-induced illnesses and cancer deaths are expected in the long term. The Chernobyl accident sparked criticism of unsafe procedures and design flaws in Soviet reactors, and it heightened resistance to the building of more such plants. Even under normal operating circumstances—when nuclear-fueled reactors operate within and according to their design parameters, the problem of how to safely dispose of spent nuclear fuel continues to be a difficult challenge. What to do with the rusting remains of inoperable nuclear submarines from the former Soviet Union and how to keep the nuclear reactor guts and fuel out of the hands of terrorists are other problematic legacies that signal an inability on the part of planners to adequately predict the dangerous unintended consequences of nuclear technology for the future. Unfortunately, we are painfully aware of the history of the destructive uses of nuclear weapons—the reasons for their design and construction—and the present state of proliferation of such armaments. Couple this with the sophisticated missile delivery systems that can reach every corner of the globe with the precision afforded by GPS satellite triangulation gives a potentially new and expanded meaning to the term "holocaust".

A half century ago, the highly cultured and technologically advanced German State sanctioned the genocide of an identifiable segment of Europe's population. The result was the engineering of an efficient technology whose sole purpose was the slaughter of millions of Jews, as part of the largest exercise in the exploitation of hatred in history. This successful commitment on the part of a so-called enlightened German society to carrying out the systematic genocide of its Jewish civilians and those of the conquered nations under its control has been tattooed into human consciousness as "The Holocaust". The description serves as a vivid reminder of that distinct singular government sanctioned program of extermination on the part of a people who, at the time, prided themselves as possessing all the attributes that define the cultured and civilized state. But, even this monumental catastrophe highlighting the tragic side of twentieth century civilization pales compared to the possibilities for the global annihilation of all of humanity by way of a "nuclear holocaust", a finite possibility, where no one—not even the perpetrators—are spared. The planet, under the control of its most intelligent species, has, for all intent and purposes, entered a distinctively precarious phase in its history—one signaled by the risk of nuclear conflagration—with the irreversible consequences for life and the LS which that presents. Within the context of recent history and a cursory examination of the directions our collective civilization is heading, constructive paranoia coupled with positive media hysteria may, not only be excusable in the circumstances, but constitute the only effective open channel of communication complacent world leaders may take seriously. Consider the following:

E) THE DOOMSDAY CLOCK—AN APOCALYPSE THERMOSTAT:

The introduction of the nuclear technology is considered a monumental turning point in human history. Its accomplishment actually gave reality to a couple of mythical and hypothetical concepts only fantasized about in the past. First, is the alchemist's dream of converting one substance into something else (ordinary lead into precious gold was the classic quest). The modern day version amounts to turning matter into instant energy with the "atoms for peace" promise of improving the lives of all. Second, is the nightmare of the apocalyptic "doomsday", that the unleashing of uncontrolled amounts of the same nuclear energy has the potential of inflicting upon our planet. The application of each reflects, in a graphic way, the dual nature of the human psyche: the result of an evolutionary past that joins the emerging technological "cultural variable (CV)" to the ever present aggressive "genetic variable (GV)"—which mandates the employment of nuclear technology toward the design and production of mass destruction weaponry. Is this a game our species can ultimately win?

There is an hypothetical "*Doomsday Clock*" ticking away on the campus of the University of Chicago established by the prestigious Bulletin of Atomic Scientists that is meant to convey how close humanity has come to the verge of self-annihilation. Every now and then, the keepers of the clock advance or retard the minute hand as a metaphoric way of demonstrating how world events—political and military—seem to be influencing our tendency to self-destruct. For example, the clock was reset in 1991 when the hands were moved back to 17 minutes to "midnight"—the symbol of nuclear apocalypse—to acknowledge the end of the Cold War. This was its furthest point (safest) since it was set at seven minutes to midnight at its inception in 1947. But then, on Friday December 8 1995, in a seeming reversal of judgment, the Bulletin pushed the hands of their Doomsday Clock three minutes closer to midnight. The reason cited by Leonard Reiser, chairman of the Bulletin, referring specifically to the end of the Cold War, was the fact that "...the world did not take full advantage of the opportunities available at the time. Nevertheless, the fact that the clock exists at all says a lot about our species' future prospects for self-destruction. When the Bulletin of Scientists came out with their first six-page letter on December 10, 1945, not that long after the first nuclear bomb was detonated, they issued a dire warning that is no less clear today. Referring to a doomsday brought upon our world by nuclear war, they warned: "This catastrophe will be inevitable if we do not succeed in banishing war from the world". They did not have to be explicit about nuclear war, because they already knew that the fundamental principle: "all's fair in love and war" applies particularly well to the search for and use of the most destructive available technology when it comes to the practice of warfare. The precedent had already been set at Hiroshima and Nagasaki. When the Soviet Union exploded its first atomic bomb in 1949, the hands of the clock were moved four minutes closer to midnight, anticipating—in a most graphic manner—the fact that human technology was about to force-feed the nuclear arms race that would come to represent, in the view of the Bulletin of Atomic Scientists, the greatest historical danger to human survival. The evolution to the next ominous level of nuclear technology, confirmed by the US hydrogen bomb test in 1952, provided accurate testimony in support of those fears, and provided, as well, a clear indication to advance the doomsday thermostat to its closest point ever—to two minutes to midnight. While past decisions to reset the clock have been made in private, the experts have more recently invited the public to lend its participation in future decisions, in deference to the uncertainties that prevail in such deliberations. Perhaps the inclusion of the public is an acknowledgment of the fact that there are today many more human activities that should be included as part of any doomsday scenario. Let us not forget that any action that renders the planetary habitat unfit environmentally, is by definition, a potential doomsday agent. It's all a question of degree and ultimate result.

Under the circumstances, any fears we may harbor as to whether such destruction is possible are not simply taken on faith alone. The Bulletin of Scientists has been monitoring our catastrophe potential for the past half century while others have ascertained that a nuclear winter represents the likely annihilation of every living thing that breaths. In addition, any such calamity would perpetuate its influence by rendering the planet's surface unfit for habitation, in virtue of life-prohibiting nuclear radiation that wouldn't quit for some thousands of years. Suffice it to say that such an occurrence would set back LS complexity (decrease the number of complex species) considerably. In other words, the only species that could be able to survive a global nuclear catastrophe would be the ones with the fewest needs in terms of resources and habitat—whose niches might remain relatively intact. That doesn't leave too much wiggle room for species of sophisticated complexity—and very little, indeed, for the perpetrator species of such an event. I trust you see where I am going with this. Let's sum it up with a set of three questions and answers:

F) THE COMPONENTS OF AN LS SELF-LIMITING SUBSYSTEM:

> 1) Question: What LS species, in virtue of its technological capabilities, could qualify as an essential operative variable for the fulfillment of a self-limiting, self-destruct, LS sub-system program?
> Answer: Only the species capable of establishing an adequately destructive technology and simultaneously harboring the potential will to use it— Homo Sapiens (humans)!
> 2) Question: Would such a self-destruct event permanently disable the LS and possibly put it out of business?
> Answer: Most certainly not. It may set back the complexity agenda a bit. But, according to the RDH there never was a complexity agenda. Furthermore, the RDH asserts that within the LS—system survival over time (and not particular species survival) is all that matters.
> And finally,
> 3) Question: What do you get when you mix "genetically derived innate aggression" with "culturally derived and universally available nuclear technology"?
> Answer: The ultimate self-destruction of the human species—a "Nuclear Holocaust".

Remember, according to the RDH the LS only needs to buy time (survival of some species). In the event of such a nuclear holocaust, it is expected that the LS's principle source of energy, the sun, will cease to shine through the resultant cloud cover composed of radiated dust and ash for many months. Under such circumstances, any species that manages to survive the effects of the initial hell fire event will have a field day just living off of the carcasses of the victims—big and small. More importantly, the LS will be able to revert back to its original survival mode in terms of primitive eukaryotic species surviving on bacteria—in the absence of a photosynthesis based food chain. As long as there exists some surviving species, anywhere on the planet, whose SAs can endure the new BA realities following such a nuclear winter scenario, the LS will continue along its merry old way—surviving, evolving and looking forward to any other challenges that it might encounter. The LS never looks back. It only moves forward in time—it never even skips a beat.

Under the circumstances, we may well come to appreciate in a refreshingly original way how the development of nuclear technology heralds a momentous milestone in the history of the human species. Now, we will highlight the rational incentive to incorporate within the LS a self-limiting subsystem, with a set of questions and answers that will serve, as well, to highlight the irony inherent within our imaginative scenario.

1) Question: With respect to a self-limiting LS subsystem, could "nuclear technology", (the cultural variable, CV) represent and contribute both a) the source of a potential problem, as well as b) the source of the remedy?

a) The potential problem would comprise the means of forbidden extraterrestrial contamination that could only come about through the (peaceful) use of nuclear engines for space travel; while

b) The remedy of the problem would comprise the destruction of the offending technology by self-using that same technology to create a nuclear conflagration (through the reliance on human innate aggression)—before space travel becomes a serious "contamination threat".

2) Question: Is it inevitable that our "ancient" genetic variable (GV), as represented by innate human aggression, will combine, with our "recent" cultural variable (CV), as represented by nuclear destructive technology: to undermine the survival of our species, before we come to realize the explosive potential for human obliteration that this explosive combination represents?

Seen in another way:

Is it mere coincidence that the cultural variable (CV),—nuclear technology, the only technology that can allow human beings to participate in serious space travel with the potential for extraterrestrial contamination— is also the same technology that can destroy the human species as a result of its genetic variable (GV)—our hard wired aggressive heritage?

We have here two distinct but related relationships to consider, which could be considered the sufficient and necessary constituents of an efficient self-limiting LS mechanism:

1) Nuclear Technology:—signifying a recently acquired source of, both present and future, extraordinarily significant capabilities:

a) Present Capability: Nuclear arms—representing the only certain means of destroying all of humanity (and its technology) and,

b) Future Capability: Nuclear powered spacecraft—representing the only certain means of spreading biological contamination extraterrestrially—a taboo possible scenario from the rational designer point of view.

2) Human Behavior Potential:—a blend of two distinct variables that could constitute an efficient LS self-limiting design feature:

a) Cultural Variable (CV): Very recent technology, capable of producing both present and future nuclear-driven capabilities referred to above, and

b) Genetic Variable (GV): Very ancient, but still operative, engine of human aggression and militant enthusiasm that overrides rational and objective reason.

The above relationships, when combined, can serve to implement a self-limiting, self-destruct mechanism to scale back LS complexity to more tolerable and less troublesome operational levels—by employing the destructive "present capability" before the contaminating "future capability" can take effect.

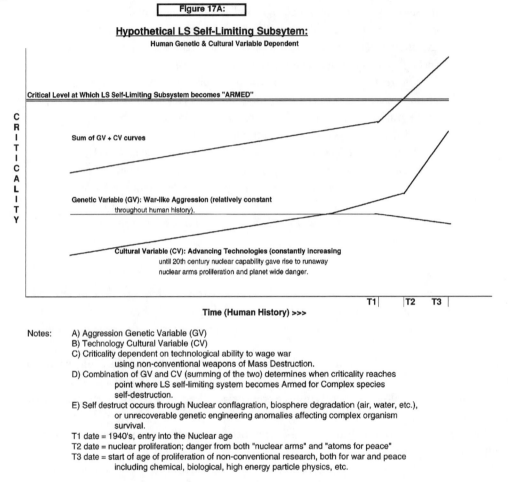

Figure 17A:

Hypothetical LS Self-Limiting Subsytem:
Human Genetic & Cultural Variable Dependent

Critical Level at Which LS Self-Limiting Subsystem becomes "ARMED"

C
R
I
T
I
C
A
L
I
T
Y

Sum of GV + CV curves

Genetic Variable (GV): War-like Aggression (relatively constant
throughout human history).

Cultural Variable (CV): Advancing Technologies (constantly increasing
until 20th century nuclear capability gave rise to runaway
nuclear arms proliferation and planet wide danger.

T1| |T2   T3 |

Time (Human History) >>>

Notes: A) Aggression Genetic Variable (GV)
         B) Technology Cultural Variable (CV)
         C) Criticality dependent on technological ability to wage war
                 using non-conventional weapons of Mass Destruction.
         D) Combination of GV and CV (summing of the two) determines when criticality reaches
                 point where LS self-limiting system becomes Armed for Complex species
                 self-destruction.
         E) Self destruct occurs through Nuclear conflagration, biosphere degradation (air, water, etc.),
                 or unrecoverable genetic engineering anomalies affecting complex organism
                 survival.
         T1 date = 1940's, entry into the Nuclear age
         T2 date = nuclear proliferation; danger from both "nuclear arms" and "atoms for peace"
         T3 date = start of age of proliferation of non-conventional research, both for war and peace
                 including chemical, biological, high energy particle physics, etc.

3) A Self-Limiting LS Subsystem:

Object: To prevent inevitable extraterrestrial contamination inherent in any extraterrestrial space activity by an evolved intelligent biological species of an LS.

Implementation: Use the same technology essential for the implementation of the undesirable behavior, by turning it in upon the offending species itself, i.e. use the same genetic variable responsible for the species' evolutionary success (aggressive nature) and the implicated technology whenever it appears (as nuclear weapons) to *self*-destroy the species in question before it can fully develop the use of such technology as the means and causative agent that could wreak contamination havoc beyond its terrestrial boundaries, i.e., design into the system the potential for self-destruction to occur all by itself.

Action on the Part of the LS to be Taken For Implementation: None! The self-limiting feature is designed to be logistically <u>self-activating</u>—on an as needed basis when circumstances warrant. The system depends on the fact that knowledge of the destructive aspects of nuclear technology by an intelligent evolved species would logically precede the discovery of the propulsion potential of nuclear engines permitting deep space exploration—in effect allowing the system to monitor itself.

G) A RACE AGAINST TIME:

Figure 17A is a hypothetical graph illustrating the crucial time lines of the two principle independent variables, GV and CV, which could comprise our suggested self-limiting destruct mechanism. It has been drawn to reflect the relationships of each for achieving the critical trigger level their sum must exceed in order that the sufficient and necessary operational conditions are met. The time line reflecting the hard-wired aggression GV indicates that its high point was reached way back before the species homo-sapiens-sapiens was well defined. This reflects our legacy of fight-to-the-death response to perceived threats that has marked our collective history since before we even became a species.

But, lest one is left with the impression that human evolution is nothing more than a haphazard stream of doom-and-gloom aggressive evolutionary strings, the direction of this most ancient independent variable time line is seen to reflect the fact that, as a species in transition (from our animal past to the human angels we aspire to be) it can be hoped that if we survive long enough, we could be successful in achieving total control over the remnants of our individual and collective aggressive natures. Total cooperation in human affairs would then be able to replace rampant competition and the incessant bouts of human self-destruction. If we should somehow manage to survive the transition, that fact would be reflected in the sufficient reduction of the GV to compensate for the rapid rise in the CV. Indeed. we must take the warning implicit in our graph—of our unrestrained technology, CV. It's direction is upward in a nearly vertical climb, and accurately indicating the runaway nature of our cultural technological advances—which, in the near future, can only bring to warfare unimagined tools of destruction.

While we have described above the dangers that derive from our built-in aggressive tendencies, aggression remains only a single human attribute—one of a number that can get us into trouble as a species. I believe that every case of excess—that acts as a negative influence on the future survival of our species—can be traced to the convergence of the two most powerful influences on our thinking and behavior—the GV and CV: the genetically derived emotions, and the culturally derived technology[1]. This explosive combination could be tolerated when our technology limited our actions to local habitat arenas with negligible effects on the planet as a whole. But, we have a strategic situation at present whereby the growth in the quality and quantity of our planet-wide technological applications threaten the air we breathe, the water we drink and the carrying capacity of the planet to support runaway population growth. Thus, the graph depicts not only the immediate threat of disaster that is aggression based, but represents, as well, the medium and long-term consequences of technology run amuck, and the questionable ability of directing human efforts to reversing the trend. In all instances, it will be the most complex species—those with the least flexibility to adapt quickly to biosphere changes—that will perish first. Where does that leave us?

The graph representing the sum of the curves of the twin independent variables reflects the inevitable convergence toward a critical threshold—a graphic race against time in which our species may well be engaged. Under this scenario, because the CV technology curve increases rapidly while the GV aggression curve tails off only incrementally—some time in the recent past the full conditions for the future assured self-destruction have been met, i.e., the system is armed, and the human species could well be primed to self-destruct according to LS system design intent. Because of the slow pace of evolution, and the quick pace of culturally driven technology, one is hard pressed to imagine an eventual positive outcome.

If there is any credibility to this tale of unbridled predicament for mankind, it can all be summed up as follows: Our species is on a critical path whose extrapolation into the future inevitably leads to both short term and long term disasters—to rival any in the 3.8 billion years of LS history. The one significant difference will be the source of that event—from within the system itself, at the hands of one of its own species. Humanity could well be the unwitting tool of its own destruction. How ironical!

H) Summary—The Human Species At the Brink:

The novel exercise we have engaged in, metaphorically juxtapositions two important attributes of our species: First, is the relatively constant aggressive trait that dates back to the early genetic history of hominids in general and humans in particular. It probably served a critical role in our evolutionary development—accounting in large part for beating out all other (probably less aggressive) competitive hominids for necessary survival resources. Our more peaceful genetic cousins probably succumbed to our particularly lethal brand of aggression—just the kind of species attribute that would fit well with the "survival of the fittest" doctrine often associated with Darwinian evolution. Second, is the intellectual and cultural advances characteristic of the last couple of hundred years, culminating in the technology cultural revolution that gained humans the capability of unleashing upon the planet a nuclear kind of holocaust that could wipe out all land based life. Such an eventuality could pollute the continents with sufficient lethal radiation to obviate any possibility of surface habitation for eons of time.

There are two questions we must now consider, that effectively summarize the case we have made above:

1] Is it mere coincidence that the LS species that has attained the highest (and perhaps the only) intellectual achievement has, as well, retained the aggressive potential to wipe itself off the face of the earth? No other species can make this claim. What we have here is the juxtaposition of a genetic trait—aggression—derived from the hard-wired emotions dating back hundreds of thousands of years, with a recent cultural trait—nuclear technology—dating back only half a century.

2] Is it mere coincidence that the same technology that could propel biological material outside of our solar system and over time contaminate the far reaches of outer space can, as well, be the identical technology that can totally destroy higher life on the planet? Here the juxtaposition comprises the two critical applications of a single technology—one able to cancel out the other.

1) THE ULTIMATE EFFECT ON THE LS:

If you can accept the possibility (even as a long shot) of negative answers to the above two questions, then you have, in effect, acknowledged the possibility that the LS was designed with a built-in self-limiting subsystem, which becomes in effect, a self—destruct mechanism for the high-end intelligence-based achievement species. One more crucial question looms within this scenario: How would a nuclear holocaust on the planet effect the survival of the LS?

I believe it is safe to predict, that the ultimate strategic defenses employed by the LS to survive both short term and catastrophic events (such as disastrous meteorites like the one responsible for the extinction of the dinosaurs 65 million years ago) would be more than sufficient to protect the system itself from annihilation—even under nuclear winter conditions. The production of many species spread out in many habitats and niches underground and deep within the oceans would permit the survival of at least some LS species that could always serve as the rootstock for evolution to work with. We could, of course, say good-by to the more complex species, in as much as the food chain would become radically disrupted, with little time for elaborate lifeforms to adapt. It is probably the lowest forms of life, capable of rapid generational turnover, that would have the best chances at survival, inasmuch as their continuance would depend on absorbing the bounties of destroyed life in the short term—surviving long enough to vary their genetic makeup through mutations in the medium and long term. The point is, that the LS has managed to endure grievous assaults to its survival in the past and could be expected to do so repeatedly and endlessly, if necessary. Complexity and higher intelligence could be set back indeterminable millions of years but again, (and we cannot overemphasize the point) complexity never was an LS imperative. Survival of self-replicating information molecules (DNA within living cells) over time, and under any contingencies, is what the LS is all about. Again, the evolutionary development of complexity and of a high-end intelligent species simply reflects the relatively lengthy period of calm between catastrophic events. The emergence of complex and more intelligent species simply reflects the longer periods of calm within the biosphere. Within this context, nuclear holocaust for higher life looms as nothing more than another in a series of twists and turns characteristic of past LS history. But the occasion will be memorable (not that anyone would be left to record the occasion) as having been instigated from within the LS itself, as the greatest lasting achievement of the human species—the unique distinction of having created its own complete and total annihilation and in Darwinian terms—its very own extinction.

For Humanity:

From the unique context described above, our discussions lend novel weight to all of the other mainstream arguments that describe humanity as being at an historic point-of-no-return for it's very survival. The dangers of a conflagration of one sort or another, derived from out-of-control technology are both obvious and insidious. In truth, it doesn't make a difference whether we do ourselves in as a result of abuses and insults that derive from nuclear, chemical, biological, or environmental technologies. On the one hand, we are witness to the dismantling of the half-century cold war between the armed camps of the East and West. One would expect one consequence to be a reduction in the threat of nuclear war. And, indeed, the two sides have made appropriate moves to substantially ease the tensions between them. With the implementation of the first Strategic Arms Limitation Treaty (START-1) both sides agreed to reduce their nuclear stockpiles to about 6000 each. One would think it an impossible task to invent targets for all of these weapons, but they exist anyway—the consequences of a universal brand of paranoia that we seem to tolerate as some bizarre, if acceptable, substitute for rational logic. Ironically, the demise of the cold war has substituted new and uncertain dangers. While the Russian nuclear arsenals were secured by the totalitarian regime of the former Soviet Union, their threat, as it turned out, remained under strict, rational, and most importantly, predictable control. But, the dismantling of the Soviet Union has had the frightening effect of dismantling, as well, whatever government controls kept nuclear warheads and their delivery systems in check. The fact is that while the Soviet government was in charge, all their weapons of mass destruction could be accounted for. Today, such essential controls are lacking among the newly emerged states that replaced it, with the real prospect of no one any longer being able to account, no less control, where these weapons, or the strategic materials for their production, end up. The radical changes to civilian and military infrastructures, plus the economic anarchy that followed the break up of the Soviet Union, has created the ideal commercial climate of exploitation, that has literally placed some of these nuclear related materials and arms up for grabs, and potentially available to terrorists. This situation has the genuine ingredients for a worst-case scenario for humankind. Not only have we witnessed these weapons of mass destruction becoming stockpiled in outrageous numbers—lunacy masquerading as self defense—but we now are faced with the challenge of finding and destroying them before they can be acquired by dangerous renegade states or worse still—terrorist organizations led by lunatics with little or nothing to lose. Consider the prospect of fanatical regimes bent upon redressing at any cost (including suicidal behavior) the imagined ills of mankind in the name of religious doctrine. Herein lies the frightening but all too realistic, potential for the implementation of our collective worst-case scenario imaginable. There is no paranoia here. None is required. We live today with the prospect of nuclear weapons in the hands of totalitarian regimes comprised of fundamentalist religious fanatics. Is this not equivalent to a basic "doomsday scenario"? Does not "the destructive products of nuclear technology, in the hands of motivated, aggressive and disturbed psychopaths" constitute enough of a threat to global stability that could potentially erupt into mutual self-destruction? We need not try to imagine the recipes for other future global disaster while the seeds of that disaster exist in our midst as you read these words. Imagine having "Attila the Hun" at the command of such weapons. Do you doubt for a single moment that he would use it? And, once the genie is unleashed from the mythical "nuclear bottle", retaliation against can be expected to be swift and ferocious—against both real (if known) and imagined (if need be) perpetrators. We all lose.

Again, back to our oft repeated question: Is it merely coincidental that the same technology that could destroy mankind is the same one that could breech the distances for space travel with the inevitability of biological contamination beyond the LS design limits? Could the juxtaposition of the genetic trait for species aggression, together with the development of nuclear technology, in fact, be the critical factor that arms the trigger of an LS self-destruct mechanism—just before that same technology becomes available for space travel? And if, following our extensive discussion, this possibility now looms possible, then the ultimate query is: Can humanity escape the path to certain destruction—a fate that arguably appears unavoidable. Should the hands on the Doomsday Clock be set to a precarious "one minute to midnight"? The answer to this question, in fact, may represent the ultimate irony of all.

The very survival of the human race could ultimately depend upon our understanding and appreciating the full implications that reside within the RDH OoL option, and in particular—the ramifications within the concept of LS design intent for human extinction. The only solution to our dilemma, in fact, may ultimately depend on a full-blown assessment of the RDH through testing of the introns as described previously. The discovery of non-genetic encoded information in eukaryotic cells would of necessity precipitate radical changes in the most fundamental arenas of human thought—including the absolute verification of the RDH—the 5th Option—leading to a sobering reassessment of our collective self-worth and realistic prospects for our future survival. Even if the results of such testing remain inconclusive, a serious consideration of the RDH must acknowledge, nevertheless, that the possibilities the RDH scenario raises lead inevitably toward logical conceptual changes in the manner in which we assess the dangers we collectively face. An analogous precedent for comparison is the effect the SETI exploration program has had on changing intellectual attitudes with respect to the legitimacy of searching both for evidence of the existence of extraterrestrial intelligence, and also of exobiological life elsewhere in the solar system. In a similar vein, a thoughtful consideration of the RDH and all of its implications must lead inexorably to the acceptance of the logical conclusion that ultimate human self-destruction may be just part of a larger LS agenda; that despite human errors of omission and commission that are laying waste increasingly large portions of our biosphere, our self-destructive tendencies transcend our own natures and derive from a more insidious source; that self-destruction is a sacrifice the LS imposes on any technologically advanced species that could interfere with its prime agenda; that there is nothing vindictive about it—it's the way the system was efficiently designed to obviate specific problems that might arise.

This scenario gives a whole new collective meaning for our species, to self-explanatory concepts such as: "Author of one's own misfortune" and "mitigating circumstances". Within the perspective of our present deliberations, the former implies that we are collectively to blame for the technological misdeeds that are seen as the causes of the various planet-wide crises we are presently facing. But, seen from the unique perspective of the ideas presented within the RDH, a compelling case can be made for mitigating circumstances—that we are unwitting agents of LS design intent—a design intent that places LS survival and containment ahead of any possible considerations for human survival and well being and that if we are, in fact, in serious trouble—it is simply because we cannot help ourselves. From the Life-system vantage point: "The needs of the many (species) outweigh the needs of the few".

Life now becomes all the more complicated as we begin to deal with the realization that the LS, of which the human species forms just a transient part, indeed could have been a product of rational design—to serve a specific and limited purpose within the confines of a limited planetary environmental space.

Complexities become compounded as we confront the new realities forced upon us. How, for example, do we respond to the forced conclusion that the evolution and existence of a complex and intelligent species such as ours has no ultimate significance other than to ourselves? This line of thinking raises the distinct possibility that human survival, in fact, could well depend upon self-imposed programs comprising specific well thought out steps to deliberately subvert the LS design intent—by seizing the initiative ourselves and taking remedial matters into our own hands, so to speak. If the concept of a self-limiting subsystem, similar to the one described above and specifically optimized toward LS containment becomes a reasonable proposition, what does it say about any relationship we could ever forge, philosophically or otherwise, with the system designer—when the destruction of our species becomes a specific design imperative?

Under the circumstances, can humanity ignore the implications implicit within the RDH? And if, indeed, it does—then does it do so, literally, at its own peril. I can make this statement only because as a legitimate OoL option, the ramifications of the RDH are too significant to dismiss out of hand. This, in effect, is a plea to apply the readily available tools and resources to the study of the information contents of eukaryotic DNA. Our future as a species could well depend on what we find.

Ironically, the molecular biologists working on curing genetic diseases can legitimately also make human-survival claims, albeit on a different scale of values, referring to the medical benefits to be derived from such work. Our focus is on the larger picture—secret messages imbedded in DNA that—besides vindicating the RDH—could also point the way to a solution to collective human species survival.

A) SICKNESS, AGING AND DEATH:

The RDH and its concept of LS design intent provides a rational scenario for why we get sick, why we age and why the ultimate destiny of all living things is death and the recycling of biological material. In the absence of the RDH, these primary aspects of all eukaryotic biological life defy rational explanation other than "things just are the way they are". Is sickness an evolved process? Is aging predictable from the SAb point of view? Wouldn't you expect that one of the most important organism properties evolution could emphasize and seek to maximize would be longevity—with perpetual life within organisms the ultimate evolutionary goal? If Darwinian evolution is everything it's cracked up to be, then why should evolutionary biologists simply accept the premise that survival of the fittest does not include the elimination of sickness, the continual extension of longevity and the elimination of death? A simple answer to be found within the RDH would be that these three characteristics of life are programmed into the PdP, are an integral of the LS design and, in fact, are immune to evolution and that only the PdP genotype ultimately survives. In the course of our deliberations, we have concluded that the LS design intent is system survival over time, and not the perpetuation of individual component organisms. That implies as well that survival of the system PdP is paramount and too important to be subjected to evolutionary change. Increased species complexity over time turns out to be merely a consequence of the adaptive evolutionary processes described in detail above, which serve the cause of LS short and long-term survival.

Design considerations might well yield some insights—including the unavoidable fact that operational biology at the micro level—based on a chemical medium—must accommodate the entropy dictates of the 2nd law. LS design does overcome entropy at the system level by insulating itself within many layers of complexity that are far removed from its basic chemical reactions. Probably the most important entropy insulating layer, from the design viewpoint is reproduction—which has the effect of insulating a successive generation from assured entropy-driven organism phenotype degradation of the previous one. Thus, within the RDH context, the attempts at changing this status quo by the only intelligent species able to do so represents one more twist of irony.

B) MEDICINE—SUBVERTING LS FORM AND FUNCTION?

Is the Fountain of Youth finally within reach? Throughout history, humans have invested much time and energy developing stratagems specifically aimed at subverting that universal characteristic of life, which condemns them to certain destruction. What is the practice of medicine if not human intervention toward altering the course of natural biological processes that threaten the lives of individuals? The whole aim of medical practice is to avoid and cure illness—its ultimate aim is to cheat death. In modern societies, medical intervention begins months before birth as both mother and child are continually monitored to detect abnormal conditions and permit timely remedial action as required—the only aim being to thwart any detectable life-threatening conditions.

And so it continues throughout our lives, that medical practitioners enthusiastically intervene in all kinds of ways—from the prescription of vitamins and powerful drugs, the monitoring and adjusting of cholesterol and glucose levels, to the removal and replacement of diseased organs—all towards the goal of maintaining health, prolonging life and delaying the inevitable death. While no one has yet achieved that ultimate goal, the fact is that longevity has increased significantly as a direct result of such contrived efforts. Stem cell research promises to accelerate these trends. In effect, these measures aimed at helping individuals on a massive scale are nothing more or less than the contrived intervention with the natural processes of LS form and function. What we fail to fully appreciate, in this massive interference with the natural dynamic biological processes, is that we have become instrumental in the shaping of attribute distribution curves—not only of species attributes (SA's) but of biosphere attributes (BA's) as well. Within the last several hundred years, the human species has extricated itself from the universal species dependency upon the interplay of SA's and BA's that have traditionally defined a species' population genetics. The individual human ability to reproduce offspring has become independent of physical conditions or even the necessity of finding a suitable mate. Neither distance in space or time, nor the health of an individual, nor, indeed, even the condition of an individual organism being alive, need determine the suitability for successful reproduction. With the advent of sperm and egg banks, biologists presently possess the technology to produce test-tube babies from donors who lived out their lives centuries apart—parents whose lives could never cross—linked only by offspring born centuries after they, themselves, had died. With the advent of cloning technology, the ultimate goal of growing and harvesting organs derived from ones own genes promises to raise the moral and ethical stakes concerning such research. Some critics of genetic engineering describe such interventions with the natural processes of Life as a dangerous subversion of natural LS biology. In fact, the interventions of medical practitioners and biologists, indeed, represent universal human experience in the modification of LS design. From the RDH perspective, we would construe such interventions at the molecular biology level as "tinkering" with LS design—the implication being that we may inadvertently be getting in over our heads and that there are unappreciated dangers in messing with the PdP of biology.

c) Cancer—A Uniquely Curious Disease:

The monumental global effort to understand and subvert the mechanisms that give rise to cancer continue in a long medical tradition of other such efforts, but may in fact represent a very special exercise with interesting implications from the RDH point of view. All of the diverse cancers have in common the cessation of cellular mechanisms that control the reproduction and division of cells. The fact that all cancers entail a suspension of cellular reproductive regulation leading to exponential cell division, in fact, could implicate some universal causal triggering mechanisms at the basic PdP level. Within the context of the RDH design intent, it may not be too farfetched to suggest that the cause of cancer could be linked to the detection of uncorrectable errors in the EI located in the introns of affected cells. Once detected and marked, it is not hard to visualize some kind of culling mechanism meant to destroy such cells. It has been suggested that cells become cancerous all the time but that our immune systems are capable of removing them from our physiological midst. The question remains as to why and when the immune system fails in this critical task. Is it simply the insidious 2nd law entropy at work?

One answer compatible with RDH thinking might consider the advent of cancer as the detection and targeting for removal of intron errors within the sperm or eggs of organisms that are considered a danger to the purity of future extraneous-information integrity. Again, we can envisage a subsystem within the LS whose goal is the eradication of bad copies of such information. Within human culture, we have as an analog the mandatory destruction of inscribed parchment segments of the Judaic Torah in which spelling errors have been detected. No matter how minute the errors or the ability to instantaneously correct them can prevent the destruction, according to strict Jewish tradition, of the whole parchment segment involved in order to guarantee the high standards imposed upon the scribes entrusted with the quality of the finished work—which ultimately relies upon the integrity of its transcribed information. The purpose of such fastidiousness is to ensure that any new copy of the Torah will reflect exactly the same information as all others and that they all precisely reflect the information from the original(s) handed down thousands of years earlier. Perhaps the LS has built within it the same high level of reproduction standards, together with a self-destruct mechanism for insuring perpetual integrity. We call it cancer. Societies invest huge budgets on medical research motivated towards the discovery and subversion of destructive biological mechanisms that manifest themselves as diseases such as cancer. The irony would be galling if one day we come to recognize the utility of such a disease as a localized LS self-destruct mechanism meant to operate at the organism level in order to preserve LS design intent. In the end, medical research aimed at curing cancer may in fact represent a front line defense whose unintentional consequence is the subversion of the LS design intent—the destruction of organisms harboring bad copies of an extraneous information library.

While the fight against disease is waged worldwide, the survival of humankind from an armed LS self-limiting subsystem described in these pages could likely entail a commensurate global effort. The only difference between the two is that in the one, the efforts are aimed at enhancing and saving the lives of associate members of humanity individually. In the other, efforts would be aimed at saving all the members of the human species collectively.

For The Drake Equation and SETI programs:

At this point, I would like to return to our discussion of the Drake Equation discussed in Chapter 4, and in particular to one variable that we would care to examine a little more closely: "f_l"—the number of planets where life actually emerges. Before any kind of estimated figure can be assigned to this variable, one important consideration must, in my view, be detailed. "f_l" will be assigned fundamentally different values depending upon how it is considered that biological life occurs in the universe. Therefore, I contend that variable "f_l" should not be considered only in the light of the singular experience of it's kind that we know of—our own—and definitely not within the presumption that it had to have been simply a chance phenomenon, with SAb as the root pathway of the OoL on our planet (and responsible for similar such phenomenon anywhere else life may be found).

As previously discussed, the Drake formula relies upon the so-called "Principle of Mediocrity (PoM)". The idea behind the PoM is that if some phenomenon is found to exist in the universe, then that particular occurrence is most likely not the sole representation, and its presence anywhere probably reflects only a single example of a wider incidence of such circumstances. The principle has particularly been aimed at the phenomenon of life and underlies the widespread belief that if it happened here, it could happen anywhere, given just the right conditions. It formalizes the idea behind the all-familiar expression: "Been there; done that!" that implies that there is nothing really new under the sun, or for that matter in the universe at large. In that respect, the PoM can be extended to the existence of intelligent life and becomes implicated in our deliberations.

But, the PoM also has to come to grips with the reality summed up in the statement quoted earlier by Enrico Fermi in reference to the question of whether ETs and UFO's exist: "So, where are they!" becomes his simplistic yet elegant retort. Then again, if life is so ubiquitous a phenomenon as implied by the invocation of the PoM, then so should be intelligent life and its bi-product, technology and the evidence for it—by way of electromagnetic radiation signals resulting from radio and television emissions and the like. We know that we are flooding the universe with such evidence of our own technology with a radiation wavefront expanding outward in space in all directions at the speed of light. Ultimately, if anybody is out there they will surely know of our existence, (or past existence) as signals that emanate from sources as diverse as the "I LOVE LUCY" TV show (the original series as well as reruns) or the U.S. president's state of the union addresses, whiz outward in deep space at light speed (literally). Then again, radio emissions preceded TV by a number of years, so that we can consider our presence to have reached deep space to a distance approaching 100 light years. But, the fact remains that here we are, sending out all this stuff, all the while awaiting ETI transmissions to arrive from out there and we have nothing to show for all of our SETI efforts. According to the RDH, this says a lot, not about the weakness of the PoM as a general guideline but about the phenomenon of ETI life in our neighborhood of the galaxy. By the same token, any PoM must impact upon the SAb hypothesis that considers life as a natural phenomenon, and therefore ubiquitous as a phenomenon in our vast galaxy (billion upon billions of stars), in proportions comparable to the variety and quantity of species on our planet. Moreover, if that were truly the case, and the OoL were truly a naturally occurring SAb phenomenon, then our galactic neighborhood should be teeming with life forms and, at the very least, their evidence should be everywhere. In other words, if indeed, the PoM can be applied to the life phenomenon, then enough time has already elapsed in our galaxy that the skies should literally be ablaze with evidence of intelligence in the frequency range of radio transmissions every bit as much as they are with starlight. This speaks to the issue of galaxies and stars within our own galaxy that had a significant headstart over OoL on earth and therefore would have spontaneously abiogenerated many representative examples of life and consequently intelligence as well. After all, you can't just limit a PoM—can you? The fact that this does not seem to be the case and that to date absolutely no SETI evidence of ETI has been received should provoke a more sobering assessment of any ideas that might tend to underestimate the special quality of the OoL on our planet (and give pause to reconsider the likelihood of any kind of SAb). Unquestionably, the jury is still out with respect to the value of "f_1" and I suspect will remain there for some time to come.

Considering the extent of confusion surrounding the other values in the Drake Equation, we needn't hold our metaphorical breaths either. Unquestionably, the curiosity concerning our "aloneness" will not go away. Thus, I merely wish to inject a bit of caution as to how we go about interpreting Drake-equation kind of solutions to the extent that they reinforce limited ideas, such as SAb—ideas that we consider to be suspect and the reason for our introduction of *The 5th OPTION* in the ongoing OoL debate. All parties in the debate can probably agree that due to the lack of evidence to the contrary (Fermi's question still stands), the probability remains high that we are alone as a technological intelligence in our immediate neighborhood in the galaxy and that life is likely not all that common to begin with, as "mediocre" phenomena go. As expected the RDH can propose its own unique interpretation of this possible eventuality.

If there is any validity to a Principle Of Mediocrity as it pertains to life in the galaxy, from the RDH point of view, the facts suggest:

1) The reason we have no evidence of other biological life in our galactic neighborhood is simply because it is not a naturally occurring phenomenon but a contrived one. Such life only appears as a limited edition, only where and when it is implanted by design to serve a specific purpose in accordance with its specific design intent.

2) As a consequence, the PoM is applicable with respect to the existence of other life in our galaxy in the following way: the implanted LS on our planet should in all likelihood be only a single example of many others within a well thought out strategy. That is, if our LS were indeed engineered and placed on planet Earth for a purpose, chances are that it would be repeated on other planets in other solar systems across the galaxy to accomplish a similar purpose and design intent. This also addresses the design cost amortization issue that is all too familiar to human engineers. The first automobile or plane

that comes off the assembly line may cost in the millions and billions respectively, if only a single copy is ever produced. On the other hand, Boeing makes money because it sells many copies of the planes it designs. In contrast, the Anglo-French consortium that designed and built the Concorde supersonic jet lost money because it did not go into production. Thus, the few prototypes in service cost more than their worth. The only way an expensive design can justify its costs is by producing enough of them in order to amortize the cost of design and of the specialized tooling required to produce the very first copy of many that may well follow. The same principle applies to any designed system—planes, trains, and automobiles. Why not bio-life systems, as well?

If indeed, the LS can serve as a repository of an EI library—possibly meant to serve the needs of space travelers to the far reaches of the galaxy, for example—then, chances are there are many such installed systems located strategically throughout the galaxy. Such installations could exist in some kind of organized pattern or density throughout the wider galactic neighborhood. Thus, bio-life systems, with PdPs virtually identical to our own, could exist in many places in our galaxy—but not as the disorganized weed-like sprouting of the phenomenon that a natural abiogenetic origin would imply. In other words, if the OoL were a natural SAb phenomenon, it should tend to be randomly scattered and plentiful—everywhere conditions permit. As well, each such incidence of SAb should be characterized by its own unique PdP—representative of the unique initial conditions from which it had sprung. The fact that the LS on planet Earth seems to be an isolated example within our sphere of detectability must lead us to consider the distinct possibility that life, as we know it, is either an extremely rare SAb anomaly as natural phenomena go, or a contrived and limited edition, as it were—implanted in specific non-overlapping planetary locations around the galaxy. As such, and according to the guidelines of the PoM, and following a RDH scenario, we are probably not the only LS of its kind established in our galaxy. Perhaps biological LS systems similar to our own are planted as distant outposts of some kind that for the sake of efficiency, as well as safety (from cross contamination), are beyond casual electronic hailing distances from each other. Thus, the lack of evidence of the existence of other life in our immediate solar system neighborhood fits in well with the RDH model. As far as the PoM is concerned, without any evidence to the contrary, SAb fails to meet its test while the RDH offers logical and valid reasons why it can.

As such, and in order to eliminate any ambiguity, the implications inherent within the RDH suggest that a SAb OoL is not likely, that intelligent life is not a widespread phenomenon in the universe, and that any kind of Life is rare and probably not within electromagnetic earshot of our immediate neighborhood (with the exception of our indigenous selves and possibly discretely visiting aliens far from home). In fact, we might surmise that if any other example of biological life exists in our galaxy, it most probably was derived from the same intelligent source. This reinforces the RDH premise that biology is not the kind of thing that starts by itself: it needs to be genetically engineered and given a jump-start. The system, (a broad spectrum of initiating eukaryotic and prokaryotic species comprising large distributions of organisms to accommodate initial foodchain and evolution imperatives) is then implanted on a suitable planet where the likelihood of survival success is assured. The PoM can be invoked to suggest that the existence of Earth-like planets, suitable as habitat for biological life, must be common throughout the galaxy. The vast number of stars alone testifies to this likely probability. It is the apparent scarcity of evidence of life other than our own that doesn't make a lot of sense, if biological life were indeed a natural, and therefore ubiquitous phenomenon. This scarcity of life can be, and indeed is, explained by the RDH. That scarcity also suggests, that biological life requires very special circumstances for its existence: an intelligent intermediary responsible for its design, jump-start, and placement in operation within a suitable environment. (Within a totally different context, the RDH validates the intuitions of many, that an extraordinary intervention was required for the origin of the LS—no different from the necessity of human intervention for the existence and operation of our own mechanical machines.) Remember—2nd law entropy at the micro level of random chemistry rules supreme.

The Existence of Extraterrestrial Intelligence:

While SETI programs continue searching the heavens for evidence of ET intelligence, the chances of actually detecting an intelligent signal coming from outer space remain unknown. While the RDH supports the pursuit of any scientific research that can shed light on the existence of other sources of intelligence in the universe, its intrinsic message would suggest we might be focusing our attention in the wrong place. While we diligently monitor electromagnetic radiation from outer space as the only potential source of evidence of intelligent life, we may in fact be neglecting the motherlode of intelligent extraterrestrial information in our midst. Instead of passively waiting for the SETI "phone" to ring, the implications of the RDH thesis suggest that extraterrestrial information may have already arrived as hard copy—just waiting to be decoded and read. We refer, of course, to the only example of a non-human derived information database of which we are aware—the DNA library. The RDH postulates that the capacity to store vast amounts of information within the DNA of eukaryotic species comprises both the purpose for the design of life as well as the likely location for a body of supplementary extraneous information (SEI). A principal conclusion of the RDH thesis is that the non-genetic information contained within the introns of DNA is of extraterrestrial origin. Thus, we are faced with the interesting prospect that future SETI programs may in fact turn from searching the vast reaches of cosmic outer space for evidence of extraterrestrial intelligence to examining the vast extant information libraries within biological inner space—the chemical medium of DNA in our midst. The encouraging news is that the technological methodology for the SETI within the minute DNA molecules of life is already in place and the exploration has already begun. Vast amounts of funding are currently financing efforts of interpreting the information available in the human genome. Of course, the incentive for such a universal effort on the part of the whole molecular biology community is geared toward the medical benefits that will accrue from the acquired knowledge of human genetics. The RDH suggests this global effort presents a unique opportunity to expand the SETI initiative, using the novel encryption tools discussed in Chapter 15. The human imagination cannot help but marvel at the poignant juxtaposition of such ultimate contrasts exemplified within the search for an extraterrestrial non-material entity—information—both in the infinite vastness of outer space and the infinitesimal realm of atoms and molecules. It is one more example of the fine line that separates the extremes within human intellectual endeavors. Another is the bringing to bear of the science of particle physics toward the study and understanding of the underlying principles of astrophysics. Are we now on the verge of applying some of the same principles of information theory—waiting to be applied if and when an ET information sequence is detected from outer space—to the non-random information sequences already apparent within the non-genetic DNA introns of human inner space? The RDH model of reality leaves no room for doubt as to the practicality and desirability of this human imperative.

For Genetic Engineering:

If anything can help humanity survive its technological phase in history, it is knowledge of what we are doing that is right, and what it is that we are doing wrong. Our present state of awareness suggests that we are too often confused when it comes to understanding the long-term effects of new and advancing technologies. It seems logical that the potential for environmental chaos and the consequential dangers for biological integrity increase in proportion to the extent our technologies permit us to tinker with nature. This is presently occurring on a number of technological fronts. On reflection, a case can be made that no greater threat exists to human life than the increasing knowledge of molecular biologists, which permits them to tamper with the most intimate workings of the PdP of bio-life. The aim of all such research, of course, is to intervene positively in order to alleviate medical problems, expand agricultural yields and enhance human existence in general. The problem is that we may be approaching a watershed stage in these kinds of activities that could result in the unthinkable—the introduction of changes that materially alter the fundamental design platform of biological life. Such changes, innocuous when they occur, could conceivably spread like wildfire throughout the LS, cascading across the whole interactive fabric of life. These kinds of statements are not meant as a warning but rather as acknowledged possibilities. The truth is that no one can predict the outcome of these kinds of applied research simply because no one can possibly know. You can never predict the consequences of activities meant to discover and apply new knowledge. Scientists proceed by creating causes and methodically measuring effects. There is nothing new here. The real danger derives from the nature of the arenas where scientists are applying their skills. There is a major difference between chemists investigating and exploring new compositions of glass and their potential uses, and biologists actively engaged in rearranging the architecture of individual cells—while totally ignorant of the delicate nature of the fabric of life they are tampering with. Living stuff has the potential to reproduce indefinitely—therefore, we had better be extra careful of what it is we create, purposefully or accidentally, and let loose from those test tubes. We have already witnessed the consequences of thoughtless tinkering with nuclear reactors—what happens when one carelessly removes constraints that maintain design intent integrity. The consequences of tinkering with the PdP of bio-life could make the Chernobyl "near miss" look like child's play. According to the RDH thesis, such activities have the potential for inadvertently changing the PdP of all of biological life, as we know it. The consequences could potentially lead to both: a) the production of improved food supplies and medical procedures that can benefit mankind and, b) the unleashing of some inadvertently contrived ruthless competing biological entity based on a PdP incompatible with our own. At worst, the result could be the pathogenic wipeout of the entire LS, as we know it—replaced by some living entity that starts from scratch. Does anyone doubt that once we begin this bio-tech journey, we really shall be relinquishing any ability to control the results, whether arrived at by commission or omission; both intended and unintended. It is not a question of "if" but "when" we shall be confronted with the consequences of biotechnologies run amok. Why the hysterics? There is ample precedent.

One of the fundamental weaknesses of science is that while we are doing it, we rarely have insight as to the ultimate consequences. Our experience with the development of the peaceful application of nuclear technology has proven the point. The irony is that for half a century, the world considered nuclear arms as the major threat to continued human existence. In fact it took a Chernobyl-like accident to point up the fact that the supposedly "Atoms for Peace" initiative—the program pushing the research and development of the peaceful uses of nuclear energy, can be every bit as much a potential villain. If *Chernobyl* teaches us anything, it is the sobering fact that to date we have probably had more luck than brains in preventing nuclear disasters. One might be forgiven for wondering how many nuclear narrow escapes 20th century human civilization has in fact experienced. It is not paranoia that voices the suggestion that the whole truth about all such near misses and nuclear safety in general will probably never be known.

Even the best of motives cannot serve as a prevention of potential disaster. The development of antibiotics and their proliferation in both human and animal populations is teaching us that immediate short-term gains can result in long-term complications. Broadband antibiotics have accomplished the removal of certain disease causing pathogens, only to pave the way for the evolution of super-resistant strains we respectfully label—"super bugs". Ironically, it is in hospitals that one is most likely to confront such powerful biological adversaries—because the hospital environment is where antibiotics and viruses are most concentrated. The panic is presently underway to develop new biological countermeasures to confront the biological enemy. Isn't there something all too familiar in this scenario? The issue is not simply the fact that we are engaged in a kind of arms race with an unknown number of innovative biological enemies, but that we were unable to predict the consequences of the applied research that got us into the mess. Of course, there is no reason to doubt that we will solve this particular problem. The truly unsolveable problem is how to stay out of serious trouble as our involvement in areas of potentially disastrous research increases, commensurate with our increasing skills of involvement. The ultimate question is whether the entire human species will one-day end up paying the ultimate price.

What are we to make of the application of genetic engineering to our food supply? The impressive results in both quality and quantity of food production have a potentially disastrous side. Let's not forget the DDT pesticide fiasco. Initially proclaimed as a miracle product in the eradication of crop pests, we are still trying to assess in some meaningful way its disastrous consequences to the biosphere. On another front, our reliance on artificial and limited numbers of genetic strains has decreased drastically the genetic variability of seed stock thereby creating a very real vulnerability to powerful pathogens that could irrevocably wipe out large portions of the human food supply. Again, the motive is positive and the desire distinctly humanitarian. However, do we really understand the potential dangers of the game we are playing? But the worst is yet to come.

The Human Genome Project, whose stated aim was the decoding of each letter in the human DNA library, has completed its first phase early into the first decade of the 21st century. This milestone of genetic research will open up new avenues of biological tinkering fraught with a whole slew of unappreciated dangers. The only difference between the past and the new eras of biological discovery that will accrue with the decoding of the Human Genome are the many new areas of disaster potential we will be opening up in the process. We have survived the processes of discovery getting to this point. Is it fair to assume we will also survive the consequences of being able to do the kinds of wholesale tinkering to the PdP that the Human Genome initiative will allow? Will such information—besides helping promote so-called medical miracles—also promote the development of the ultimate in biological weapons? This open question is more than just idle speculation. We know of at least one instance where the products of a genetics experiment performed in Brazil in 1957—the cross between domestic honeybees and African "killer" bees—have, through neglect, escaped the laboratory. Since that time, these aggressive insects have multiplied rapidly in the wild, threatening humans and wildlife alike as they migrate north. There is no suggestion here that these bees present any kind of serious threat to the survival of any specie other than, perhaps, to domestic bees. But, the event represents an ominous paradigm that can easily be emulated. This precedence of tampering with genetics without considering the possible consequences and taking the necessary precautions can serve as a credible warning of the very real dangers that lie ahead. And we shall be upping the stakes considerably as we begin tampering with the innermost workings at the very heart of the LS—its PdP. And, even if we do take every conceivable precaution—will that suffice over long periods of time? There is the very real potential for inadvertent errors to produce lethal results on a planet wide scale.

Together with the all of the other recognized threats looming within the framework of advancing bio-technological activities, the RDH thesis implies that we may have reached a seminal point in our techno-cultural history. The good news is: we may still have a limited window of opportunity to consider the seriousness of the survival threats and dangers we face by our own hand, and to consider as well the kinds of choices available to us that might minimize or remove some of the threats to the future survival of humankind. The less-than-good news is: considering the present state of the human condition one must logically question whether we are up to the task.

Conclusions:

As demonstrated above, the RDH represents more than simply a static solution to the question of OoL. Unlike the other OoL options, the RDH serves as a model of reality for the existence of bio-life on our planet, which, if tested and found to have validity, has important implications that impact on many levels, including our future survival.

There is a widely publicized mission statement put out by supporters of SETI. Besides the obvious subjective curiosity of wanting to know whether other intelligent civilizations exist, there is another compelling and very objective personal human reason for searching out the heavens: It is considered relevant and important for humans to find evidence we are not alone because such evidence impacts directly on our own potential for survival. If we can detect the existence of another intelligent civilization—no matter how distant—that fact alone will provide us hope that we have a future. For, the existence of another civilization will signal that technologically advanced civilizations need not succumb to the dangers inherent in the development of their technologies but can indeed survive them. While that interpretation of SETI motives may offer humans hope, it can only be of the slimmest variety inasmuch as we may be waiting a very long time for SETI to produce results. And, the Principle of Mediocrity—as applied to our aloneness—does not offer much by way of encouragement. While we are waiting, perhaps the only real direction we can turn for answering the important questions rests with the testable RDH—answers that not only relate to whether our species can survive into the future, but perhaps can provide, as well, solutions for how that might be achieved. In fact it is a logical possibility that if intelligent alien civilizations have managed to survive their technologies, their solution may very well have involved the discovery of their own rationally designed origins and the positive effects that ensued as a result (more of this in the final chapter).

In the final analysis we, as intelligent organisms, are searching for more in life than just facts. Each one of us thinking individuals, fully in accordance with long-standing tradition, wants to be able to interpret the facts of the reality in which our lives are immersed, in such a way that they offer some modicum of personal "hope"—for the future as well as the present. Humans, collectively—as societies and as individuals—even in our darkest moments have always thrived on hope, even when the slimmest of reasons for maintaining hope seem to evaporate. Thus, any thesis that claims to be an accurate model of LS reality must also provide a framework for hope—along with whatever intellectual platform it claims to support. In the next and final chapter, we explore ways in which the RDH—the 5TH OoL option—meets this important test.

---

[1]The Hare and the Tortoise: Culture, Biology and Human Nature; D P Barash; 1987

18. "Hope" Springs Eternal

Who are we? We find that we live on an insignificant planet of a
humdrum star lost in a galaxy tucked away in some forgotten corner of a
universe in which there are far more galaxies than people.
                                            —Carl Sagan (1934–1996), Astronomer

The Rational Design Hypothesis—The Ultimate Message of Hope:

With the exception of Creationism—based on the logic of religious belief—the other four OoL options, including our own RDH, suggest strictly scientific arguments in support of their respective positions. Non-believers would argue that the religious aspect of Creationism renders it scientifically untenable as an OoL option. Creationists, for their part, distrust many of the assumptions upon which scientific OoL claims depend, with particular emphasis on evolution. OoL arguments aside for the moment, Creationists bolster their underlying and scientifically insupportable belief in a purposeful supreme creator by pointing out that the moment you abandon your link with "God", you do so at the peril of losing as well the only possible source of ultimate purpose in your life—and consequently your only possible link with "hope". Thus, one important motive for adopting any theistic belief system begins with the very human necessity to believe in some ultimate something—anything that will confer desperately desired hope. The need to believe that human life has an importance that transcends physical existence is sufficient justification in favor of some divine entity as the basis of a belief system—a God endowed with the infinite power and wisdom with which to create and manage this complicated universe in which fragile humans find themselves. Essentially, the OoL question is only incidental for Creationists—considered by them to be a mysterious event, but only one among many others where explanations can be deduced and interpreted from an ancient text that essentially defers all unanswerable questions to an omnipotent creator. The cynics and non-believers among us would argue that ultimately hope is futile, and more than likely embrace the quotation attributed to the American writer, Henry Thoreau: "The mass of men lead lives of quiet desperation." But, no-one—believers and non-believers alike—would attempt to refute the desirability of finding ways of instilling hope in our lives even while some of us may be somewhat hardpressed to define exactly what it is we can expect 'hope' to accomplish.

After all is said and done, there is a practical side to our desire for hope—it would seem to be of little value unless we could believe it possible to make radical improvements to the human condition in general and our individual prospects of living happier and healthier lives. The religious position holds that it alone can furnish 'hope' as a replacement for despair, and following its own logic, attempts to replace the cold and hard facts that suggest we are in a losing race with time for our collective survival, with the "belief" that somehow, somewhere there is a godly plan that will favour believers through any and all their difficulties. But, that same argument reflects a sad acknowledgment that there are in fact no foreseeable solutions to the escalating set of problems the human species faces, and that the only hope we may have rests, not with human derived solutions, but within a belief that solutions indeed are out of our own hands and rest exclusively with divine forces. And, in a sense, this argument underscores the debate between science and religion. The former offers the cold hard testable facts that define our temporal world, letting the chips fall wherever they may; the latter offers 'hope against hope'—meant to sustain us through the perils of this life and beyond. As we shall soon come to appreciate, the RDH occupies a rather unique position within this somewhat polarized environment.

The RDH—Something for Everyone?

As stated, the RDH, in postulating a rational designer of biological life, inadvertently validates the basic creationist doctrine—that of a "creator" of life. Semantics aside, the very logical introduction of the concept of an intelligent designer of life on our planet becomes a fundamental provision shared by both the RDH as well as Creationism. However, it is obvious that each defines its interpretation of design in fundamentally different terms. The interesting thing here is that in a sense, the debate on the subject has come nearly full circle. Religious doctrine predates science as a way of dealing with and explaining the OoL and its universe habitat—evolving in the process a set of guidelines postulating a purposeful creator, able to interfere in the affairs of men. The RDH is a science based OoL hypothesis that postulates—and might eventually scientifically affirm—the existence of an intelligent and purposeful rational designer-creator of life.

Interestingly, despite its strictly scientific underpinnings, the dependence of the RDH on the intervention of a prior intelligence as designer, allows us to seek and explore avenues from which we might be able to extract some tangible measure of hope upon which an evolved intelligent LS species might satisfyingly depend. The 'hope' that the RDH can deduce from its OoL deliberations derives not from any kind of wishful thinking that drives religious belief, but directly from the scientifically testable conclusions upon which its thesis is based. Moreover, the RDH can do so without sacrificing its scientific integrity and objectivity. This is indeed 'hope' with a difference.

Ironically, scientific testing of the RDH may eventually provide the Creationist school with the formal proof of design it holds to be true. Scientific validation of the fundamental premises of the RDH may unwittingly furnish Creationists with evidence of the existence of a set of awesome and universal texts that would rival and, indeed, supplant the "holy" documents of any religion. The writings we refer to would not be written in stone or parchment nor handed down to humans through intermediary prophets. They would be written in the universal genetic language of the four nucleic acid letters in the intron chapters of DNA located in the nuclei of each and every eukaryotic cell. And, if this DNA intron library can be located and proven to exist, as the RDH speculates, it's scientific verification may afford all the world religions together with the scientific community a unique opportunity to share in the quest to decode and make intelligible the information contained therein. No interest group could claim exclusivity to such information. Biologists may be able to patent genes; they will enjoy no such benefits with respect to non-genes. The revelation of a body of EI could conceivably motivate the whole of humanity to set aside its petty differences and unite in the acceptance of the "encoded scriptures"—written in biological DNA. The discovery of an encrypted message placed among the introns of eukaryotic DNA—copied generation after generation since the very OoL on our planet—could only be the product of the rational designer and creator of life—hidden and awaiting the momentous day when an evolved intelligent product of the LS would first lay eyes on it. We can only begin to speculate upon the nature of such information—and that is where the hope comes in.

Considering that recent computer analysis has revealed the startling fact—that the introns alone (as opposed to the exons, that do not) obey the Zipf mathematical statistical tests for language (demonstrating as well a host of other such language characteristics) should, together with the RDH claims, encourage ambitious new efforts to uncover the language mystery that attends such a large proportion of DNA. According to RDH claims discussed above, there are urgent and compelling reasons to do so. The consequences of determining that every human being contains within each of its cells the full text of a message from the designer would undoubtedly spark a timely positive cultural revolution as a bonus, the likes of which have no comparison in our history. It could very well foment a movement of religious, scientific and cultural unity that could truly be termed universal, as no one could claim exclusivity, or custodial ownership, over such information. And, if it were found to exist as well within the introns of other species, the realization could then impose itself upon us, that perhaps we have an increased moral obligation and responsibility to treat all such life with greater consideration than we presently accord them. Of course that state of affairs—the treatment of all life as though it were our responsibility to do so—could only come about if we could redefine ourselves into worthy custodians of the planet, replacing the traditional religion-inspired self image as deserved exploiters and destroyers of other species. If we ever get to discover a message encoded in DNA, not only will it confirm the RDH OoL option, but just as importantly, the information contained therein could conceivably have a profound and hopefully positive influence on human culture and, indeed, human survival—an influence that could justifiably be interpreted as "interference in the affairs of men".

We can judge the importance that belief systems—whether political or religious—have had throughout history, by the extent and importance of the conflicts, divisions and debilitating wars provoked by differences of interpretation of such respective doctrines. We are still living in a time in history where diverse beliefs, and the consequential divisions they provoke, endure on a planet wide scale—continuing to incite the suspicions, hatreds and intolerance that fuel our self-destructive tendencies—a state of affairs that has endured throughout human history. It is apparent that after all this time—we humans still "don't get it"! Even though human culture has developed the scientific means to comprehend, in a limited but meaningful way, the true nature of our existence on a number of different scales, we still find it difficult to redress the egocentric and self-inflated importance we attach to our species' role in the universe. It is as though we can do no wrong. Nevertheless, the wrongs have been accumulating rapidly and while technology holds out the promise of a better world, it is ironically proving to be the curse of mankind for all but a few of the privileged among us. The RDH, if tested and validated, could help change attitudes—and provide a legitimate basis for a major reassessment of the human condition. One of its major advantages in this regard is that the RDH parallels, albeit in a limited way, the basic premise of creationism—just enough, perhaps, to maintain among creationists a certain minimal level of credibility. At the same time, as its name implies, the RDH is rational in the extreme, with no vested doctrine of its own that could affect its scientific credibility. As such, 'rational design' can easily be considered by religionists of all persuasions to be the logical modernization of Creationist thought and doctrine—Creationism turned "Rational-Designism", if you will, in the age of science and rationale. Interestingly, the RDH is well positioned to serve as that essential bridge that straddles science and religion—such that both can find common cause, an essential ingredient during this critical period in human history. We may, indeed, be on the critical path that defines whether future human generations continue as a species. The RDH could serve as that essential focal point for the unity that must precede any concerted efforts in defense of our collective children's future.

I believe that the RDH could have an important role to play; it does represent an evolution in thought, in the sense that it spans and preserves successfully the vital interests of both creationism and science. And, most importantly, within the RDH thesis there does exist a body of ideas that can engender the kind of hope that satisfies our longing for purpose but does not end up denying us of our logical basis of thought; i.e.—one that conveys hope we can truly believe in because it is logically believable. It also has the considerable advantage, for people still comfortable with religious beliefs, of making no fundamental demands incompatible with those present beliefs, while putting an end to the destructive dichotomy of logic responsible for so much personal and collective conflict.

If you have followed the reasoning in these pages and have truly opened up your mind to the many novel and logical ideas that have developed during our SE analysis of the LS, you can now walk away from this exercise with a unique sense of renewed hope and anticipation. In a nutshell, if you are a God-fearing believer in a creator, you can remain satisfied that this very rational exercise has left that belief relatively intact while providing you with good and valid reasons for accepting the logic of evolution. You will recall that we have concluded that evolution is entirely compatible with a design OoL and that it can be viewed as an effective strategic adaptive subsystem of the LS—part and parcel of the designer's design intent, the goal of which is to perpetuate the survival of the LS. You can now appreciate the fact that increased complexity that results from evolution is not an end in itself, but a simple strategy to transcend time—in order to preserve indefinitely the body of information locked up in DNA. In fact, the creator is no longer placed in the embarrassing position of keeping a "Noah's ark" variety of species agenda, as religions have always argued—the very idea of which is contradicted by evolution. The RDH has now removed, in effect, any obstacle, intellectual or otherwise, to an acceptance of evolution as part of the creator's grand design. We don't even deprive you of your Holy Scriptures: the true word of god, according to the RDH, may be written in the intron DNA of every cell in your body and everybody else's body, as well. In that respect, the word of the creator is both "wholly" in its universality as well as "holy" in a personally held sacred sense. The RDH can thus serve as an effective neutral middle ground where people of all persuasions, fundamentalist to atheist—can find common cause and understanding because the intellectual obstacles that have stood in the way are removable.

For those who have lost interest in religious dogma or are less inclined toward a religious explanation for their existence, the RDH offers renewed hope based on strictly logical grounds. This comes with the appreciation that only scientific research and reasoning can discover how to read the language of the designer, once its location can be acknowledged. That hoped-for discovery, could signify the greatest positive leap forward in virtually all areas of human thought. Within that potential may reside the unprecedented hopes and dreams of the entire human race. From a sociological standpoint, the RDH represents, indeed, the greatest measure of collective hope because it does not conflict with the interests of any special interest group while treating all humans, regardless of religious or political persuasion with equal dignity. And from a strictly pragmatic point of view, the RDH is important because it may possibly represent the only hope of humanity for its future survival. The RDH is unique as a body of thought in its suggestion that within the equivalent of roughly two million pages of language-like intron information to be found within the human DNA may well be discovered (but, only if we look for it) the only workable prescription that could advise and guide us through the perilous days ahead, and perhaps even instruct us how to neutralize our innate aggression towards each other—carry-over relics from our sub-human past. Religious teachings may have been the vehicle through which we sought solutions to such problems in the past. The fact is that too many parochial religions competing amongst themselves for membership, (money), power and influence can hardly be considered a likely prescription for solving today's complex planet-wide problems. Yet, it is within some form of religious thought wherein the majority of people seek and find hope—not that their confidence in religion is necessarily justified—it's just that in a world becoming increasingly complex, religion continues to be some refuge of last resort. But, as the people of the world become increasingly exposed to the growing list of dilemmas caused directly from the diminishing ability of the constant resource biosphere to support geometric population growth, their traditional sources of hope will be increasingly put to the test. But by that time, it may be too late to do anything about it. Catastrophism could indeed become a self-fulfilling prophecy. Perhaps now, while we can still make choices, the time has come to pass the baton to a new player armed with new strategies—and that new player is the Rational Design Hypothesis...all in the name of hope.

Hope As Strategy:

Nevertheless, there is another aspect of hope that has a much deeper importance than our narrow and selfish personal interests. I refer to the whole question of how we should interpret the finding of a body of information placed within the genetic library of a founder species of the LS some 3.8 billion years ago, accurately replicated from generation to generation and specifically to be accessed by any evolved and technologically sophisticated species that survives long enough to discover it. The answer is two-fold: The less important interpretation is to congratulate ourselves—firstly on being smart enough and lucky enough to evolve, and then secondly on surviving long enough to have developed the technology with which to access the information that may well insure the future of our lifeform. Congratulations indeed! Just as important, I would suggest, is the profound interpretation we must place on the fact that the designer might be of such a nature as to care to communicate with an intelligent LS species—a species the designer had no way of knowing would ever evolve. In this regard, that act of discovery on our part may say as much about the designer as it says about us. The discovery of the placement of information meant for a chance evolved intelligent species of unknown characteristics other than its intelligence, would provide a meaningful insight into the "mind" and nature of such a designer—that can only be interpreted as a profound optimism on its part—an optimism that must be matched by an equal measure of hope on ours. The point is, that at this moment in time, and until we begin to look, we have no way of knowing whether a message meant for us does indeed exist. And, by the very same token, if it does exist, the designer may have no way of knowing whether that personal message, riding piggy-back within the system genetic libraries that control LS form and function, will ever be discovered by us. This uncertainty places us both—designer and designee, in essentially the same boat, intimately connected by a slim thread of hope and optimism. We are in the same position as lovers separated forever by distance and time. After many years of separation, one of them wonders whether the other ever sent a promised letter. The sender wonders if the receiver ever got the letter he has sent. Meanwhile the letter itself may sit at the bottom of a dresser drawer in some forgotten attic with the distinct possibility it will forever remain undiscovered.

Probably the most hopeful aspect of the RDH thesis is the fact that we need not await the discovery of the designer's message in order to benefit from the hope we can experience individually and collectively. This common understanding of the logical possibility that the creator of the LS may have made demonstrable provisions to communicate with some future progeny of its LS design—a species capable of discovering and decoding it—can serve as a genuine unifying influence. As we launch ourselves headlong into the 3rd millennium, humankind must acknowledge the real uncertainties of whether we shall ever be able to successfully mount the essential worldwide cooperative efforts to focus upon and confront the many challenges it faces. The ideas presented within the RDH can only help further such a cause.

Radical changes to ideas that constitute communal wisdom have been introduced, at times, under the persuasion of a conqueror's sword—at other times under the persuasion of emotional appeal. The timing is always a critical factor, as both politicians and theologians will attest. But, I would suggest that the most important factor in the equation of the composition of the body of ideas held by communities concerns the relationship between the collective genetic and cultural variables of its members—GV & CV respectively (discussed in chapter 17), that characterize human nature, and the human condition in general. Those discussions suggest that if we have survived to the third millennium of the Common Era in human history, it is not through the collective skills of our politicians or religious leaders but, indeed, in spite of them. As our previous discussions suggest, the only reason we have not self-destructed in the two world wars this century is due to the simple fact that the resources both quantitative and qualitative brought to the task were insufficient to accomplish the job. Now, for the first time in history, all that has changed. The human species has finally accumulated and placed in position, the sufficient and necessary resources to destroy itself. And, while we all wait for that to happen, the military industrial complexes of our world continue their diligent efforts to design, test and create the next generations of unconventional weapons of mass destruction. The truly fascinating aspect to this gruesome tale is that at no time during the process of producing the nuclear, chemical, and biological weapon stockpiles to do the job—together with the sophisticated delivery systems that can transport them with pinpoint accuracy—has any serious thought gone into the logical consequences of their existence. History teaches us that it is normal for communities to have differences (relating to political, religious, territorial, natural resources, water, etc.) and that their legitimate settlement of last resort has traditionally been through armed conflict. Thus, it is that soldiering has always been and continues to be a legitimate and noble profession. We will defer to Kanrad Lorenz's "theory of innate aggression" relating to his concept of "militant enthusiasm" (discussed in chapter 17) to fill in the details on how leadership throughout history has exploited the GVs of their citizenry to patriotically offer up the lives of their fathers and sons—on the altars of war. The philosophy of "mutual deterrence" has historically been considered a cornerstone of the defense posture of nations between wars. Times have changed and mutual deterrence has evolved—with the advent of weapons of mass destruction—into "mutual assured destruction (MAD)". The former sought to limit an arms race to the maintenance of parity of offensive capabilities between potential adversaries. The new modern posture of deterrence that has replaced parity constitutes a virtual free-for-all and mandates the open-ended and unlimited production of weapons, ostensibly to deter a war that can result in no winners—everybody loses. Under these unique circumstances, the question of whether the human species can survive another world war becomes trivial. It follows that the question: "Under what circumstances could another world war occur?" verges on obscenity. Still, a cursory examination of the current state of world geopolitics will convince even the skeptics among us that there are any number of scenarios that could escalate quickly into an "Armageddon scenario" that no part of the globe can escape.

The RDH interpretation of LS design intent suggests that human technology (the cultural variable) may well have reached the sufficient and necessary threshold capable of arming a potential self-limiting mechanism. One suggested target is to eliminate nuclear technology, an essential component for deep space propulsion systems. The idea behind the LS self-limiting mechanism is to rely on the combination of built-in genetically derived species aggression with the destructive power of nuclear weapons to destroy the agents of that technology—humanity, before it can perfect nuclear propulsion technology. As elaborated in detail in the last chapter, the mechanisms that could trigger such an LS sub-system would be the consistent genetic variable GV, which predates human history as innate aggression and presently manifests itself as Lorenz's "militant enthusiasm". Given the universal human appreciation of the extreme damage to the planet that non-conventional weapons represent (whether nuclear, biological or chemical) it is safe to conclude that only irrational beings could seriously consider their use. This appraisal flows logically from the understanding that no community can seriously expect to be immune from the consequential fallout that would ensue. The Earth is after all a small planet with no escape route from any phenomenon creating planet wide effects. It is within this context that the

RDH serves as a warning that our species has outgrown its ability to afford the excesses of intolerance whether political, racial or religious. What we can learn from history is the predictability of human nature and how religious and political leaders at any time seem to be able to tap into the apparently endless potential for militant enthusiasm among their constituents—resulting in debilitating wars that depreciate all humanity, and extinguish hope as well. Where history fails us miserably, I suspect, is in helping us appreciate the unprecedented novelty of our approaching dillema. The unconventional tools with which we will fight future wars virtually render that human practice untenable. Yet, there are reasons to suspect that that simple logic will fail to impress certain kinds of reasoning and thinking. Consider the following.

The Kamikaze Frame of Mind:

The word kamikaze means "divine wind," a reference to a typhoon that fortuitously dispersed a Mongol invasion fleet threatening Japan from the west in 1281—not something Japanese military planners could have predicted. During WWII, rather than depend on unreliable natural causes, the desperate Japanese military decided to take matters into their own hands by creating a different kind of kamikaze strategy. The modern version relied on convincing "kamikaze" suicide bomber pilots to crash their bomb-laden aircraft into enemy ships. The pilots who flew these one-way missions were delivering, in effect, human-guided missiles. Kamikazes showed that determined suicide bombers, on sufficient occasion, could get through otherwise impenetrable defenses. The keys to the kamikaze strategy are two-fold: 1) a willingness on the part of the bomber to sacrifice his life in the service of a cause—risk management is therefore not a consideration, and 2) the ability to send sufficient kamikazes until the job is done. We have come a long way since the Kamikazes of WWII. Modern warfare has seen sophisticated "intelligent" hardware replace human "wetware" as the essential expendable component of "kamikaze" missile-guidance systems. The modern notion of kamikaze has come to represent a reckless disregard for personal welfare or safety. Recent history indicates that the kamikaze philosophy sadly persists into the modern era among fanatical groups determined to achieve their narrow agendas regardless of the cost in human lives. Nonetheless, the same arguments that render warfare using weapons of mass destruction untenable for enlightened nations must also apply to rogue nations and terrorist groups for whom, theoretically, the kamikaze option remains viable. The difference, of course, is summed up in the question of whether their leaders would resort to kamikaze tactics and under what conditions.

If the terrorist attacks on the United States, September 11, 2001 proves anything; it is the reality that the kamikaze mindset—in the guise of suicide bombers in support of terrorism—is alive and well. There is a sense that World War Three has begun without any formal declaration of war. You will not find the rules of engagement of this conflict in the Geneva Convention. Nor will there be a sense any time soon of who has the upper hand in this conflict. And while the arms scorekeeper of record— London based Janes Defence Weekly—can provide an impressive portrait of the soldiers, arms, and training possessed by one side in this conflict (the western democracies), it can't even hazard a guess as to the ability and resourcefulness of the other (all of the terrorist groups that share common cause against western values) to do great harm. But, while kamikazes and terrorism are anything but new in the history of conflict, the weapons of mass destruction becoming available to modern day terrorists will radically change how we assess the dangers to innocent civilians they represent. And since 9/11 the world has been waiting for the "other shoe to drop".

Is it conceivable that an absolute despot of questionable sanity, seeking to secure his place in infamy, could commit the unthinkable kamizaze act of unleashing upon an unsuspecting planet the nuclear option, or the unconventional chemical option, or the unconventional biological option, any one of which could trigger massive retaliatory responses? Or, how about a terminally ill dictator with nothing to lose committing his nation as a willing or unwilling accomplice to a kamikaze campaign to be memorialized in the history books? In the modern era of high tech unconventional weapons of mass destruction, these kinds of scenarios represent a very real potential danger to the future of our species. Moreover, with the passage of time, the disaster potential only increases. It pays to remember that there is no negotiation possible with the kamikaze—you have nothing they want—they're only interest is the terror the deed inflicts. Ultimately we shall come to the understanding that there are too many such scenarios that have the potential to do us in—as a species.

I would suggest that the patently absurd state of affairs as exemplified by the above scenarios can exist only because the human mindset of many community leaders is conditioned by the inertia of past history and the few enlightened policy makers, who appreciate full well the problems we face, are powerless to influence those who don't or won't. While the absurdity of future warfare on a worldwide scale, under the present technological circumstances, becomes obvious, the real question is how to mobilize the communities of the planet to guarantee present and future generations that it will never happen. If, as previous arguments insist, any changes in human attitudes must deal with the influences of both GVs and CVs on human nature, and since we can have little influence in changing the genetic component in the human equation, we are left to consider only cultural changes. The only way to achieve a universal solution to a universal problem is through a universal program designed to access and solicit human cooperation worldwide. A primary logistical problem centers on whether any program that requires global cooperation is at all possible, considering the present state of geopolitics on our planet. This issue is not raised as some noble and enlightened call to respect and understanding in the name of worldly brotherhood. While worthy in itself as a motive, our intent is more pragmatic and consistent—to draw attention to the consequences raised in the last chapter that derive from the RDH paradigm. The RDH offers a novel and interesting context from which to assess the precariousness of the human condition—much of which derives directly from the age-old differences that divide our species. If, indeed, the danger to our future survival as a species stems from the existence of some built-in LS self-limiting mechanism, the implications are that there is precious little we can do about it. If the mechanisms and conditions for triggering our destruction are integral to LS design intent, chances are the solution to our self-destruct problem may be entirely out of our hands, so to speak. Accordingly, we may have little choice but to wait and see how events unfold. What are our options, if any?

The logistical problems can be summarized as two distinctly separate scenarios—one that addresses the human perspective and one that addresses the LS perspective:

A) THE HUMAN PERSPECTIVE:

1] Nations have collectively developed and positioned on the planet a sufficient quantity of sophisticated weaponry that could destroy humanity outright.

2] Over time, it is expected that the quantities, sophistication, and degree of miniaturization of weapons of mass destruction will become such that it will be impossible to effectively control their existence, location, or distribution, opening up the real prospect some fall into irresponsible hands.

3] History and experience have taught us that there will always be fanatical groups led by individuals seeking ways of acquiring such weaponry, lying in wait while creating the opportunity to use them.

4] The present state of technology permits a small number of fanatics to hold the entire planet hostage to their demands. Logic dictates that eventually we will have to confront a "doomsday" scenario that threatens all of humanity.

5] Far from being oblivious to the danger, with few exceptions responsible community leaders are well aware of the dangers this state of affairs poses but are powerless to do anything about it.

6] It is only a matter of time!

B) THE LS PERSPECTIVE (ACCORDING TO RDH INTERPRETATION):

1] The LS was designed, jump-started and implanted on planet Earth in order to serve as a glorified DNA photocopy machine—whereby a body of extraneous information is replicated in each new generation of eukaryotic cells along with the genetic libraries responsible for the bio-life processes.

2] Integral to LS design intent is the imperative that no biological contamination occurs outside of the host planetary biosphere. The LS incorporates elaborate self-limiting provisions to enforce compliance.

3] The only possible condition that could give rise to extraterrestrial biological contamination comprises the evolution from within the LS of a species capable of developing within its cultural activities the technology that permit it to engage in deep space travel (e.g., nuclear propulsion systems).

4] The designer would normally count on the expected occasional meteor bombardment of the planet to destroy any species with such future evolutionary potential. However, the designer would be presumed to appreciate that a longshot possibility exists that a lapse in such bombardments could permit the uninterrupted evolution of a technologically capable species. It is to cover such an eventuality that LS design would include an effective mechanism to replace a naturally occurring conflagration with one artificially induced from within.

5] The ideal automatic LS self-limiting mechanism would take advantage of the marriage of two assured traits of the transgressing species: a) a genetic variable (GV) dating back hundred of thousands of years—the prevalent tendency for aggressive behaviour responsible for such a species' evolutionary competitive success; and b) the cultural variable (CV) dating back only decades—responsible for the discovery of nuclear technology that eventually could evolve into deep space propulsion technology.

A consideration of both perspectives above—the human and the LS—suggests novel solutions to the problems we face. Until now, the human focus on our place in the universe has always been both narrow and egocentric. Our interest in exobiology is only recent and centers on such questions as "Are <u>we</u> alone in the universe?" or "Can <u>we</u> establish extraterrestrial bases on other planets in our solar system?" The RDH affords a timely opportunity to expand our perspective to include a new context in which we can understand and appreciate human circumstances. Extending our perspective of the human condition by separating our interests from that of the system from which we are derived, provides a new sense into how much more precarious our survival position is than previously considered.

But, all of this is mere speculation—we don't actually know if our species, in virtue of our technological development, actually does represent some clear and present danger to LS design intent interests. We don't actually know that a self-limiting feature is armed and ready to engage in setting back evolution to so-called safe levels—do we? Moreover, you can be sure that until we have compelling evidence that will shock us out of our collective lethargy, nothing in the human condition is going to change—it hasn't in the past and there is nothing foreseeable that could be sufficiently influential to suggest humanity will change from its fatalistic path, despite all of the acknowledged or imagined dangers to its future. So, what is the point? Actually, the point is a rather simple one.

From the beginning of our exercise, we have stressed repeatedly that there is one advantage the RDH has over all of the other OoL options—that of testability. And, from the scientific point of view, testability in an hypothesis is everything. From the human point of view, testability means verifiability and therefore relevance in the affairs of humankind. The RDH provides—not only the ideas and concepts that describe and warn in a novel way about the imminent dangers we face as a species, but as well the prescription for its own verification. We must test the introns for extraneous information and do it soon.

Now is indeed the time for a reassessment of human priorities, in order to defuse all of the differences between communities that have the potential to ignite into conflicts where everyone loses. Perhaps it is time for the introduction of a new scientific program of exploration of the information encoded in intron DNA—the discovery of which could well result in a positive shift in human priorities and simultaneously positively satisfy the human psychological dependency on hope.

Hope Springs Eternal—Now, Perhaps With Good Reason:

It may be a while yet before we know how to discover, translate and read a message meant for us hidden within the 4000-volume equivalent of the introns within the human genome. But, the RDH gives us every reason to hope that it is there, hidden somewhere for the finding. It would be an ironic shame if we destroyed the planetary biosphere and ourselves before its discovery. Talk about hope? The RDH gives reason to hope by the barrel-full. Yet, it is done without dropping our intellectual standards, nor requiring us to engage in a dichotomy of logic that insults anyone's intelligence. It is hope based on a logic that favors neither the observant follower of some religious persuasion, the materialistic atheist, the philosopher, nor the scientist. It is inclusive to the extent that no matter what logic one presently follows, or school of thought one is affiliated with, the logic and relevance of the RDH stands on its own, as an independent plug-in. But, it is not meant to be some kind of panacea that purports to please everyone, and ends up satisfying only a few. This message of hope is one we can all share, with the certainty that its proof of validation remains within our own hands, and need not await the arrival of some divine emissary. Indeed, the best hope one can experience is that which can be satisfied by one's own means subject only to one's abilities and ambitions. That offered by the RDH, is just that kind of collective hope for all of humanity. The prospect of the placement of an encoded message by the designer-creator that could be discovered, translated and understood by us at some future time implies a tacit understanding of the conditions upon which any relationship between the designer-creator and ourselves can assume. It's summed up in the classic phrase:

"God helps those who help themselves'"

i.e., "If you want to understand ultimate truth, you're going to have to find it, decode it, and translate it all by yourselves. If your species survives long enough to be able to bring to bear sufficient technology to the task—there is something wonderful that awaits you. Until then, if you have already figured out the purpose of the system of which you are an integral part (the Rational Design Hypothesis fills the bill), then you have passed an important first milestone. Now your next crucial task is to allow the hope and anticipation of that fateful day—sometime in the future—to fuel your resolve, not to wait, but to unite and come together to begin the task of earnestly solving the problems that threaten the premature destruction of your habitat and species. If you truly want salvation and redemption, it is there waiting for you—but, you're going to have to earn it".

A Magnificent Obsession:

If ever there was a time in human history for a magnificent common human obsession to take hold, that time may be at hand. And the obsession I refer to is the quest to analyze the genetic information in the intron sections of the human genome for extraterrestrial information. That search and exploration should be fueled by the hope that such a discovery could turn out to be every bit as valuable as the effort being waged currently to map each of the 30 thousand or so human genes in the strictly genetic library of exon DNA. We can only speculate what may be written there. We may indeed be speculating a long time in as much as we cannot take it for granted that such a message would or could be understandable within the confines of our language skills and linguistic experience. Nevertheless, we have reason to be optimistic in the light of all of the language research alluded to earlier. However, with the introduction of the RDH model of reality, the speculation takes on an urgency that may have critical implications for mankind—not only for its future survival as discussed above, but also for the very real hope it offers mankind in the present.

We Wish You Happy Trails:

Our challenge in these pages began with a search to uncover the mysteries that surround the OoL on our planet. As you can see, it is difficult to constrain the considerations to that simple question alone. As we have discovered, when you deal with fundamental questions, one easily becomes entangled within the maze of subsidiary issues. Our exercise—in addition to everything else it may have taught us—has demonstrated that there is no shortage of subject matter that might be included—which could provide additional perspectives within the discourse. Obviously, while choices have had to be made as to what to include and more importantly, what to exclude, the task of discrimination may have proven too much, as is evidenced by the far ranging menu of issues and side issues included. If we have missed some topic or issue that seems important to the reader, as I'm sure we have, I would welcome hearing about it. I would welcome as well any and all comments—pro and con, in agreement or disagreement, from readers—whomever and wherever they may be. This is not an esoteric topic restricted to ivory tower musings. The process we embarked upon was meant to be inclusive and not remain the exclusive domains of self-proclaimed wise men. Life is a process we all share. All too often, through the life journey we are told what life is supposed to be all about and what our individual responsibilities are. If asked to describe what kind of contribution to that end this work may have made, I would, first and foremost, assert that this study of life as part of the greater LS phenomenon has shown that it is just as important to understand "what Life is not all about", as it is to have a sense of what Life truly "is about". I trust we have shed some light on both. In the process of learning the differences on a generic and fundamental scale, it is up to each individual to determine for themselves how to interpret where their personal life fits into the larger picture. Life is a system that seems to be independent of the fate of the individual organisms that it comprises. As such, while Life, the system continues indefinitely, the species of which we form a part—like all other species—appears to serve only a temporary role on the way to extinction, while the lives of the individual organisms themselves are patently transient. Thus, we can only conclude that any designer's master plan, if it did exist, would reflect itself upon the overall system—and not individual organisms. Furthermore, any problems we as a species may be facing can only be solved by us, individually and collectively alone, if indeed we are to survive at all. Thus, the lesson in all of this is that we had better start thinking and acting individually and collectively in the responsible ways that our intellect is capable of by understanding that it is high time we understood when we are thinking with our brains (CV influence) and when we are thinking with our emotions (GV influence)—what is helpful and what is not. Tough decisions have to be made soon if we are to succeed in reversing the trends that inevitably will lead to human self-destruction. Selfish short-term partisan interests that interfere with such a process must be identified and reversed at all costs: "planet-wide solidarity" and "focus" must be the watch-phrase for the new millennium.

The Rational Design Hypothesis provides us with not only a "5"th OPTION for the OoL on our planet, but also the hope and resolve that the next generation of humankind will be required to bring to the task of reorganizing the planet—if the human species is to survive. The "5"th OPTION is first and foremost an attempt, to understand the true significance of human existence—an absolute necessity in terms of ascribing some kind of value to the living exercise we are all engaged in. Truth is an easy enough and variable commodity to come by in our pluralistic world, but one very difficult to distill into its pure essence. It generally ends up in our minds as a very personal interpretation of reality—like beauty in the eyes of the proverbial beholder. As such, we have traditionally turned to the professionals—the philosophers and theologians for an understanding of truth. Nevertheless, two proverbs have emerged in western culture that can help us to clarify for ourselves our thoughts on the subject of truth:

1] "Truth is stranger than fiction!" and,

2] "The truth will set you free!"

The first imposes on each of us an obligation to keep an open mind with respect to strange and new ideas. Ideas introduced to human culture as science fiction fantasies have emerged in the modern era as science fact. It suggests also that even if the truth we seek today appears to be beyond our limited understanding of reality; we can still count on our unbounded imaginations to fill in the blanks. The suggestion a mere 50 years ago that biological Life was a designed system would have been considered to be an exercise either in theology or science fiction. The Rational Design Hypothesis and the "5"th OPTION are a poignant reminder that indeed the truth may turn out to be stranger than both.

The second challenges us to accept the premise that as strange and outlandish as new ideas may seem, each new inclusion within our individual mental database of facts and theories that alters how we view reality represents an important step in changing our mental state. By continually widening the possibilities for understanding the greater reality—within which the existence of each one of us is immersed, we are able to more effectively assess the significance of our own personal lives within the wider context. The freedom comes both from being better able to dissociate our conscious selves from the physical constraints imposed upon our daily lives as well as freeing ourselves from a too narrow interpretation of a reality that has been imposed upon us. The closer we come to a true understanding of the significance of our existence—both individually and collectively within the broader realities of biological life within its biosphere setting—the more likely we are to face up to the enormous survival challenges with which humanity will soon have to deal. The future of our children's children may well depend upon the advance in the time frame available between the acknowledgment of the multitude of problems we face as a species—any one of which could deliver the fateful blow—and the implementation of a focused plan of action by a united humanity. Nobody is crying, "wolf"! The "5"th OPTION can be considered, among other things, as a sobering wake-up call —intent upon finding the ultimate truth within a sea of half-truths that have yet to stir a common spirit within the human consciousness.

It is my own personal hope that this exercise of discovery of LS form and function—utilizing the SE reverse engineering methodology to shed light on its design intent, purpose and use—has stimulated your imagination and that the RDH provides you with good and valid reasons to believe in life, humanity, and, most importantly, to believe in yourself. My own sense of hope is based on the very human capacity to believe, that any designer of our kind of LS would, indeed, have the moral capacity (which quite possibly may be a universal trait of sentient intelligence) to care enough to make provisions for communicating with an intelligent species that might eventually evolve within that system. There is a human kind of logic that says loud and clear, that if an LS design has sufficient room and flexibility that allows for the inclusion of a body of extraneous information within its information library, then the designer of such a system would not let that opportunity pass without doing so. At the very least, we would expect any system designer to stamp its mark where it could be found—for reasons as simple as to protect its proprietary rights to its design patent. We already know that there is indeed plenty of room for loads of extraneous information that can ride piggyback, together with the information data bank that forms the system design intent, as well as the genetic information library that is at the heart of the system PdP operation. To date, we can be greatly encouraged by the results of preliminary computer analysis that, you will recall, has yielded the conclusion that introns do indeed have language qualities in accordance with Zipf's rules. (See Ch 15). So far, everything is on track and we have reason to be optimistic.

But, hope comes as well in another more subtle form. In the end, the very idea of the additional inclusion within DNA of a message meant specifically for us, within the genetic information library of each and every one of us, without the sender ever knowing whether we, or any other intelligent species would ever evolve represents nothing, if not the ultimate message of hope on the part of a would-be designer. This sense of hope is further heightened with the realization that it would be considered the supreme true gift because it is tendered without any expectation of reciprocation. This follows along the lines of the Judaic tradition of "Chesed Emet"—wherein a proper burial was considered the ultimate legacy that a human being can bestow upon another human being. This, in virtue of the fact that the benefactor understands full well that the consideration can never be reciprocated. We may come to appreciate it as such in practical terms, if it turns out that not only does such a message exist, but also that it translates into the prescription for the survival of our technologically developed, but environmentally challenged and endangered species. Then, in a marvelous twist of irony, the Rational Design Hypothesis may bring human culture full circle: a universal belief in a pragmatic "designer-Creator" that can indeed "deliver" on salvation. Hope does, indeed, spring eternal!

Author's Note:

The author believes that the discourse must be kept alive and open. This book is part of an ongoing process of discovery. The questions raised are all too important to be left to those living in ivory towers. One of the benefits of living in a time and place where innovative thought is encouraged is the freedom to participate in this kind of exercise. You are encouraged to do so. Another book is already in the works in order to expand and clarify as well as revise some of ideas put forth in this first effort. You can help be part of the process. It is hoped that the questions we have raised here together with some of the insights we have offered will serve well the quest for an understanding of the OoL and also persuade you, the reader, to become part of the process. Please e-mail your comments or inquiries to Bryant Shiller: bryshill@The5thOPTION.com.

Apppendix
(refer to Chapter 13)

Point Mutation Tables
AmAcid Node Diagrams

Table 13B

TABLE 13-B			Table of All Possible Mutations (9 per Codon)																												
			(nonsense)														Nonpolar															
20 Amino Acids >			SToP			ALA				GLY				ILE			LEU						MET	PHE		PRO				VAL			
			stp			A				G				I			L						M	F		P				V			
64 Original Codons (shown vertically) >>			u a a	u a g	u g a	g c u	g c c	g c a	g c g	g g u	g g c	g g a	g g g	a u u	a u c	a u a	u u a	u u g	c u u	c u c	c u a	c u g	a u g	u u u	u u c	c c u	c c c	c c a	c c g	g u u	g u c	g u a	g u g
Resultant AmAcid Following all Possible Single Point Mutations (576 in all)			Q	Q	R	S	S	S	S	S	S	C	C	stp/W	F	F	L	X	X	F	F	X	X	L	L	L	S	S	S	S	F	F	L	L
			K	K	R	P	P	P	P	R	R	R	R	L	L	L	M	I	I	I	M	L	I	I	T	T	T	T	L	L	L	M
			E	E	G	T	T	T	T	S	S	R	R	V	V	V	V	V	V	V	V	V	I	V	A	A	A	A	I	I	I	M
X = Synonymous Mutation i.e., no AmAcid change			L	L	L	V	V	V	V	V	V	V	V	T	T	T	S	S	P	P	P	P	T	S	S	L	L	L	L	A	A	A	E
			S	S	S	D	D	E	E	A	A	A	A	N	N	K	stp	W	H	H	Q	Q	K	Y	Y	H	H	Q	Q	D	D	E	E
			X	W	X	G	G	G	G	D	D	E	E	S	S	R	stp	stp	R	R	R	R	R	C	C	R	R	R	R	G	G	G	G
			Y	Y	C	X	X	X	X	X	X	X	X	X	X	X	F	F	X	X	X	X	I	X	X	X	X	X	X	X	X	X	X
			Y	Y	C	X	X	X	X	X	X	X	X	X	X	X	F	F	X	X	X	X	I	L	L	X	X	X	X	X	X	X	X
			X	X	W	X	X	X	X	X	X	X	X	X	X	X	M	M	M	X	X	X	I	L	L	X	X	X	X	X	X	X	X
Possible Single Mutations >			27			36				36				27			54						9	18		36				36			
No Change: (138/576 = 24%) >			4			12				12				6			18						0	2		12				12			
Nonsense (stp) Codons (23/576) >			NA			0				1				0			3						0	0		0				0			
% Nonsense Codons (4%) >			NA			0%				3%				0%			6%						0%	0%		0%				0%			
Diff Kinds of AmAcids Out of 20 >			10			7				8				9			9						6	6		6				8			
% Out of 20 Choices >			50%			35%				40%				45%			45%						30%	30%		30%				40%			
No of non-polar AmAcids >			1	1	2	6	6	6	6	5	5	5	5	6	6	6	6	6	7	7	7	7	6	6	6	5	5	5	5	8	8	8	8
No of polar AmAcids >			4	5	4	2	2	2	2	2	2	0	0	3	3	1	1	2	0	0	1	1	1	3	3	2	2	3	3	0	0	0	0
No of Acidic AmAcids >			1	1	0	1	1	1	1	1	1	1	1	0	0	0	0	0	0	0	0	0	0	0	0	0	0	0	0	1	1	1	1
No of Basic AmAcids >			1	1	2	0	0	0	0	1	1	2	2	0	0	2	0	0	2	2	1	1	2	0	0	2	2	1	1	0	0	0	0
Nonsense (SToP) Codons >			2	1	1	0	0	0	0	0	0	1	0	0	0	0	2	1	0	0	0	0	0	0	0	0	0	0	0	0	0	0	0
		Ttl>	9	9	9	9	9	9	9	9	9	9	9	9	9	9	9	9	9	9	9	9	9	9	9	9	9	9	9	9	9	9	9
Codons per AmAcid																																	
SToP Codon	3	stp	2	1	1	0	0	0	0	0	0	1	0	0	0	0	2	1	0	0	0	0	0	0	0	0	0	0	0	0	0	0	0
	4	Ala (A)				3	3	3	3	1	1	1	1																	1	1	1	1
	4	Gly (G)		1		1	1	1	1	3	3	3	3																	1	1	1	1
Neutral	3	ILE (I)												2	2	2	1		1	1	1		3	1	1					1	1	1	
Nonpolar	6	LEU (L)	1	1	1									1	1	2	2	2	3	3	4	4	2	3	3	1	1	1	1	1	1	2	2
Amino Acids	1	MET (M)												1	1	1	1					1	0										1
(hydrophobic)	2	PHE (F)												1	1		2	2	1	1				1	1					1	1		
	4	PRO (P)				1	1	1	1								1	1	1	1						3	3	3	3				
	4	VAL (V)				1	1	1	1	1	1	1	1	1	1	1	1	1	1	1	1	1	1	1	1					3	3	3	3
	2	ASN (N)												1	1																		
Neutral	2	CYS (C)			2					1	1													1	1								
Polar	2	GLN (Q)	1	1																	1	1						1	1				
Amino Acids	6	SER (S)	1	1	1	1	1	1	1	1	1			1	1		1	1						1	1	1	1	1	1				
(hydrophilic)	4	THR (T)				1	1	1	1					1	1	1							1			1	1	1	1				
	1	TRP (W)		1	1							1						1															
	2	TYR (Y)	2	2																				1	1								
Acidic	2	ASP (D)				1	1			1	1																				1	1	
Amino Acids	2	GLU (E)	1	1				1	1			1	1																				1	1
Basic	6	ARG (R)			2					1	1	2	2			1			1	1	1	1	1			1	1	1	1				
Amino Acids	2	HIS (H)																		1	1					1	1						
	2	LYS (K)	1	1												1							1										
Totals>	64		9	9	9	9	9	9	9	9	9	9	9	9	9	9	9	9	9	9	9	9	9	9	9	9	9	9	9	9	9	9	9

TABLE 13-B

	Polar								Acid		Basic				
ASN	CYS	GLN	SER		THR	TRP	TYR	ASP	GLU	ARG		HIS	LYS		
N	C	Q	S		T	W	Y	D	E	R		H	K		

Codon nucleotides (read top to bottom per column):

	ASN	CYS	GLN	SER	THR	TRP	TYR	ASP	GLU	ARG	HIS	LYS
nt1	a a	u u	c c	u u u u a a	a a a a	u	u u	g g	g g	c c c c a a	c c	a a
nt2	a a	g g	a a	c c c c g g	c c c c	g	a a	a a	a a	g g g g g g	a a	a a
nt3	u c	u c	a g	u c a g u c	u c a g	g	u c	u c	a g	u c a g a g	u c	a g

Single-base mutation results (amino acid / stp):

ASN	CYS	GLN	SER	THR	TRP	TYR	ASP	GLU	ARG	HIS	LYS
Y Y	R R	stp stp	P P P P C C	S S S S	R	H H	Y Y	stp stp	C C stp W stp W	Y Y	stp stp
H H	S S	K K	T T T T R R	P P P P	R	N N	H H	Q Q	S S X X X X	N N	Q Q
D D	G G	E E	A A A A G G	A A A A	G	D D	N N	K K	G G G G G G	D D	E E
I I	F F	L L	F F L L I I	I I I M	L	F F	V V	V V	L L L L I M	L L	I M
T T	S S	P P	Y stp stp T T	N N K K	S	S S	A A A A	A A	P P P P T T	P P	T T
S S	Y Y	R R	C stp W N N	S S R R	stp	C C	G G G G	G G	H H Q Q K K	R R	T R
X X	X X	H H	X X X X X X	X X X X	C	X X	X X	D D	X X X X S S	X X	N N
K K	stp stp	H H	X X X X R R	X X X X	C	stp stp	E E	D D	X X X X S Q	Q Q	N N
K K	W W	X X	X X X X R R	X X X X	stp	stp stp	E E	X X	X X X X X Q	Q Q	X X

	ASN	CYS	GLN	SER	THR	TRP	TYR	ASP	GLU	ARG	HIS	LYS	Ttls	
	18	18	18	54	36	9	18	18	18	54	18	18	576	< Possible Mut'ns
	2	2	2	14	12	0	2	2	2	18	2	2	138	< No chnge (X's)
	0	2	2	3	0	2	4	0	2	2	0	2	23	< "SToP" Codons
	0%	11%	11%	6%	0%	22%	22%	0%	11%	4%	0%	11%	4%	< % SToP Codons
	7	6	6	11	8	5	6	7	6	12	7	7		<<Diff AmAcids
	35%	30%	30%	55%	40%	25%	30%	35%	30%	60%	35%	35%		<% of 20 Choices

ASN	CYS	GLN	SER	THR	TRP	TYR	ASP	GLU	ARG	HIS	LYS	Ttls	
1 1	2 2	2 2	3 3 3 3 2 2	3 3 3 3	2	1 1	3 3	3 3	3 3 3 2 4 4	2 2	1 1	252	Non-polar (np)
4 4	5 5	0 0	6 6 4 5 4 4	6 6 4 4	3	4 4	2 2	1 1	2 2 1 2 4 4	4 4	1 1	171	Polar (p)
1 1	0 0	1 1	0 0 0 0 0 0	0 0 0 0	0	1 1	3 3	3 3	0 0 0 0 0 0	1 1	1 1	36	Acid
3 3	1 1	4 4	0 0 0 0 3 3	0 0 2 2	2	1 1	1 1	1 1	4 4 4 3 2 2	2 2	2 2	90	Basic
0 0	1 1	1 1	0 0 2 1 0 0	0 0 0 0	2	2 2	0 0	1 1	0 0 1 0 1 0	0 0	1 1	27	SToP
9 9	9 9	9 9	9 9 9 9 9 9	9 9 9 9	9	9 9	9 9	9 9	9 9 9 9 9 9	9 9	9 9	576	

Codons

ASN	CYS	GLN	SER	THR	TRP	TYR	ASP	GLU	ARG	HIS	LYS	Total	
0 0	1 1	1 1	0 0 2 1 0 0	0 0 0 0	2	2 2	0 0	1 1	0 0 1 0 1 0	0 0	1 1	27	SToP
			1 1 1 1			1 1 1 1			1 1 1 1			36	A
	1 1			1 1		1			1 1 1 1			36	G
1 1			1 1 1 1		1				1		1	27	I
		1 1	1 1		1				1 1 1 1	1 1		54	L
			1						1		1	9	M
	1 1		1 1				1 1					18	F
		1 1	1 1 1 1	1 1 1 1					1 1 1 1	1 1		36	P
							1 1 1 1					36	V
1 1			1 1 1 1			1 1 1 1	1 1			1 1	2 2	18	N
	1 1		1 1	1 1	2	1 1			1 1			18	C
		1 1						1 1	1 1	2 2	1 1	18	Q
1 1	2 2		3 3 3 3 1 1	2 2 1 1	1	1 1			1 1 2 2			54	S
1 1			1 1 1 1 1 1	3 3 3 3					1 1	1 1		36	T
	1 1		1 1	1		0			1 1			9	W
1 1	1 1		1 1			1 1	1 1		1 1	1 1		18	Y
1 1			1 1			1 1	1 1	2 2		1 1		18	D
		1 1					2 2	1 1		1 1		18	E
	1 1 1 1		3 3	1 1	2				3 3 4 4 2 2	1 1	1 1	54	R
1 1		2 2				1 1	1 1		1 1	1 1		18	H
2 2		1 1		1 1					1 1		1 1	18	K
9 9	9 9	9 9	9 9 9 9 9 9	9 9 9 9	9	9 9	9 9	9 9	9 9 9 9 9 9	9 9	9 9	576	

Tables 13C, 13D, & 13E

TABLE 13-C: All Possible AmAcid Substitutions

Resultant SUBSTITUTIONS Of One AMINO ACID For Another Following Basepair Mutations

To / From>>	SToP	ALA	GLY	ILE	LEU	MET	PHE	PRO	VAL	ASN	CYS	GLN	SER	THR	TRP	TYR	ASP	GLU	ARG	HIS	LYS	No M's	No CDNs
SToP	4				1			3			2	2			2	4		2	2		2	27	3
ALA A		12	4				4		4				4	4			2	2	2			36	4
GLY G	1	4	12						4		2		2	4			2	2				36	4
ILE I				6	4	3	2		3	2		2		3					6		1	27	3
LEU L	3			4	18	4	2	6	4			2	2		1		4	2		1		54	6
MET M				3	2	0			1					1					1			9	1
PHE F				2	6		2		2		2					2						18	2
PRO P		4			4			12				2	4	4			4	2				36	4
VAL V		4	4	3	6	1	2		12								2	2				36	4
ASN N				2						2			2	2		2	2			2	4	18	2
CYS C			2				2				2		4			2	2		2			18	2
GLN Q	2				2			2				2		4					2	4	2	18	2
SER S	3	4	2	2	2		2		4	2	4		14	6	1	2			6			54	6
THR T		4		4	3	1			4	2			8	12					2		2	36	4
TRP W	2		1	1							2		1		0				2			9	1
TYR Y	4						2				2		2			2	2			2		18	2
ASP D		2	2						2	2						2	2	4		2		18	2
GLU E	2	2	2						2			2					4	2			2	18	2
ARG R	2		6	1		1		4			2	2	6	2	2				18	2	2	54	6
HIS H					2		2			2	4	2				2			2	2	2	18	2
LYS K	2			1		1				4		2		2					2	2	2	18	2
Total Substitutions>>	27	36	36	27	54	9	18	36	36	18	18	18	54	36	9	18	18	18	54	18	18	576	64

Note: Bold Figures represent Synonymous Substitutions

TABLE 13-D: Percent Change - All Possible AmAcid Substitutions

Resultant SUBSTITUTIONS Of One AMINO ACID For Another Following Basepair Mutation

To / From>>	STP	ALA	GLY	ILE	LEU	MET	PHE	PRO	VAL	ASN	CYS	GLN	SER	THR	TRP	TYR	ASP	GLU	ARG	HIS	LYS
SToP	#NAME?	0.00	2.78	0.00	5.56	0.00	0.00	0.00	0.00	0.00	11.11	11.11	5.56	0.00	22.22	22.22	0.00	11.11	3.70	0.00	11.11
ALA A	0.00	33.33	11.11	0.00	0.00	0.00	11.11	0.00	11.11	0.00	0.00	0.00	7.41	11.11	0.00	0.00	11.11	11.11	0.00	0.00	0.00
GLY G	3.70	11.11	33.33	0.00	0.00	0.00	0.00	0.00	11.11	0.00	11.11	0.00	3.70	0.00	0.00	0.00	11.11	11.11	11.11	0.00	0.00
ILE I	0.00	0.00	0.00	22.22	7.41	33.33	11.11	0.00	8.33	11.11	0.00	0.00	3.70	8.33	0.00	0.00	0.00	0.00	1.85	0.00	5.56
LEU L	11.11	0.00	0.00	14.81	33.33	22.22	33.33	11.11	16.67	0.00	0.00	11.11	3.70	0.00	11.11	0.00	7.41	11.11	0.00	0.00	0.00
MET M	0.00	0.00	0.00	11.11	3.70	0.00	0.00	0.00	2.78	0.00	0.00	0.00	0.00	2.78	0.00	0.00	0.00	0.00	1.85	0.00	5.56
PHE F	0.00	0.00	0.00	7.41	11.11	0.00	11.11	0.00	5.56	0.00	11.11	0.00	0.00	0.00	0.00	11.11	0.00	0.00	0.00	0.00	0.00
PRO P	0.00	11.11	0.00	0.00	7.41	0.00	0.00	33.33	0.00	0.00	0.00	11.11	7.41	11.11	0.00	0.00	7.41	11.11	0.00	0.00	0.00
VAL V	0.00	11.11	11.11	11.11	11.11	11.11	11.11	0.00	33.33	0.00	0.00	0.00	0.00	0.00	0.00	0.00	11.11	11.11	0.00	0.00	0.00
ASN N	0.00	0.00	0.00	7.41	0.00	0.00	0.00	0.00	0.00	11.11	0.00	0.00	3.70	5.56	0.00	11.11	11.11	0.00	0.00	11.11	22.22
CYS C	0.00	0.00	5.56	0.00	0.00	0.00	11.11	0.00	0.00	0.00	11.11	0.00	0.00	0.00	22.22	11.11	0.00	0.00	3.70	0.00	0.00
GLN Q	7.41	0.00	0.00	0.00	3.70	0.00	0.00	5.56	0.00	0.00	0.00	11.11	0.00	0.00	0.00	0.00	0.00	11.11	3.70	22.22	11.11
SER S	11.11	11.11	5.56	7.41	3.70	0.00	11.11	0.00	11.11	11.11	22.22	0.00	25.93	16.67	11.11	11.11	0.00	0.00	11.11	0.00	0.00
THR T	0.00	11.11	0.00	11.11	0.00	11.11	0.00	0.00	11.11	11.11	0.00	0.00	11.11	33.33	0.00	0.00	0.00	0.00	3.70	0.00	11.11
TRP W	7.41	0.00	2.78	0.00	0.00	0.00	0.00	0.00	0.00	0.00	11.11	0.00	1.85	0.00	0.00	0.00	0.00	0.00	3.70	0.00	0.00
TYR Y	14.81	0.00	0.00	0.00	0.00	0.00	11.11	0.00	0.00	0.00	11.11	0.00	3.70	0.00	0.00	11.11	11.11	0.00	0.00	11.11	0.00
ASP D	0.00	5.56	5.56	0.00	0.00	0.00	0.00	0.00	5.56	11.11	0.00	0.00	0.00	0.00	0.00	11.11	11.11	22.22	0.00	11.11	0.00
GLU E	7.41	5.56	5.56	0.00	0.00	0.00	0.00	0.00	5.56	0.00	0.00	11.11	0.00	0.00	0.00	0.00	22.22	11.11	0.00	0.00	0.00
ARG R	7.41	0.00	16.67	3.70	0.00	7.41	11.11	0.00	11.11	0.00	11.11	11.11	11.11	5.56	22.22	0.00	0.00	0.00	33.33	11.11	11.11
HIS H	0.00	0.00	0.00	0.00	3.70	0.00	5.56	0.00	0.00	11.11	22.22	11.11	0.00	0.00	0.00	11.11	0.00	0.00	3.70	11.11	11.11
LYS K	7.41	0.00	0.00	3.70	0.00	11.11	0.00	0.00	0.00	22.22	0.00	11.11	0.00	5.56	0.00	0.00	0.00	0.00	3.70	11.11	11.11
Ttl Substitutions (%) >	#NAME?	100	100	100	100	100	100	100	100	100	100	100	100	100	100	100	100	100	100	100	100

Note: Bold Figures represent Synonymous Substitutions

TABLE 13-E: Percent Change - All Possible AmAcid Substitutions

Resultant SUBSTITUTIONS Of One AMINO ACID For Another Following Basepair Mutations

	STP	ALA	GLY	ILE	LEU	MET	PHE	PRO	VAL	ASN	CYS	GLN	SER	THR	TRP	TYR	ASP	GLU	ARG	HIS	LYS	
Ttl Subs: >>	27	36	36	27	54	9	18	36	36	18	18	18	54	36	9	18	18	18	54	18	18	576
SToP	4	0	1	0	3	0	0	0	0	0	2	2	3	0	2	4	0	2	2	0	2	
% ->	14.81	0.00	2.78	0.00	5.56	0.00	0.00	0.00	0.00	0.00	11.11	11.11	5.56	0.00	22.22	22.22	0.00	11.11	3.70	0.00	11.11	
Nonpolar	4	24	20	18	40	9	12	20	32													
% ->	14.81	66.67	55.56	66.67	74.07	66.67	66.67	55.56	88.89	11.11	22.22	22.22	29.63	33.33	22.22	11.11	33.33	33.33				
Polar	13	8	5	7	5	1	6	10	0										14	8	8	
% ->	48.15	22.22	13.89	25.93	9.26	11.11	33.33	27.78	0.00	44.44	55.56	11.11	53.70	55.56	33.33	44.44	22.22	11.11	25.93	44.44	44.44	
Acid	2	4	4	0	0	0	0	0	0	2	0	2	0	0	0	0	6	6	0	2	2	
% ->	7.41	11.11	11.11	0.00	0.00	0.00	0.00	0.00	11.11	11.11	0.00	11.11	0.00	0.00	0.00	11.11	33.33	33.33	0.00	11.11	11.11	
Basic	4	0	6	2	6	2	0	6	0	6	2	8	4	2	2	2	2	2	14	8	8	
% ->	14.81	0.00	16.67	7.41	11.11	22.22	0.00	16.67	0.00	33.33	11.11	44.44	11.11	11.11	22.22	11.11	11.11	11.11	40.74	22.22	22.22	
Ttl Subs (%) ->	100	100	100	100	100	100	100	100	100	100	100	100	100	100	100	100	100	100	100	100	100	

Table 13F

Table 13-F	All COMPLIMENTARY TRANSVERSION MUTATIONS
REVERSAL Of COMPLIMENTARY BASES (Purine/Pyramadine) a to u; u to a; c to g; and g to c	

Column groups: STOP | Nonpolar Amino Acids — ALA · GLY · ILE · LEU · MET · PHE · PRO · VAL

Row	uaa	uag	uga	gcu	gcc	gca	gcg	ggu	ggc	gga	ggg	auu	auc	aua	uua	uug	cuu	cuc	cua	cug	aug	uuu	uuc	ccu	ccc	cca	ccg	guu	guc	gua	gug
20 Amino Acids > / code	stp	stp	stp	A	A	A	A	G	G	G	G	I	I	I	L	L	L	L	L	L	M	F	F	P	P	P	P	V	V	V	V
64 Codons	uaa	uag	uga	gcu	gcc	gca	gcg	ggu	ggc	gga	ggg	auu	auc	aua	uua	uug	cuu	cuc	cua	cug	aug	uuu	uuc	ccu	ccc	cca	ccg	guu	guc	gua	gug
192 Possible	aaa	aag	aga	ccu	ccc	cca	ccg	cgu	cgc	cga	cgg	uuu	uuc	uua	aua	aug	guu	guc	gua	gug	uug	auu	auc	gcu	gcc	gca	gcg	cuu	cuc	cua	cug
Mutations	uua	uug	uca	ggu	ggc	gga	ggg	gcu	gcc	gca	gcg	aau	aac	aaa	uaa	uag	cau	cac	caa	cag	aag	uau	uac	cgu	cgc	cga	cgg	gau	gac	gaa	gag
X = No Change	uau	uac	ugu	gca	gcg	gcu	gcc	gga	ggg	ggu	ggc	aua	aug	auu	uuu	uuc	cua	cug	cuu	cuc	auc	uua	uug	cca	ccg	ccu	ccc	gua	gug	guu	guc
Only 158 (82%)	K	K	R	P	P	P	P	R	R	R	R	F	F	L	I	M	V	V	V	V	L	I	I	A	A	A	A	L	L	L	L
Amino Acid	L	L	S	G	G	G	G	A	A	A	A	N	N	K	stp	stp	H	H	Q	Q	K	Y	Y	R	R	R	R	D	D	E	E
Changes Occur	Y	Y	C	X	X	X	X	X	X	X	X	X	M	X	F	F	X	X	X	X	I	L	L	X	X	X	X	X	X	X	X

		#	STOP	ALA	GLY	ILE	LEU	MET	PHE	PRO	VAL
No-Changes (X)		34	0	4	4	2	4	0	0	4	4
STOP	4.7%	9	0	0	0	0	2	0	0	0	0
Nonpolar	42.7%	82	2	12	8	6	12	2	4	8	8
Polar	29.7%	57	4	0	0	2	2	0	2	0	0
Acid	7.3%	14	0	0	0	0	0	0	0	0	4
Basic	15.6%	30	3	0	4	1	2	1	0	4	0

No of Codons

Grp	#	Amino	code	uaa	uag	uga	gcu	gcc	gca	gcg	ggu	ggc	gga	ggg	auu	auc	aua	uua	uug	cuu	cuc	cua	cug	aug	uuu	uuc	ccu	ccc	cca	ccg	guu	guc	gua	gug
	3	SToP	stp															1	1															
N	4	ALA	A				1	1	1	1	1	1	1	1													1	1	1	1				
o	4	GLY	G				1	1	1	1	1	1	1	1																				
n	3	ILE	I												1		1	1						1	1	1								
p	6	LEU	L	1	1												1			1	1	1	1	1	1	1					1	1	1	1
o	1	MET	M													1			1															
l	2	PHE	F												1	1		1	1															
a	4	PRO	P				1	1	1	1																	1	1	1	1				
r	4	VAL	V																	1	1	1	1								1	1	1	1
	2	ASN	N												1	1																		
P	2	CYS	C			1																												
o	2	GLN	Q																			1	1											
l	6	SER	S			1																												
a	4	THR	T																															
r	1	TRP	W																															
	2	TYR	Y	1	1																				1	1								
Acid	2	ASP	D																												1	1		
	2	GLU	E																														1	1
	6	ARG	R			1					1	1	1	1													1	1	1	1				
Base	2	HIS	H																	1	1													
	2	LYS	K	1	1												1							1										
		Totals>		3	3	3	3	3	3	3	3	3	3	3	3	3	3	3	3	3	3	3	3	3	3	3	3	3	3	3	3	3	3	3

64 codons

Table 13-F

	Polar																		Acid				Basic								
ASN		CYS		GLN		SER						THR				TRP	TYR		ASP		GLU		ARG						HIS		LYS	
N		C		Q		S						T				W	Y		D		E		R						H		K	
aau	aac	ugu	ugc	caa	cag	ucu	ucc	uca	ucg	agu	agc	acu	acc	aca	acg	ugg	uau	uac	gau	gac	gaa	gag	cgu	cgc	cga	cgg	aga	agg	cau	cac	aaa	aag
uau	uac	agu	agc	gaa	gag	acu	acc	aca	acg	ugu	ugc	ucu	ucc	uca	ucg	agg	aau	aac	cau	cac	caa	cag	ggu	ggc	gga	ggg	uga	ugg	gau	gac	uaa	uag
auu	auc	ucu	ucc	cua	cug	ugu	ugc	uga	ugg	acu	acc	agu	agc	aga	agg	ucg	uuu	uuc	guu	guc	gua	gug	ccu	ccc	cca	ccg	aca	acg	cuu	cuc	aua	aug
aaa	aag	uga	ugg	cau	cac	uca	ucg	ucu	ucc	aga	agg	aca	acg	acu	acc	ugc	uaa	uag	gaa	gag	gau	gac	cga	cgg	cgu	cgc	agu	agc	caa	cag	aau	aac
Y	Y	S	S	E	E	T	T	T	T	C	C	S	S	S	S	R	N	N	H	H	Q	Q	G	G	G	G	stp	W	D	D	stp	stp
I	I	S	S	L	L	C	C	stp	W	T	T	S	S	R	R	S	F	F	V	V	V	V	P	P	P	P	T	T	L	L	I	M
K	K	stp	W	H	H	X	X	X	X	R	R	X	X	X	X	C	stp	stp	E	E	D	D	X	X	X	X	S	S	Q	Q	N	N

Summary (per amino acid):

ASN	CYS	GLN	SER	THR	TRP	TYR	ASP	GLU	ARG	HIS	LYS
0	0	0	4	4	0	0	0	0	4	0	0
0	1	0	1	0	0	2	0	0	1	0	2
2	0	0	0	0	0	2	2	2	8	2	2
2	5	0	15	10	2	2	0	2	5	2	2
0	0	2	2	0	0	0	2	2	0	2	0
2	0	2	2	2	1	0	2	0	4	0	0

Tally grid (per codon):

aau	aac	ugu	ugc	caa	cag	ucu	ucc	uca	ucg	agu	agc	acu	acc	aca	acg	ugg	uau	uac	gau	gac	gaa	gag	cgu	cgc	cga	cgg	aga	agg	cau	cac	aaa	aag
		1				1										1	1											1			1	1
																							1	1	1	1						
1	1																														1	
				1	1																								1	1		
																																1
																			1	1			1	1	1	1						
																			1	1											1	1
						1	1			1	1					1													1	1		
		2	2			1	1	1	1			2	2	1	1	1											1	1				
				1	1	1	1	1	1	1	1	1	1	1	1												1	1				
1	1										1			1													1					
																			1	1								1	1		
				1	1			1	1							1			1	1			1	1	1	1						
1	1			1	1														1	1												
3	3	3	3	3	3	3	3	3	3	3	3	3	3	3	3	3	3	3	3	3	3	3	3	3	3	3	3	3	3	3	3	3

Tables 13G, 13H & 13I

TABLE 13-G: Complimentary Transversion Basepair Substitutions
Resultant SUBSTITUTIONS Of One AMINO ACID For Another Following Basepair Mutations

Column groups: SToP | Nonpolar (hydrophobic, neutral): ALA GLY ILE LEU MET PHE PRO VAL | Polar (hydrophilic, neutral): ASN CYS GLN SER THR TRP TYR | Acid: ASP GLU | Basic: ARG HIS LYS | No M's | No CDNs

(Left vertical label: RESULTANT AMINO ACID SUBSTITUTIONS)

To \ From	SToP	ALA	GLY	ILE	LEU	MET	PHE	PRO	VAL	ASN	CYS	GLN	SER	THR	TRP	TYR	ASP	GLU	ARG	HIS	LYS	No M's	No CDNs
SToP	0				2						1		1			2			1		2	9	1
ALA A		**4**	4					4														12	1
GLY G		4	**4**																4			12	1
ILE I				**2**	1	1	2			2											1	9	1
LEU L	2			1	**4**	1	2		4			2								2		18	2
MET M				1	1	**0**															1	3	0
PHE F				2	2		**0**									2						6	1
PRO P		4						**4**											4			12	1
VAL V					4				**4**								2	2				12	1
ASN N				2						**0**						2					2	6	1
CYS C	1										**0**		4		1							6	1
GLN Q					2							**0**						2		2		6	1
SER S	1										4		**4**	6	1				2			18	2
THR T													6	**4**					2			12	1
TRP W											1		1		**0**				1			3	0
TYR Y	2						2			2						**0**						6	1
ASP D									2								**0**	2		2		6	1
GLU E									2			2					2	**0**				6	1
ARG R	1		4					4					2	2	1				**4**			18	2
HIS H					2							2					2			**0**		6	1
LYS K	2			1		1				2											**0**	6	1
Total Substitutions>>	9	12	12	9	18	3	6	12	12	6	6	6	18	12	3	6	6	6	18	6	6	192	21

Note: Bold Figures represent Synonymous Substitutions

TABLE 13-H: Percent Change - Complimentary Transversion Substitutions
Resultant SUBSTITUTIONS Of One AMINO ACID For Another Following Basepair Mutation

To \ From	STP	ALA	GLY	ILE	LEU	MET	PHE	PRO	VAL	ASN	CYS	GLN	SER	THR	TRP	TYR	ASP	GLU	ARG	HIS	LYS
SToP	0.00	0.00	0.00	0.00	11.11	0.00	0.00	0.00	0.00	0.00	16.67	0.00	5.56	0.00	0.00	33.33	0.00	0.00	5.56	0.00	33.33
ALA A	0.00	**33.33**	33.33	0.00	0.00	0.00	0.00	33.33	0.00	0.00	0.00	0.00	0.00	0.00	0.00	0.00	0.00	0.00	0.00	0.00	0.00
GLY G	0.00	33.33	**33.33**	0.00	0.00	0.00	0.00	0.00	0.00	0.00	0.00	0.00	0.00	0.00	0.00	0.00	0.00	0.00	22.22	0.00	0.00
ILE I	0.00	0.00	0.00	**22.22**	5.56	33.33	33.33	0.00	0.00	33.33	0.00	0.00	0.00	0.00	0.00	0.00	0.00	0.00	0.00	0.00	16.67
LEU L	22.22	0.00	0.00	11.11	**22.22**	33.33	33.33	0.00	33.33	0.00	0.00	33.33	0.00	0.00	0.00	0.00	0.00	0.00	0.00	33.33	0.00
MET M	0.00	0.00	0.00	11.11	5.56	**0.00**	0.00	0.00	0.00	0.00	0.00	0.00	0.00	0.00	0.00	0.00	0.00	0.00	0.00	0.00	16.67
PHE F	0.00	0.00	0.00	22.22	11.11	0.00	**0.00**	0.00	0.00	0.00	0.00	0.00	0.00	0.00	0.00	33.33	0.00	0.00	0.00	0.00	0.00
PRO P	0.00	33.33	0.00	0.00	0.00	0.00	0.00	**33.33**	0.00	0.00	0.00	0.00	0.00	0.00	0.00	0.00	0.00	0.00	22.22	0.00	0.00
VAL V	0.00	0.00	0.00	0.00	22.22	0.00	0.00	0.00	**33.33**	0.00	0.00	0.00	0.00	0.00	0.00	0.00	33.33	33.33	0.00	0.00	0.00
ASN N	0.00	0.00	0.00	22.22	0.00	0.00	0.00	0.00	0.00	**0.00**	0.00	0.00	0.00	0.00	0.00	33.33	0.00	0.00	0.00	0.00	33.33
CYS C	11.11	0.00	0.00	0.00	0.00	0.00	0.00	0.00	0.00	0.00	**0.00**	0.00	22.22	0.00	33.33	0.00	0.00	0.00	0.00	0.00	0.00
GLN Q	0.00	0.00	0.00	0.00	11.11	0.00	0.00	0.00	0.00	0.00	0.00	**0.00**	0.00	0.00	0.00	0.00	0.00	33.33	0.00	33.33	0.00
SER S	11.11	0.00	0.00	0.00	0.00	0.00	0.00	0.00	0.00	0.00	66.67	0.00	**22.22**	50.00	33.33	0.00	0.00	0.00	11.11	0.00	0.00
THR T	0.00	0.00	0.00	0.00	0.00	0.00	0.00	0.00	0.00	0.00	0.00	0.00	33.33	**33.33**	0.00	0.00	0.00	0.00	16.67	0.00	0.00
TRP W	0.00	0.00	0.00	0.00	0.00	0.00	0.00	0.00	0.00	0.00	16.67	0.00	5.56	0.00	**0.00**	0.00	0.00	0.00	5.56	0.00	0.00
TYR Y	22.22	0.00	0.00	0.00	0.00	0.00	33.33	0.00	0.00	33.33	0.00	0.00	0.00	0.00	0.00	**0.00**	0.00	0.00	0.00	0.00	0.00
ASP D	0.00	0.00	0.00	0.00	0.00	0.00	0.00	0.00	16.67	0.00	0.00	0.00	0.00	0.00	0.00	0.00	**0.00**	33.33	0.00	33.33	0.00
GLU E	0.00	0.00	0.00	0.00	0.00	0.00	0.00	0.00	16.67	0.00	0.00	33.33	0.00	0.00	0.00	0.00	33.33	**0.00**	0.00	0.00	0.00
ARG R	11.11	0.00	33.33	0.00	0.00	0.00	0.00	33.33	0.00	0.00	0.00	0.00	11.11	16.67	33.33	0.00	0.00	0.00	**22.22**	0.00	0.00
HIS H	0.00	0.00	0.00	0.00	11.11	0.00	0.00	0.00	0.00	0.00	0.00	33.33	0.00	0.00	0.00	0.00	33.33	0.00	0.00	**0.00**	0.00
LYS K	22.22	0.00	0.00	11.11	0.00	33.33	0.00	0.00	0.00	33.33	0.00	0.00	0.00	0.00	0.00	0.00	0.00	0.00	0.00	0.00	**0.00**
Ttl Substitutions (%)>	100.00	100.00	100.00	100.00	100.00	100.00	100.00	100.00	100.00	100.00	100.00	100.00	100.00	100.00	100.00	100.00	100.00	100.00	100.00	100.00	#####

Note: Bold Figures represent Synonymous Substitutions

TABLE 13-I: Percent Change - Complimentary Transversion Substitutions
Resultant SUBSTITUTIONS Of One AMINO ACID For Another Following Basepair Mutations

To: \ From>	STP	ALA	GLY	ILE	LEU	MET	PHE	PRO	VAL	ASN	CYS	GLN	SER	THR	TRP	TYR	ASP	GLU	ARG	HIS	LYS	
Ttl Subs >>	9	12	12	9	18	3	6	12	12	6	6	6	18	12	3	6	6	6	18	6	6	192
SToP	0	0	0	0	2	0	0	0	0	0	1	0	1	0	0	2	0	0	1	0	2	
% ->	0.00	0.00	0.00	0.00	11.11	0.00	0.00	0.00	0.00	0.00	16.67	0.00	5.56	0.00	0.00	33.33	0.00	0.00	5.56	0.00	33.33	
Nonpolar	2	12	8	6	12	2	4	8	8	2	0	2	0	0	0	2	2	2	8	2	2	
% ->	22.22	100.00	66.67	66.67	66.67	66.67	66.67	66.67	66.67	33.33	0.00	33.33	0.00	0.00	0.00	33.33	33.33	33.33	44.44	33.33	33.33	
Polar	4	0	0	2	2	0	2	0	0	2	5	0	15	10	2	2	0	2	5	2	2	
% ->	44.44	0.00	0.00	22.22	11.11	0.00	33.33	0.00	0.00	33.33	83.33	0.00	83.33	83.33	66.67	33.33	0.00	33.33	27.78	33.33	33.33	
Acid	0	0	0	0	0	0	0	0	4	0	0	2	0	0	0	0	2	2	0	2	0	
%Acid ->	0.00	0.00	0.00	0.00	0.00	0.00	0.00	0.00	33.33	0.00	0.00	33.33	0.00	0.00	0.00	0.00	33.33	33.33	0.00	33.33	0.00	
Basic	3	0	4	1	2	1	0	4	0	2	0	2	2	2	1	0	2	0	4	0	0	
% ->	33.33	0.00	33.33	11.11	11.11	33.33	0.00	33.33	0.00	33.33	0.00	33.33	11.11	16.67	33.33	0.00	33.33	0.00	22.22	0.00	0.00	
Ttl Subs (%)	100	100	100	100	100	100	100	100	100	100	100	100	100	100	100	100	100	100	100	100	100	

Figures 1a & 1b

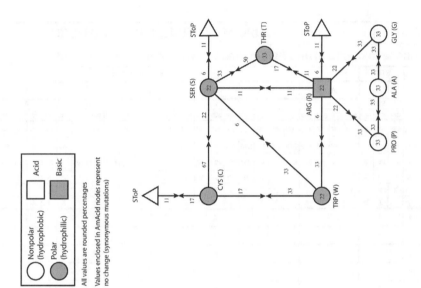

Complementary Transversions AmAcid Node Diagrams
Nonpolar (hydrophobic)
Polar (hydrophilic)
Acid
Basic
All values are rounded percentages
Values enclosed in AmAcid nodes represent no change (synonymous mutations)
STOP
TYR (Y)
ASN (N)
LYS (K)
PHE (F)
ILE (I)
MET (M)
LEU (L)
GLN (Q)
GLU (E)
HIS (H)
VAL (V)
ASP (D)
CYS (C)
SER (S)
THR (T)
TRP (W)
ARG (R)
PRO (P)
ALA (A)
GLY (G)

Figure 1a

Figure 1b

Table 13J

Table 13-J — Table of all TRANSITION MUTATIONS

Purine to Purine (a to g; g to a) and Pyramidine to Pyramidine (u to c; c to u)

20 Amino Acids > — STOP | **Nonpolar Amino Acids**

Codon-level detail (group headers: STOP, ALA (A), GLY (G), ILE (i), LEU (L), MET (M), PHE (F), PRO (P), VAL (V)):

	uaa	uag	uga	gcu	gcc	gca	gcg	ggu	ggc	gga	ggg	auu	auc	aua	uua	uug	cuu	cuc	cua	cug	aug	uuu	uuc	ccu	ccc	cca	ccg	guu	guc	gua	gug
64 Codons >	uaa	uag	uga	gcu	gcc	gca	gcg	ggu	ggc	gga	ggg	auu	auc	aua	uua	uug	cuu	cuc	cua	cug	aug	uuu	uuc	ccu	ccc	cca	ccg	guu	guc	gua	gug
192 Possible ▷	caa	cag	cga	acu	acc	aca	acg	agu	agc	aga	agg	guu	guc	gua	cua	cug	uuu	uuc	uua	uug	gug	cuu	cuc	ucu	ucc	uca	ucg	auu	auc	aua	aug
Mutations ▷	uga	ugg	uaa	guu	guc	gua	gug	gau	gac	gaa	gag	acu	acc	aca	uca	ucg	ccu	ccc	cca	ccg	acg	ucu	ucc	cuu	cuc	cua	cug	gcu	gcc	gca	gcg
X = No Change ▷	uag	uaa	ugg	gcc	gcu	gcg	gca	ggc	ggu	ggg	gga	auc	auu	aug	uug	uua	cuc	cuu	cug	cua	aua	uuc	uuu	ccc	ccu	ccg	cca	guc	guu	gug	gua
Only 126 (65%) ▷	Q	Q	R	T	T	T	T	S	S	R	R	V	V	V	X	X	F	F	X	X	V	L	L	S	S	S	S	I	I	I	M
Amino Acid ▷	X	W	X	V	V	V	V	D	D	E	E	T	T	T	S	S	P	P	P	P	T	S	S	L	L	L	L	A	A	A	A
Changes Occur ▷	X	X	W	X	X	X	X	X	X	X	X	X	X	M	X	X	X	X	X	X	I	X	X	X	X	X	X	X	X	X	X

Category summary by group:

Category	%	Total	STOP	ALA	GLY	ILE	LEU	MET	PHE	PRO	VAL
No-Changes (X)		66	4	4	4	2	10	0	2	4	4
SToP	4.7%	9	4	0	0	0	0	0	0	0	0
Nonpolar	43.8%	84	0	8	4	6	16	2	4	8	12
Polar	29.7%	57	4	4	2	3	2	1	2	4	0
Acid	6.3%	12	0	0	4	0	0	0	0	0	0
Basic	15.6%	30	1	0	2	0	0	0	0	0	0

No of Codons matrix (columns are the 64 source codons; totals per column = 3):

Group	No.	AA		uaa	uag	uga	gcu	gcc	gca	gcg	ggu	ggc	gga	ggg	auu	auc	aua	uua	uug	cuu	cuc	cua	cug	aug	uuu	uuc	ccu	ccc	cca	ccg	guu	guc	gua	gug
	3	SToP	stp	2	1	1																												
N	4	ALA	A				1	1	1	1																					1	1	1	1
o	4	GLY	G								1	1	1	1																				
n	3	ILE	I												1	1								1							1	1	1	
p	6	LEU	L															2	2	1	1	2	2		1	1	1	1	1	1				
o	1	MET	M														1																	1
l	2	PHE	F																	1	1				1	1								
a	4	PRO	P																	1	1	1	1				1	1	1	1				
r	4	VAL	V				1	1	1	1					1	1	1							1							1	1	1	1
	2	ASN	N																															
P	2	CYS	C																															
o	2	GLN	Q	1	1																													
l	6	SER	S								1	1						1	1						1	1	1	1	1	1				
a	4	THR	T				1	1	1	1					1	1	1							1										
r	1	TRP	W		1	1																												
	2	TYR	Y																															
Acid	2	ASP	D								1	1																						
	2	GLU	E										1	1																				
	6	ARG	R			1							1	1																				
Base	2	HIS	H																															
	2	LYS	K																															
		Totals >		3	3	3	3	3	3	3	3	3	3	3	3	3	3	3	3	3	3	3	3	3	3	3	3	3	3	3	3	3	3	3

64 codons

Table 13-J

N	N	C	C	Q	Q	S	S	S	S	S	S	T	T	T	T	W	Y	Y	D	D	E	E	R	R	R	R	R	R	H	H	K	K
Polar																			Acid				Basic									
ASN		CYS		GLN		SER						THR				TRP	TYR		ASP		GLU		ARG						HIS		LYS	
aau	aac	ugu	ugc	caa	cag	ucu	ucc	uca	ucg	agu	agc	acu	acc	aca	acg	ugg	uau	uac	gau	gac	gaa	gag	cgu	cgc	cga	cgg	aga	agg	cau	cac	aaa	aag
gau	gac	cgu	cgc	uaa	uag	ccu	ccc	cca	ccg	ggu	ggc	gcu	gcc	gca	gcg	cgg	cau	cac	aau	aac	aaa	aag	ugu	ugc	uga	ugg	gga	ggg	uau	uac	gaa	gag
agu	agc	uau	uac	cga	cgg	uuu	uuc	uua	uug	aau	aac	auu	auc	aua	aug	uag	ugu	ugc	ggu	ggc	gga	ggg	cau	cac	caa	cag	aaa	aag	cgu	cgc	aga	agg
aac	aau	ugc	ugu	cag	caa	ucc	ucu	ucg	uca	agc	agu	acc	acu	acg	aca	uga	uac	uau	gac	gau	gag	gaa	cgc	cgu	cgg	cga	agg	aga	cac	cau	aag	aaa
D	D	R	R	stp	stp	P	P	P	P	G	G	A	A	A	A	R	H	H	N	N	K	K	C	C	stp	W	G	G	Y	Y	E	E
S	S	Y	Y	R	R	F	F	L	L	N	N	I	I	I	M	stp	C	C	G	G	G	G	H	H	Q	Q	K	K	R	R	R	R
X	X	X	X	X	X	X	X	X	X	X	X	X	X	X	X	stp	X	X	X	X	X	X	X	X	X	X	X	X	X	X	X	X

Counts per amino acid:

ASN	CYS	GLN	SER	THR	TRP	TYR	ASP	GLU	ARG	HIS	LYS
2	2	2	6	4	0	2	2	2	6	2	2
0	0	2	0	0	2	0	0	0	1	0	0
0	0	0	10	8	0	0	2	2	2	0	0
4	4	2	8	4	0	4	2	0	5	2	0
2	0	0	0	0	0	0	2	2	0	0	2
0	2	2	0	0	1	2	0	2	10	4	4

Lower matrix (entries of 1 per codon column, final row all 3):

N	N	C	C	Q	Q	S	S	S	S	S	S	T	T	T	T	W	Y	Y	D	D	E	E	R	R	R	R	R	R	H	H	K	K
				1	1														2				1									
												1	1	1	1																	
										1	1								1	1	1	1										
												1	1	1																		
								1	1																							
															1																	
				1	1																											
				1	1	1	1																									
1	1							1	1										1	1												
		1	1																		1	1	1	1								
				1	1																				1	1						
1	1					1	1	1	1	1	1																					
												1	1	1	1																	
																													1			
		1	1																		1	1							1	1		
1	1																		1	1												
																					1	1									1	1
		1	1			1	1									1							1	1	1	1	1	1	1	1	1	1
																					1	1			1	1			1	1		
																					1	1									1	1
3	3	3	3	3	3	3	3	3	3	3	3	3	3	3	3	3	3	3	3	3	3	3	3	3	3	3	3	3	3	3	3	3

Tables 13K, 13L, & 13M

TABLE 13-K: Transition Basepair Substitutions
Resultant SUBSTITUTIONS Of One AMINO ACID For Another Following Basepair Mutations

To \ From	STP	ALA	GLY	ILE	LEU	MET	PHE	PRO	VAL	ASN	CYS	GLN	SER	THR	TRP	TYR	ASP	GLU	ARG	HIS	LYS	No M's	No CDNs
SToP	4											2			2				1			9	1
ALA A		**4**							4				2				2	2	2			12	1
GLY G			**4**											3								12	1
ILE I					4		2		4													10	1
LEU L					**10**		2	4					2									18	2
MET M				1		**0**							1									2	0
PHE F					2		**2**						4									6	1
PRO P						2		**4**	4													12	1
VAL V		4		3		1			**4**	2			2				2					12	1
ASN N										**2**						2			2			6	1
CYS C											**2**								2			6	1
GLN Q	2											**2**										6	1
SER S			3		2		2	4		2			**6**									18	2
THR T		4		3		1								**0**					1			12	0
TRP W	2										2				**0**						2	3	0
TYR Y										2						**2**						6	1
ASP D			3														**2**					6	1
GLU E			3											4				**2**		2	2	6	1
ARG R	1		3								2	2			1				**6**	2	2	18	2
HIS H												2							2	**0**	2	6	1
LYS K																				2	**0**	6	1
Total Substitutions>>	9	12	12	9	18	3	6	12	12	6	6	18	12	3	6	6	6	18	6	6		192	21

Note: Bold Figures represent Synonymous Substitutions

TABLE 13-L: Percent Change - Transition Substitutions
Resultant SUBSTITUTIONS Of One AMINO ACID For Another Following Basepair Mutation

To \ From	STP	ALA	GLY	ILE	LEU	MET	PHE	PRO	VAL	ASN	CYS	GLN	SER	THR	TRP	TYR	ASP	GLU	ARG	HIS	LYS
SToP	44.44	0.00	0.00	0.00	0.00	0.00	0.00	0.00	0.00	0.00	0.00	33.33	0.00	0.00	66.67	0.00	0.00	0.00	5.56	0.00	0.00
ALA A	0.00	**33.33**	0.00	0.00	0.00	0.00	0.00	0.00	33.33	0.00	0.00	0.00	11.11	0.00	0.00	0.00	33.33	33.33	11.11	0.00	0.00
GLY G	0.00	0.00	**33.33**	0.00	0.00	0.00	0.00	0.00	0.00	0.00	0.00	0.00	0.00	25.00	0.00	0.00	0.00	0.00	0.00	0.00	0.00
ILE I	0.00	0.00	0.00	**0.00**	22.22	0.00	33.33	0.00	33.33	0.00	0.00	0.00	0.00	0.00	0.00	0.00	0.00	0.00	0.00	0.00	0.00
LEU L	0.00	0.00	0.00	0.00	**55.56**	0.00	33.33	33.33	0.00	0.00	0.00	0.00	11.11	0.00	0.00	0.00	0.00	0.00	0.00	0.00	0.00
MET M	0.00	0.00	0.00	11.11	0.00	**0.00**	0.00	0.00	0.00	0.00	0.00	0.00	8.33	0.00	0.00	0.00	0.00	0.00	0.00	0.00	0.00
PHE F	0.00	0.00	0.00	0.00	11.11	0.00	**33.33**	0.00	0.00	0.00	0.00	0.00	22.22	0.00	0.00	0.00	0.00	0.00	0.00	0.00	0.00
PRO P	0.00	0.00	0.00	0.00	22.22	0.00	0.00	**33.33**	0.00	0.00	0.00	0.00	0.00	0.00	0.00	0.00	0.00	0.00	0.00	0.00	0.00
VAL V	0.00	33.33	0.00	33.33	0.00	33.33	0.00	0.00	**33.33**	33.33	0.00	0.00	11.11	0.00	0.00	0.00	33.33	0.00	0.00	0.00	0.00
ASN N	0.00	0.00	0.00	0.00	0.00	0.00	0.00	0.00	0.00	**33.33**	0.00	0.00	0.00	0.00	0.00	33.33	0.00	0.00	11.11	0.00	0.00
CYS C	0.00	0.00	0.00	0.00	0.00	0.00	0.00	0.00	0.00	0.00	**33.33**	0.00	0.00	0.00	0.00	0.00	0.00	0.00	11.11	0.00	0.00
GLN Q	22.22	0.00	0.00	0.00	0.00	0.00	0.00	0.00	0.00	0.00	0.00	**33.33**	0.00	0.00	0.00	0.00	0.00	0.00	0.00	0.00	0.00
SER S	0.00	0.00	16.67	0.00	11.11	0.00	33.33	33.33	0.00	33.33	0.00	0.00	**33.33**	0.00	0.00	0.00	0.00	0.00	0.00	0.00	0.00
THR T	0.00	33.33	0.00	33.33	0.00	33.33	0.00	0.00	0.00	0.00	0.00	0.00	0.00	**0.00**	0.00	0.00	0.00	0.00	5.56	0.00	0.00
TRP W	22.22	0.00	0.00	0.00	0.00	0.00	0.00	0.00	0.00	0.00	33.33	0.00	0.00	0.00	**0.00**	0.00	0.00	0.00	0.00	0.00	33.33
TYR Y	0.00	0.00	0.00	0.00	0.00	0.00	0.00	0.00	0.00	33.33	0.00	0.00	0.00	0.00	0.00	**33.33**	0.00	0.00	0.00	0.00	0.00
ASP D	0.00	0.00	16.67	0.00	0.00	0.00	0.00	0.00	0.00	0.00	0.00	0.00	0.00	0.00	0.00	0.00	**33.33**	0.00	0.00	0.00	0.00
GLU E	0.00	0.00	16.67	0.00	0.00	0.00	0.00	0.00	0.00	0.00	0.00	0.00	0.00	33.33	0.00	0.00	0.00	**33.33**	0.00	33.33	33.33
ARG R	11.11	0.00	16.67	0.00	0.00	0.00	0.00	0.00	0.00	0.00	33.33	33.33	0.00	0.00	33.33	0.00	0.00	0.00	**33.33**	0.00	0.00
HIS H	0.00	0.00	0.00	0.00	0.00	0.00	0.00	0.00	0.00	0.00	0.00	33.33	0.00	0.00	0.00	0.00	0.00	0.00	11.11	**0.00**	33.33
LYS K	0.00	0.00	0.00	0.00	0.00	0.00	0.00	0.00	0.00	0.00	0.00	0.00	0.00	0.00	0.00	0.00	0.00	33.33	0.00	33.33	**0.00**
Ttl Substitutions (%) >	100.00	100.00	100.00	100.00	100.00	100.00	100.00	100.00	100.00	100.00	100.00	100.00	100.00	100.00	100.00	100.00	100.00	100.00	100.00	100.00	#####

Note: Bold Figures represent Synonymous Substitutions

TABLE 13-M: Percent Change - Transition Substitutions
Resultant SUBSTITUTIONS Of One AMINO ACID For Another Following Basepair Mutations

To: \ From	STP	ALA	GLY	ILE	LEU	MET	PHE	PRO	VAL	ASN	CYS	GLN	SER	THR	TRP	TYR	ASP	GLU	ARG	HIS	LYS	
Ttl Subs: >>	9	12	12	9	18	3	6	12	12	6	6	6	18	12	3	6	6	6	18	6	6	192
SToP	4	0	0	0	0	0	0	0	0	0	0	2	0	0	2	0	0	0	1	0	0	
% ->	44.44	0.00	0.00	0.00	0.00	0.00	0.00	0.00	0.00	0.00	0.00	33.33	0.00	0.00	66.67	0.00	0.00	0.00	5.56	0.00	0.00	
Nonpolar	0	8	4	6	16	2	4	8	12	0	0	0	10	8	0	0	2	2	5	0	0	
% ->	0.00	66.67	33.33	66.67	88.89	66.67	66.67	66.67	100	0.00	0.00	0.00	55.56	66.67	0.00	0.00	33.33	33.33	11.11	0.00	0.00	
Polar	4	4	2	3	2	1	2	4	0	4	4	8	4	4	3	6						
% ->	44.44	33.33	16.67	33.33	11.11	33.33	33.33	33.33	0.00	66.67	66.67	33.33	44.44	33.33	0.00	66.67	33.33	0.00	27.78	33.33	0.00	
Acid	0	0	4	0	0	0	0	0	0	2	0	0	0	0	0	0						
% ->	0.00	0.00	33.33	0.00	0.00	0.00	0.00	0.00	0.00	33.33	0.00	0.00	0.00	0.00	0.00	0.00	33.33	33.33	0.00	0.00	33.33	
Basic	1	0	2	0	0	0	0	0	0	0	2	2	0	0	1	2						
% ->	11.11	0.00	16.67	0.00	0.00	0.00	0.00	0.00	0.00	0.00	33.33	33.33	0.00	0.00	33.33	33.33	0.00	33.33	55.56	66.67	66.67	
Ttl Subs (%) >	100	100	100	100	100	100	100	100	100	100	100	100	100	100	100	100	100	100	100	100	100	

Figures 2a & 2b

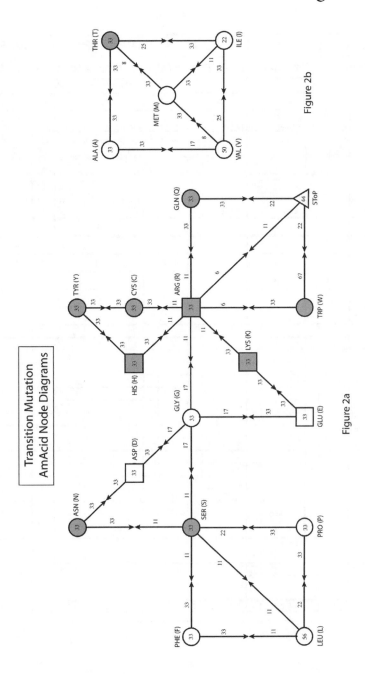

Transition Mutation
AmAcid Node Diagrams

○ Nonpolar (hydrophobic)
● Polar (hydrophilic)
□ Acid
■ Basic

All values are rounded percentages

Values enclosed in AmAcid nodes represent
no change (synonymous mutations)

Figure 2a

Figure 2b

Table 13N

Table 13-N — Table of all NON-COMPLIMENTARY TRANSVERSION MUTATIONS

Reversal of Non-Complimentary Bases (Purine / Pyramadine) a to c; c to a; g to u; u to g

		STOP			Nonpolar Amino Acids																											
20 Amino Acids >		stp			ALA (A)				GLY (G)				ILE (I)			LEU (L)						MET (M)	PHE (F)		PRO (P)				VAL (V)			
64 Codons >		uaa	uag	uga	gcu	gcc	gca	gcg	ggu	ggc	gga	ggg	auu	auc	aua	uua	uug	cuu	cuc	cua	cug	aug	uuu	uuc	ccu	ccc	cca	ccg	guu	guc	gua	gug
192 Possible ▷		gaa	gag	gga	ucu	ucc	uca	ucg	ugu	ugc	uga	ugg	cuu	cuc	cua	gua	gug	auu	auc	aua	aug	cug	guu	guc	acu	acc	aca	acg	uuu	uuc	uua	uug
Mutations ▷		uca	ucg	uua	gau	gac	gaa	gag	guu	guc	gua	gug	agu	agc	aga	uga	ugg	cgu	cgc	cga	cgg	agg	ugu	ugc	cau	cac	caa	cag	ggu	ggc	gga	ggg
X = No Change ▷		uac	uau	ugc	gcg	gca	gcc	gcu	ggg	gga	ggc	ggu	aug	aua	auc	uuc	uuu	cug	cua	cuc	cuu	auu	uug	uua	ccg	cca	ccc	ccu	gug	gua	guc	guu
Only 154 (80%) ▷		E	E	G	S	S	S	S	C	C	stp	W	L	L	L	V	V	I	I	I	M	L	V	V	T	T	T	T	F	F	L	L
Amino Acid ▷		S	S	L	D	D	E	E	V	V	V	V	S	S	R	stp	W	R	R	R	R	R	C	C	H	H	Q	Q	G	G	G	G
Changes Occur ▷		Y	Y	C	X	X	X	X	X	X	X	X	M	X	X	F	F	X	X	X	X	I	L	L	X	X	X	X	X	X	X	X

Summary by block

	Total	STOP	ALA	GLY	ILE	LEU	MET	PHE	PRO	VAL
No-Changes (X)	38	0	4	4	2	4	0	0	4	4
SToP 4.7%	9	0	0	1	0	1	0	0	0	0
Nonpolar 43.8%	84	2	4	8	6	12	2	4	4	12
Polar 29.7%	57	5	4	3	2	1	0	2	6	0
Acid 6.3%	12	2	4	0	0	0	0	0	0	0
Basic 15.8%	30	0	0	0	1	4	1	0	2	0

No of Codons

		n	uaa	uag	uga	gcu	gcc	gca	gcg	ggu	ggc	gga	ggg	auu	auc	aua	uua	uug	cuu	cuc	cua	cug	aug	uuu	uuc	ccu	ccc	cca	ccg	guu	guc	gua	gug
	SToP	3	stp															1																
N	ALA	4	A				1	1	1	1																								
o	GLY	4	G			1					1	1	1	1																	1	1	1	1
n	ILE	3	I													1	1							1										
p	LEU	6	L			1														1	1	1	1		1	1								
o	MET	1	M												1																			
l	PHE	2	F															1	1												1	1		
a	PRO	4	P																								1	1	1	1				
r	VAL	4	V								1	1	1	1				1	1												1	1	1	1
	ASN	2	N																															
P	CYS	2	C			1					1	1													1	1								
o	GLN	2	Q																										1	1				
l	SER	6	S	1	1		1	1	1	1					1	1																		
a	THR	4	T																								1	1	1	1				
r	TRP	1	W											1					1															
	TYR	2	Y	1	1																													
Acid	ASP	2	D				1	1																										
	GLU	2	E	1	1				1	1																								
	ARG	6	R														1			1	1	1	1	1										
Base	HIS	2	H																								1	1						
	LYS	2	K																															
	Totals>			3	3	3	3	3	3	3	3	3	3	3	3	3	3	3	3	3	3	3	3	3	3	3	3	3	3	3	3	3	3	3

64 codons

Table 13-N

							Polar												Acid							Basic						
ASN		CYS		GLN		SER						THR				TRP	TYR		ASP		GLU		ARG						HIS		LYS	
N		C		Q		S						T				W	Y		D		E		R						H		K	
aau	aac	ugu	ugc	caa	cag	ucu	ucc	uca	ucg	agu	agc	acu	acc	aca	acg	ugg	uau	uac	gau	gac	gaa	gag	cgu	cgc	cga	cgg	aga	agg	cau	cac	aaa	aag
cau	cac	ggu	ggc	aaa	aag	gcu	gcc	gca	gcg	cgu	cgc	ccu	ccc	cca	ccg	ggg	gau	gac	uau	uac	uaa	uag	agu	agc	aga	agg	cga	cgg	aau	aac	caa	cag
acu	acc	uuu	uuc	cca	ccg	uau	uac	uaa	uag	auu	auc	aau	aac	aaa	aag	uug	ucu	ucc	gcu	gcc	gca	gcg	cuu	cuc	cua	cug	aua	aug	ccu	ccc	aca	acg
aag	aaa	ugg	uga	cac	cau	ucg	uca	ucc	ucu	agg	aga	acg	aca	acc	acu	ugu	uag	uaa	gag	gaa	gac	gau	cgg	cga	cgc	cgu	agc	agu	cag	caa	aac	aau
H	H	G	G	K	K	A	A	A	A	R	R	P	P	P	P	G	D	D	Y	Y	stp	stp	S	S	X	X	X	X	N	N	Q	Q
T	T	F	F	P	P	Y	Y	stp	stp	I	I	N	N	K	K	L	S	S	A	A	A	A	L	L	L	L	I	M	P	P	T	T
K	K	W	stp	H	H	X	X	X	X	R	R	X	X	X	X	C	stp	stp	E	E	D	D	X	X	X	X	S	S	Q	Q	N	N

Summary counts (per amino-acid group):

ASN	CYS	GLN	SER	THR	TRP	TYR	ASP	GLU	ARG	HIS	LYS
0	0	0	4	4	0	0	0	0	8	0	0
0	1	0	2	0	0	2	0	2	0	0	0
0	4	2	6	4	2	0	2	2	6	2	0
2	1	0	6	6	1	2	2	0	4	4	6
0	0	0	0	0	0	2	2	2	0	0	0
4	0	4	4	2	0	0	0	0	8	0	0

Final totals row (all columns): 3 3 3 3 3 3 3 3 3 3 3 3 3 3 3 3 3 3 3 3 3 3 3 3 3 3 3 3 3 3 3 3 3

Tables 13O, 13P, & 13Q

TABLE 13-O: Non-Complimentary Transversions
Resultant SUBSTITUTIONS Of One AMINO ACID For Another Following Basepair Mutations

To \ From>>		SToP	ALA	GLY	ILE	LEU	MET	PHE	PRO	VAL	ASN	CYS	GLN	SER	THR	TRP	TYR	ASP	GLU	ARG	HIS	LYS	No M's	No CDNs
			Nonpolar (hydrophobic, neutral)								*Polar (hydrophilic, neutral)*							*Acid*		*Basic*				
SToP				1		1						1					2	2	2		2		9	1
ALA	A		**4**								2		4	1				2	2				12	1
GLY	G	1		**4**						4	2		2							1			9	1
ILE	I				2	3	1									1				4			18	2
LEU	L	1			3	**4**	1	2		2										1			3	0
MET	M				1	1						2											6	1
PHE	F					2		**4**		2	2	2	4							2			12	1
PRO	P								**4**														12	1
VAL	V		4	2		2		2		**4**						2				2	2		6	1
ASN	N														1								6	1
CYS	C	1		2					2							2				2	2	2	6	1
GLN	Q			2		2								4			2		4			2	18	2
SER	S	2	4		2						2			**4**	4							2	12	1
THR	T								4														3	0
TRP	W			1		1						1					2						6	1
TYR	Y	2												2				2	2				6	1
ASP	D		2														2			2	2		6	1
GLU	E	2	2										4							8			18	2
ARG	R				1	4	1			2													6	1
HIS	H										2	2	2										6	1
LYS	K										2	2		2									6	1
Total Substitutions>>		9	12	12	9	18	3	6	12	12	6	6	6	18	12	3	6	6	18	6	6	6	192	21

Note: Bold Figures represent Synonymous Substitutions

TABLE 13-P: Percent Change - Non-Complimentary Transversions
Resultant SUBSTITUTIONS Of One AMINO ACID For Another Following Basepair Mutation

To \ From>		STP	ALA	GLY	ILE	LEU	MET	PHE	PRO	VAL	ASN	CYS	GLN	SER	THR	TRP	TYR	ASP	GLU	ARG	HIS	LYS
			Nonpolar								*Polar*							*Acid*		*Basic*		
SToP		0.00	0.00	8.33	0.00	5.56	0.00	0.00	0.00	0.00	0.00	16.67	0.00	11.11	0.00	0.00	33.33	33.33	0.00	0.00	0.00	0.00
ALA	A	0.00	**33.33**	0.00	0.00	0.00	0.00	0.00	0.00	0.00	0.00	0.00	0.00	22.22	0.00	0.00	0.00	33.33	33.33	0.00	0.00	0.00
GLY	G	11.11	0.00	**33.33**	0.00	0.00	0.00	0.00	0.00	33.33	0.00	33.33	0.00	0.00	0.00	33.33	0.00	0.00	0.00	0.00	0.00	0.00
ILE	I	0.00	0.00	0.00	**22.22**	16.67	33.33	33.33	0.00	16.67	0.00	0.00	0.00	0.00	0.00	33.33	0.00	0.00	0.00	22.22	0.00	0.00
LEU	L	11.11	0.00	0.00	**33.33**	**22.22**	33.33	33.33	0.00	16.67	0.00	0.00	0.00	0.00	0.00	0.00	0.00	0.00	0.00	5.56	0.00	0.00
MET	M	0.00	0.00	0.00	11.11	5.56	**0.00**	0.00	0.00	16.67	0.00	33.33	0.00	0.00	0.00	0.00	0.00	0.00	0.00	0.00	0.00	0.00
PHE	F	0.00	0.00	0.00	0.00	11.11	0.00	**0.00**	0.00	16.67	0.00	33.33	0.00	0.00	0.00	0.00	0.00	0.00	0.00	0.00	33.33	0.00
PRO	P	0.00	0.00	0.00	0.00	0.00	0.00	0.00	**33.33**	0.00	0.00	0.00	33.33	0.00	33.33	0.00	0.00	0.00	0.00	0.00	0.00	0.00
VAL	V	0.00	0.00	33.33	0.00	11.11	0.00	33.33	0.00	**33.33**	0.00	0.00	0.00	0.00	0.00	0.00	0.00	0.00	0.00	0.00	33.33	33.33
ASN	N	0.00	0.00	0.00	0.00	0.00	0.00	0.00	0.00	0.00	**0.00**	0.00	0.00	0.00	16.67	0.00	0.00	0.00	0.00	0.00	0.00	0.00
CYS	C	11.11	0.00	16.67	0.00	0.00	0.00	0.00	33.33	0.00	0.00	**0.00**	0.00	0.00	0.00	33.33	0.00	0.00	0.00	33.33	33.33	33.33
GLN	Q	0.00	0.00	0.00	0.00	0.00	0.00	0.00	0.00	16.67	0.00	0.00	**0.00**	0.00	0.00	0.00	0.00	0.00	0.00	22.22	0.00	0.00
SER	S	22.22	33.33	0.00	22.22	0.00	0.00	0.00	0.00	0.00	33.33	0.00	0.00	**0.00**	**33.33**	0.00	0.00	0.00	0.00	0.00	0.00	33.33
THR	T	0.00	0.00	0.00	0.00	0.00	0.00	0.00	33.33	0.00	0.00	0.00	0.00	0.00	**0.00**	0.00	0.00	0.00	0.00	0.00	0.00	0.00
TRP	W	22.22	0.00	8.33	0.00	5.56	0.00	0.00	0.00	0.00	0.00	16.67	0.00	0.00	0.00	**0.00**	0.00	33.33	0.00	0.00	0.00	0.00
TYR	Y	22.22	0.00	0.00	0.00	0.00	0.00	0.00	0.00	0.00	0.00	0.00	0.00	11.11	0.00	0.00	**0.00**	33.33	33.33	0.00	0.00	0.00
ASP	D	0.00	16.67	0.00	0.00	0.00	0.00	0.00	0.00	0.00	0.00	0.00	0.00	0.00	0.00	0.00	33.33	**0.00**	0.00	0.00	0.00	0.00
GLU	E	22.22	16.67	0.00	0.00	0.00	0.00	0.00	0.00	0.00	0.00	0.00	0.00	0.00	0.00	0.00	0.00	0.00	**0.00**	**44.44**	0.00	0.00
ARG	R	0.00	0.00	0.00	11.11	22.22	33.33	0.00	0.00	0.00	0.00	0.00	0.00	22.22	0.00	0.00	0.00	0.00	0.00	**0.00**	0.00	0.00
HIS	H	0.00	0.00	0.00	0.00	0.00	0.00	0.00	16.67	0.00	33.33	0.00	33.33	0.00	0.00	0.00	0.00	0.00	0.00	0.00	**0.00**	0.00
LYS	K	0.00	0.00	0.00	0.00	0.00	0.00	0.00	0.00	0.00	33.33	0.00	33.33	0.00	0.00	16.67	0.00	0.00	0.00	0.00	0.00	**0.00**
Ttl Substitutions (%)>		100.00	100.00	100.00	100.00	100.00	100.00	100.00	100.00	100.00	100.00	100.00	100.00	100.00	100.00	100.00	100.00	100.00	100.00	100.00	100.00	100.00

Note: Bold Figures represent Synonymous Substitutions

TABLE 13-Q: Percent Change - Non-Complimentary Transversions
Resultant SUBSTITUTIONS Of One AMINO ACID For Another Following Basepair Mutations

To: \ From>	STP	ALA	GLY	ILE	LEU	MET	PHE	PRO	VAL	ASN	CYS	GLN	SER	THR	TRP	TYR	ASP	GLU	ARG	HIS	LYS	
		Nonpolar								*Polar*							*Acid*		*Basic*			
Ttl Subs: >>	9	12	12	9	18	3	6	12	12	6	6	6	18	12	3	6	6	18	6	6	6	192
SToP	0	0	1	0	1	0	0	0	0	0	1	0	2	0	0	2	2	0	0	0	0	
% ->	0.00	0.00	8.33	0.00	5.56	0.00	0.00	0.00	0.00	0.00	16.67	0.00	11.11	0.00	0.00	33.33	33.33	0.00	0.00	0.00	0.00	
Nonpolar	2	4	8	6	12	2	4	4	12	0	4	2	6	4	2	4	4	6	4	4	0	
% ->	22.22	33.33	66.67	66.67	66.67	66.67	66.67	33.33	100.00	0.00	66.67	33.33	33.33	33.33	66.67	0.00	33.33	33.33	33.33	33.33	0.00	
Polar	5	4	3	2	1	0	2	6	0	2	1	0	6	6	1	2	0	2	2	4	6	
% ->	55.56	33.33	25.00	22.22	5.56	0.00	33.33	50.00	0.00	33.33	16.67	0.00	33.33	50.00	33.33	33.33	0.00	22.22	66.67	100.00		
Acid	2	4	0	0	0	0	0	0	0	0	0	0	0	0	0	2	0	0	0	0	0	
% ->	22.22	33.33	0.00	0.00	0.00	0.00	0.00	0.00	0.00	0.00	0.00	0.00	0.00	0.00	0.00	33.33	33.33	0.00	0.00	0.00		
Basic	0	0	0	1	4	1	0	2	0	4	0	4	2	2	0	0	0	8	0	0	0	
% ->	0.00	0.00	0.00	11.11	22.22	33.33	0.00	16.67	0.00	66.67	0.00	66.67	22.22	16.67	0.00	0.00	0.00	44.44	0.00	0.00		
Ttl Subs (%) ->	100	100	100	100	100	100	100	100	100	100	100	100	100	100	100	100	100	100	100	100	100	

Figures 3a & 3b

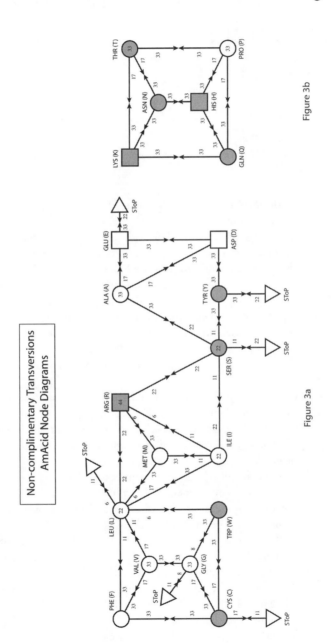

Nonpolar (hydrophobic)
Polar (hydrophilic)
Acid
Basic
All values are rounded percentages
Values enclosed in AmAcid nodes represent no change (synonymous mutations)
Non-complimentary Transversions
AmAcid Node Diagrams
PHE (F)
LEU (L)
VAL (V)
GLY (G)
TRP (W)
CYS (C)
MET (M)
ILE (I)
ARG (R)
SER (S)
ALA (A)
TYR (Y)
GLU (E)
ASP (D)
STоP
LYS (K)
ASN (N)
THR (T)
HIS (H)
GLN (Q)
PRO (P)

Figure 3a

Figure 3b

Glossary of Terms and Abbreviations Used in The 5th OPTION

NOTE: *All bold italics used in the Glossary indicate original terms, expressions and/or ideas developed in this book.*

ACP	**A**nthropic **C**osmological **P**rinciple: "The universe is fine-tuned for the evolution of intelligent life"
ADP	"Discharged" biochemical fuel cells that can be recharged into ATP.
Adaptive Evolution	*Evolution by means of 'adaptive selection': species' built-in propensity to anticipate changes to external biosphere conditions.*
Adaptive Selection	*A more precise description of 'Natural Selection' as the prime mover of evolution whereby LS species come equipped to survive by anticipating changes to external biosphere conditions ('species biosphere-attribute anticipation' (SBAA)).*
AmAcid Node Diagram	*Visual representation of the special relationship between the codons and their single basepair mutations.*
Anticodon	The basepair compliment of a codon that forms part of transfer DNA.
Apoptosis	Programmed cell death.
Archeabacteria	Considered the most ancient prokaryotic life-form in biology.
Artificial Life (AL)	Computerised metaphoric analog of living entities.
ATP	Chemical "storage batteries" that provide energy to fuel all cellular activity.
BA	***B**iosphere **A**ttribute: A single variable biosphere condition affecting organism survival.*
Basepair	A single chemical letter in the genetic alphabet.
Chemical Soup	The aqueous environment within which biological life is thought to have self-generated (abiogenesis), according to the 2nd OoL option.
Chromosome	A collection of genetic and "junk" sequences of DNA.
Coded Self-Assembly	Self-replication that occurs under the control of coded information.
Codon	A single chemical word composed of three letters of the genetic alphabet (signifies one of 20 amino acids or "stop" instruction).
Complexity	A nebulous description of convenience applied to any complicated phenomenon.
Creationism	The 1st OoL Option: "God created Life on Earth!"
Distribution Curve	A plot of the distribution of measurable species attributes (SA's).
DNA	The chemical medium where the species genome is written.

DPS	<u>D</u>irected <u>P</u>an<u>s</u>permia - The 4th OoL Option: "The seeds of Life were purposely dispersed from somewhere in outer space."
Ecosphere	Areas of the universe habitable by living things.
Elan Vital	Suggested "life-force" ingredient that permeates the living phenomenon.
Embryogenesis	The formation of a complete organism from a single cell.
Emergence, Theory of	Essentially: "the whole is greater than the sum of its parts".
EpE	*<u>E</u>quivilency <u>P</u>rinciple of <u>E</u>volution: "Fitness derived from changes to BA's are equivalent to that derived from SA's."*
Eukaryotic Cell	Nucleated biological cell from which all higher life forms are derived.
Eubacteria	More recent bacteria considered to be derived from archaebacteria.
ETI	<u>E</u>xtra <u>T</u>errestrial <u>I</u>ntelligence
Evolution	The subsystem of the life-system (LS) responsible for species adaptation to changing external biosphere conditions. Also, the results of such adaptation.
Evolution Filter	*Function of the specific degenerate form of the genetic code.*
Exobiology	**Field of research into the likelihood of the existence of extraterrestrial biological life.**
Exon	<u>Ex</u>pressible sequence of genetic DNA.
Fortuitous Emergence	*System change (characteristic of life) that is neither deterministic nor retraceable.*
FPE	*Formitive Period of Evolution*
Gene	A single genetic instruction (usually a recipe for a protein).
Genetic Code	The 64 possible combinations of chemical 3-letter words that code for the 20 amino acid and the instruction "stop" used throughout the LS.
Genotype	All of the expressible information contained within an organism's genetic library.
Hydrothermal Vents	Light deprived hydrothermal deep sea ecosystems that support unique life-forms.
Inevitable Emergence	*System change (characteristic of non-life) that is deterministic and therefore retraceable.*
Information	A set of data.
Intron	<u>Int</u>ervening information DNA sequence commonly referred to as "junk DNA".
ISRN	<u>I</u>nverse <u>S</u>quare <u>R</u>oot of <u>N</u> rule: A mathematical expression of confidence for a group of observations, dependent on the number of events "N"
Intelligence (generic)	*System capacity to: counteract entropy of information; differentiate information from randomness; affect "choice" over "chance".*
LS	*The <u>L</u>ife <u>S</u>ystem: The total interactive system comprising biological life on the planet.*
"M" mutation	*Basepair mutations to genetic information that occur in sex cells between the time an organism emerges (is produced) and the time it reproduces offspring.*
"m" mutation	*Basepair mutations to genetic information that occur only during the actual replication processes involved from the time offspring replication begins until the emergence of a fully formed offspring (embryogenesis).*
mRNA	<u>M</u>essenger <u>RNA</u>: Edited working copy of a gene
Militant Enthusiasm	Term coined by Kanrad Lorenz to describe the human propensity for attitudes that fuel human aggression that leads to "warfare".
Morphogenesis	The formation and differentiation of tissues and organs during embryogenesis..

Mosaic gene	A gene which contains both introns and exons.
NASA	<u>N</u>ational <u>A</u>eronautical and <u>S</u>pace <u>A</u>dministration
Natural Selection	Darwinian doctrine of evolution by selection of the fittest organisms that pass on their genes to future generation(s).
Occam's Razor	The maxim: "Entities are not to be multiplied without necessity."
OGEF	*<u>O</u>perational <u>G</u>enetic <u>E</u>volution <u>F</u>ilter: The capacity of the form and function of the genetic code to control and guide the consequences of random mutations within the genotype in specific non-random directions within the phenotype.*
Phenotype	The physical expression of the information contained within the genetic library of an organism.
Polypeptide	A chain of linked amino acids.
PoM	<u>P</u>rinciple <u>of</u> <u>M</u>ediocrity (as it applies to Life): Chances are that life is a common occurrence in our universe.
PdP	*<u>P</u>rimary <u>D</u>esign <u>P</u>latform of Life: The basic irreducible operational framework of bio-life <u>not</u> subject to evolution.*
PdPe	*Generic eukaryotic PdP.*
PdPp	*Generic prokaryotic PdP.*
Prokaryotic Cell	Primitive cell from which all bacteria are derived.
Protein	A polypeptide chain of amino acids folded in three-dimensional space.
PS	<u>P</u>anspermia - The 3rd OoL Option: "Life originated from seeds from outer space."
QO	*<u>Q</u>uantized <u>o</u>rganism = Quantized genotype (QG) expressible as Quantized phenotype (QP)*
QTE	*<u>Q</u>uantum <u>T</u>heory of <u>E</u>volution: A proposed theory that only certain "quantized" genotypes (QG) can qualify as capable of being translated and expressed as viable phenotypes (QP). The theory is meant to explain both missing transitions in the fossil record as well as 'punctuated evolution'.*
Rational	Having reason or understanding; relating to, based on, or agreeable to reason:
RDH	*The <u>R</u>ational <u>D</u>esign <u>H</u>ypothesis - The 5th OoL option: "Life was purposefully engineered and implanted on planet Earth to solve a utilitarian problem.*
Ribosome	Cellular machine tool that translates genetic instructions into proteins.
RNA	The chemical medium where genetic information is transcribed from DNA into a "working instruction", before being translated into a physical protein.
RNA World	A general solution for the 2nd OoL option that suggests RNA as a chemical precursor molecule predating biology.
SA	*<u>S</u>pecies <u>A</u>ttribute: A single variable within a species phenotype important for survival.*
SAb	<u>S</u>pontaneous <u>A</u>biogenesis - The 2nd OoL Option: The "primordial chemical soup" OoL theory – life spontaneously happened all by itself
SBAA	*<u>S</u>pecies <u>B</u>iosphere <u>A</u>ttribute <u>A</u>nticipation: The primary mechanism of Adaptive Evolution responsible for species Adaptive Selection.*
SE	<u>S</u>ystems <u>E</u>ngineering: The "intellectual catalyst" used in <u>The 5th OPTION</u> to

analyze the form, function, and design intent of biological Life.

SEGI	<u>S</u>earch for <u>E</u>xtraneous <u>G</u>enomic <u>I</u>nformation
SETI	The "<u>S</u>earch for <u>E</u>xtra-<u>T</u>errestrial <u>I</u>ntelligence".
Synonymous Mutation	Basepair change that yields no amino acid substitution.
UDIF	<u>U</u>niversal <u>D</u>ogma of <u>I</u>nformation <u>F</u>low: *"Design must derive from information; information must derive from intelligence; intelligence must derive from intelligence;..."*